HEALTHY FOUNDATIONS

in Early Childhood Settings

HEALTHY FOUNDATIONS

in Early Childhood Settings

Sixth Edition

Barbara Pimento

Deborah Kernested

NELSON

NELSON

Healthy Foundations in Early Childhood Settings, Sixth Edition

by Barbara Pimento and Deborah Kernested

VP, Product Solutions, K–20:
Claudine O'Donnell

Director of Softside Publishing:
Jackie Wood

Publisher:
Carmen Yu

Executive Marketing Manager:
Amanda Henry

Content Manager:
Courtney Thorne

Photo and Permissions Researcher:
Jessie Coffey

Senior Production Project Manager:
Natalia Denesiuk Harris

Production Service:
SPi Global

Copy Editor:
Marcia Gallego

Proofreader:
SPi Global

Indexer:
Belle Wong

Design Director:
Ken Phipps

Higher Education Design PM:
Pamela Johnston

Interior Design:
Jennifer Stimson

Cover Design:
Diane Robertson

Cover Image:
Gaston Comeau

Compositor:
SPi Global

Library and Archives Canada Cataloguing in Publication Data

Pimento, Barbara
[Healthy foundations in child care]
  Healthy foundations in early childhood settings / Barbara Pimento, Deborah Kernested. — Sixth edition.

First edition published under title:
  Healthy foundations in child care / Barbara Pimento, Deborah Kernested.
Includes bibliographical references and index.
Issued in print and electronic formats.
ISBN 978-0-17-673917-1 (softcover).— ISBN 978-0-17-689088-9 (PDF)

  1. Children—Health and hygiene—Canada—Textbooks. 2. Early childhood education—Health aspects—Canada—Textbooks. 3. Health promotion—Canada—Textbooks. 4. Child welfare—Canada—Textbooks. 5. Textbooks. I. Kernested, Deborah, author II. Title. III. Title: Healthy foundations in child care.

HQ778.7.C3P55 2018   613'.0432
C2018-905512-X
C2018-905513-8

ISBN-13: 978-0-17-673917-1
ISBN-10: 0-17-673917-3

Contents

Unit 2
Occupational Health

Unit 3
Illness Prevention

Unit 4
Illness Management

Unit 5
Nutrition

Unit 7
Safety Promotion

Unit 8
Preventing Child Maltreatment

Unit 9
Supporting Children's Development

List of Tables, Figures, and Appendixes

Tables

Figures

Appendixes

Before You Begin

Health is a complex subject that is interesting, challenging, thought-provoking, and always dynamic. It includes a wide range of perspectives. We are confident that this edition of *Healthy Foundations in Early Childhood Settings*, like the previous ones, reflects all of these attributes and addresses more fully those issues that are of greater concern today. As the title of this book implies, health is a cornerstone of ensuring high-quality early childhood learning and care (ECLC). Development and learning are fostered and supported when children are healthy and able to participate fully in a child-centred, play-based curriculum. Health is integrated with children's growth, development, and cultural realities, and each of this book's units reflects this belief.

In collaboration with families, educators have an integral role in maintaining or improving children's overall health status through a health promotion philosophy. This role requires an anti-bias attitude, respect, and sensitivity to diverse ethnocultural and family health beliefs and practices. Each of us has a responsibility for our own health, yet we can't dismiss the responsibility of our communities and society.

The third edition (revised) of *Well Beings: A Guide to Health in Child Care* (2015), by the Canadian Paediatric Society, provides the Canadian early childhood learning and care community with a comprehensive health resource manual. The book's audience extends beyond directors and educators to include child care office personnel, public health staff, physicians, and early childhood education instructors and students. As with previous editions, we refer to *Well Beings* and use selected material from it throughout this textbook. *Healthy Foundations in Early Childhood Settings*, Sixth Edition, provides you with an overall health promotion philosophy and entry-level knowledge and skills, and introduces you to *Well Beings*, Third Edition (revised), which you will use as a resource manual upon graduation to expand your knowledge and skills.

The emphasis in *Healthy Foundations in Early Childhood Settings* is on the overall health needs of all children. We have not included discussion of physical, cognitive, or socioemotional challenges and long-term medical conditions such as epilepsy or diabetes. In most, if not all, early childhood education training programs, students are required to complete a course on working with children with special needs and working effectively with families and others involved in their care. Students then combine the knowledge, skills, and attitudes that they learn in their courses and program placements to meet the physical, emotional, and social needs of each child. Many training institutions also offer post-diploma education in this area. Special Link: The National Centre for Child Care Inclusion provides researchers, policymakers, parents, and early childhood educators and directors with the best inclusive practices on the front lines of Canadian child care. Their findings are available to everyone on their website (see Resource Materials).

Healthy Foundations in Early Childhood Settings, Sixth Edition, reflects a national perspective while recognizing differences among the provinces' and

NELSONstudy

To access Resource Materials, visit NelsonStudy, available at NELSONbrain .com. See page xxvii for more information.

territories' child care regulations. As a result, we have selected a number of terms that are used throughout the textbook.

Educator

Regardless of the term used officially in any particular province or territory, people working in the field use different titles for their profession. Here are a few:

- educator
- early childhood professional
- facilitator
- teacher
- caregiver
- child care worker
- child care provider
- child care practitioner
- early childhood educator
- child care professional

At the national level, there is ongoing discussion about selecting one term that can be used to designate a person who has formal early childhood education training, one term that reflects the complexity of roles in working with children and their families in child care programs. There is no national consensus. Ontario's College of ECE is the first regulatory college for early childhood educators (ECEs) in Canada. The College monitors and supports high standards in early childhood education. It also helps ensure that Ontario's children who attend early learning and care programs are being cared for by qualified professionals. Only those educators who are registered with the Ontario College can use the designation RECE (Registered Early Childhood Educator). Complicating the discussion is the fact that in most of the literature, the term "early childhood" applies to the ages between birth and 8 years, thus excluding school-agers between the ages of 9 and 12 and, by extension, those who work with them.

We have chosen to use the term "educator." We recognize that trained, qualified professionals who work in ECLC programs care, support, facilitate, and educate.

Director

The daily operation of an ECLC program is often determined by the number of children enrolled and the organization's management style. As a result, in some situations, the director is responsible for the program's overall administration, is responsible for the supervision of staff, and sometimes also works with children. In other situations, the director oversees the finances and policy and staffing decisions and takes primary responsibility for networking in the community and formally representing the program. In addition, one or more supervisors oversee the staff and work directly with children and families for all or part of each day. The term "director" refers to the individual who has primary responsibility for supervising educators and managing day-to-day operations. Programs that operate as cooperatives do not have directors. In these programs, "director" refers to the collective that makes decisions.

Program and Setting

In this edition, we use the terms "program" and "setting."

The term "program" refers to the learning environment planned and implemented by educators, who base it on the children's emerging needs and interests.

The term is also used to refer to the program in a more general sense, as an ECLC program that is licensed by a province or a territory. The term "setting" generally refers to the physical space—the structure, the building—that houses the program. Educators work not only in child care centres but in a variety of programs, such as family resource centres, family daycare homes, and nursery school programs. For this reason, the term "centre" is used minimally.

Parents and Families

The terms "parents" and "families" refer to any adult who has primary responsibility for the child. The terms encompass legal guardians and foster parents. We recognize that the child's immediate family may comprise individuals other than biological or adoptive parents, and we hope that our use of these terms reflects inclusiveness.

Child Care Licensing Agency

The term "child care licensing agency" refers to the office or department primarily responsible for licensing programs in individual provinces and territories. When we refer to child care regulations, we mean those that apply to your province or territory.

Age Groups of Children

Classifications for age groups vary with child care regulations. We use these definitions throughout the textbook:

- infants: birth to 12 months
- toddlers: 12 to 24 months
- preschoolers: 2 to 5 years
- school-agers: 6 to 12 years

NEW TO THE SIXTH EDITION

The new edition contains updated information and statistics in all units. Other significant changes are as follows:

- Unit 1: Adequate housing in Canada is a primary concern relating to social determinants of health. The national housing strategy requires immediate action for improved population health. The situation of Indigenous peoples highlights Canada's failure to address needs for people who have the poorest health status in all of Canada. With basic needs such as safe water supplies and housing not available to many communities, it is no wonder that health status has not improved significantly, but improvements are underway. With regard to health promotion, the definition and awareness of mental health promotion have become more current considering its importance in persons of all ages to enhance their ability and to enjoy life and deal with challenges.
- Unit 2: Recent research on the *Wellbeing of Educators in the Workplace* (Ioannone & Pimento, 2017) has been added to this unit using the three levels of health promotion. The research highlights the importance of support in

the well-being of the early childhood workforce and workplace predictors of health and well-being, with particular focus on psychological protection, professional development, and recognition, benefits, and wages.

- Unit 3: This unit provides a general update on content and references.
- Unit 4: This unit provides a general update on content and references.
- Unit 5: Health Canada's multi-year revision process of the 2007 food guide is outlined in this unit to support student understanding of the upcoming changes. Guiding principles will be more direct than those in 2007 and will reflect concerns regarding many Canadians' low intake of vegetables and fruit; high consumption of saturated fats, sugar, and salt; and insufficient plant-based protein.
- Unit 6: Updated information on many aspects of health, including childhood obesity and how sleep relates to healthy active living, is provided. There is also an addition regarding risky play, which is not referring to the past definition of dangerous or hazardous. Today risky play refers to situations whereby a child can take manageable risk as part of building confidence. It is an educator's role to support each child's developmental needs and skills and to let children take and manage risks to keep them safe.
- Unit 7: There are updates to the most recent Canadian Standard Association's *Children's Playspaces and Equipment* requirements. Additions in this unit include updates in air quality, climate change, and environmental contaminants, with particular concerns for the health and well-being of Indigenous peoples. The call for action on radon in ECLC settings, as well as family homes across Canada, is currently of huge concern. Radon is the number one cause of lung cancer in non-smokers.
- Unit 8: This unit provides a general update on statistics and references. In addition, we are very fortunate to have important information from Boost Child & Youth Advocacy Centre's well-respected *Making a Difference: The Community Responds to Child Abuse* (Eighth Edition). The relevant and current suggestions are essential to the role of educators in responding to the possibility of child maltreatment and family violence.
- Unit 9: The topic of sexual development is updated, including a more current view of gender behaviour: gender identity and gender independent children. We have also added more fulsome discussions regarding napping needs, tips to support children's napping or relaxation, as well as nighttime sleep requirements for children's well-being and updates regarding oral health.

Two or more Critical Thinking questions are asked in each unit, enabling students to explore the issues introduced.

Updates to resources, including websites for further reference, are available on NelsonStudy.

LEARNING OUTCOMES

Educational reform and initiatives across Canada—such as prior learning assessment, standards, and outcomes—are catalysts for some educational institutions to embark on the process of establishing learning outcomes. These are clear, broad statements that embody the necessary and significant knowledge, skills, and attitudes that learners are expected to demonstrate to successfully complete each course or program.

We have examined this textbook for significant learning statements. On completion of this textbook, in conjunction with studies in health, it is expected that students will have demonstrated the ability to

1. represent the holistic nature of health through examining its physical, emotional, and social dimensions;

2. identify the scope and limits of the educator's roles with regard to health in ECLC settings, recognizing the importance of sensitivity and respect for the primary role of parents and family;

3. apply the principles of a health promotion philosophy to their own lives as well as to their work with children;

4. promote children's health based on knowledge of child development and observation within the context of the family culture;

5. assimilate the importance of collaborating and networking with other professionals and agencies on an ongoing basis to enhance health in ECLC programs; and

6. transfer the principles of essential health policies and practices to new situations in ECLC programs.

Acknowledgments

It is hard to believe that this edition marks the 25th anniversary of our first, published in 1994. I am retired after close to 40 years of teaching (and learning) at Lambton and George Brown Colleges. I have combined dedication for early childhood education with health promotion. I value the benefits of shared knowledge and a broader perspective in health promotion practice from my recent work at the WAVE (Wellness, Applied Research, and Visionary Education) as Health Promotion Specialist. I continue to gain knowledge and discuss points of view through my relationships with family, friends, previous colleagues, and graduates. Cheers to the wonderful faculty, staff, managers, and, of course, students from across the college and others with whom I had the opportunity to meet and work.

My husband and life partner, Michael, is wonderful—always there to listen, share ideas, and offer his wisdom and support in countless ways. Our adult daughters, Taryn (and wife Margo) and Taylor (with partner Zach), radiate love for life and passion for social justice issues, sharing their knowledge and insights, which influence my views. As a new grandparent, I love observing Ivy's growth, development, and vivacious personality. Michael and I feel blessed to be part of Ivy's life.

Deborah and I continue to work a province apart, but it feels as if we are sitting side by side. I marvel at Deborah's many strengths and enjoy the ongoing discussions and laughs we have through the process. It is a privilege to write with a long-time friend!

—Barbara Pimento

To Ali, thank you for your patience and support and for taking care of me through so many time crunches this edition. To my mother, Rhoda, my sister, Carla, and my friends, thank you all for your love and encouragement. To my niece and nephew, Anastasia and Erik, over the past 25 years I've had the privilege of watching you both grow into wonderful, engaging, and creative adults, both graduating and embarking on your professional careers this year. I so look forward to seeing what your futures hold.

In 1993, Barb and I sat at her dining room table for about a year writing our first edition. At that time, we could not have imagined reaching the point of writing six. Over the past year and half, there were times when I wasn't sure we'd finish this edition, but we did. This edition, like the earlier ones, could not have happened without the best writing partner and friend I could have.

—Deborah Kernested

There are several people whom we would like to thank for sharing their knowledge in the development of *Healthy Foundations in Early Childhood Settings*, Sixth Edition. Special thanks to Pearl Rimer, Director of Research and Training, Boost Child & Youth Advocacy Centre. Pearl recently updated the well-respected *Making a Difference: The Community Responds to Child Abuse*, Eighth Edition. Pearl dedicated much time and expertise in her contribution to Unit 8 (Preventing Child Maltreatment), which has resulted in up-to-date information and changes to ensure that students and educators are well informed in this essential area of health promotion.

Also, our sincere appreciation to Palmina Ioannone, PhD, RECE, and Professor at George Brown Cellege. Palmina headed the recent research on the *Wellbeing of Educators in the Workplace* (2017) with colleague Barb Pimento. We have incorporated the research findings, highlighting the importance of support for the well-being of the early childhood workforce, with primary focus on psychological protection. Palmina and Barb would like to acknowledge the George Brown College students who assisted in our research: Haniya Mohamed, BECL, RECE; Natalie Murree, BECL, RECE; Daniel Foster, RECE; and Jenny Rajewski, MEd, RECE. (Note: BECL is Bachelor in Early Childhood Leadership; RECE is Registered Early Childhood Educator.) We also wish to thank Melanie Dixon, Director of Professional Practice, Ontario's College of Early Childhood Educators, for granting permission to offer the Ontario RECEs the opportunity to complete the research survey, at their discretion.

To Carla Kernested, Policy Analyst, Department of Families (Government of Manitoba), sincere thanks for your ongoing consultation on issues throughout the textbook for all six editions! To Courtney Thorne, our Content Manager, your enduring attention to detail and your patience and support while moving us along the development schedule deserves our admiration and thanks! Thank you to Carmen Yu, Publisher, and Paul Fam, Director of Hardside Publishing, who helped guide the process along the way. Thanks also to the many others at Nelson whose hard work helped make this book possible: Amanda Henry, Executive Marketing Manager; Natalia Denesiuk Harris, Senior Production Project Manager; Pamela Johnston, Higher Education Design Project Manager; Marcia Gallego, Copy Editor; Lynn McLeod, Project Manager, Rights Acquisition & Policy; Jessie Coffey, Permissions Researcher; Kavitha Ram, Proofreader; and Belle Wong, Indexer. Sincere gratitude to Magesh Rajagopalan, Team Lead-Project Management at SPi. To all of you who have contributed to the production of this edition, we are delighted with the results.

A textbook is not complete without its photographs. A special thank-you to Sister Celeste, who went above and beyond to provide us with wonderful photos from their program in Tulita, NWT. Thank you so much to the children, families, and educators at Downtown Montessori at Coatsworth who generously welcomed us into their ECLC program. Special thanks to Franca Tarantino, supervisor, and Elizabeth (Liz) Ferguson (co-director, Day Care Connection), who organized our visit. We have also continued to benefit from previous photos taken (with thanks) at George Brown College ECLC settings, especially at the Casa Loma Child Care Centre and Richmond-Adelaide Child Care Centre, who opened their doors for us to capture photos depicting best practices. Some of the photographs in this book are courtesy of Carla Kernested, Winnipeg; several families across Canada; and Ryerson University's Early Learning Centre.

Finally, thank you to all who reviewed the fifth edition of this text to provide us with the direction required to develop the sixth edition. The information and insight provided by these reviewers proved invaluable in ensuring the quality of this resource and, most of all, in keeping us abreast of the needs of our colleagues, who bring this material to life. Special thanks, therefore, go to the following:

Lori Culleton, St. Lawrence College
Karen Davis, Mohawk College
Tricia Dumais, Conestoga College
Dale Kern, Mohawk College
Dale Long, Seneca College
Lisa McCaie-Watters, Centennial College

Instructor Resources

All key instructor ancillaries are provided on the Instructor Companion Site at nelson.com/instructor, giving instructors the ultimate tool for customizing lectures and presentations.

PowerPoint: Microsoft® PowerPoint® lecture slides that support each unit have been created by the text authors, Barbara Pimento and Deborah Kernested. Many slides feature key figures, tables, and photographs from *Healthy Foundations in Early Childhood Settings*, Sixth Edition.

Instructor's Manual and Test Bank: The Instructor's Manual and Test Bank to accompany *Healthy Foundations in Early Childhood Settings*, Sixth Edition, have been prepared by the text authors, Barbara Pimento and Deborah Kernested. The manual contains suggested classroom activities and ideas for assignments, questions to promote critical thinking and help students to assess their learning, and other resource materials to give you the support you need to engage your students within the classroom.

Additionally, each chapter contains a set of test questions for each section, including a mix of multiple choice, true/false, fill-in-the-blank, short answer, reordered list, and matching questions that you may use to evaluate the class. There are approximately 100 examples of each question type in the Instructor's Manual and Test Bank as a whole.

Student Resources

NelsonStudy: The NelsonStudy website is available for purchase and brings course concepts to life with engaging and interactive learning tools, including chapter summaries, self-study practice quizzes, case studies, and self-reflection exercises. Students easily access NelsonStudy online from any device—no set up, just success! Access NelsonStudy by visiting NELSONbrain.com and registering the access code from the card included with the textbook. If a code card is not provided, instant access can be purchased at NELSONbrain.com.

NELSONstudy

Health Promotion

1

CONTENTS

Promoting the health of children and families in early childhood learning and care (ECLC) programs is one of the most important roles of educators. So much of what educators do is interconnected with health and well-being. In this introductory unit, we establish what health is, and we look at what determines our health. We explore health promotion and our changing attitudes toward health and well-being. The unit closes with an introduction to the health promotion action plan and how it can be incorporated into ECLC programs. It is important for early childhood educators to recognize their essential responsibilities as health promoters. The action plan is revisited in subsequent units.

OBJECTIVE

To identify the World Health Organization's definition of health. (LO 1)

WHAT IS HEALTH?

The most influential definition of health in the 20th century was introduced by the World Health Organization (WHO) in 1948. Health, said WHO, is "a state of complete physical, mental and social well-being and not merely the absence of disease or infirmity" (World Health Organization [WHO], 2013b). The definition has been criticized over the years because of, among other reasons, its use of the word "state" rather than "process" and for the impossibility of achieving a "complete" state of health. Yet there is no doubt that this definition paved the way for a social model of health and health promotion in Canada, broadening the concept of health from a medical one to one that encompasses quality of life.

In 1986, WHO revised its definition of **health** to

> the extent to which an individual or group is able, on the one hand, to … realize aspirations and satisfy needs, and, on the other hand, to change or cope with the environment. Health is therefore seen as a resource for everyday life, not the objective of living; it is a positive concept, encompassing social and personal resources as well as physical capacities. (WHO, 2005, p. 3)*

This momentous change in how health is defined in 1986 was primarily a response to growing expectations for a new public health movement around the world, recognizing the impact of the community and society on individual health. The ever-changing nature of our health means that our adaptability to change is an important lifelong attribute and influences our health. All people are unique in how they define their own health. Health is enhanced by reasonable lifestyles and the equitable use of public and private resources that permit people to maintain and improve their own quality of life and well-being, however they define health.

"Quality of life" has varied definitions. It is a term that is now used in everyday life. It is generally subjective because it is based on how each of us sees our life, including our race, culture, economic situation, stage of life, and many other factors. For this reason, the following definition, originally developed by the University of Toronto's Quality of Life Research Unit over 25 years ago, is the authors' choice. **Quality of life** refers to the degree to which an individual enjoys the important dimensions of her or his life, including the fulfillment of physical and emotional needs, social belonging, and the realization of goals, hopes, and aspirations. Quality of life is relevant to all humans, at any time and from their own perspectives. The quality of life index developed by the research unit includes being (who one is), belonging (connections with one's environments), and becoming (achieving personal goals, hopes, and aspirations) (Raphael et al., 1999).

Quality of life is essential to all human beings for a life of fulfillment. Consider this fact in your life, and with the children, families, and colleagues with whom you will come in contact. High-quality ECLC programs enable parents to participate

---

*Source: *Health Impact Assessment Toolkit for Cities. Document 1. Background Document: Concepts, Processes, Methods. Vision to Action.* World Health Organization, 2005.

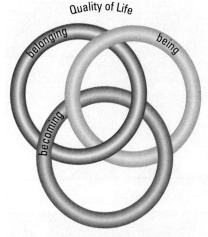

Quality of Life

belonging   being

becoming

Source: Reprinted by permission of Quality of Life Research Unit, Occupational Science and Occupational Therapy, University of Toronto.

OBJECTIVES

To list the 12 social determinants of health, as defined by the Government of Canada. (LO 1)

To define the term "population health." (LO 1)

To list the features of a population health approach. (LO 1)

fully in their work or education, which enhances the quality of their lives and the lives of their children. "All Canadians would benefit from improved early childhood development in terms of improved community quality of life, reduced social problems, and improved Canadian economic performance" (Mikkonen & Raphael, 2010, p. 24). And yet, although known as an important contributor to child well-being, only 17% of Canadian families have access to regulated child care (Mikkonen & Raphael, 2010, p. 24).

SOCIAL DETERMINANTS OF HEALTH

Health is a basic human right, so why are some of us more likely to enjoy good health than others? To answer this question, we first need to consider health determinants. There are no guarantees of good health, and many aspects of our lives affect our health status. Maintaining our health is the combined responsibility of all of us, as members of our community and of society. In addition to our biology and genetics, there are many factors that influence our health status, and the Government of Canada has identified what are known as the (12) **social determinants of health (SDH),** based on those set forth by WHO in 1986. A wealth of evidence supports the view that the social, economic, and physical environmental circumstances of individuals and groups are equally or more important to our health status than medical care and personal health behaviour (Government of Canada, 2015b). For the most part, SDH are the circumstances in which people are born, grow up, live, work, and age (WHO, 2008, p. 6).

There is a complex interplay of the social determinants of health; some have a broader impact than others and may be more or less significant to our health at different times in our lives (see Table 1.1).

It is likely that many Canadians are unaware that the social and economic circumstances of their lives have a greater influence on individual and community health status than do medical care and personal health behaviours.

Each of the 12 social determinants recognized by WHO and Government of Canada has been shown to have strong effects upon the health of Canadians. In addition, there are several current (and historical) issues that require much political attention for change, and many would consider that they require immediate and fulsome action. For example, in *Social Determinants of Health: The Canadian Facts*, the authors offer a more specific model of (14) social determinants, which includes housing and Indigenous status (Mikkonen & Raphael, 2010, p. 9).

One of Canada's primary concerns for population health is housing. Although housing is identified as part of the "income and social status" social determinant of health, it deserves additional and immediate focus. The Canadian Paediatric Society's (CPS) position statement *Housing Need in Canada: Healthy Lives Start at Home* states that "one-third of households in Canada live in substandard conditions or in housing need" (CPS, 2015, p. 403).

TABLE 1.1 Canada's Social Determinants of Health

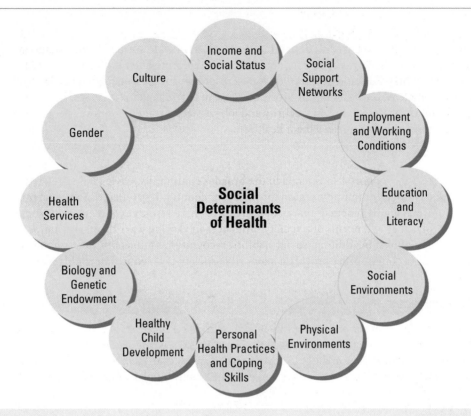

Income and Social Status

There is strong and growing evidence that higher social and economic status is associated with better health. Health status improves at each step up the income and social hierarchy. High income determines living conditions such as safe housing and the ability to buy sufficient good food. The healthiest populations are those in societies that are prosperous and have an equitable distribution of wealth. Why are higher income and social status associated with better health? Considerable research indicates that the degree of control people have over life circumstances, especially stressful situations, and their options to act are the key influences. Higher income and social status generally result in more control and options. And the biological pathways for how this could happen are becoming better understood. A number of recent studies show that limited options and poor coping skills for dealing with stress increase vulnerability to a range of diseases through pathways that involve the immune and hormonal systems.

Social Support Networks

Support from families, friends, and communities is associated with better health. Such social support networks could be very important in helping people solve problems and deal with adversity, as well as in maintaining a sense of mastery and control over life circumstances. The caring and respect that occur in social relationships, and the resulting sense of satisfaction and well-being, seem to act as a buffer against health problems.

Employment and Working Conditions

Unemployment, underemployment, and stressful or unsafe work are associated with poorer health. People who have more control over their work circumstances and fewer stress-related demands on the job are healthier and often live longer than those in more stressful or riskier work and activities.

(continued)

TABLE 1.1 Canada's Social Determinants of Health (*continued*)

Education and Literacy

Health status improves with level of education. Education is closely tied to socioeconomic status, and effective education for children and lifelong learning for adults are key contributors to health and prosperity for individuals and for the country. Education contributes to health and prosperity by equipping people with knowledge and skills for problem solving and helps provide a sense of control and mastery over life circumstances. It increases opportunities for job and income security and job satisfaction, and it improves people's ability to access and understand information to help keep them healthy.

Social Environments

The importance of social support also extends to the broader community. Civic vitality refers to the strength of social networks within a community, region, province, or country. It is reflected in the institutions, organizations, and informal giving practices that people create to share resources and build attachments with others. The array of values and norms of a society influences in varying ways the health and well-being of individuals and populations. In addition, social stability, recognition of diversity, safety, good working relationships, and cohesive communities provide a supportive society that reduces or avoids many potential risks to good health.

Physical Environments

The physical environment is an important determinant of health. At certain levels of exposure, contaminants in our air, water, food, and soil can cause a variety of adverse health effects, including cancer, birth defects, respiratory illness, and gastrointestinal ailments. In the built environment, factors related to housing, indoor air quality, and the design of communities and transportation systems can significantly influence our physical and psychological well-being.

Personal Health Practices and Coping Skills

Personal health practices and coping skills refer to those actions by which individuals can prevent diseases and promote self-care, cope with challenges, develop self-reliance, solve problems, and make choices that enhance health. Definitions of lifestyle include not only individual choices but also the influence of social, economic, and environmental factors on the decisions people make about their health. There is a growing recognition that personal life "choices" are greatly influenced by the socioeconomic environments in which people live, learn, work, and play. These influences impact lifestyle choice through at least five areas: personal life skills, stress, culture, social relationships and belonging, and a sense of control. Interventions that support the creation of supportive environments will enhance the capacity of individuals to make healthy lifestyle choices in a world where many choices are possible.

Healthy Child Development

New evidence on the effects of early experiences on brain development, school readiness, and health in later life has sparked a growing consensus about early child development as a powerful determinant of health in its own right. At the same time, we have been learning more about how all of the other determinants of health affect the physical, social, mental, emotional, and spiritual development of children and youth. For example, a young person's development is greatly affected by his or her housing and neighbourhood, family income and level of parents' education, access to nutritious foods and physical recreation, genetic makeup, and access to dental and medical care.

(*continued*)

TABLE 1.1 Canada's Social Determinants of Health (*continued*)

Biology and Genetic Endowment

The basic biology and organic makeup of the human body are a fundamental determinant of health. Genetic endowment provides an inherited predisposition to a wide range of individual responses that affect health status. Although socioeconomic and environmental factors are important determinants of overall health, in some circumstances, genetic endowment appears to predispose certain individuals to particular diseases or health problems. Aging is not synonymous with poor health. Active living and the provision of opportunities for lifelong learning may be particularly important for maintaining health and cognitive capacity in old age. And studies on education level and dementia suggest that exposure to education and lifelong learning may create reserve capacity in the brain that compensates for cognitive losses that occur with biological aging.

Health Services

Health services, particularly those designed to maintain and promote health, to prevent disease, and to restore health and function, contribute to population health. The health services continuum of care includes treatment and secondary prevention.

Gender

Gender refers to the array of society-determined roles, personality traits, attitudes, behaviours, values, relative power, and influence that society ascribes to the two sexes on a differential basis. "Gendered" norms influence the health system's practices and priorities. Many health issues are a function of gender-based social status or roles.

Culture

Some people or groups may face additional health risks due to a socioeconomic environment that is largely determined by dominant cultural values that contribute to the perpetuation of conditions such as marginalization, stigmatization, loss or devaluation of language and culture, and lack of access to culturally appropriate health care and services.

Source: © All rights reserved. *Toward a Healthy Future: Second Report on the Health of Canadians.* Public Health Agency of Canada, 2013. Adapted and reproduced with permission from the Minister of Health, 2018.

Housing insecurity includes the following:

- the need to spend at least half or more of an individual's or family's income on housing costs
- living in unsafe housing
- use of short-term shelters
- homelessness

These and other inadequate housing situations can obviously have appalling and even disastrous impacts on the health and well-being of individuals and families across the country. To date, Canada has failed to meet the needs of many people in this regard, with the most profound failures regarding safe housing for Indigenous peoples (Macdonald & Wilson, 2016).

On a positive note, after commissioning four months of countrywide consultation, the federal government released their report titled *What We Heard: Shaping Canada's National Housing Strategy* (Government of Canada, 2016b). *Canada's National Housing Strategy* was published in November 2017 (see Resource Materials).

NELSONstudy

To access Resource Materials, visit NelsonStudy.

HOUSING ISSUES ACROSS CANADA

The following is what the federal government reported they heard from the more than 7000 Canadians who participated in consultations on housing in Canada. The consultations brought healthy debate and discussion to housing issues, generating the following priority themes:

- "Helping those in greatest need."
- "Helping Indigenous peoples achieve better housing outcomes for themselves."
- "Eliminating homelessness."
- "Making housing more affordable."
- "Adopting a ... National Housing Strategy to better coordinate the various housing initiatives ... and to tackle housing needs across the entire continuum."
- "Housing policies and programs should center on people and place."
- "Setting clear outcomes and targets."
- "Delivering long-term and predictable funding."
- "Realizing the right to housing."
- "Improving data collection, analysis and research."
- "Taking a collaborative approach to housing." (Government of Canada, 2016b, pp. 4–5)

Governments are responsible for many aspects of the regulating, planning, financing, designing, constructing, and operating of housing in Canada. They provide financial assistance and housing to those who cannot meet their housing needs in the private housing market. Governments are also the primary source of housing research, data, demonstration, and knowledge that support informed decision making across the sector.

WHO's Commission on the Social Determinants of Health wrote in their final report that the "unequal distribution of health-damaging experiences is not in any sense a 'natural' phenomenon but is the result of a toxic combination of poor social policies and programmes, unfair economic arrangements, and bad politics" (2008, p. 1). The commission's overarching recommendations for action to improve the SDH are as follows:

- "Improve daily living conditions."
- "Tackle the inequitable distribution of power, money, and resources."
- "Measure and understand the problem and assess the impact of action." (WHO, 2008, p. 2)

Ideally, this is what a national housing strategy will accomplish.

Population Health and a Population Health Approach

Population health studies why some groups of people are healthier than others. Populations include large groups of people within a boundary, be that a neighbourhood, a city, or a country. A **population health approach**, widely accepted by the Government of Canada, aims to improve the health of the entire population and to reduce health inequities among population groups. Since those inequities have a lot to do with the social, economic, and physical environmental aspects of life (i.e., social determinants), a population health approach recognizes the essential role of public social policy to reduce the gaps among groups in the population (Government of Canada, 2013). "The outcomes or benefits of a population health approach, therefore, extend beyond improved population health outcomes to include a sustainable and integrated health system, increased national growth and productivity, and strengthened social cohesion and citizen engagement" (Government of Canada, 2013, p. 2).

What is the population health approach in Canada? Here is a brief introductory explanation of the multipronged approach used to improve the health of Canadians (Government of Canada, 2013, pp. 2–3):

> *Invest Upstream:* Efforts and investments in a population health approach are directed at root causes to increase potential benefits for health outcomes.*

You may have heard the term "upstream," but how does it apply to your health? The basic premise is that when we understand what happens before we get sick (upstream), we can take action to eliminate the cause of an illness (downstream). The quicker that a root cause is found, the greater the opportunity to take actions to improve the population's health.

For example, we all know that access to clean water is vital to one's health. A community's water source is a river. Upstream from where the community draws the water is a factory that dumps waste into the river. That waste mixed in the river travels downstream into the community's water source. The community members then consume the factory's pollutants when they drink and cook with this water. The root cause of the illness is the pollutants. By eliminating the pollutants upstream, the cause of the illness is eliminated downstream.

> *Base Decisions on Evidence:* A population health approach uses "evidence-based decision making."*

Scientific evidence is used to make decisions about the cause and effect of the determinants of health. This evidence is used to set priorities and strategies to improve health.

Let's continue with the example about the contaminated water source. Tests on the factory's waste and the concentration of pollutants in the water upstream and at the community's water source are measured, combined with the health issues that are presenting in the community. All of the evidence is evaluated to determine if the root causes of the illnesses are, in fact, linked with the polluted water.

> *Apply Multiple Strategies to Act on the Determinants of Health:* A population health approach takes action based on analyses and understandings of the entire range of the determinants of health. A population health approach recognizes the complex interplay between the determinants of health.*

There are 12 social determinants of health. Understanding illness and promoting health are complex. Some or all [or additional] health determinants come into play. Not every illness is going to have a straightforward root cause upstream.

In the example of the community's polluted water, fixing the problem isn't as straightforward as one might think. The factory is the sole employer for more than 100 kilometres. If the factory were to close, many of the people in the community would not have jobs. The impact of poverty on one's health is known to be very significant to individual, family, and community health. Poverty leads to inadequate nutrition and food insecurity, inadequate housing, or even homelessness. These and many other circumstances can have short- or long-term appalling consequences on health. In addition to the concerns about job losses, the community is in a remote location, making another source of clean water challenging and expensive. The complexity can be overwhelming.

> *Collaborate across Levels and Sectors:* A population health approach calls for shared responsibility and accountability for health outcomes with groups not normally associated with health, but whose activities may have an impact on health or the factors known to influence it.... It then ensures coordinated planning, development and implementation of their related policies, programs, and services.*

In the Canada's Health Care System section (see page 12), we discuss the areas of responsibilities between the federal and provincial/territorial governments. But it is important to recognize that health promotion is not solely the responsibility of those levels of governments. Groups that are connected to health and others that represent social well-being and community planning are all players in health promotion.

In the polluted water example, the community's mayor and council and chamber of commerce; the factory's owner, board, and management; and governmental legislative representatives from agencies such as the conservation and water stewardship, family services, and labour collaborate to address the water contamination.

> *Employ Mechanisms to Engage Citizens:* A population health approach promotes the participation of all Canadians in developing strategies to improve health. The approach ensures appropriate opportunities for Canadians to have meaningful input into the development of health priorities, strategies and the review of outcomes.*

You have likely heard the term "buy-in." When we participate in developing strategies for improving health, we believe in the plan and the actions needed.

Those living in the community with the contaminated water are essential players in addressing the health issue. Meaningful citizen involvement, including but not limited to representation from child and family agencies, schools, services for the elderly, and environmental activism, ensures that the strategies developed are practical and viable. It is essential that those directly affected by the pollution will have the desired outcome of improved health and minimal future risk.

> *Increase Accountability for Health Outcomes:* Regular and timely reporting of results and sharing of information with partners and Canadians is an integral part of a population health approach.*

Implementing a health promotion strategy isn't the whole story. Without measuring outcomes and sharing those findings with the population, we don't know if the strategies are having the intended positive impact on our health.

It isn't enough to implement the solution for eliminating the community's water pollution. Progress must be monitored and concerns reported to the community. For example, if there is a continued health impact on a faction of the community (e.g., young children, the elderly, or residents who live closer to the source), ongoing monitoring will quickly draw attention to this, resulting in immediate response by the appropriate agencies. These reports can lead to changes being made to the health promotion strategy or to assurances that the resolution is on track.*

CRITICAL THINKING

Referring to the preceding discussion on the multipronged population health approach and the example of a community's polluted water, let's take a look at the ongoing discussion around another issue: harmonizing Canada's immunization schedule. As you may or may not know, the provincial and territorial governments have responsibility for determining which routine immunizations will be recommended and funded. This results in a patchwork of routine schedules for infants and children, with possible serious health consequences. One example is the hepatitis B vaccine, where provinces and territorial programs vary widely in age of immunization. Some require it to begin at birth, whereas others have it available routinely as late as Grade 7. One major consideration that puts children in Canada at risk for inadequate immunization coverage is the reality that many families move from one province to another annually. Inconsistent immunization schedules result in infants and children missing doses, putting them unnecessarily at risk for certain contagious illnesses (CPS, 2018).

Consider the following points to develop a population health strategy to harmonize the delivery of vaccines in Canada, which would address inequity and safety problems for children:

- **Invest Upstream** We have a national immunization schedule, yet the provinces and territories create their own and determine which vaccines are covered by their health plan (see The Federal and Provincial/Territorial Roles and Responsibilities, page 13).

- **Base Decisions on Evidence** Science has demonstrated the effectiveness and safety of immunizing children and adults (see Immunization, page 139). There are parents who choose not to immunize their children. There continue to be claims that immunizations are responsible for causing autism, yet science has proved that this is not true. Would these unfounded claims impact the lobbying effort to harmonize immunization and ensure that as many children's immunizations as possible are up-to-date?

- **Apply Multiple Strategies to Act on the Determinants of Health** If we were to snap our fingers and all the provinces and territories implemented the national immunization schedule tomorrow, the work still wouldn't be done. What else would need to be done to support this program? (Examples include reducing the cost of vaccines, educating health care providers and the public on the national schedule, and catching up children's immunizations.)

(continued)

- **Collaborate across Levels and Sectors** The National Advisory Committee on Immunization (NACI) consists of a wide range of governmental, public health, and medical representatives. Aside from health care, who else in Canada may join the lobby nationally and locally to move to a harmonized program?
- **Employ Mechanisms to Engage Citizens** Ultimately, families are responsible for ensuring that their children are immunized. How does your strategy bring families into supporting the harmonization? Does the "one size fits all" approach work when developing educational material for families? If not, what factors do the writers need to keep in the forefront when developing material? (Some examples might be using social media or sending out reminders that a child is due for a vaccine using an automated phone and/or email system.)
- **Increase Accountability for Health Outcomes** What kind of research and feedback do you think needs to be shared with public health professionals and families as a harmonized program is rolled out and into the future?

In terms of the health of populations, it is well documented that the wider the gap between the socioeconomic "have" and "have not" groups in a society, the lower the health status of the overall population (Wilkinson & Marmot, 2003). This is evident internationally when we consider the positive population health outcomes in countries such as Sweden, Japan, and New Zealand, whose socioeconomic gap is narrower and health outcomes are better than those of countries such as Canada and the United States. "Worldwide, there are over 170 studies on income inequality and its relation to health. Data has demonstrated that in more unequal countries people live shorter lives, a higher proportion of children die in infancy, [and] obesity is more common, as is mental illness and the use of illicit substances" (Block, 2013, p. 3).

CANADA'S HEALTH CARE SYSTEM

Where does Canada's health care system fit in this picture? As discussed earlier, social, economic, and physical environmental factors have a greater impact on our health than does health care, and improvement in health for populations is strongly linked to policies and programs that address inequities. However, the quality of that health care also influences our health, in both prevention and management of disease and injury.

The *Canada Health Act* (passed into law in 1984) is the federal legislation that includes the five **national principles of medicare** and establishes criteria for individual provinces and territories to receive federal funding for health care services. In Canada, our system of universal medical and hospital insurance tries, although it does not always succeed, to provide all citizens with equal access to health care. Canada has made the right to health care one of the priorities on its political agenda. We are treated by doctors and are hospitalized when necessary.

The Canadian health care system has faced challenges in the past three decades, due to numerous factors. Some of these factors are changes in the way services are delivered, financial constraints, the aging of the baby boom generation, and the

THE FEDERAL AND PROVINCIAL/TERRITORIAL COLLABORATION TO DELIVER MEDICARE

THE NATIONAL PRINCIPLES OF MEDICARE

- Publicly administered—A public authority is accountable to its provincial/territorial government.
- Comprehensiveness—Medicare covers all necessary medical procedures.
- Universality—Medicare is available to all Canadians.
- Accessibility—All Canadians have an equal opportunity to obtain necessary medical services.
- Portability—Medical coverage in one province/territory is accepted in the others and pays for a limited number of medical costs outside Canada.

THE FEDERAL AND PROVINCIAL/TERRITORIAL ROLES AND RESPONSIBILITIES

The following is a snapshot of the roles and responsibilities for delivering health care within Canada (Government of Canada, 2018a, pp. 3–5).

FEDERAL GOVERNMENT	PROVINCIAL AND TERRITORIAL

- Sets and administers the national principles of the *Canada Health Act*, which establishes criteria and conditions for health insurance plans that must be met by provinces and territories in order for them to receive full federal cash transfers in support of health.
 	
 - Supports the provinces and territories financially through the Canada Health Transfer and Equalization payments.
 	
 - Funds and/or delivers primary and supplementary services to certain groups of people, such as First Nations people living on reserves, Inuit, and active members of the Canadian Forces.
 	
 - Regulates and protects health (e.g., regulation of pharmaceuticals, food, and medical devices), consumer safety, and disease surveillance and prevention.
 	
 - Provides support for health promotion and health research.
	- Provides reasonable access to hospital and doctors' services expected to meet national principles set out under the *Canada Health Act*. For example:
	   - Plans and funds the care in hospitals and other health facilities.
	   - Funds doctors and other health professionals.
	   - Plans and implements health promotion and public health initiatives.
	
	 - Most offer and fund supplementary benefits for certain groups (e.g., low-income residents and seniors), such as drugs prescribed outside hospitals, ambulance costs, and hearing, vision, and dental care, that are not covered under the *Canada Health Act*. Those outside these groups pay for these services out of pocket or with private health insurance.
	
	 - Provides an independent workers' compensation agency.

high cost of innovative, new technology, including electronic health technologies (such as health records and telehealth). These and other factors, albeit essential drivers to respond to changing needs, are expected to continue to challenge our health care system into the future.

Health care reform has proved to be an immense task in Canada. Health care reform—rethinking and restructuring—is being taken on worldwide. What has been a somewhat rigid structure in Canada's health care system is now striving to provide the flexibility needed to meet the diverse needs of a rapidly changing society. If our health care system were being established today, the system would likely rely less on hospitals and doctors and provide a broader range of community-based services. A high standard of care remains essential, but simply doing more of the same with less doesn't work. All levels of government in Canada have been calling for a more community- and home-based approach to health care, yet some of these same governments are also cutting social services that are needed in an infrastructure for an integrated and comprehensive system. For example, simply sending patients home from hospital earlier without adequate support for care at home in differing situations does not address the problem.

With an agenda to make recommendations for reforming Canada's "ailing" health care system, the Health Council of Canada (2013) put forward their suggestions in a report: *Better Health, Better Care, Better Value for All: Refocusing Health Care Reform in Canada*. The following is a short list of several key recommendations:

- Investing significantly more money in our health system is unrealistic. The need is to "refocus health care reform. Choices need to be made. We must, and we can, do better" (p. 34).
- A clear vision and a set of balanced goals are needed, rather than tackling individual components of the health system (p. 21).
- Focus needs to shift to efficiency, such as reducing waste and duplication, improving management processes, and reducing the overuse of services (pp. 6, 7).
- "The health system has not kept pace with the evolving needs of Canadians. Expenditures on hospital care, drugs, and physicians continue to dominate Canada's health care spending despite the growing need for better prevention and management of chronic disease, improved primary care, and expanded home care services to meet the needs of our aging society" (p. 4).

The Canadian Medical Association (CMA) culminated its two-year National Dialogue on Health Care Transformation across Canada with the 2013 report *Health Care in Canada: What Makes Us Sick?* The report summarizes the public dialogues and includes the CMA's 12 recommendations for change. Income, housing, nutrition, and early childhood development have very high influence in determining health. The medical profession is ethically bound to work on building a society in which all have the opportunity for a healthy life. The report recommends

- implementing a national food security program to safeguard equitable access to nutritious food for all Canadians; and
- moving forward with investments in early childhood development (Canadian Medical Association, 2013, pp. 1–2).

Components of Canada's Health Care System

There are two components of the health care system: primary health and public health.

Primary Health Care System

Although health care reform is effecting change, the **primary health care system** essentially includes conventional medical services available to people who want to maintain their health and seek cures for illness. General practitioners, family physicians, and pediatricians are the physicians we first contact when seeking medical care or advice. In certain situations, these physicians consult with specialists (e.g., gastroenterologists, cardiologists) and other medical professionals, such as physiotherapists, dietitian-nutritionists, and audiologists. We are seeing a movement toward including complementary medical practices in the medical services available through medicare, such as chiropractic services. Social workers and other relevant professionals are often brought into patients' medical care when nonphysical factors affect health (e.g., housing, poverty, substance abuse, child abuse). With wide recognition that the social determinants of health must be integrated into a framework for the future of our health care system, this movement will be expanding with time.

Public Health System

In Canada, public health services are provided regionally within each province and territory. Each public health department serves a specific geographic area. Usually, each public health agency within a province or territory is headed by a medical officer of health, who is a physician with specialty training in community medicine. The medical officer of health is given legal powers to prevent health hazards through provincial/territorial public health legislation.

Public health measures have been responsible for many of the major improvements in the health of Canadians, particularly around issues related to clean water and infectious diseases. Recently, however, the risks to health have been changing. The leading causes of death for all ages are now chronic diseases and injuries. Today's public health challenges include epidemic numbers of obese adults and children, continued smoking rates, and increasing rates of asthma in children. The threat of infectious diseases has not disappeared, with the return of age-old problems (e.g., syphilis, community waterborne disease outbreaks), age-old nuisances (e.g., bedbugs), and the appearance of new infectious diseases and threats (e.g., West Nile virus, severe acute respiratory syndrome [SARS], Lyme disease, and bioterrorism). Most current public health legislation focuses on the control of infectious diseases. The new reality is initiating legislation directed at public health prevention and health promotion focused on chronic conditions such as obesity, diabetes, and asthma.

The **public health system** provides and supports a wide range of programs, including the following examples:

- disease surveillance and responses to outbreaks
- health promotion to advocate for and facilitate healthier public policies, improve skills, and support individual and community-level behaviour change

- immunization programs
- inspection of restaurants and child care facilities

The local public health agency usually provides a variety of services when budgets permit. The medical officer of health designates services to address the public health needs in that geographic area. Large urban communities, for example, have a higher concentration of individuals addicted to drugs than do rural communities. When a region has a number of ECLC programs, ideally, the public health agency responds to each program's unique needs for information, consultation, and education.

As an educator, you will be involved with the public health system. Public health agencies are responsible for inspecting and approving health standards in ECLC programs, particularly licensed centres. Many centres, however, also actively seek an ongoing relationship with their public health professionals, to maximize the potential for health promotion. Directors commonly seek guidance for infectious disease control, immunization, safety, nutrition, and dental health.

Financial restraints have meant larger workloads for public health personnel. Often the agency's priority for health promotion and chronic disease prevention makes a relationship with an ECLC program mutually beneficial. Directors or educators may need to initiate contacts with the designated public health nurse or inspector due to great demands on the official's time.

OVERALL GOALS OF PUBLIC HEALTH IN CANADA

- Promote health;
- Prevent and control chronic diseases and injuries;
- Prevent and control infectious diseases;
- Prepare for and respond to public health emergencies;
- Serve as a central point for sharing Canada's expertise with the rest of the world;
- Apply international research and development to Canada's public health programs; and
- Strengthen intergovernmental collaboration on public health and facilitate national approaches to public health policy and planning.

Public health focuses on the entire population at both the individual and the community level. It encompasses a range of activities performed by all three levels of government (federal, provincial/territorial, and municipal) in collaboration with a wide variety of stakeholders and communities across the country.

Through our research, programs, and services, our goals are to bring about healthier Canadians, reduced health disparities, and a stronger capacity to deliver on and support public health activities.

Source: © All rights reserved. *Mandate*. Public Health Agency of Canada, date modified: June 16, 2016. Adapted and reproduced with permission from the Minister of Health, 2018.

CHANGING ATTITUDES TOWARD HEALTH CARE

OBJECTIVES

To discuss a holistic view of health and its effect on Canada's changing health care system. (LO 1)

To describe how complementary health practitioners contribute to a collaborative approach to health care. (LO 1)

To define the term "interprofessional collaboration." (LO 1)

To define the term "natural health products." (LO 1)

To describe the role that the federal government has in regulating natural health products. (LO 1)

Although Canada still largely operates an illness care system, there is now broader awareness of the power that social determinants of health hold in promoting health and reducing risks of various illnesses and injuries. Of course, treatment and cure needs are essential and require adequate resources. However, when we consider the "invest upstream" population health approach, more and more Canadians are questioning the curative approach to conventional medicine and are considering the merits of a holistic approach to health care. The holistic approach encompasses health promotion as a way of reducing health risks to individuals and the community at large. Reduced health risks means that less money would be needed for curative treatments and more money could be reallocated to health promotion measures, which include prevention.

Conventional medical care has become established in Western countries only over the past 200 or so years. Medical care primarily focuses on treating people after they become sick and on health maintenance, rather than on health care based on promotion. Most people seek medical advice only after experiencing the symptoms of illness. Physicians evaluate the symptoms, look for a cause, and decide on a treatment. The recommendations can be narrow in focus. Often physicians treat the physical symptoms rather than consider the connections among the patient's dimensions of well-being. Treatments commonly include surgery, medication, physical or occupational therapy, or a change in nutritional habits—or any combination thereof, all of which relate to the patient's physical health. This style of medical care is one in which the doctor is in charge and the patient asks few questions. When a patient is hospitalized, other health care professionals, such as dietitian-nutritionists, occupational therapists, and respiratory technicians, see the patient when the doctor requests a consultation.

Conventional medicine is extremely expensive because of its reliance on highly specialized professionals, institutions (hospitals and clinics), and expensive equipment. Moreover, often it does not care for the patient as a whole. It does not routinely use the expertise and skills of a variety of health professionals within a collaborative team approach; rather, it uses them as consultants if the doctor deems their input necessary.

This curative or health recovery approach was, and still is to some degree, widely held among many in the medical community and society, although this is changing. Many patients expect doctors to be miracle workers—to cure all their ills without patients accepting any responsibility for their unhealthy lifestyles. But another health care delivery system is gaining support, one that takes a holistic or broader view of health. We are becoming more informed consumers, asking our physicians questions and viewing ourselves as partners or advocates in our health care. Many Canadians are taking more individual control over accessing health professionals—chiropractors, physiotherapists, naturopaths—rather than waiting for a doctor's referral.

Traditionally, health care providers have been the main source of information and advice for patients. Although this is still true, increasing numbers of individuals are using the Internet to do extensive research on their conditions and come to their doctor appointments loaded with printouts and questions. This can result in some patients then thinking that they know more than their physician in regard to the condition and treatment. However, without the background, health knowledge, and experience of a physician, the average Canadian is not prepared to make decisions based on publicly accessible information because so much of the medical information found on the Internet is unreliable. It is imperative that patients visit reputable websites when using the Internet. Nevertheless, the demand by patients for greater involvement in decision making has made it essential that the public has access to user-friendly, accurate, and current information. In turn, health care providers are called upon to interpret the vast amount of public health information.

An Emerging Interprofessional Approach in Health Care

Medicine is a business, and doctors are adapting to the changing attitudes and expectations of consumers. Examples of the changing direction in Canada's health care system include a revamping, on the part of some medical schools, of teaching programs to a community-based model, a movement toward community medicine, interprofessional collaboration, and the licensing of complementary practitioners such as midwives and acupuncturists.

Interprofessional collaboration gives professionals the opportunity to learn with, from, and about one another, building mutual respect as well as shared knowledge and decision making in the best interests of patients. This collaboration has been linked to greater provider satisfaction, leading to enhanced recruitment and retention and improved patient safety and outcomes (Government of Canada, 2010).

Community medicine, such as that practised in community health centres, has an interprofessional approach to health care. Under one roof, community health centres may provide the services of professionals such as physicians, nurses, public health nurses, nurse practitioners, dietitian-nutritionists, social workers, physical and occupational therapists, health advocates, counsellors, interpreters, massage therapists, and pharmacists. These professionals work together to meet the diverse needs of individuals and their families. Community health centres refer patients to and work with other community services, such as job retraining, English as an additional language (EAL) lessons, housing and income agencies, legal aid, and so on. Often programs related to prenatal health, early childhood, and parenting are important components of their organizations.

These and other measures benefit patients and the public by reducing overuse and misuse of the system and by providing alternatives that may be more appropriate for the health and well-being of some individuals. Obviously, the expertise of doctors remains essential to Canada's health care system, but a team, interprofessional approach uses the expertise of many health and health-related professionals effectively, and includes team communication strategies to keep everyone informed.

This change moves away from the doctor's office and hospitals to clinics that provide a variety of services in collaboration. Community health centres also make a statement that health and social services should not be separated. Many people, such as those who live in poverty or on the street, who are not fully literate, or who have recently immigrated to Canada, are unable to obtain the level or quality of health care that others can in the conventional medical care system. Ideally, community health centres are designed and administered by the community to meet its unique needs.

Complementary Health Practitioners

Historically, **complementary (or traditional) health practitioners** such as homeopaths, naturopaths, acupuncturists, and midwives have long been part of a tradition in other parts of the world but have been excluded from the conventional medical model in Canada. Many alternative practices and products have not been scientifically proven to be effective or safe and so are unregulated and not covered by medical insurance or drug benefit plans. Conversely, critics of conventional medicine question whether some treatments covered by medicare are medically necessary or effective, or at least they question those that are overused (e.g., the high number of sonograms [ultrasounds] done during most healthy pregnancies). Some individuals may assume that using a complementary practitioner is a step toward holistic health; however, that may not always be the case. Anyone who chooses to consult a complementary practitioner—or a physician, for that matter—must be a very conscientious consumer. Moreover, urgent attention on the part of governmental authorities is needed to ensure the safety and effectiveness of complementary interventions.

Chiropractors have been regulated by provincial statute in all provinces. Chiropractors, just like medical doctors, dentists, psychologists, and optometrists, have the legislated right and obligation to communicate a diagnosis and to use the title "doctor." Two examples of complementary practitioners who have been approved in many, but not all, provinces and territories are acupuncturists and midwives.

Acupuncture is an ancient form of Chinese medicine involving the insertion of very fine, solid needles into the skin at specific points on the body to achieve a therapeutic effect. No drug is injected. The needles alone create the beneficial effects of acupuncture. Acupuncture is used to encourage natural healing, improve mood and energy, reduce or relieve pain, and improve the function of affected areas of the body.

As of January 2018, "traditional acupuncturists are regulated in British Columbia, Alberta, Quebec, Ontario and Newfoundland. The title of 'Acupuncturist' is protected in those provinces. In provinces without regulation it is the consumers' responsibility to inform themselves of the practitioner's level of training" (Acupuncture Canada, n.d., p. 1). Furthermore, "in most Canadian provinces, but not all, health care practitioners must be trained in acupuncture in order to practice it as a complement to their own professional training. Standards for training are set by the regulatory bodies for each health care profession" (Acupuncture Canada, n.d., p. 1). For example, "medical doctors and dentists may practice acupuncture in all Canadian provinces and territories. Chiropractors may practice acupuncture in all provinces but Quebec and British Columbia" (Acupuncture Canada, n.d., p. 1).

Source: Reprinted by permission of Acupuncture Canada.

Midwifery has been a legal and legitimate profession in England for over 500 years, but the publication of the *Midwifery Act* in Ontario on January 1, 1994, was the first legal acknowledgment in Canada of the legitimacy of birthing babies beyond the medical model approach. Pregnancy and childbirth are natural and low-risk processes for most women. Midwives provide continuity of care by supporting the woman and family throughout the pregnancy, during the birth, and for six weeks or longer after delivery.

Almost all provinces and territories in Canada have now legislated midwifery as of 2017.

Natural Health Products

Natural health products (NHPs) are now the most popular form of complementary health care in North America. NHPs were regulated according to the *Natural Health Products Regulations* (NHPR), which came into effect on January 1, 2004. Recently, the regulation title has been changed to *Natural and Non-prescription Health Products Directorate* (NNHPD) subsequent to its recently expanded mandate to include the oversight of nonprescription and disinfectant drugs in addition to natural health products.

The Licensed Natural Health Products Database contains information about natural health products that have been issued a product licence by Health Canada.

Products with a licence have been assessed by Health Canada and found to be safe, effective and of high quality under their recommended conditions of use. You can identify licensed natural health products by looking for the eight-digit Natural Product Number (NPN) or Homeopathic Medicine Number (DIN-HM) on the label.

This Licensed Natural Health Products Database is managed by Health Canada and includes information on *licensed* natural health products, including:

- vitamin and mineral supplements
- herb and plant-based remedies
- traditional medicines like Traditional Chinese Medicines or Ayurvedic (Indian) Medicines
- omega 3 and essential fatty acids
- probiotics
- homeopathic medicines
- many everyday consumer products, like certain toothpastes, antiperspirants, shampoos, facial products and mouthwashes (Government of Canada, 2015a, p. 1)*

NHPs must be safe for consideration as over-the-counter products, be available for self-care and self-selection, and not require a prescription to be sold. For further information, refer to the Government of Canada's Licensed Natural Health Products Database (see Resource Materials).

"Natural," however, doesn't always mean safe. For example, just like all medications, some NHPs are toxic in large doses; some can cause side effects or allergic

NELSONstudy

To access Resource Materials, visit NelsonStudy.

---

*Source: © All rights reserved. *Licensed Natural Health Product Database*. Health Canada 2011. Adapted and reproduced with permission from the Minister of Health, 2018.

reactions or interact with other medications; and some may be harmful for people in certain circumstances (e.g., with heart disease, during pregnancy). It is therefore important to consult your doctor, naturopath, or pharmacist before trying a product and to read the written material that comes with the natural product. This is where those in Canada who have a low literacy level, or who read in languages other than English or French, are at a disadvantage—it affects their health literacy as well.

CANADIANS' ATTITUDES TOWARD NATURAL HEALTH PRODUCTS (NHPs)

In 2010, Ipsos Reid Public Affairs surveyed 2001 Canadian adults (18 and older) across Canada for Health Canada. The survey measured awareness and attitudes regarding natural health products and their regulation, labelling, and safety. The following were some of Ipsos Reid's conclusions and recommendations (2011, p. 13):

- Three in four used NHPs, and a third used them every day.
- There was a great deal of confusion as to what an NPH actually is, and many assumed that certain types of products (e.g., organic food products) are NHPs, which they are not.
- The public was divided about whether or not NHPs were approved by Health Canada and about their quality and safety.
- Seven in 10 indicated that they read the NHP labels; 2 in 10 looked for either a Natural Health Product License Number (NPN) or a Drug Identification Number for Homeopathic Remedies (DIN-HM) on the product.
- Canadians agreed that they need more information on NHPs, including safety, regulation, side effects, benefits, information on recalls, and safety advisories.
- Many Canadians rely on traditional health care professionals for their information and feel that these providers would benefit from more NHP information as well.

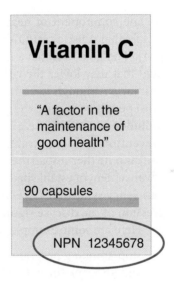

Source: © All rights reserved. *Licensed Natural Health Product Database.* Health Canada 2011. Adapted and reproduced with permission from the Minister of Health, 2018.

Some families with children in ECLC programs use complementary practitioners and medicines. Remedies and medicines may come from either cultural or traditional backgrounds or from a philosophy that differs from the established medical model. It is important to respect health practices different from your own and to be aware of your role in promoting the health of each child in your care. If you question an aspect of the family's health practices, find out more about it before taking action. However, many ECLC programs have written policies restricting the administering of nonprescribed medication in your program (see Administering Medication, page 195).

In Canada, some alternative health care is covered, at least partially, by the discretion of provincial and territorial health insurance plans (e.g., osteopaths, chiropractors, midwives). As stated earlier, some medical doctors are incorporating complementary practices into their patients' care. These doctors are under increasing scrutiny from their licensing body. As our health care system becomes more collaborative and interprofessional in nature, Canadians may see changes.

PREVENTION AND HEALTH PROMOTION

Prevention and health promotion activities have been practised for centuries. In the 1970s, a more committed and conscious movement toward healthy living began in Canada.

What Is Prevention?

As one component of health promotion, **prevention** involves identifying the factors that cause a condition and then reducing or eliminating them (Epp, 1986, p. 4). The goal is to have individuals adopt preventive strategies in their daily lives that may lower the risk of occurrence or recurrence of a particular illness or injury. Although lowering a risk doesn't guarantee that a disease is prevented, most people recognize the positive elements of this change. Primary prevention includes strategies (e.g., immunization) to prevent disease. Secondary prevention includes strategies to detect and treat disease as soon as possible and stop further impairment. Tertiary prevention tries to stop or slow down the advancement of established disease. For example, persons with acquired immune deficiency syndrome (AIDS) can undergo antiretroviral therapy to slow the progression of the disease significantly.

Here are some examples of primary prevention strategies:

- stop-smoking programs and no-smoking policies for preventing lung cancer and lowering the risk of heart disease and other major diseases
- monthly breast self-examinations and regular Pap smears for women for early identification of disease
- regular dental checkups
- hand-washing and immunization programs for children to reduce the spread of infectious diseases
- the design of play equipment for safety and appropriateness for the ages and number of children using it
- the use of Canadian Standards Association (CSA)–approved car seats and seat belts in cars and CSA-approved bike helmets on bicycles and scooters

There is not always evidence to support cause-and-effect relationships between health behaviour and disease. In fact, the many interrelated factors involved in disease make prevention complex. Also, popular opinion often promotes certain preventive lifestyle behaviours. These situations highlight the importance of the informed consumer, who weighs the pros and cons of specific behaviour. In particular, we cannot assume that every preventive practice we recommend for adults can be applied to children.

What Is Health Promotion?

Health promotion is "the process of enabling people to increase control over, and to improve their health. To reach a state of complete physical, mental and social well-being, an individual or group must be able to identify and to realize aspirations, to satisfy needs, and to change or cope with the environment" (WHO, 2013a, p. 1). To an extent, this also requires decreasing their risk of disease. But disease prevention is not the primary goal of health promotion; it is a secondary goal. Health promotion focuses on strengths rather than only risk factors.

A health promotion program can improve health (well-being) without necessarily reducing the prevalence of disease or of specific disease risk factors, such as smoking, high fat intake, or lack of fitness.

What Is Mental Health Promotion?

The Public Health Agency of Canada (PHAC) "defines positive mental health as 'the capacity of each and all of us to feel, think, act in ways that enhance our ability to enjoy life and deal with the challenges we face. It is a positive sense of emotional and spiritual well-being that respects the importance of culture, equity, social justice, interconnections and personal dignity'" (Government of Canada, 2014, p. 1).*

Although the general term "health promotion" includes mental health, there has been growing concern over the past few years regarding mental health issues for persons of all ages. PHAC has developed the only federal program with a focus on **mental health promotion** in Canada. The program, Promoting Mental Health Means Promoting the Best of Ourselves,

- coordinates federal/provincial/territorial action on mental health promotion;
- collaborates with stakeholders and partners to generate evidence-based knowledge to assist in the design of policies and programs; and
- develops public education and awareness activities on positive mental health and its relationship to overall health. (Government of Canada, 2014, p. 1)*

The program's primary goal "is to enable key mental health stakeholders and partners to develop and deliver policies and programs which address positive mental health and the underlying conditions of poor mental health, such as poverty, homelessness and unemployment. Programs which promote positive mental health have been found to reduce the risks of mental illness and related disorders" (Government of Canada, 2014, p. 1).*

The Library of Parliament published a brief titled *Current Issues in Mental Health in Canada: Child and Youth Mental Health* (Butler & Pang, 2014). The introduction begins with some startling facts:

- By the time they turn 19 years of age, 15 to 25% of children in Canada experience at least one mental health problem or mental illness, and have a good chance of facing another one sometime in their lifetime.
- "Only one in six people under 19 is adequately diagnosed and only one in five under 12 receives the treatment he or she needs."
- Positive mental health is associated with greater likelihood of completing school, more positive social relations, more self-confidence, better income potential, and increased resilience (Library of Parliament, 2014, p. 1).

In upcoming units, such as Unit 2: Occupational Health and Unit 9: Supporting Children's Development, further attention will be given to the essential nurturing and promotion of mental health and well-being.

The Health Promotion logo was created for the First International Conference on Health Promotion held in Ottawa, Ontario, in 1986. Since then, WHO has kept this symbol as the logo because it stands for the approach to health promotion as outlined in the Ottawa Charter:

> The logo represents a circle with 3 wings. It incorporates five key action areas in Health Promotion (build healthy public policy, create supportive environments for health, strengthen community action for health, develop personal skills, and re-orient health services) and three basic HP strategies (to enable, mediate, and advocate). (WHO, 2013a, p. 5)*

Areas in which the federal government has implemented healthy public policy are restrictions on the sale and advertising of tobacco, publicity to reduce impaired driving, a ban on bisphenol A in plastic baby bottles, and a ban on the production and commercial use of industrially produced trans fats. Over time, our understanding of the factors that contribute to better health has deepened. At first, government policies focused on lifestyle choices and on healthy public policy. Now, largely because of research on the nonmedical social determinants of health and how they profoundly affect health, the focus has shifted to the societal level (e.g., safe and affordable housing, enhanced maternity/parental leave, reduction of environmental contaminants), beyond factors that are within the immediate control of individuals and communities.

With a holistic view of health, everyone can be involved in promoting health. It is becoming increasingly apparent that people who believe they can control aspects of their lives and have choices are more likely to be action oriented and self-confident. It is easy to lose hope or view ourselves as ineffective when we believe that we have no control over our destiny. In your work with children, you will model and foster feelings of self-confidence and belief in yourself within a realistic framework of what we may or may not be able to control.

---

*Source: Reprinted from The Ottawa Charter for Health Promotion, First International Conference on Health Promotion, Ottawa. 2013. http://www.who.int/healthpromotion/conferences/previous/ottawa/en/index4.html. Reprinted by permission of the World Health Organization.

Build Healthy Public Policy

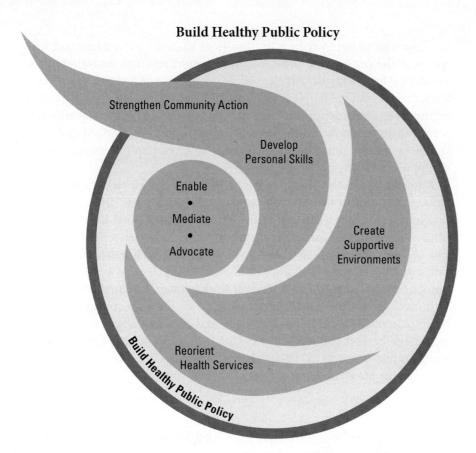

Strengthen Community Action

Develop
Personal Skills

Enable
•
Mediate
•
Advocate

Create
Supportive
Environments

Reorient
Health Services

Build Healthy Public Policy

Source: Reprinted from The Ottawa Charter for Health Promotion, First International Conference on Health Promotion, Ottawa. 2013. http://www.who.int/healthpromotion/conferences/previous/ottawa/en/index4.html. Reprinted by permission of the World Health Organization.

Integrating Prevention into a Health Promotion Approach

You may be saying to yourself, "I have control over most aspects of my life," and that is true to a degree. Many of us did not succumb to outside influences and start smoking. Perhaps we made other lifestyle decisions based on positive or negative influences. No one can claim, for example, "Cigarette advertising and peer pressure made me smoke." To focus solely on individual lifestyle decisions is to ignore the complex aspects of health behaviour. Nor can society simply blame the victim, absolving itself of its responsibility for coordinating healthy public policy, fostering public participation, and strengthening community health services (Epp, 1986, p. 8). An individual's ability to implement specific prevention strategies and the likelihood of success or failure are directly related to additional factors that affect that person's life. To think otherwise is to blame the victim (e.g., "It is the teenage girl's fault that she has anorexia," or "If he had been stronger willed and stopped smoking, he wouldn't have lung cancer," or "She's fat because she's lazy"). This attitude toward prevention is unacceptable and does nothing to enhance our understanding of health and improve our well-being.

Sarah quit smoking to reduce her health risks. She can't understand why everyone else can't do the same. For others, quitting smoking is more than withdrawal from addiction to nicotine. Malcolm has tried to quit a few times, but he recently lost his job, and smoking helps reduce his overwhelming feelings of stress. Most of Malcolm's friends smoke, and their social activities permit them to smoke. Moreover, his father and uncles smoked and lived long lives without developing lung cancer, so he has no firsthand evidence in support of claims made by experts.

A health promotion perspective takes into account the challenges of reducing inequities in Malcolm's life and enhancing his capacity to quit smoking. He enters a job-retraining program that results in meaningful employment. His standard of living improves, as do his self-esteem and outlook on his future. With lowered stress levels, Malcolm is better able to cope with everyday stress by walking to and from work. He now works in a non-smoking workplace. His new friends at work happen to be nonsmokers, and he is involved in different social activities. With the high cost of cigarettes, no-smoking legislation in public places, and concerns about second-hand smoke, smokers are feeling society's pressure to stop smoking. Consequently, Malcolm now has a much better chance of success because so many other factors in his life are in place to support his decision.

In summary, health promotion involves all aspects of a person's life that affect his or her well-being, and prevention focuses on particular risks or behaviour believed to be causal factors in disease or injury.

CRITICAL THINKING

Serena, a young woman who spends most of her time on social media, sneaks away at work whenever possible and can't wait for her next break time to check who has responded to her latest tweet or posted on Instagram. As coworkers stop talking to her, and friends only contact her on social media, Serena begins to realize that she has an addiction that has actually resulted in loneliness and isolation, rather than social well-being. Serena's best friend, as well as her siblings, have told her that she doesn't look or listen to anyone; she just stares at her phone. Her boss just gave Serena a final notice in writing that she will be fired if she doesn't focus on her work.

Give an example of a prevention strategy within a health promotion framework. Which of the social determinants of health could be affected by Serena's addiction to social media?

Public Policy and Health Promotion

NELSONstudy
To access Resource Materials, visit NelsonStudy.

The Canadian Medical Association's *Health Care in Canada: What Makes Us Sick?* report (see Resource Materials) was based on wide-ranging consultations around the country gathering input on Canadians' views of the social determinants of health:

At all the meetings, speakers confirmed the impact of socioeconomic factors on health outcomes and life expectancy. Four factors were seen as having the most substantial impact on health in Canada at this time: income, housing, nutrition, and early childhood development. Other topic areas mentioned were the environment, specifically air and water quality; the need to create healthy communities; the impact of addictions; the need for a national pharmaceutical plan; and the impact of systemic racism on the health of Indigenous people. The impact of race or culture was also seen as an important factor in determining health outcomes in Canada, especially for immigrants. Many speakers talked about the need for reform to the health care system, specifically for a better primary care system, more coordinated care, and improved access to health care services for vulnerable individuals.

Several other social determinants of health were mentioned, such as culture, the environment, education, and health literacy. Participants stressed that society, governments and health care providers all have an obligation to address such problems as poverty, inadequate housing, and nutrition.

Because the health of Indigenous people in Canada was seen as being particularly influenced by the social determinants of health, the CMA held a town hall meeting to address the challenges facing Indigenous people and communities (Canadian Medical Association, 2013, pp. 1, 3).

The many recommendations coming out of this report focused on public policy—involving all levels of government—necessary to have the kind of impact on Canadians that will have lifelong benefits to the health of individuals, communities, and the entire country. The CMA, with the input of regular Canadians, has strongly voiced the opinion that "the health care system is not the only place, or even the most important place, to focus on improving the health of the population" (O'Campo, 2013, p. 2).

The solution is to establish policies that address the social determinants of health, such as poverty, housing, employment, and education, to change the circumstances of people's lives. This is in alignment with WHO's focus on "health in every policy" because, in many ways, social policy can be equated to health policy! Collaboration in all sectors and levels of government is needed toward this goal.

HEALTH PROMOTION IN EARLY CHILDHOOD LEARNING AND CARE PROGRAMS

Promoting health is something we can do to improve the quality of our own life and the lives of those around us. How can ECLC programs be part of this movement?

Social Determinants: The Five Most Applicable to Early Childhood Learning and Care Programs

How do the social determinants of health relate to daily work in the field of child and family services? Although all 12 of them are linked, 5 in particular are present in ECLC programs on a day-to-day basis:

1. healthy child development
2. income and social status
3. education and literacy
4. social support networks
5. culture

OBJECTIVES

To list and describe the five determinants of health most applicable to ECLC programs. (LO 2)

To identify at least one strategy to promote health in the ECLC setting for each of the five determinants. (LO 2)

To list the elements of quality in an ECLC program. (LO 2, 4)

To list the purposes of program policies in an ECLC program. (LO 6)

To discuss student and educator strategies to advocate for high-quality ECLC programs. (LO 2, 3, 4)

"Early childhood experiences have strong immediate and longer lasting biological, psychological and social effects upon health" (Mikkonen & Raphael, 2010, p. 23). A healthy start in life has a great impact on the well-being of children and throughout life, providing opportunities for children to develop the attributes and resilience needed to mature into healthy adults in our complex society. A child's experiences during early childhood become embedded in the individual's biology.

Retrospective studies in humans have shown that development in the utero period and infancy influences risks for adult diseases (type 2 diabetes, hypertension, heart attacks, obesity, cancer, and aging). The Kaiser Permanente studies in California found that "adults with mental health problems, addiction, obesity, type II diabetes, coronary artery disease, and other conditions in adult life had poor early child development" (Mustard, 2010, p. 2).

Neuroscience is helping us understand how social determinants affect the body through biological pathways. We now know that although the brain has all its areas and neurons at birth, it is far from fully developed. "Wiring" or setting learning pathways essentially takes place during the first few years of life. The neuron connections strengthen from care and nurturing. Positive relationships with adults in the early years are investments in optimal brain development.

"The challenge of reducing the gap between what we know and what we do to promote the healthy development of young children is to view current best practices as a starting point and to leverage scientific concepts to inspire fresh thinking" (Shonkoff, 2010, p. 357). Shonkoff, among renowned researchers in early childhood development, acknowledges that solid evidence emphasizes that positive, early experiences strengthen brain formation. Shonkoff also points out that there is increasing understanding of "how significant adversity damages brain circuits and undermines lifelong learning, behaviour, physical and mental health. Moreover, neurobiology tells us that the later we wait to invest in children at greatest risk, the more challenging to achieve optimal outcomes, especially for children who experience the early biological disruptions of toxic stress" (Shonkoff, 2010, p. 365). (See Toxic Stress Response, page 541.)

During the investment phase from pregnancy through early childhood, stable, responsive relationships and rich learning experiences in all the environments in which children live and learn have a significant positive impact on every aspect of their development. The brain's capacity for change decreases with age. It is most flexible, or "plastic," early in life. Since the central nervous system communicates with all systems in the body (e.g., immune, hormonal, gastrointestinal), it follows that brain development affects the long-term functioning of the body—hence the incidence of disease (Hertzman, 1998, p. S16).

Young children develop best in warm, responsive environments that protect them from inappropriate disapproval and punishment—environments in which there are opportunities to explore their world, to play, and to learn how to speak and listen to others. "Stimulation has an independent effect on perceptual motor development outcomes among stunted children, over and above nutritional supplementation" (Hertzman, 2010, p. 2).

Parenting style has long been recognized as a critical influence on healthy child development; nurturing relationships support all areas of development. Fortunately, most children live with parents who have supportive and positive approaches to parenting. In fact, the vast majority of parents score well on a scale that looks at "effective parenting," including approaches to discipline and consistency. The good news is that according to a scale that measures positive parenting behaviours such as talking, playing, and laughing together, 92% of children under age two and a significant majority of older children lived with parents who demonstrated a positive parenting style.

The "family-time famine," a reality in many homes, is problematic because families need time together to nurture relationships and enhance members' sense of security, belonging, and competence. *Overwhelmed*, by Brigid Shulte (2015), is a book on the complexities of work–life balance that reminds parents that work shouldn't define them. However, with modern-day expectations on workers, employers often expect them to devote a lot of extra time to a multitude of tasks and deadlines. Part of the reason is that many workplaces develop policies without devoting time or resources to effectively implement them. Families need to work for salaries that are adequate enough to pay the bills, but one of the drawbacks is that long work hours means less time with their children. Parents need to be available to build communication, respond to children's needs, and support their development of skills (e.g., problem solving) and values as role models. Time together enhances children's feelings of security, belonging, and competence.

Developmental Health

As discussed earlier in the unit, a population health approach recognizes the value of public policy that strives to improve the health of the entire population while reducing inequities among population groups. Developmental psychology studies the biological and environmental factors in brain development. **Developmental health** combines these two fields of study in recognizing the impact of early childhood experiences on lifelong health:

- Illnesses and disabilities that emerge in adult life have their roots in early childhood and prenatal development (Hertzman & Power, 2004).
- Measures of physical growth, cognition, and behaviour in early childhood predict health status in adult life (Hertzman & Power, 2004).
- Research over decades concludes that high-quality, developmentally appropriate early childhood programs produce short- and long-term positive effects on children's development.

Quality ECLC programs foster many skills and gains in all areas of children's development, including cognitive, social, emotional, and physical gains. In addition, programs that provide health-promoting supports such as good nutrition, nurturance, safety, and stimulation offer investment in social determinants of health over life's progression (Hertzman, 2010, p. 3).

Two: Income and Social Status

A significant measure of the health and strength of a society is the well-being of its children and families. By that measure, Canada is failing. Currently, over 1.3 million children and families in Canada live in poverty (Campaign 2000, 2017, p. 2). Evidence is overwhelming that poverty is the greatest barrier (or threat) to health—people living in poverty are much more likely to develop health problems, including chronic illnesses such as heart or lung disease, and to die at an earlier age than people living above the poverty level.

Poverty is more than socioeconomic status. It is also relative to what many Canadians have access to—security when it comes to housing, food, clothing, work, educational opportunities, dental care, medication when needed, and options for activities (e.g., vacation) to nourish the soul. For children to have optimal developmental possibilities, it goes without saying that child poverty is based on family poverty.

Although we know that not every child who grew up in poverty does poorly in the long term, the preferred long-term strategy is not to build resilience in poor children but to eliminate child poverty. Having choices and control over many of the decisions in your life contributes to your well-being, and a degree of control is enjoyed by most wealthy Canadians. It follows, then, that poverty, unemployment, and cuts in social supports have a dramatic impact on the health of many Canadians. A standard of living that fosters well-being is achieved when adults have the opportunity to work at meaningful jobs, have access to affordable housing, and have high-quality ECLC for their children.

UNICEF's *Innocenti Report Card 13* (UNICEF Office of Research, 2016) surveyed 35 industrial nations on inequalities in child well-being. Canada was at a grim 26th place out of 35 rich countries in four key areas of child well-being: income, education, health, and life satisfaction. Lower life satisfaction can have an impact on a child's mental health and is associated with low physical activity, weaker relationships with parents and peers, and greater inequality in family wealth. Comparison of child poverty across industrialized countries shows that government action is a key driver to reduce child poverty. Higher levels of child poverty in some countries, such as Canada, are a function of not just chance or necessity but policy and priorities. "While Canada is doing relatively well in some areas such as education and low-rates of neonatal mortality, our rankings are woefully low in others. For instance, our country ranks 32 out of 41 rich nations in its efforts to meet the global goal to 'end poverty in all its forms' and 37 out of 41 in reaching the goal to 'end hunger, achieve food security and improved nutrition'" (Campaign 2000, 2017, p. 22). "As Canada's 150th year since confederation closes, it is time to usher in a new poverty-free era.... With over 1.2 million children and families in poverty, a transformational response to the complexity of poverty is overdue. It is time for a new social contract with a renewed foundation built on equity and dignity. The goal must be that no person in Canada lives in poverty, no matter their age, ethnicity, gender, religion, ability, sexual orientation or education. To do this, governments need to adopt a poverty reduction lens on all economic, fiscal, taxation and social policy decisions and budgetary priorities" (Campaign 2000, 2017, p. 1) (see Appendix 8.1, page 529).

Some children move into and out of poverty, usually as a result of their parents' opportunities to find and maintain adequate employment. Other families depend on two wages to provide basic needs, and even the two combined may be insufficient. The gap between poor and well-off families in Canada has been widening steadily since 1973. This is mainly due to the lack of access to adequately paid, secure jobs that can support families. Most of the jobs that have been created are part time, low wage, contractual, or seasonal, with few or no benefits. Furthermore, in recessionary times, people who have been gainfully employed for

FIGURE 1.1   Child Poverty Rates in the Provinces, 2015

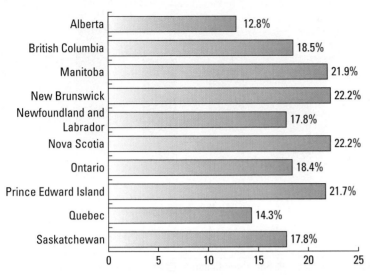

Source: Statistics Canada, 2017. *Census in Brief: Children Living in Low-income Households,* September 13, http://www12.statcan.gc.ca/census-recensement/2016/as-sa/98-200-x/2016012/98-200-x2016012-eng .cfm. Reproduced and distributed on an "as is" basis with the permission of Statistics Canada.

years may lose their jobs, putting them a paycheque away from short- or long-term poverty situations, including inadequate housing or homelessness. Consequently, many families are excluded from participation in the economic and social fabric of their communities. This undermines the connectedness that communities need to maintain and build public support for social programs. In households in which one of the adults is physically or emotionally challenged, or must be the primary caregiver for a family member with substantial special needs, that person may be unable to find employment that provides an adequate income—or to find any employment at all. The financial impact of a family breakup or reconstitution also moves families into or out of poverty.

Children who live in persistent poverty are less likely to be academically prepared to start school, especially if they have not had the opportunity to attend a high-quality ECLC program. It is not surprising that children who are poor are not likely to enjoy the same feelings of self-worth or quality of life as their more financially stable peers (e.g., they are less likely to participate in sports or other organized physical activities because of high costs).

The risk of poverty is not the same for all children. The poverty of opportunity speaks to the reality that, in Canada, we are not usually talking about absolute poverty. Nonetheless, this is the situation for most persons living in Indigenous communities and homeless families in urban areas. However, a "poverty of opportunity" refers to the relative poverty experienced by more than a million children in Canada.

In the realities of day-to-day life, there are parents and families who require more than social supports, such as some parents with low incomes. Resourceful educators recognize and seek out respectful means to assist parents if they are willing. Along with discreetly sharing information on local food banks, clothing

FIGURE 1.2   Risk of Poverty

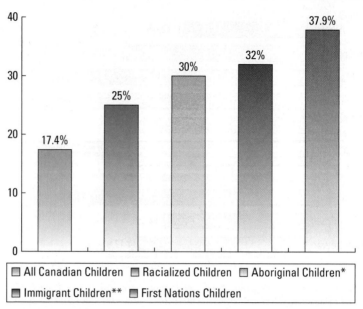

* Aboriginal children includes persons who are First Nations, Métis, or Inuit and/or those who
are Registered or Treaty Indians and/or those who have membership in a First Nation or band.
** Refers to children of current or former landed immigrants and permanent residents.
Source: Statistics Canada, Census of Population, 2016. Catalogue Number
98-400-X2016206.

Source: From Campaign 2000, *2017 Report Card on Child and Family Poverty in Canada,* p. 10.
Reprinted by permission of Campaign 2000.

exchanges, and training and skills development opportunities, some educators
actively advocate for universally accessible child care so that parents can engage in
work, training, and other opportunities—a longer-term strategy than food banks.
However, the short-term reality often means that the small ways to support families are important for children and their families.

Poverty, particularly as it affects children and families, must be addressed to
improve health. The Government of Canada's discussion paper *Towards a Poverty
Reduction Strategy* (2016a) discusses the multiple dimensions of poverty, including
effects on health.

Someone who lives in poverty is at higher risk for poor health; the cycle
tends to lead to further poverty. This is due to illness affecting job opportunities
and/or inability to remain in a job for various reasons, including unmet health
needs. Other dimensions of well-being are affected as well, such as the lack of the
necessary income for adequate housing and nutrition needs, low health literacy,
little socialization with others, and lack of full participation in the community.
Canadians in poverty statistically tend to have a shorter life span and higher rates
of serious and often chronic diseases, such as cancers, and mental health issues
(Government of Canada, 2016a, p. 11).

Campaign 2000, a nonpartisan, cross-Canada coalition of over 120 national,
provincial, and community organizations, is committed and has been working
tirelessly to end child and family poverty in Canada. In their 2017 report card
on child poverty, the primary message is that "the goal must be that no person

in Canada lives in poverty, no matter their age, ethnicity, gender, religion, ability, sexual orientation or education. To do this, governments need to adopt a poverty reduction lens on all economic, fiscal, taxation and social policy decisions and budgetary priorities" (Campaign 2000, 2017, p. 2).

The Health Status of Indigenous Peoples' Communities

The situation of Indigenous peoples highlights Canada's failure to address social and economic determinants of health. Indigenous peoples have the poorest health status of all Canadians. The federal government holds the primary responsibility to support Indigenous communities in addressing the health gap. When basic needs such as safe water supplies and housing are not available to many communities, it is little wonder that health status is not significantly improving. To meet the challenge of administering and controlling their own health care, Indigenous communities require adequate investment from the federal government to build infrastructure. They also need continued support for initiatives that draw on traditional knowledge and culture to develop culturally relevant approaches to problems such as substance abuse and family violence. Indigenous peoples in Canada have contributed a rich heritage to the country, and have not shared fully in its social and economic development.

RECENT STEPS

June 11, 2008: The federal government publicly apologized to Indigenous peoples for enduring generations of torment that saw the federal government strive to extinguish their language and eradicate their culture in residential schools. It was a historic moment when Indigenous peoples finally heard a prime minister at the time, Stephen Harper, say, "We are sorry" (CBC News, 2008).

November 12, 2010: Canada joined other countries in supporting the United Nations Declaration on the Rights of Indigenous Peoples. In doing so, Canada reaffirmed its commitment to promote and protect the rights of Indigenous peoples at home and abroad. This came three years after Canada's refusal to support the United Nations Declaration on the Rights of Indigenous Peoples in 2007 (Lum, 2014).

October 19, 2015: In his prime minister elect victory speech, Justin Trudeau stated the government's intention for a "renewed nation-to-nation relationship with Indigenous Peoples that respects rights and honours treaties" ("Justin Trudeau, for the Record," 2015, p. 4).

The federal government soon sent a strong signal that they prefer the term "Indigenous peoples" and changed the name of the Department of Aboriginal Affairs and Northern Development Canada to Indigenous and Northern Affairs Canada (INAC) (Indigenous Corporate Training Inc., n.d., p. 3).

One in four Indigenous children in Canada lives in poverty. "The Federal government must work with all levels of government now to lower shameful poverty rates that trespass on the rights of current and future generations to live in dignity" (Campaign 2000, 2012, p. 6).*

*Source: From Campaign 2000, *2016 Report Card on Child and Family Poverty in Canada*, p. 6. Reprinted by permission of Campaign 2000.

"The facts are stark and grim, demanding immediate action. There are more children in child welfare care today than residential school populations at the height of the residential schools era. From 1989 to 2012, Indigenous children spent 66 million nights or 187,000 hours of their lives in foster care away from their families. Suicide rates among First Nations youth are 5 to 7 times higher than non-Indigenous youth and the Inuit youth suicide rate is 11 times the national average" (Campaign 2000, 2016, p. 7). Canada's legacy of racism, colonialism, and neglect cannot delay concerted action any longer.

Eliminating appalling poverty levels among Indigenous children and families leads the national commitment to reconciliation. Expectations for the government to act are high, including implementing the 94 calls to action from the Truth and Reconciliation Commission of Canada (2015) to address the legacy of residential schools. Child welfare reform and implementation of Jordan's Principle are the top two calls to action from the Truth and Reconciliation Commission. Jordan's Principle was designed to ensure that Indigenous children do not experience delays, disruptions, or denials of services ordinarily available to other Canadian children. Unfortunately, the bulk of spending on child welfare and other needs for Indigenous children is slated for 2020–2021 (Campaign 2000, 2016, p. 7). (See Resource Materials.)

NELSONstudy

To access Resource Materials, visit NelsonStudy.

The above dates and information denote small steps. The insidious multigenerational damage to Indigenous nations and communities and people cannot be undone; moving forward requires much effort. The magnitude of suffering that many Indigenous peoples and communities continue to struggle with includes appalling living conditions that are particularly shocking in such a prosperous country.

Three: Education and Literacy

As future educators, you can likely relate to the fact that the more educated a person is, the more likely he or she is to be healthy. While we care for young children, we also play a tremendous role in their education. Children's introduction to the world of learning is, in partnership with their parents, very often through their first experiences in group-based ECLC settings. Children learn through play, and we are great promoters of play! As already mentioned, brain research tells us that the early years set the foundation for lifelong learning, behaviour, and health. Play-based problem solving is an optimal approach to early learning. One of our most important roles is in supporting and promoting early and emerging literacy in young children through a rich play environment and opportunities for problem solving, especially in pretend play. Also, educators and families are mutual resources, directly and indirectly supporting the child's education. Programs may also hold events with guest speakers, such as the local public health nurse or dietitian, or may offer a book-lending library with parenting titles, all of which benefit the child's education.

Communication skills include the ability to speak and be understood, as well as literacy. In Canada, literacy is defined as being able to read and write in one or both of our official languages, English and French. A large number of adults, over five million Canadians age 16 to 65, have problems dealing with printed materials and most likely identify themselves as people who have difficulty reading.

Statistics from the Conference Board of Canada in 2012 highlight the low adult (16 to 65 years of age) literacy skills in Canada:

- Forty-eight percent had inadequate literacy skills—a noteworthy increase from a decade earlier (p. 1).
- No province was graded above a "C" for inadequate literacy skills (p. 1).
- Canada also had a "C" grade on inadequate literacy skills in a 2012 international comparison study (p. 3).

Additional significant information from the Conference Board of Canada (2012) includes the following:

- Most immigrants to Canada have adequate or high literacy in their native language, but approximately 65% of recent immigrants (in Canada for 10 years or less) are not adequately literate in English or French, Canada's official languages (p. 4).
- From literacy data in 2011, Indigenous peoples (in Canada as a whole and in Ontario, Manitoba, Saskatchewan, and British Columbia) are more likely to have lower literacy skills than the non-Indigenous population. Although the gap may be alarming, Indigenous and non-Indigenous people with comparable education levels have similar literacy skills levels (p. 5).

Adults whose first language is English (or French) may have low literacy skills; so, too, may adults whose first language is not English (or French). These individuals may be literate in their first language (e.g., Mandarin, Italian, Cree) but not in English or French; however, statistically, they are not considered literate by Canadian standards and are at a disadvantage in the larger community.

In addition to the broader disadvantages (e.g., lack of career opportunities, much lower pay) that are associated with illiteracy, there are often specific concerns contributing to poor health, such as the inability to read printed information about health or illness. People who do not speak or understand one of the official languages well are at a disadvantage because they may not seek information or must depend on someone else's interpretation. A person who is illiterate or with low literacy skills, and has no access to an interpreter, may be unable to make effective use of health or social services.

"In Canada health literacy is defined as 'the ability to *access, comprehend, evaluate and communicate* information as a way to promote, maintain and improve health in a variety of settings across the life-course.' Figures show that 60% of adults and 88% of seniors in Canada are not health literate. People who are not health literate have difficulty using the everyday health information that is routinely available in health care facilities, grocery stores, retail outlets, schools, through the media, and in their communities" (Government of Canada, 2018b, p. 1).*

Some examples are as follows:

- A person may not adequately understand a physician's or pharmacist's instructions.

---

*Source: © All rights reserved. *Health Literacy.* Public Health Agency of Canada, date modified: January 30, 2018. Adapted and reproduced with permission from the Minister of Health, 2018.

- Parents who are not sufficiently fluent in the same language as the educators in an ECLC program may not understand when they are asked to bring in their child's immunization record.

- Parents who are illiterate or have low literacy may not disclose that they can't read the program's parent handbook outlining the health policies.

To improve readability, many public materials are now written in plain and simple language. In large cities, or areas where many people speak, read, and write in languages other than English or French, municipal governments often publish pamphlets and other documents in other languages. This service has had a positive effect on the well-being of people in the community.

Health, social services, and educational departments continue to find ways to increase the number of informational resources accessible to those who do not speak, read, and write English or French. As well, individuals and their cultural or ethnic communities have a responsibility to seek language and literacy programs in English or French so that they can use the available resources. Consider new immigrants to Canada, especially those who have come from war-torn countries, such as Syria. Even those who have come with high literacy skills in their first language, in addition to learning a new language, may have a lower degree of health literacy in a particular context, such as being in a new country or when facing or remembering stressful situations (Ng & Omariba, 2010, pp. 42–49).

Immigrants originating from Asia and Africa tend to have languages and cultures very dissimilar to those in Canada and thus may face adjustment challenges. Immigrants who are less proficient in English or French are often less able to function in society and, as a result, are likely to have lower health literacy (Ng & Omariba, 2010, p. 10). Early childhood educators and all other professionals working with children and families new to Canada need to take steps to communicate by

- providing information that is appropriate and easy to use,

- using straightforward language and culturally appropriate messages and body language,

- recognizing that familiarizing themselves with Canada's health care system can be complicated for new immigrant families, and

- ensuring through various ways that communication is being understood by both parties.

CRITICAL THINKING

NELSONstudy

To access Resource Materials, visit NelsonStudy.

For the education and literacy determinant of health, particularly health literacy, give an example of how an early childhood learning and care program can support newcomer families in promoting their health. Refer to CPS's *Caring for Kids New to Canada* website (see Resource Materials).

Four: Social Support Networks

Educators engage in family support and believe in the value of social support networks. Healthy social environments and strong support networks promote the emotional and physical well-being of children. Many ECLC programs proactively establish networks among the parents in their programs, encouraging mutual support and connecting parents with services and supports.

Community as Context

You share a partnership with parents and other family members in enabling the child to be the best that he or she can be—physically, emotionally, socially. The ECLC program should provide a welcoming community for families in the context of their lives at that time. Parents know their child best, and it is important that you respect their values and parenting practices. After all, the child is part of that family for a lifetime but is part of your ECLC program for only a limited time. Parents are the decision makers about their child's health. Educators, however, may be able to provide information such as referrals to agencies, books, articles, and other individuals who help parents consider new information or another perspective in their decisions. Building relationships with parents on a daily basis benefits everyone involved. With the busy lives that families lead, as well as the busy days in the ECLC programs, communication is increasingly less face-to-face time and more communication via written and online approaches. Finding best ways to communicate in an ongoing way with individual families is one of the ways that educators demonstrate a caring and responsive attitude.

After you graduate as an early childhood educator, you may at times be concerned about the effects of a family's health values or practices on the child's well-being. You must determine whether your concern stems from a value or practice that is different from any to which you are accustomed. This contrast may reflect sociocultural differences, a term that refers to ethnicity, race, socioeconomic status, religion, or any other aspect of a social group that shapes values and practices. This value or practice may be very different from, or even in conflict with, one that you grew up with. If it is, you must decide whether this value or practice is simply another way of looking at something or is potentially harmful to the child's physical, emotional, or social well-being. You broaden your awareness by learning about other perspectives. You may or may not decide to adopt this value or practice, but it is important that you not judge others solely on the basis of your limited view. Competent educators strive to communicate with families and support each family's values as much as possible while maintaining standards of high-quality ECLC.

If, on the other hand, you are unsure about the parents' values or practices because of the potential for physical, emotional, or social harm to the child, you have a responsibility to follow up. Effective communication with parents ensures that you understand the value or practice. Ineffective communication frequently results in assumptions and

Adam Crowley/Photodisc/Getty Images

judgments based on incomplete information. It is possible, often with the help of community resources, to make a more informed decision on the issue and decide, likely with the director, on a plan of action. Keep in mind that most parents care about their children and believe that their parenting reflects this care. This principle can be very helpful in deciding what to do next.

In addition to pre-enrollment interviews, parents and educators find out more about each other through day-to-day communication, regular parent–educator interviews, the parent handbook, bulletin boards, email, newsletters, and other communication vehicles. If differences exist between the program's philosophy and policies and the parents' values and practices, the parents might consider using an ECLC program that better reflects their attitudes. In most situations, however, educators and the director will have tried to negotiate a mutually acceptable situation before that happens.

"**Social capital**" is a term that means the power of socially cohesive communities that benefits all children and families, as communities support healthy practices by making a healthy choice the easy choice. Social networks can include family, acquaintances, work colleagues, neighbours, and friends, such as other parents from their child's early learning and care program. Participation or membership in a long list of possible informal or formal organizations and associations can also help families and children to communicate with and build trust in others. Communication can be face-to-face or through many other possibilities such as social media (e.g., parents' groups on Facebook), telephone, and text messaging. The more social resources that adults, especially parents of young children, have access to and are able to use to share ideas and supportive suggestions, the greater the benefits to children and families.

The following are highlights from *Trends in Social Capital in Canada* (Turcotte, 2015, p. 3), comparing statistics in surveys of Canadians in 2003 and 2013:

	2003	2013
The percentage of Canadians having three or more close friends increased.	70%	75%
The percentage of Canadians who reported having done a favour for a neighbour in the past month increased.	61%	70%
Canadians' social networks, particularly among young people, have become more ethnically diverse.	54%	59%
The percentage of Canadians who participated in or were a member of a group, an association, or an organization increased.	61%	65%
The number of Canadians agreeing that, generally speaking, "most people can be trusted" remained the same.	54%	54%
The number of Canadians reporting that "you cannot be too careful in dealing with people" remained the same.	46%	46%

Source: Martin Turcotte, 2015. *Trends in Social Capital in Canada*, May 20, http://www.statcan.gc.ca/pub/89-652-x/89-652-x2015002-eng.pdf. Reproduced and distributed on an "as is" basis with the permission of Statistics Canada.

In summary, ongoing communication in ECLC settings and socially cohesive neighbourhoods and communities are great ways to build trust, create social networks, and buffer some of the stressors in the lives of families.

Because families are so diverse, educators also recognize the importance of culture in people's health and well-being. "**Culture**" sounds like a simple word, but it can actually be a very complex term. It is probably best defined by each individual. "Inherited" culture can include race, ethnicity, language, and religion. "Personal" culture, on the other hand, is acquired and often reflects shared values and attitudes and similarities in ideology.

You may define your personal culture primarily by your family structure, your race or ethnic background, the language you speak (e.g., deaf culture), your religion, your sexual orientation (e.g., lesbian), and so on. People usually define their culture by the aspects of their lives that most affect their day-to-day living, and some aspects of culture are learned and passed on through generations.

As noted by the Government of Canada (2011), some people face additional health risks due to marginalization, stigmatization, and lack of access to culturally appropriate services. Culture-specific practices can also have an impact on the overall health of a population. The skilled educator respects and accommodates, as much as possible, the cultural preferences of a family—everything from respecting religious dietary restrictions to toilet learning preferences. Referring families to culturally relevant services and agencies in the community is one way to support their inclusivity and access.

CRITICAL THINKING

Your program's philosophy places a high value on helping children develop independence. However, one family in the program places a high value on interdependence (i.e., a long-term commitment to depending on one another, remaining close to family). How do the staff and parents compromise in the best interest of the child?

It is important to recognize that there are different ways of being and doing, and not all ways will be familiar to you. By asking parents informal questions such as "How do you handle this type of situation at home?" you can gain insight into why a child doesn't respond well to the educators' strategy, and you can also acquire another way of looking at the issue. In a program that has an open view to diversity, this would simply be viewed as a different way—a way to be respected. Children can be caught between two value systems. When issues about value differences arise, it is a priority to negotiate a cultural conflict so that neither way is devalued (see What's Good for Children: A Multiethnic View, page 40).

Educators have a responsibility to find out as much as possible about the child and family and to be sensitive and responsive to differences. It is certainly possible for children to move comfortably between the ECLC setting and the home culture, where roles, expectations, and interactions may differ considerably, if there is mutual respect between and interest from educators and parents. A climate of acceptance paves the way for understanding and learning for everyone involved. To be effective professionals, educators need to respect diversity and difference, gender equality, and inclusion of children with disabilities.

If a child and his or her family believe that the ECLC environment supports the child's individuality and cultural values, beliefs, and practices, they will feel emotionally secure and comfortable contributing to others' awareness of their values and practices. Children are profoundly influenced by the attitudes of their adult community. The term "**cultural safety**" refers to the outcome of interactions in which individuals experience their cultural identity and way of being as having been respected or, at least, not challenged or harmed (Early Childhood Development Intercultural Partnerships, n.d.). It is essential for educators to remember the importance of this outcome in their relationships with families and coworkers.

WHAT'S GOOD FOR CHILDREN: A MULTIETHNIC VIEW

It's good for children to receive culturally competent care that is sensitive and has a global, multiethnic view.

Culturally competent care requires that:

- Adults in children's lives respect each other.

- Adults in children's lives work to understand each other's perspectives.

- Caregivers and parents understand how program and family values may differ and work together toward blending differing value systems.

- Adults in children's lives create ongoing dialogues.

DIALOGUES

- Dialogues ensure that information is exchanged so that good judgment can result from the blending of shared points of view.

- Dialogues require that everyone who works with children is both a teacher and a learner. Professionals must be willing to understand each other and to view parents as the experts who know what's good for their children.

- Dialogues occur when the people involved begin by listening to each other instead of judging each other. (Gonzalez-Mena, 2014)

People from common ethnic backgrounds may have shared traits (e.g., skin colour, language), customs, and behaviour. How people view health and illness, doctors, medicine, and approaches to healing may be influenced by their ethnicity. In addition to finding out about these beliefs directly from parents, you can contact agencies that are aware of an ethnoculture's health beliefs and practices. However, we can't assume from general information that a family has particular health beliefs or practices. Individuals and families are unique in their situations and beliefs—ethnicity is just one aspect of many that shape people's lives.

CRITICAL THINKING

Your main responsibility as an educator is to focus on each child's healthy development and communicate updates with the child's family on a regular basis. However, you may find that it is challenging for families, especially newcomer families, to focus on these discussions when they are facing immediate issues and problems. Refer to the most applicable social determinants of health to ECLC programs (page 27) to identify two relevant determinants that may be at the forefront of family concerns after arriving in Canada. Think of at least one positive, respectful way to support parents in becoming more ready to discuss their child's development with staff (see *Growing Up in a New Land: A Guide for Newcomer Parents* in the Resource Materials).

NELSONstudy

To access Resource Materials, visit NelsonStudy.

High-Quality Early Childhood Learning and Care Programs

Tens of thousands of young children in Canada are enrolled in licensed ECLC programs. Many thousands who would benefit do not have the opportunity to attend licensed programs based on limited spaces. High-quality programs support children's lifelong learning and families' needs. Consequently, society must acknowledge that these programs are essential services for families, recognize the indicators of high-quality programs, and support the delivery of service through legislative and financial changes. If parents have access to high-quality ECLC programs, they can participate fully in their work or education, which enhances the quality of their lives and the lives of their children.

ECLC programs support parents in their role as their children's primary educators. High-quality ECLC programs have positive long-term health effects for children, as discussed earlier. "The positive relationship between child care

Courtesy of George Brown College/Richmond Adelaide Child Care Centre

Courtesy of Barb Pimento

quality and virtually every facet of children's development …
is one of the most consistent findings in developmental science" (Shonkoff & Phillips, 2001, p. 313).

A baseline for quality is found in the legislation in each province and territory. Regulations for licensed ECLC programs include specifications for the following matters, among others:

- early childhood learning and care training requirements
- group size
- staff–child ratios
- space requirements
- program planning
- nutrition requirements
- management of ill children

Every licensed ECLC program has a copy of its provincial or territorial regulations. It is important to understand that these regulations ensure a minimum standard. A minimum level of care is *not* high-quality early childhood learning and care. Because licensing early childhood settings is a provincial and territorial responsibility, regulations vary greatly across Canada. An area of particular concern is the wide variation in levels of early childhood education (ECE) training required for staff working in the field.

Your role as a student and entry-level educator in providing quality care is crucial in promoting the physical, emotional, and social well-being of the children and families you serve.

Early Childhood Learning and Care Program Policies

An ECLC program can ensure that they implement a high-quality program by having

- a written philosophy that states its ideology about children's learning and care;
- policies that guide decisions and plans of action;
- procedures that answer the who, what, when, where, and why for each policy; and
- educators who consistently implement the policies and procedures. Educators and parents need to understand the rationale behind the policies before they can see the big picture in procedures.

ECLC is a cooperative effort shared by staff and families. Preparing a policy manual is one way to demonstrate that shared commitment. Writing, reviewing, and revising the manual annually draw on the expertise of the staff, families, and professionals in the community (e.g., public health, child abuse prevention, social services). The reviewers evaluate the effectiveness and relevance of the policies and procedures. Health information, circumstances, and priorities change. Staff or parents may raise new issues and concerns.

TABLE 1.2 The Elements of Quality Early Childhood Learning and Care

Children can experience high-quality early childhood education and care in any type of child care setting. High quality begins by protecting a child's health and safety but goes much further to provide an experience that actively supports the child's development. Research tells us that the following characteristics are fundamental to high-quality education and care:

ELEMENT DESCRIPTION	BENEFITS TO CHILDREN
Environment	
High Ratio of Adults to Children*	
- Children under 2 years: 1:3	- Closer relationships between children and educators
- Children ages 2–3: 1:6	- Less aggressive, more considerate, and more self-confident children in the early childhood environment
- Preschoolers: 1:8	- By Grade 1, children demonstrate more independence, superior social and communication skills, and better cognitive development
Group Sizes	
- Smaller groups show benefits	- More cooperative and generally better behaviour in children
	- Communication and play with others is increased
	- Higher scores on tests of social ability and readiness to read

(continued)

TABLE 1.2 The Elements of Quality Early Childhood Learning and Care *(continued)*

ELEMENT DESCRIPTION	BENEFITS TO CHILDREN
Environment	
Well-Defined Spaces	
• Indoor and outdoor group space and activity areas are well-defined, with obvious boundaries	• Positive interactions between children and between children and adults
	• Children are better engaged with their surroundings and spend more time exploring the environment
Approach	
Education	
• Post-secondary college diploma or university degree in early childhood education	• Children score higher than others of the same age on standard tests of language development
• Care is more specialized to the needs and abilities of each child	
• Activities are carefully chosen to match appropriate development level and degree of stimulation	
Curricula Are Well Structured and Planned	
• Daily schedules are familiar to children and include routines	• Children show higher creativity
• Activities are organized and age-appropriate while also allowing for choice	• Cognitive and language test scores are higher
	• Children are less likely to show signs of stress
Relationships	
Positive Relationships between Children and Educators	
• Educators show an active interest in the children and encourage them to communicate	• Higher levels of language development and play
• Educators are sensitive and responsive to each child	• Children demonstrate better engagement with the world around them and less tendency to wander
Positive Relationships between Educators and Families	
• Educators and parents or families of children demonstrate mutual respect	• More interaction between the educator and child
• Communication is open	• Children interact better with peers
• Family is involved as a partner in the child's care	
Responsive Care	
• Care based on sensitivity to physical and emotional needs (e.g., food, sleep, attention)	• Gradually builds tolerance for stimulation and new experiences
• Acknowledges verbal and non-verbal signals used to communicate	• Prevents overstimulation
• Respects each child's unique threshold for new experiences or stimulation at a particular time	• Avoids forcing children into dealing with more than he or she can comfortably manage

*Although there are recommended ratios for age groups, how your province or territory defines age groups and group sizes may differ from ratios as stated here.

Source: Canadian Council on Learning (2006), *Why Is High-Quality Child Care Essential? The Link between Quality Child Care and Early Learning,* pp. 2–4 (July 2013).

Health Policies

Policy manuals are legal documents that outline the program's philosophy, its goals and objectives, and how the educators intend to meet the regulations and implement the procedures. Well-written policies combine the child care regulations, early childhood education training, the expertise of other professionals and parents, and the most current health information available, in addition to drawing upon what staff have learned from managing previous health and safety issues. However, regulations are only minimum requirements based on legislation. High-quality programs build on that foundation to develop fuller, broader, inclusive **health policies** that reflect their knowledge and skills in caring for children daily. When a policy is well written, its rationale is clearly understood and the stated procedures obviously promote the well-being of children, staff, and families.

Policy manuals are living documents. Our knowledge of children's well-being, including health, nutrition, hygiene, safety, growth and development, illness, medical conditions, and physical or emotional challenges, evolves more quickly than legislators make or change regulations. Furthermore, educators use past experiences to identify additional policy issues. Policy manuals incorporate the unexpected—"What will we do if this happens?" (The manual outlines the steps to follow if, for example, a child's noncustodial parent arrives to take the child from the centre, as well as what to do when a child vomits medication.) An effective policy manual adapts to the changing needs of individual programs.

An infant program has an outbreak of diarrhea. Hand-washing and diapering routines should be suspected of causing the spread of the virus or bacteria responsible for the gastrointestinal infection. Without the policy manual setting out the steps for diapering and hand washing, staff are not able to evaluate the educators' compliance with the routines that would have prevented the spread. Perhaps the policy and procedures are not effective. Perhaps educators need retraining in the routines and closer supervision.

Beyond the legal licensing requirement for having a manual, policies have a variety of purposes. They can explain how to

- conduct staff orientation, in-service training, and job performance appraisals;
- extract the most relevant policies to be developed into parent handbooks; and
- define lines of communication and confidentiality.

They also

- contain the administrative and medical/health forms and specify who has access to that information;
- contain information sheets and handouts and routines that can be used for posters on such topics as diapering, toileting, hand washing, and exclusion criteria; and
- identify the names and associations related to ECLC programs so that staff stay current with related research.

Each regulation provides directors, educators, their boards, and parents with the basis for developing policies and procedures for the individual day-to-day program, the ages of the children, and their location. The following illustrates a few of the issues that may be included in discussions about policies and procedures:

- The medication policy indicates what medications are permitted and why. Procedures are clearly spelled out and cover administration, storage, and record keeping; identification and reporting of side effects and medication errors; and the management of emergency situations. The program's expectations of parents regarding medications would also be included. In the event of a medication incident, comparing the procedures with the actions of the educator will determine whether precautions were in place and carried out to the best of the person's ability to prevent the error. Perhaps such a review would determine that the current medication procedures require revision.

- A child falls from a climbing structure in the winter and breaks his arm. On examination, the impact-absorbing surface is found to be covered with a sheet of ice. Does the program have an outdoor play policy and procedures in place that, when implemented, would prevent children from using a climber when the surface does not meet safety requirements? In addition, the policy handbook needs to clearly state what to do, what to document, and whom to contact if there is a serious occurrence.

- A school-age program located in an elementary school establishes clear lines of communication with the principal and the children's teachers to ensure the consistent coordination of health policies.

- All legislated requirements (e.g., suspected child abuse reporting) must be included, with the necessary procedures.

- When a child gets sick during the day, does the school notify the parents, or is doing so the program's responsibility?

- Are the regular safety checks of the playground and equipment a shared responsibility of the ECLC program staff and the school, or are they solely the school's responsibility? Are the expectations about the use of the playground equipment consistent between the program and the school? When issues arise, how are they reported and recorded? Who is responsible for record keeping?

- Do the educators and teachers consistently teach and model healthy habits?

- When concerns are raised about a child or a family by either the educators or a teacher, do both parties work together to address the concerns?

Advocating for High-Quality Early Childhood Learning and Care Programs

In the 1980s, advocates for a national child care plan agreed on three fundamental principles for a child care system: universal accessibility, comprehensiveness, and high quality. Their continued advocacy for child care indirectly promotes children's health. High-quality ECLC benefits all children.

A universal, publicly-funded, high quality childcare system has always been a key element in Campaign 2000's anti-poverty plan. Universal early childhood education and care (ECEC) is necessary for parents to escape poverty through workforce and education participation, for making women's equality a reality and for ensuring that all children, including those who are low income, Indigenous and newcomers to Canada, can benefit from quality ECEC. Quality ECEC supports child development and school readiness and is an important buffer from the negative effects of poverty. (Campaign 2000, 2017, p. 16)

After decades of federal government promises, Canada is one of only a few wealthy countries that still does not have a national child care plan to serve all families. Uneven distribution and underfunding is the reality across Canada, leading to failure to meet the needs of the majority of children and families.

The limited supply of spaces covers only 1/4 of children aged 0–5 years; childcare for infants/toddlers is even more scarce. Regulated childcare is unaffordable for most families. A 2016 study found that 75% of Toronto families cannot afford childcare; median fees outside Quebec reach $1600/month/per child. Fee subsidy schemes fail the low income families they are intended for; long wait lists and hefty surcharges keep many out. (Campaign 2000, 2017, p. 17)

The evidence is compelling and overwhelming: well-funded, integrated ECLC programs improve the cognitive and social functioning of all children and affect education, health, the social capital, and overall equity within populations. This is key for stable, cohesive societies and economic growth. ECLC programs have the capacity to support pluralism and reduce inequities. If properly linked to labour, health, and social services, ECLC programs can deliver additional outcomes, such as enhanced maternal employment, less family poverty, better parenting skills, and greater family and community cohesion. Quality ECLC programs are not only good for children and families, they are also good for the bottom line. Focused public spending on young children provides returns that outstrip any other type of human capital investment (McCain et al., 2007, p. 135).

Photo by Roberto Machado Noa/LightRocket via Getty Images

Advocacy doesn't occur only at the national level. Advocates for high-quality ECLC are working to improve standards of care in each province and territory by ensuring that revisions made to legislation reflect the indicators of high-quality ECLC.

How can early childhood educators and students deliver high-quality early childhood learning and care that supports health promotion? Your training provides you with the entry-level knowledge and skills to provide a level of care higher than the minimum set out in the legislation. Your training also helps you recognize the importance of delivering a high-quality ECLC program. This commitment to ongoing learning and professional behaviour makes you a "personal" advocate. To be a public policy advocate, you can be involved in local, provincial/territorial, or federal early childhood education organizations that address issues of quality, accessibility, and compensation for educators. "Policies that cannot measure up in addressing all three issues are not solutions and may become part of the problem" (Gestwicki & Bertrand, 2012, p. 252). We need to speak with one voice to safeguard accomplishments and move forward.

WHAT QUALITY CHILD CARE CAN DO FOR ALL OF US

- Ensure that all young children have the very best opportunity to thrive.
- Allow parents to work to support their families.
- Support women's equality.
- Strengthen the economy through returns on women's education, training, and workforce participation.
- Build strong local communities by generating ongoing economic activity.
- Allow Canada to meet its human rights obligations to children and women.

Source: From Campaign 2000, *Needed: A Federal Action Plan to Eradicate Child Poverty in Canada, 2012 Report Card on Child and Family Poverty*, p. 15. Reprinted by permission of Campaign 2000.

In Canada, only 24.1% of children under the age of five have access to regulated child care spaces. However, 73.5% of mothers with young children do paid work (Savigny, 2017, pp. 17–19). The most recent year Canada reported early childhood learning and care enrollment numbers to the Organisation for Economic Co-operation and Development (OECD) was in 2010. The OECD is an assembly of 35 countries committed to democracy and the market economy, using "its wealth of information on a broad range of topics to help governments foster prosperity and fight poverty through economic growth and financial stability" (OECD, n.d., p. 1). Based on this information, it seems that Canada's statistics regarding regulated ECLC spaces are far from updated.

OBJECTIVES

To identify the three components of a health promotion action plan and describe how they can be implemented. (LO 3)

To list three reasons why a health promotion action approach contributes to ECLC programs. (LO 2, 3)

To discuss student and educator strategies to advocate for high-quality ECLC programs. (LO 3, 5)

In Canada, only 24.1% of children under the age of five have access to regulated child care spaces. However, 73.5% of mothers with young children do paid work (Savigny, 2017, pp. 17–19). The most recent year Canada reported early childhood learning and care enrollment numbers to the Organisation for Economic Co-operation and Development (OECD) was in 2010. The OECD is an assembly of 35 countries committed to democracy and the market economy, using "its wealth of information on a broad range of topics to help governments foster prosperity and fight poverty through economic growth and financial stability" (OECD, n.d., p. 1). Based on this information, it seems that Canada's statistics regarding regulated ECLC spaces are far from updated.

HEALTH PROMOTION ACTION PLAN

Health promotion, in a broad sense, enables individuals, the community, and levels of government to identify health risks and make positive changes at the individual, community, and societal (population health) levels. It moves beyond a focus on individual behaviour toward a wide range of social and environmental interventions. However, not all health promotion can happen at the macro level. A population health approach will effect social change, but the day-to-day realities of life necessitate action on a range of scales—from the individual to societal change.

Action Plan

Health promotion activities enable us to take action to improve our own health and that of all Canadians. A **health promotion action plan** establishes a set of strategies that can be divided into three components:

- individual problem solving and self-reliance
- community action
- societal change

Optimally, when all three components are at work, the likelihood of significant change is high. At the individual level, one is benefiting from the action, either in the short or long term. But all health promotion is positive and should not be underestimated. At the community level, small or larger numbers and groups of people are involved, and, of course, societal change is at the level of population health, improving outcomes locally, provincially, or territorially and sometimes improving outcomes for all Canadians. Realistically, however, we are not always successful in achieving our original goals. During the process, we may need to adjust the vision. Barriers may be impossible to overcome. But even these situations usually have outcomes that contribute to good health, such as developing coping skills, increased social supports, networking, and a long-term commitment to work for change.

Individual Problem Solving and Self-Reliance

As individuals, we solve problems all the time, and many of our behavioural changes occur when we focus on improvements or solutions. However, changing our behaviour is easier when we do not have to overcome barriers or when we have the resources to effect change.

- Because Alyssa's parents provide a variety of nutritious foods, she has learned to make healthy food choices. They guide their daughter's development of healthy eating habits by modelling. By the time she is of school age, she will have developed the knowledge and decision-making skills to make choices. Then when she becomes influenced by peers and the media and may not always make the healthiest choices, she will at least be aware when she is eating less nutritious foods and can therefore balance her choices.
- You decide to add more physical activity to your life by regularly walking to work or school.

Societal barriers or influences can affect our ability to make healthy lifestyle decisions either positively or negatively. In the past, smoking was accepted by society. The media depicted it as fun, sophisticated, and elegant. Smokers could smoke almost anywhere, and no one was concerned about second-hand smoke or about pregnant women smoking. There were no barriers; in fact, society encouraged people to smoke. Today, smoking is recognized as one of the most serious public health concerns, and this has resulted in public education on the risks of smoking, support and products to help stop smoking, legislation from all three levels of government on smoke-free environments, taxes on tobacco, strict limitations on advertising, and limitations on availability (e.g., pharmacies do not sell tobacco, and cigarette vending machines have been banned). Long-time smokers are quitting, supported and encouraged by society. People are more comfortable in asking smokers not to smoke in their cars or homes, and many smokers ask permission before lighting up. Smoking in public has been severely restricted, with the knowledge now that both second-hand (nonsmokers taking in smoke from others in the vicinity) and third-hand (toxins brought indoors on smokers' clothes, etc.) smoke pose health hazards.

Even with relative numbers of smokers in Canada decreasing, public health officials remain concerned about the number of teenagers (more girls than boys) who are first-time smokers. From a developmental perspective, it's not surprising that adolescents are exerting control over their lives and may, in fact, make decisions counter to parental or public opinion. This is complicated by the fact that teenagers and young adults may view themselves as invincible.

Community Action

When individuals come together as a community, they pool skills, knowledge, and resources to support one another and work toward change. A health promotion strategy oriented toward community action is an effective way to make change to meet the health needs of a community, particularly where barriers are present. Community action may occur in settings such as workplaces, schools, clinics, and communities with partnership and capacity building across multiple sectors and diverse organizations. The workplace, for example, is an important community setting for health promotion. While physical factors such as air quality and injuries are still of concern, the focus in the workplace is moving to the social issues of health, particularly mental health. This will be evident in Unit 2: Occupational Health.

Health promotion aims for changes that will involve and have an impact on the whole group (whether big or small), a process known as community capacity building. Community capacity building can happen when groups of people

- work together to identify issues and priorities that reflect their needs;

- develop and implement an action plan, which usually involves communication with a number of agencies and resources; and

- evaluate the strengths and deficiencies of their actions and the extent to which they have realized their goals.

A group of tenants in an apartment building has recognized that grocery shopping is difficult because of issues such as

- their low income,
- the lack of public transportation to affordable stores, and
- the many single-parent families who have no one to care for their children while the parents are grocery shopping.

As a small community, the tenants organize a food depot that is open once a week and sells fresh fruit and vegetables. A food produce supplier provides the local produce at a reasonable cost.

A community doesn't always have to be a large group of people.

Several neighbours organize an informal babysitting system that lets one parent shop for groceries while another cares for the children. This allows the parents to shop without taking tired, bored, or hungry children with them, which often results in impulse buying and angry parents or frustrated children.

Although this example reflects cooperation, the group is somewhat self-reliant. Often, once a small group has worked together in this way, the participants begin to identify broader social and health issues or concerns (e.g., causes of ill health) and may move toward more of a larger community action model.

A group of directors that meets regularly as a network shares a concern about the food that parents are providing for their school-age children. The directors organize a parent meeting, invite a dietitian-nutritionist and social worker, and provide child care and dinner. At the meeting, participants identify a number of issues:

- lack of affordable food
- lack of nutrition resources that fit the literacy and interest levels of a number of the parents
- time constraints for parents and their need for ideas for nutritious lunches that can be easily prepared
- children's practice of trading lunch items with peers and a concern that nutritious foods won't be desirable
- children's beliefs that foods from their ethnocultural backgrounds will not be accepted by their peers

In the example about nutrition for school-age children, the small community's work led the participants to develop an action plan that included reaching out into the larger community for resources. This had benefits not only for the immediate issue but also for long-term well-being. Regular links with the broader community tend to foster an active problem-solving approach to life.

All participants involved have some role in the process, including evaluating whether goals have been met. Parents and staff may have different responsibilities and perspectives, but everyone works toward the same goal. Depending on the ages of the children and the actions being taken, some or all of the children may be involved in the process (e.g., if a community vegetable garden is part of the solution).

A few people in a neighbourhood are concerned about the quality of the air due to smokestack emissions at a local factory. Together, they go door to door to gain citizen support and they meet with public health officials, governmental officials, and the factory management. Then they develop a plan of action to reduce the emissions.

Societal Change

Depending on the extent of the issue and who is involved, community action can lead to legislative changes—locally, provincially, or federally—that affect everyone in a community (e.g., city or town), a province, a territory, Canada, or even world-wide (e.g., issue such as air quality or climate change). If we take the example of the smokestack emissions a step further, stricter government regulations for companies to reduce air pollution levels (societal change) may emerge from what began as a small community action.

Societal changes often result from changes in legislation or public health policy, the mandate of a population health approach. Social responsibility for health is reflected by the actions of decision makers in both the public and the private sector to pursue policies and practices that promote and protect health (WHO, 1997, p. 5).

Here are some examples:

- air pollution controls
- provincial legislation to ban smoking in cars with child passengers
- drinking-and-driving legislation
- legislative bans on manufacturing and selling equipment that doesn't conform to safety regulations

Of course, even more sweeping changes than public health policy are the social policy changes that can come about when the social determinants of health are addressed. *For example, if a provincial minimum wage is legislated to increase substantially, a significant decline in poverty rates for families could mean improved health for many. Another example would be to implement the harmonization of the immunization schedule in Canada (see Critical Thinking, page 11). And a third example would include a "health in all policies" approach across all government departments' policy initiatives aimed to improve population health (e.g., a national child care plan, with support and likelihood of increased wages and benefits for educators).*

Let's take one last look at the example of staff and parents and their concerns about children's nutrition. As a group, they recognize that their experience is not isolated, that the issue and solutions go beyond their own community and into society at large. Consequently, some participants join a lobby group that is trying to ban television advertising of junk food aimed at children, whereas others work with a national antipoverty group advocating a federal policy for a national child nutrition program. As discussed earlier in this unit, a focus on the bigger issue of reducing and eliminating poverty is, ultimately, the most effective health promotion approach. A collective vote is a powerful tool for effecting change. Find out where political candidates stand on various issues and cast your vote accordingly.

Health Promotion Action Plan in the Early Childhood Learning and Care Program

An action approach to promoting health in programs is positive for a number of reasons:

1. *It fosters partnerships with parents and other family members.* Working together for common goals recognizes and builds on people's knowledge and strengths. In addition to getting the job done, you develop relationships with the families—a benefit to everyone involved.

2. *An action approach helps people learn to solve problems and experience the value of working cooperatively.* When individuals see results, they are more likely to view themselves as having enough personal and collective power to effect change. When all the players are committed to the issue, there are fewer barriers. Of course, there are times when interactions among employers, administrators, and boards or budget restraints result in insurmountable obstacles. Although this will be disappointing, it is helpful to view what has been gained through the process. Obviously, in addition to the benefits from the action itself, working cooperatively also models a cooperative approach for children that is crucial for adapting in our ever-changing world.

3. *An action approach increases the individual's and group's awareness of community resources, knowledge of community need, and community capacity building.* An action plan will probably include communication with public health and other municipal departments, community health centres, social service agencies, and so on. An active approach to promoting health in ECLC settings can lead to improved accessibility for children and families to the larger community as information is shared through family and friends. This leads to community capacity building, whereby groups share common needs and a commitment to turning their ideas into reality.

NETWORKING WITH THE COMMUNITY

Networking with the community contributes to the well-being of children, families, educators, and the overall ECLC program. Educators working effectively as a team contribute significantly to the level of quality provided by the program. No one works in isolation, and ECLC programs are no exception. Staff cannot and should not try to be all things to all people. Staff must establish a network with professionals, agencies, and associations in their community (see Figure 1.3, page 55). This network allows the staff to grow both personally and professionally, resulting

OBJECTIVES

To list ways that educators and ECLC programs benefit from networking with the community. (LO 5)

To describe strategies to handle "mixed messages" that families and educators are faced with around health issues. (LO 5, 6)

Courtesy of Barb Pimento, taken at the Downtown Montessori (Coatsworth) Childcare Centre

in higher-quality ECLC programs. Your early childhood education training and skills equip you to work as an effective member of the network of professionals concerned with the growth, development, and health of children (e.g., public health departments, child abuse prevention teams, school boards, public health, community health centres).

Interprofessional collaboration is recognized as one of the best ways to move forward in effective health and social service practice, as discussed in An Emerging Interprofessional Approach in Health Care (page 18). When different professionals work collaboratively to support children and families, everyone benefits. The professionals are learning with, from, and about each other, building mutual respect as well as shared knowledge and decision making in the best interests of the child and the family. The additional benefits of drawing a number of services together include reduced duplication, improvements to the delivery of service, and lower costs. As students in an early childhood education program, you may be overwhelmed when you think about developing relationships with individuals and groups, but be assured that it doesn't happen overnight. It is important that you see the benefits of working collaboratively, learning from others, and sharing your expertise. In ECLC settings where staff and the director do not work collaboratively, children, families, and staff are at a real disadvantage. No one person or agency can do it all or know it all. Networking increases resources and decreases educator stress levels (see Figure 1.3).

As you can see from our discussion on health promotion, your approach to your work can affect the health and well-being of children and families. For those educators who are committed to their profession, what you think (attitude), what you know (knowledge), and what you do (behaviour) are evolving positively through education and experience. We must recognize our strengths and limitations throughout this lifelong learning process and make responsible decisions

FIGURE 1.3   Groups and Individuals Who Interact with ECLC Programs

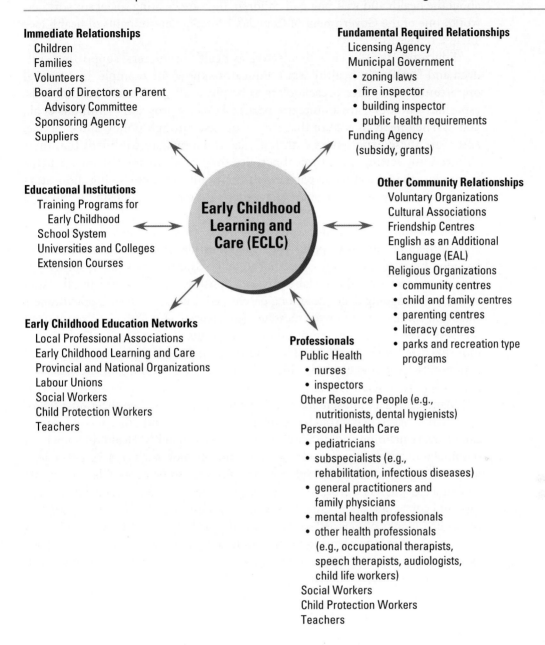

Immediate Relationships
 Children
 Families
 Volunteers
 Board of Directors or Parent
   Advisory Committee
 Sponsoring Agency
 Suppliers

Fundamental Required Relationships
 Licensing Agency
 Municipal Government
  • zoning laws
  • fire inspector
  • building inspector
  • public health requirements
 Funding Agency
   (subsidy, grants)

Educational Institutions
 Training Programs for
   Early Childhood
 School System
 Universities and Colleges
 Extension Courses

**Early Childhood
Learning and
Care (ECLC)**

Other Community Relationships
 Voluntary Organizations
 Cultural Associations
 Friendship Centres
 English as an Additional
   Language (EAL)
 Religious Organizations
  • community centres
  • child and family centres
  • parenting centres
  • literacy centres
  • parks and recreation type
    programs

Early Childhood Education Networks
 Local Professional Associations
 Early Childhood Learning and Care
 Provincial and National Organizations
 Labour Unions
 Social Workers
 Child Protection Workers
 Teachers

Professionals
 Public Health
  • nurses
  • inspectors
 Other Resource People (e.g.,
   nutritionists, dental hygienists)
 Personal Health Care
  • pediatricians
  • subspecialists (e.g.,
    rehabilitation, infectious diseases)
  • general practitioners and
    family physicians
  • mental health professionals
  • other health professionals
    (e.g., occupational therapists,
    speech therapists, audiologists,
    child life workers)
 Social Workers
 Child Protection Workers
 Teachers

accordingly. All educators and directors need access to resources; a student or recent graduate of an early childhood education program needs to have increased support that is readily available.

Mixed Messages

Parents of young children and educators are inundated with many mixed and competing messages about health issues as they try to determine how best to promote children's optimal well-being. These messages come from the media, the Internet, printed materials, family members, public health departments, and other sources.

An everyday strategy is communication. When parents and educators connect about the health and well-being of children, they are creating social support networks, one of the Government of Canada's 12 social determinants of health (see Table 1.1, page 5).

Educators need to view themselves as health promoters, supporting children and families in healthy ways. Educators know, for example, that several opportunities a day for preschoolers to be physically active for short periods, especially outdoors, are an integral part of a quality program (Timmons et al., 2007). They need to ensure that this happens, through policy and practice, and share these experiences with families. If parents are confident that their children are getting the physical activity they need during the day, it helps them view the educators as partners in their child's healthy living. Educators and families may be able to share suggestions for enjoyable but simple physical activity ideas.

On the flip side, educators are responsive to families' concerns, creating an environment of mutual respect. As discussed earlier, educators take care not to abandon important cultural values but to make adjustments when it seems reasonable and recognize that collaborative relationships are key to effective decision making. An ongoing dialogue among parents, educators, and health practitioners can avoid confusion and mixed messages (e.g., fear of germs) that can result from one perspective that is not tempered by other points of view. This dialogue is also more likely to lead to healthy policy at the program level and possibly advocacy at community levels and beyond, which can contribute to health improvements for greater numbers of children.

Many Canadian households now have Internet access. The sheer quantity of information accessible through the Internet, television, and other media sources can be overwhelming and difficult to evaluate for reliability. Health literacy is an essential tool for parents and educators. Invaluable tools such as *A Parent's Guide to Health Information on the Internet* by CPS need to be accessible for parents and educators. CPS's *Caring for Kids* website is designed for parents and educators, and educators can include the site in communication tools such as parent or policy handbooks or newsletters. CPS's *Caring for Kids New to Canada* website is for health professionals working with immigrant and refugee children and youth and includes valuable information for parents and educators, such as culture and health. (See Resource Materials.)

NELSONstudy

To access Resource Materials, visit NelsonStudy.

CONCLUSION

As educators, we can contribute to the health promotion plan. In our daily work with children and families, we can put into practice a health promotion philosophy by

- developing and following healthy policies and procedures;
- modelling healthy habits ourselves;
- communicating in an ongoing way with the families, demonstrating sensitivity and openness to their health beliefs and practices; and
- networking with the community, including interprofessional collaboration, realizing that we all benefit through sharing resources and expertise.

Each of the following units in this book discusses health-related practices in the ECLC program.

Healthy lifestyles, the physical environment, and genetics are significant determinants of health. To improve the quality of life for all Canadians, however, action needs to be taken on the social and economic determinants of health in particular, giving priority to the serious problem of income inequity. According to the Canadian Institute for Health Information, "research on health inequalities has consistently shown that individuals with higher income tend to have better health outcomes; this is the socio-economic gradient in health" (2016, p. 33). The Health Council of Canada reported that "Canadians with higher incomes and levels of education have longer lifespans, are less likely to suffer from chronic conditions such as diabetes, and report better overall health status than those with lower incomes and levels of education" (Canadian Institute for Health Information, 2016, p. 17). The wider the gap in population income, the poorer the population health. As Nelson Mandela, the renowned South African civil rights activist, wisely stated, "Security for a few is insecurity for us all."

ASSESS YOUR LEARNING

Define terms or describe concepts used in this unit.

- complementary (or traditional) health practitioners
- cultural safety
- culture
- developmental health
- health
- health policies
- health promotion
- health promotion action plan
- interprofessional collaboration
- mental health promotion
- national principles of medicare
- natural health products
- networking
- population health approach
- prevention
- primary health care system
- public health system
- quality of life
- social capital
- social determinants of health

Evaluate your options in each situation.

1. Your doctor hands you a prescription. When you ask him what it's for and whether there are side effects, he replies, "Don't worry about it. Just take these pills and you'll feel better."

2. Classes have been cancelled for the day to allow students to attend a child care rally at the legislature. You are tempted to skip it because you have to study for a test.

3. A parent is angry at pickup time because his daughter's sleeves are damp from water play even though she was wearing a smock. He believes that this is how someone gets a cold. He asks that his daughter never play at the water table again.

4. One of the parents of a child in the infant room says she doesn't know what to do because she gets different messages at every turn. The information in her magazines and what she finds on the Internet differs from what her husband's family tells her, and that differs from what the educators say and do in the ECLC program.

5. A safety issue arises at the centre. None of the staff can think of a suitable response, and you suggest that consulting with another centre may provide options. The director insists, "We can work this out ourselves," and does not want outside interference.

Courtesy of George Brown College/Casa Loma Child Care Centre

Occupational Health

2

CONTENTS

TABLES

FIGURES

APPENDIXES

Students in colleges and universities are not a homogeneous group but reflect the communities in which they live. Many students are right out of high school; others are mature students returning to school after time spent in the workforce. Some are parents. Some are in their first educational program since arriving in Canada. Many are juggling school and part-time jobs or other commitments. You, too, are entering your early childhood education (ECE) studies with experiences different from those of your classmates, and you have responsibilities beyond the classroom and placements in early childhood learning and care (ECLC) settings.

Even at the best of times, school can be stressful. It is a period of transition: establishing new friendships and study habits, trying to budget your time and money. There can be additional adjustments to make, such as moving away from home for the first time or to a new community. It's not surprising if you are experiencing stressors, suffering emotional ups and downs, feeling tired and at times discouraged, feeling pulled in different directions. A survey of over 30,000 postsecondary students across Canada at 34 colleges and universities found that "89 per cent of students said they were overwhelmed by all they had to do; nearly 54 per cent reported being hopeless and 64 per cent lonely sometime in the past 12 months; 86.9 per cent said they were exhausted, [and] 56 per cent felt overwhelming anxiety" (Winsa, 2013, p. 2).

Occupations that we tend to think of as stressful are those that are inherently dangerous, such as mining, operating heavy machinery, firefighting, and police work. Yet every occupation presents potential risks to its employees' physical and emotional health. Store clerks who repeatedly drag groceries over the scanner at the checkout counter can develop severe wrist pain as well as sore legs or varicose veins from standing. People who work at computer terminals all day may suffer from eyestrain, lower back pain, and carpal tunnel syndrome. Employees who perform repetitive tasks and work that permits them little control over their jobs experience a low level of autonomy, which leads to job dissatisfaction. Every profession has stressors; ECLC is no exception. Thankfully, it also includes many benefits and opportunities. In this unit, the focus is on the challenges, in order to impress upon you the importance of managing stressors over which you have control, while joining those who advocate to build a national system that will benefit children, families, and educators.

ECLC is *not* babysitting! Many still believe that working in a licensed ECLC setting is just an extension of minding other people's children. In addition, the fact that ECLC is a predominantly female profession has historically accorded it low status, and many people believe that women naturally have the aptitude, knowledge, and skills needed to care for groups of children. In other words, the popular myth is that anyone can look after children. The reality is that, as discussed in Unit 1, one of the key determinants of health is child development, which highlights the essential role of increasing and retaining qualified and skilled professionals in the early childhood workforce. Many people also don't believe that ECLC (unlike education and health care) constitutes an essential service to families. These attitudes contribute to the low status, low salaries, and lack of respect at times accorded to early childhood educators. There is a wide discrepancy in wage rates for centre-based staff, even within the same province or territory. To address this reality, most provinces have made strides to increase the income levels of early childhood educators (Child Care Human Resources Sector Council, 2013b, p. 18).

Staff turnover has a detrimental effect on everyone involved—children, families, and remaining educators—and is a very significant issue. "Employers in Newfoundland and Labrador, and Alberta reported the highest average number of permanent staff with an ECE credential leaving in the past 12 months (4.0% and 3.8% respectively) and in PEI, Québec and Manitoba the lowest (1.5%, 1.6% and 1.7% respectively). The Canada-wide average was 2.4%" (Child Care Human Resources Sector Council, 2013b, p. 21).

Fortunately, change is happening, however slowly:

There have been significant changes in Canada's ECEC [early childhood education and care] sector since the 1998 *You Bet I Care!* study was carried out. Key informants and focus group participants identified significant program and policy changes since that time that have impacted human resources, and include:

- Introduction of provincial/territorial (PT) policy and funding initiatives that influence human resources, including wage subsidies, educational support, bursaries and incentives, and revised policies regarding recognition of post-secondary early childhood credentials.

- Increasing involvement and oversight of ECEC programs from ministries of education.

- Introduction of early childhood curriculum frameworks.

- Increased support for human resources from . . . national/provincial/territorial early childhood organizations.

- Changing relationships between child care centres and school based kindergarten programs.*

The ECLC community and its professional associations tirelessly advocate at all levels of government. Most families recognize that ECLC programs are an essential service and that children's positive early experiences are critical to their overall development.

As in any other occupation, not everyone is suited to the work. Yes, children are amazing, energetic, curious, active learners. Yes, it can be exciting and rewarding to be involved in their lives and development. But contrary to the stereotype addressed earlier, educators must develop the attitudes, knowledge, and skills necessary to be competent in their career. In addition, ECLC is physical and emotional work. Always having to be "on" with children can be emotionally tiring. Combine this with the working dynamics of coworkers, administration, and management styles of supervisors and directors, and educators can experience excessive job stress leading to burnout.

Most of those who work in ECLC settings do not belong to ECE organizations and, as a result, may have little access to supports such as collegial networking, topical and timely sector information, and professional development opportunities. Educators working in smaller centres are often isolated and have limited interaction with colleagues. Those who provide family home child care usually work alone. Professional affiliation is a critical support to individuals

---

*Source: *You Bet We Still Care! A Survey of Centre-Based Early Childhood Education and Care in Canada*. Highlights Report, Child Care Human Resources Sector Council, 2013, pg. 2. Retrieved November 2017 from http://www.ccsc-cssge.ca/sites/default/files/uploads/Projects-Pubs-Docs /EN%20Pub%20Chart/YouBetSurveyReport_Final.pdf

and the workforce. Professional affiliation in this sector is typically voluntary. In Ontario, educators' registration in the College of Early Childhood Educators is legislated. Other provinces and territories may consider registration or other required professional affiliation in the future. Although there are some stressors that you may not be able to control, you can control many aspects of the work to increase your job satisfaction. In recent decades, a holistic approach to health has often been translated into dimensions of wellness to facilitate self-awareness and enhance individual goal setting. Although dimensions are listed separately in the accompanying table, there is recognition that all aspects of wellness are interrelated. Table 2.1 provides descriptions of eight commonly identified dimensions of wellness.

TABLE 2.1   Dimensions of Personal Wellness

Physical Dimension: met through respect for your body by participating in physical activity regularly; "make healthy food choices and avoid harmful behaviours such as tobacco use, drug misuse, and excessive alcohol consumption." (Hales & Lauzon, 2018, p. 10)

Intellectual Dimension: "refers to your ability to think and learn from life experience"; active mind—gather, process, and "act on information; to think through your values" and "use your critical thinking skills, including your ability to evaluate health information, to safeguard your well-being." (Hales & Lauzon, 2018, p. 10)

Emotional Dimension: "the degree to which one feels positive and enthusiastic about oneself and life, . . . awareness and acceptance of a wide range of feelings in oneself and others; . . . capacity to express and manage your own feelings;" recognition of your strengths and limitations, while effectively coping with stressors. (Hales & Lauzon, 2018, p. 10)

Social Dimension: "encourages a collectivist view of the world—that of contributing to society, helping others, and valuing the concept of interdependence between ourselves and our environment. . . . Individuals who have a sense of connection to others are more likely to have a secure attachment style and benefit from supportive relationships." (Hales & Lauzon, 2018, p. 9)

Occupational Dimension: "Finding enrichment through your work or vocation can enhance your well-being. . . . In a well work environment, you contribute your skills and talents to your community and enjoy work that is meaningful and rewarding. Occupational wellness follows the tenet that it is healthy to balance work and other life commitments." (Hales & Lauzon, 2018, p. 9)

Spiritual Dimension: "Identifying our basic purpose in life; learning how to experience love, joy, peace and fulfillment;" finding things that nourish the soul. (Hales & Lauzon, 2018, p. 10)

Environmental Dimension: being respectful of and trying to live in harmony with nature. It demands leadership and a long-term, coordinated effort from all of us. (Hales & Lauzon, 2018, pp. 10–11)

Financial Dimension: becoming financially literate; learning to take control over money; having the ability to meet basic needs.

Goals can be short term (usually accomplished within a year), long term, or ongoing (e.g., lifelong inclusion of daily physical activity). You're more likely to achieve success in lifestyle changes if your goals are

- specific—Identify in exact terms what you hope to achieve and set out a detailed action plan.

- personalized—Set your own goals rather than having someone set them for you.

- written—Write down your goals and keep a journal of your progress and setbacks; make a contract with yourself.

- realistic—Be realistic. Unattainable goals will discourage you.

- measurable—Ensure that you can measure your goals, for example, "To be able to climb stairs to my apartment (six floors) without being out of breath within eight weeks." or "I will walk briskly with Marnie and Brandon during lunch break for 25 minutes, three days a week for the next six weeks." Goals such as "I'm going to get fit" or "I'm going to lose weight" are not measurable.

- time specific—Establish target dates for your goals. Deadlines are motivational; however, keep in mind that adjustments may be necessary. Behaviour change is always possible but may take a little longer than you predict. Remember to always acknowledge your accomplishments and keep moving forward.

- evaluated—Monitor your progress. This will help you keep on track and determine when a goal may be unrealistic or too easy. Make the necessary goal adjustments to support you in moving forward (Hoeger et al., 2009, pp. 42–43).

This unit begins with an exploration of the physical dimension of early childhood work for educators and students. The second section explores the social and emotional dimensions. Although the topics are organized in sections, they are all interrelated. To explore other dimensions (e.g., spiritual, environmental) more specifically, you may want to refer to wellness manuals such as the one by Hales and Lauzon (2018) (see Resource Materials). It is also important to acknowledge that a common source for health information is the Internet. If this is a significant vehicle of health information for you, ensure that the site is credible (see Appendix 2.1, page 119).

PROMOTING YOUR PHYSICAL WELL-BEING

What are your health concerns about working with children? When instructors ask new ECE students this question, many students worry about head lice, bed bugs, colds, and the flu. We know that when children are first enrolled in programs, they get sick more often, but as time passes, the rate of illness declines. This pattern applies to students as well. Adults benefit from a mature immune system; they are fully immunized, one hopes, and most have already experienced the common childhood diseases (e.g., chickenpox). Adults can also implement hygiene practices that protect them and reduce the opportunities for illness to spread among children and adults. Even so, you may experience a few viral infections when you begin your ECLC program placements.

It probably will take only a couple of days of work in a program to experience firsthand how physically demanding caring for children can be. It's a strain for educators to lift and carry infants and toddlers; move play equipment; sit on the floor; lean over child-sized tables, sinks, and toilets; and be constantly on the move in the playground to supervise children or take part in a physical activity. The positive side is that this constant and varied movement, when performed correctly, contributes to physical fitness. It is also rewarding to care for children, both in terms of the close relationships you begin to develop and the role modelling that calm, empathic care is for children and families.

Achieving a Balance in Your Lifestyle

As adults, we make individual lifestyle choices that can have positive or negative effects on our health.

Nutrition

One of our basic needs is food. However, the amount of emphasis placed on food and our health varies among individuals and throughout society. The bottom line—nutrition has a significant impact on our health and well-being. The principles of nutrition discussed in Unit 5 apply to children's nutritional status and to your own. As well, factors that shape eating habits are discussed; these can assist you in developing insight into why, what, and when you eat. Some people's habits fall far short of the recommended principles of nutrition. Others know what good nutrition includes and put these principles into practice every day.

Everyone wants to be healthy, which makes many of us eager for the newest information about which foods are good and not good for our health. It's easy for us to be influenced or overwhelmed by conflicting nutrition messages. Diet books that present a range of leading-edge nutrition research and claims by the authors can be difficult to understand from the science. Unless you are under the care of a doctor or a dietitian, your best judgment is to maintain eating habits based on a balanced amount of protein, fat, and carbohydrates with plenty of whole grains, vegetables, and fruit. Knowledge of beverages and foods with low or no nutritive value (e.g., soft drinks, chips, candy) can help us make choices that keep these types of foods to a minimum.

Of course, there are times when nutrition is less of a priority—especially to someone experiencing a great deal of stress. There is concern, however, that this becomes a pattern of behaviour or a vicious circle because our bodies have increased nutrient needs at times of emotional or physical stress.

Parvati, an ECE student, is studying frantically for midterm tests and is trying to stay awake by drinking a lot of coffee. Not surprisingly, the coffee keeps her awake even when she wants to sleep. Parvati doesn't believe she has time for sit-down meals and instead eats doughnuts and other low-nutritive foods in the cafeteria. By week's end, Parvati is snapping at everyone and can't imagine how she'll ever survive her weekend job at the mall.

This example highlights the interplay between nutrition and physical, social, and emotional well-being. Parvati's nutritional habits have raised her stress level rather than lowered it. How can she use nutrition in her favour when she is stressed out during test week? Recognizing the problem, Parvati makes a point to learn more about nutrition and how nutrients (especially B and C vitamins) nourish the nervous system. As test week approaches, Parvati eats a variety of foods high in these vitamins—whole-grain breads and cereals, milk and yogurt, dark-green leafy vegetables, broccoli, tomatoes, oranges, and bananas. During that week, she brings in nutritious snacks such as cut fresh vegetables or whole-grain crackers with cheese or hummus and fruit that she can refuel on. She limits her coffee to a couple of cups during the morning. Parvati is pleasantly surprised that by the end of the week, she isn't a bear! Let us hope that this experience has a positive impact on Parvati and that she makes some permanent changes to her eating patterns that help her in the long term.

Eating nutritiously confers benefits daily and over time for all of us. Foods that are high in nutrients keep our minds and bodies in good working order, providing ongoing energy. Eating patterns that maximize the intake of wholesome foods while minimizing the intake of processing and additives may contribute to the prevention of serious chronic diseases. In addition to feeling good and possibly preventing disease, we also provide healthy role models for children. *Eating Well with Canada's Food Guide* (Health Canada, 2018, pp. 7–8) includes three principles:

1. Guiding Principle 1: A variety of nutritious foods and beverages are the foundation for healthy eating.

2. Guiding Principle 2: Processed or prepared foods and beverages high in sodium, sugars or saturated fat undermine healthy eating.

3. Guiding Principle 3: Knowledge and skills are needed to navigate the complex food environment and support healthy eating.

Today's food environment makes it very difficult for Canadians to make healthy food choices: There is a constant flow of changing and often conflicting messages on healthy eating; there is widespread availability and promotion of foods that do not contribute to a healthy eating pattern; and Canadians face challenges in understanding and using reliable nutrition information. (Health Canada, 2016, p. 8)*

Healthy Eating Strategy

The Government of Canada is taking action to make the healthier choice the easier choice for all Canadians. . . . Healthy eating can be challenging due to several factors, some beyond the control of the consumer.

[All Canadians play a part] in a future in which better food environments enable Canadians to make healthier eating choices as part of a healthy lifestyle. . . . Health Canada will consult Canadians on front of package food labels aimed at helping Canadians make healthier and more informed choices, particularly on sugars, sodium and saturated fats.

Health Canada will improve the quality of foods available for Canadians by implementing measures that reduce sodium levels and eliminate industrially-produced trans fat . . . [and] will work with its partners and remain committed to evidence-based decision making, openness, transparency and meaningful engagement with the public and stakeholders on healthy eating initiatives.*

---

*Source: © All rights reserved. *Healthy Eating Strategy.* Health Canada 2016. Adapted and reproduced with permission from the Minister of Health, 2018.

Health Canada does not recommend strict dieting, which is recognized as counterproductive. Canadians are urged to reject the popular myth that a healthy body size is narrowly defined. Realistically, a healthy body size is achieved and maintained through nutritious eating, without dieting, and through incorporating regular physical activity into your lifestyle. Age, gender, body type, and other factors influence our body size. It is noteworthy, however, that the dramatic increase in the rate of obesity in Canada is of concern to our mortality and morbidity. Statistics Canada (2012, p. 1) reported: "Among Canadians aged 18 to 79, almost 2 out of every 3 (60%) adults aged 18 to 79 were overweight or obese while 2% were underweight, based on their measured BMI."

Body mass index (BMI) is calculated as weight in kilograms divided by height in metres squared. Although internationally used, BMI is not an ideal measure. For example, individuals who are quite muscular may be inaccurately considered to be overweight or obese. (See Concern about Body Weight, page 358.) Currently, the World Health Organization's (n.d.) international classification guidelines for BMI and measures of fat distribution (waist-to-hip ratio) are used to define obesity. With regard to BMI,

- adults with less than 18.5% body fat may have risks associated with being underweight,
- 18.5 to 24.9% body fat is optimal for adults, and
- adults with 25% or higher body fat may have increased risks associated with being overweight.

By society's standards, Alexa is obese. She has spent years yo-yo dieting and trying to attain a body size that is acceptable to those around her. Whenever she loses weight, even under a physician's care, she quickly regains it. She feels like a failure because she believes she will never be able to lose the weight that she wants to. Family and strangers joke about Alexa's size, which is hurtful and disrespectful and diminishes her self-esteem (e.g., "You would be so pretty if you would only lose weight"). Alexa's anger is understandable—prejudice against large persons is one of the last forms of discrimination in which disparaging attitudes and comments seem to remain socially acceptable.

Alexa's friend Hercilia is a large woman yet is much more self-assured. She suggested that Alexa consult with her dietitian-nutritionist, who follows a health promotion model. This was the turning point for Alexa. Two years later, Alexa's body size still does not fit society's standard. However, she has become much more aware of what is important to her and has a quality of life that far surpasses that of her past, when she was always on hold until she lost weight. She consistently makes healthy food choices and incorporates physical activity into her daily routine. For the past year, Alexa and her counsellor have worked through her feelings of failure, and that work has improved her feelings of self-worth and body image (see Body Image, page 235). The self-help group that she attends provides mutual support in coping with society's prejudice against people who are larger, their putdowns, and intrusive questions (e.g., a taxi driver asks his passenger, "So how much do you weigh?"). Since Alexa has stopped focusing on weight loss and has incorporated a health promotion model into her approach, she has more energy than ever before and is slowly losing weight.

Today, there is some recognition of a wide range of healthy body sizes. Fashionable and affordable clothes are more readily available in a range of sizes. Fast-food restaurants have started to offer foods with nutrition information that help people make healthy choices. A physically active lifestyle is essential for the long-term well-being of all Canadians.

NELSONstudy

To access Resource Materials, visit NelsonStudy.

Following *Eating Well with Canada's Food Guide* and putting consistent effort into normalizing routine physical activity will help adults who are considered overweight move into a healthier range. Individuals who may be considered obese will probably require guidance and supervision by a physician and a dietitian.

How does your eating pattern rate? Try recording what you eat for the next few days or, even better, for a week. To see how your choices compare with *Eating Well with Canada's Food Guide* recommendations, connect to My Food Guide by Health Canada, an interactive tool that helps you personalize the information (see Resource Materials). Another online tool is Dietitians of Canada's eaTracker, which lets you easily check your food and activity choices, analyze your recipes, and plan your meals. Sign up to set goals and track your progress. (See Resource Materials.)

You may find that

- you are doing everything right, and this review confirms and supports your healthy lifestyle.

- you have a low energy level and feel that your overall health (e.g., complexion, dullness of hair, frequency of colds, headaches) can be improved.

- if you are a woman, perhaps you have chronic premenstrual syndrome (PMS) and have heard that changes in diet, such as reducing or eliminating caffeine and alcohol, may help reduce the symptoms.

- you know that you overeat when you're bored or that you crave salty, high-fat food when you study.

Any habit is hard to break or adjust, so don't expect change to happen overnight. The first step is to find out what influences your eating. As children, we develop positive and negative associations with food. Using examples, Table 5.1 illustrates what food can mean to someone (see page 234). Sometimes you eat food because you feel like it, whether it is nutritious or not! If we feel deprived of food we enjoy, we are more likely to abandon our progress in making changes. Here are a few additional suggestions:

- If you are not currently a breakfast eater, try to make changes gradually. Eating from three or all four food groups in the morning can contribute to a more productive day, building your energy to focus on the children in your care.

- Fat is an essential nutrient for good health. However, it is easy to get too much or the wrong kind of fat. More specifically, the Dietitians of Canada (2016, p. 1) recommend that adults should "consume a small amount (about 30–45 mL or 2–3 tablespoons)" of unsaturated fats daily. Unsaturated fats include vegetable oil, salad dressing, and mayonnaise, and are also found in nuts, seeds, avocado, and fatty fish such as salmon. Note that too much fat from meats and dairy products (i.e., more than 10% of daily calories) can raise low-density lipoprotein (LDL) cholesterol levels which can increase cholesterol levels.

- Follow the age and stage recommendations in Health Canada's *Eating Well with Canada's Food Guide.* For example, women who could become pregnant or are pregnant or breastfeeding should take a multivitamin daily containing 400 micrograms of folic acid (Health Canada, 2011b, p. 42). Folic acid is a B vitamin that is known to reduce the risk of a fetus developing a neural tube defect and also supports the growth of maternal and fetal tissue. Men and women over the age of 50 need more vitamin D than can be obtained from food to reduce the risk of osteoporosis and fractures. A supplement containing 400 IU of vitamin D in addition to consuming 500 mL of milk each day is recommended (Health Canada, 2011b, p. 43).

- Gradually reduce the number of processed foods you buy, although some convenience foods may seem too convenient to give up! Most, but not all, processed foods have a lot of saturated fat, salt, sugar, and additives. Read labels to determine nutrition content.

- Bring your own food to school or work as often as possible, or bring at least part of the meal, or bring snacks to ensure some high-nutritive foods.

- Share ideas with your friends. Potluck lunches or two or three friends taking turns bringing lunch may be enjoyable and save time. This idea can promote openness to try new foods.

- When possible, plan ahead if you will be eating out. Most chain restaurants have websites that have the nutrient and calorie content of their menu items. Staff in restaurants will often have the nutritional analysis of the menu items available if you ask. Some post the nutrient content of their menu items for their customers.

The *Healthy Menu Choices Act* (Government of Ontario, 2017) came into effect to promote informed, healthy eating choices for the consumer and family. Here are some highlights related to menus:

- The act applies to food service providers (with 20 or more locations in Ontario) that sell food prepared to be eaten right away (e.g., fast-food or dine-in restaurants, grocery stores, hotels, movie theatres).

- The food service providers are required to display caloric information on standard food and drink menu items (i.e., items offered for sale in standardized portions).

- There are display requirements (e.g., font, place on menu) for menus and anywhere else the food item is listed.

- "As of January 1, 2017, businesses covered by the new rules must post the following statement: Adults and youth (ages 13 and older) need an average of 2,000 calories a day, and children (ages 4 to 12) need an average of 1,500 calories a day. However, individual needs vary" (pp. 2–3).*

- This information can help the consumer and "family make informed choices and discuss healthy options when ... getting takeout, stopping for a treat or eating out [at] a restaurant" (p. 3).*

---

*Source: From Ministry of Health and Long-Term Care, 2016. "Calories on Menus," https://www.ontario.ca/page/calories-menus. © Queen's Printer for Ontario, 2016. Reproduced with permission.

"Inspectors from local public health units will visit all businesses that must follow the law. After that, public health units will respond to any complaints about a business not following the law. This could lead to education, a warning and then a fine if they continue not to follow the law" (p. 3).*

Physical Activity

Generally, physical activity includes any bodily movement caused by muscle contraction that results in using energy. Balancing healthy eating with daily physical activity is a winning combination. Health Canada's (2011a) proclamation to "Eat well and be active today and every day!" can include benefits such as better overall health, lower risk of disease, feeling and looking better, more energy, and stronger bones and muscles. These benefits have a positive impact on our sense of well-being and enhance our physical and intellectual abilities, now and as we get older.

The fitter you are, the better your body is able to deal with the everyday demands you put on it and to recover from any injury. Ratey (2008, pp. 37–38) highlights the important role exercise plays in elevating and balancing the three brain (neuro) transmitters that have a powerful influence in supporting mental health:

- Serotonin influences mood, impulsivity, anger, and aggressiveness.
- Norepinephrine can amplify signals that influence attention, perception, motivation, and arousal.
- Dopamine is thought of as the learning, satisfaction, attention, and movement transmitter.

Research is finding that fitness, not low body weight, is the more significant predictor of a longer life. Recent studies, for example, are finding that in adults, those who are obese but physically fit may have a lower risk of dying early or of developing cardiovascular disease than those who are of normal weight but are physically inactive (Ortega et al., 2013). In one study (Kuk et al., 2011), researchers looked at the mortality risk of 6000 obese compared to lean Americans for over 16 years. This study found that obese individuals who were otherwise healthy live just as long as their lean counterparts. This illustrates that not all obese individuals are at an elevated health risk and that body weight alone cannot distinguish healthy and unhealthy obese individuals.

Some people don't give exercise a second thought because being active is just part of their lifestyle (e.g., they walk or ride a bicycle to work rather than drive). Those of us who have not incorporated regular physical activity into our lives may find it easier to start by taking small steps rather than big leaps. A drastic change can be motivating at first but soon becomes discouraging if the work and effort don't bring quick results. It may be difficult to fit one more thing into an already crowded schedule, and exercise may seem to be expendable. Single parents of young children, for example, may not see how it is possible. Maybe riding a stationary bike while watching television with the children would be workable, or taking the stairs rather than an escalator whenever possible. Often making

Roberto Westbrook/Blend Images/Getty Images

---

*Source: From Ministry of Health and Long-Term Care, 2016. "Calories on Menus," https://www.ontario.ca /page/calories-menus. © Queen's Printer for Ontario, 2016. Reproduced with permission.

a conscious effort to be more active while at work or school is a possibility. While supervising on the playground, educators can keep moving as much as possible, or they can go for a brisk walk during the coffee break or lunch break.

Lepp et al. (2013, p. 8) studied a sample of U.S. college students and identified a possible relationship between cellphone use, physical and sedentary activity, and cardiovascular fitness. Their data suggested that high-frequency cellphone users

- are more likely to miss opportunities for physically active recreation in order to use their cellphones for sedentary activities such as social media, games, apps, and surfing the Internet; and
- have a broader pattern of leisure-time sedentary behaviour, in addition to cellphone use, such as watching television, playing video games, and using the computer.

The negative association between cellphone use and fitness illustrated in this study deserves further attention as cardiorespiratory fitness is an excellent indicator of an individual's risk for a number of health concerns. Cellphone use, like computer use, may disrupt physical activity and reduce cardiovascular fitness.

The Alberta Centre for Active Living (n.d.-a, n.d.-b, n.d.-c) reminds employers that workplace physical activity programs can reduce sick leave by up to 32% and increase productivity by up to 52%. The centre offers ideas for each of the three levels of the health promotion action plan to make physical activity at work a reality. Here are a few examples for each of the three levels, focusing on how employers can support employee fitness:

Individual Level
- "Start a physical activity closet filled with low-cost sport and activity equipment (e.g., basketballs, fitness bands, pylons, skipping ropes, Frisbees)" (n.d.-b, p. 1).
- Track your physical activity week by week.
- "Buy one or two bikes and helmets for employees to use at work to get fresh air and sunshine or run errands" (n.d.-b, p. 1).
- "Produce or link to an active living screensaver with physical activity tips that employees can download" (n.d.-b, p. 1).
- "Post a sign-up board where staff can join a group or find a buddy to partici-pate in activities of interest" (n.d.-c, p. 1).
- "Co-ordinate a stair climb challenge. Post a chart at the top of the stairwell, and encourage employees to track the number of flights of stairs they climb each workday" (n.d.-c, p. 1).* Organize teams and have a goal (e.g., to climb the equivalent of Mount Logan).

Community (Employer) Level
- "Help employees develop time-management skills. These skills can help employees make time for physical activity" (n.d.-b, p. 1).
- "Arrange a company badminton [tennis, softball, soccer, golf, or other] tour-nament that lasts several months, with each employee playing once a week. Post the results as the tournament progresses" (n.d.-c, p. 1).

---

*Source: Physical Activity @ Work, 2007a, 2007b, 2007c. Alberta Centre for Active Living. University of Alberta.

- Extend the walking or stair-climbing programs to other workplaces or community groups.

- "Post and promote a sign-up board for lunchtime walking groups" (n.d.-c, p. 1). "Co-ordinate a walk to work club. Acknowledge employees who either walk to work or walk to public transit" (n.d.-c, p. 1).*

- Plan a workplace health fair involving other ECLC programs in the community, or plan a walking or biking marathon for a charitable cause.

- Link employees with community facilities that can assess fitness levels, or hire a qualified fitness professional to provide this service onsite.

- Include a physical activity account in the employer's benefit plan to pay for or subsidize fitness memberships, assessments, classes, counselling, or instruction.

Societal Level

- Lobby the municipal government for more bicycle lanes and green space for walking and public transportation expansion.

- Lobby public and private employers to commit to workplace physical activity in policy statements and designate funding to physical activity initiatives.

- Mandate that employers must ensure inclusive policies for physical activity opportunities to all employees. Adapting information and activities for any staff who are visually impaired or physically disabled as well as for those who speak English as a second language are examples of inclusivity. Note that the *Canadian Human Rights Act* protects all Canadians from 11 grounds of discrimination. Some of the grounds include disability, race, national or ethnic origin, sexual orientation, and gender identity or expression.

Four components of physical fitness are universally recognized as promoting good health: **aerobic (cardiovascular) fitness**, **flexibility**, **strength**, and **endurance** (see Table 2.2).

*Source: Physical Activity @ Work, 2007a, 2007b, 2007c. Alberta Centre for Active Living. University of Alberta.

TABLE 2.2 Four Fitness Components

Fitness Components	Definition	Examples
Aerobic (Cardiovascular) Fitness	- How well your heart is able to pump oxygen-rich blood to your cells and carry waste out of your cells. The term "aerobic" means "with oxygen." - The body performs low- to moderate-intensity tasks over an extended period of time. By working our heart muscle at 60 to 80% of its capacity for a minimum of 10 minutes (progressing to 30 minutes) 4 days a week, we increase and maintain our aerobic fitness level.	- Walking, hiking, cross-country skiing, cycling, dance aerobics or water aerobics, rope skipping, in-line skating, rowing, and stair climbing are some possibilities. - Choose activities and times that suit your life situation. Busy people often try to fit aerobic activity into their workday by walking or climbing stairs at lunch or getting off public transit a few kilometres before their stop and walking the rest of the way.

(continued)

TABLE 2.2 Four Fitness Components (*continued*)

Fitness Components	Definition	Examples
Flexibility	• The ability of your joints to move through the full range of their motion. Proper stretching is the best way to increase flexibility. • Good back health and the prevention of pulls and other muscle damage are important benefits of flexibility (see Preventing Musculoskeletal Injuries, page 81). • Stretching each major muscle group after a few minutes of warm-up and before you begin vigorous aerobic or strength training is an important way to prevent strains and sprains.	• Some stretching exercises can be incorporated into your day, such as head tilts, side stretches, arm circles, and sit/reach stretches. • Even stretching in the morning before getting out of bed can contribute to your flexibility and back health. • You may also enjoy yoga or tai chi classes for many benefits, including flexibility (e.g., mindfulness and stress management).
Strength	• The ability of one of your muscle groups to exert force in one motion (e.g., lifting a toddler or moving a table). Strength training in a gym usually involves a range of machines with weights, strengthening different muscles. To a certain extent, this can also be done with free weights. • A set is the number of repetitions performed for a given exercise, such as lifting a certain weight. • It is important to build strength and endurance gradually, to prevent muscle fatigue and injury.	• Strength-training exercises usually involve weights. • Alternatively, you can use your body resistance to build strength. This includes activities such as push-ups, sit-ups, step-ups, pull-ups, arm curls, and abdominal curl-ups. Climbing stairs instead of taking elevators and escalators helps to build strength as well.
Endurance	• The ability of one of your muscle groups to perform muscular contractions of moderate force over an extended period (e.g., lifting half of your maximum capacity a few times a minute over five minutes). • Both strength and endurance increase through activity involving resistance training because your muscles get stronger when you condition them to lift more weight and gain endurance when you gradually increase repetitions. It is essential that you learn and practise the proper techniques to prevent injury.	• If you walk, ride a bike, dance, or climb a hill, you are working on your aerobic fitness, strength, and muscular endurance all at the same time. • In the work environment, muscular endurance may translate into putting all the cots away after nap time or being able to lift 10 toddlers—one at a time—off the change table.

An active lifestyle should include all four fitness components, but your goals and the level of activity you want in your life will help determine how much of each component will be included. For example, someone who wants to improve overall well-being but doesn't have the time or interest in focusing a lot of attention on a program may place more emphasis on aerobic activities and some gentle stretching to improve flexibility. Regardless of the aerobic activity chosen, strength and endurance should be relatively easy to incorporate. Although programs such as yoga, Pilates, and tai chi do not focus on aerobic activity, they improve flexibility, strength, and endurance.

Recognizing the short- and long-term benefits of moderate physical activity for your personal and professional lives is the first step toward fitness. Remember the following:

- Start your program gradually and choose activities you enjoy.
- Make sure that you have the right equipment and clothing for the activity. If cost is a factor, choose an activity that has lower equipment costs.
- Learn and use the proper techniques to prevent injury and maximize fitness benefits.
- Stop if it hurts! Listen to your body. Pain means that there is something your body is not ready for and you can injure yourself if you continue.

Optimal intensity tends to be at the moderate level. As you build your fitness level, such as walking farther, more briskly, or up inclines more easily, you'll find that you are able to do more with less intensity. To build your fitness level, it is important to "step up" your workout and increase the challenge. Make sure you know the basics, such as footwear and gear/equipment best suited to your activity and how to monitor your heart rate. ParticipACTION and many other agencies and resources are available to help you get started with suggestions for fitness activities.

Leisure and Rest

Balancing our need for meaningful work with our need for leisure contributes to well-being. Leisure means different things to different people. For example, most individuals have a need for solitude that can be fulfilled through a variety of activities, such as completing puzzles, doing crafts or artwork, or meditating. Many people use meditation to relax and manage stress. Although different techniques and philosophies are advocated, in general, meditation uses deep breathing, allowing tension to leave the body. Most forms of meditation involve sitting or lying quietly for anywhere from five or more minutes, perhaps focusing on a particular word or symbol (a mantra), controlling breathing, and becoming more in tune with the inner self. Mindfulness is a type of meditation that essentially involves focusing your mind on the present. To be mindful is to be aware of your thoughts and actions in the present, without judging yourself.

With meditation, as with other forms of coping with or managing stress, the individual determines how effective it is as a tool. To satisfy our need to relate to others, we may like going to a movie with a friend, talking on the phone, entertaining at home, fishing with others, or going camping. Religious, political, or other community meetings may also fulfill this need. We might satisfy our need to participate through organized sports or physical activity, a gardening club, or an ethnocultural group. Most individuals also need to observe at times. They may satisfy that need by visiting amusement parks, watching parades, sitting on the porch and watching passersby, or browsing in a bookstore.

These are but a few examples, but they highlight the fact that for most of us, there is an overlap between physical activity and relaxation because going to the gym or taking a brisk walk may achieve both ends. In the discussion on stress later in this unit, the topic of leisure activities—whether physically active and social or quiet and solitary—as a means to cope with stress appears again. Being aware of what is relaxing for you and finding regular opportunities to unwind are part of everyday health promotion.

Our bodies need time to rest and sleep to revitalize and to provide time for bodily functions and organs to slow down. The duration of sleep that individual adults need varies. Illness, pregnancy, or other factors may increase the amount of sleep needed.

Stress factors such as financial or personal problems, exam-time worry, or a colicky baby can affect the amount or quality of our sleep. Here are some common-sense suggestions for having a better sleep:

- Avoid alcohol (which can disrupt sleep patterns) or smoking (because nicotine makes you wakeful) before going to bed.
- Eliminate or reduce consumption of caffeinated drinks (e.g., coffee, cola drinks) starting in late afternoon.
- Do something relaxing before going to bed.
- Maintain a regular schedule and routine for going to bed and getting up.
- Get out of bed and do something (e.g., read a relaxing book, write a list to reduce worries) rather than watch the clock when you are unable to sleep.
- Stress coupled with sleep deprivation is very taxing on one's emotional and physical health, and talking with a friend or counsellor can help you find short- or long-term solutions.

Especially when we are young, and often as students, socializing in the evenings may take precedence over getting enough sleep every night. When lack of sleep affects our health or work/school performance, we are faced with making some decisions and establishing priorities. And when we work with children, we must be especially alert to our surroundings from the standpoint of safety. As well, sleep deprivation often makes us irritable—not an appropriate frame of mind when working with children and coworkers. These decisions are sometimes difficult, especially for young adults who are training for a career, but responsibility does involve setting priorities. Balancing our need to socialize (e.g., on the weekend) with our responsibilities is essential to becoming a professional.

Reducing Other Risk Factors

Health behaviour either promotes your health or undermines it. Here are important examples of health behaviour that contribute positively to our health:

- quitting smoking and avoiding passive (second-hand) smoke (includes tobacco and marijuana, e-cigarettes, and vaping)
- limiting your consumption of alcohol and refraining from drinking alcohol during pregnancy and breastfeeding
- avoiding illegal drugs and being careful about medication use
- practising safer sex to prevent sexually transmitted infections (STIs), including human papilloma virus (HPV), human immunodeficiency virus (HIV), and hepatitis B
- maintaining a regular schedule of physical and dental checkups and monthly self-exams of breasts or testicles for early detection of breast or testicular cancer

In keeping with the health promotion philosophy discussed in Unit 1, the continuum of responsibility between individual and society depends very much on your circumstances.

Selecting health care professionals who best suit our health needs can play a significant role in health promotion. If you live in an area where there is more than one choice, choose the health professional or agency that

- answers your questions clearly and directly;
- gives you access to your medical file, should you choose to see it; and
- is linguistically and culturally relevant to you (e.g., Shawn is Indigenous, and when he feels sick, he sees his family doctor as well as an Elder who is a traditional healer).

You may have additional criteria, and it is important that you feel like a partner in your health care. It's in your best interest to take an active role in decision making about your medical treatments. This is our individual responsibility. When in doubt, ask for a second or third opinion. Women in particular often feel uncomfortable with or even intimidated by some physicians and do not ask them questions about their own health care. Even today, some physicians prescribe tranquilizers for women with complaints such as PMS or symptoms of menopause.

One of the best ways that people who smoke can improve their long-term health is by quitting, but that may not be easy. It's especially difficult when other stress factors are present and beyond the smoker's control. Smoking may be relaxing or a stress reliever for that person in that situation. Pursuing ways to quit smoking, however, is well worth the effort, and many communities have support systems that can help. At a time when so many Canadians are quitting smoking, it is discouraging that teens and young women are the fastest-growing groups starting to smoke. Young people who have been smoking only a short time are strongly encouraged to quit before the addiction becomes stronger. What messages are educators and ECE students sending to children who see them smoking outside the building on breaks, who smell the smoke on their clothes and hair, who see them smoking outside the mall or on the street?

The issue of partner abuse is included to raise awareness and sensitize readers to the possibility that fellow students, future coworkers, children's parents, or even you yourself may be a victim. Violence can take many forms, including physical, sexual, emotional, social, and financial. You will need to expand your knowledge in this area because we are only touching the surface of the problem of abuse. In Canada, self-reported data have shown that violence in spousal and dating relationships affects hundreds of thousands of people and results in both physical and psychological injuries (Burczycka, 2016, p. 47).

Lidia was a victim of spousal abuse. She felt powerless to escape. She believed that if she left her husband, he would find and possibly kill her. Her coworkers talked among themselves about how weak Lidia was for not leaving her husband. Yet it's too simple to say, "Just leave him!" Family violence is a very complicated situation. Lidia eventually found the support and legal assistance she needed at the local women's shelter, but not before years of violence had taken a great toll on her well-being.

FAMILY VIOLENCE IN CANADA

- In 2015, almost 92,000 people in Canada were victims of intimate partner violence, representing just over a quarter (28%) of all victims of police-reported violent crime. Four out of five victims of police-reported intimate partner violence were women (79%)—representing about 72,000 female victims . . .

- Victimization by an intimate partner was the most common form of police-reported violent crime committed against females (42% of female victims, compared to 12% of male victims). In contrast, more males relative to females were victimized by a friend or an acquaintance (40% versus 28%) or by a stranger (36% versus 15%) . . .

- In 2015, violence within dating relationships was more common than violence within spousal relationships, according to police reported data. A current or former dating partner was the perpetrator against 54% of intimate partner violence victims, compared to a current or former legally married or common-law spouse (44% of victims). These proportions were similar among male and female victims. . . .

- A current dating partner was most often the perpetrator against young victims of intimate partner violence: 51% of victims aged 15 to 19 years and 46% of victims aged 20 to 24 years were victimized by a current dating partner. These age groups were also more often victimized by former dating partners. . . .

- Those aged 65 years and older had the highest proportion of victimization by a current spouse, with 7 out of 10 (68%) intimate partner victims in this age group having been victimized by their current husband, wife or common-law partner. (Statistics Canada, 2017, pp. 47–48)

Source: Statistics Canada. 2017. *Family Violence in Canada: A Statistical Profile,* 2015 http://www.statcan .gc.ca/pub/85-002-x/2017001/article/14698-eng.pdf. Reproduced and distributed on an "as is" basis with the permission of Statistics Canada.

Intimate partners who are being abused stay in the relationship for a number of reasons: fear, low self-esteem, a lack of economic and social supports, cultural taboos, religion, obligation, and oppression. When an individual discloses abuse to you, listen and believe that person. This is the first step, and the emotional support you provide may encourage that person to take action, although the decision should be hers or his. In the future, possibly with your support, she or he may seek options (e.g., shelters, legal advice, services sensitive to specific needs) and make a safety plan.

Familiarize yourself with your community's emergency shelters and the telephone hotline as well as any available long-term services. Partner abuse, date rape, and other forms of violence, particularly against women, are known to be prevalent in our society. For victims of intimate-partner abuse, the abuse "follows" them to work as the abuser may call and harass them or their coworkers, and the stress affects the quality of their work or the amount of time off work.

With support, many can escape the vicious circle of violent relationships. Stopping the violence is a complex task and requires a multifaceted societal response. Training programs for early childhood educators are important tools to support the non-offending parent and children in these difficult circumstances. (See Boost in Resource Materials.) Shelters are available in most communities across Canada.

NELSONstudy

To access Resource Materials, visit NelsonStudy.

Infectious Diseases and You

When you start working in programs, you'll probably find that you get sick more often than usual. Although this is to be expected, there are things you can do to prevent being ill so frequently, including being immunized, implementing hygiene practices, and maintaining a well-balanced lifestyle.

ECE training programs should require students to have up-to-date immunizations before they do their first placement in a program. The training institution's health personnel collect and review students' immunization records and other related medical information.

Standard immunization requirements for prospective child care practitioners are as follows:

1. Proof that immunizations against diphtheria, tetanus, polio, and pertussis are up-to-date, with tetanus–diphtheria (as Td or dTap) received within the last 10 years and at least one dose of dTap received in adulthood.

2. Documentation of one MMR (measles, mumps, and rubella) vaccination if a prospective child care employee was born after 1970. A laboratory-confirmed proof of immunity against these diseases is also acceptable.

3. Documentation of two doses of chickenpox (varicella) vaccine or a doctor's documentation of the person having had chickenpox or laboratory-confirmed proof of immunity against chickenpox.

4. Documentation of a negative TB skin or blood test. Neither test can differentiate between latent and active disease. Before beginning work in child care, a person testing positive must undergo further assessment and present a doctor's note confirming that active TB has been ruled out.

5. Annual influenza vaccine if the child care practitioner will be caring for children under 24 months of age or children with chronic diseases. (Canadian Paediatric Society [CPS], 2015, p. 373)*

*Source: Reprinted with permission from the Canadian Paediatric Society.

In addition to routine immunizations outlined above, there may be additional immunizations required in your public health department jurisdiction. There are a number of optional but recommended vaccinations. It is recommended that educators receive the following:

- **Hepatitis A vaccine**, especially in programs serving vulnerable communities (e.g., in rural or remote areas with inadequate water or sewage purification systems). A child care practitioner would receive two doses of hepatitis A vaccine, given 6 to 12 months apart.

- **Hepatitis B vaccine**, especially in programs serving children whose families have come from countries where hepatitis B is common, or in communities where hepatitis B is common. The usual adult schedule is three doses: one at the first visit, a second one month later, and a final dose 6 months after that. Follow-up testing for antibody response may also be necessary to verify immunity.

Courtesy of George Brown College/Scotia Plaza Child Care Centre

- **Booster shots for mumps and measles**. While vaccines protecting against both these illnesses are universally administered in early childhood under the routine schedule, a booster shot may be required for those who received only one dose. Local public health recommendations should be followed. Child care practitioners can ask their doctor for advice. (CPS, 2015, p. 374)*

To reduce the spread of infectious diseases in programs, educators are responsible for implementing hygiene practices. Steps taken to reduce the spread of germs among children will have a positive effect on educators' health. On a daily basis, educators must pay particular attention to how and when they wash their hands. Unit 3 outlines what you need to know, including the ins and outs of hand washing and information on hygiene practices.

There will be times when educators who are ill should be excluded from work. An early childhood program's exclusion policy for educators and others working in the program should include the following conditions. The individual should be excluded when she or he

- cannot fulfill her [or his] responsibilities because her [or his] illness compromises the care of the children.

- is sick with a respiratory infection. Facility supervisors should encourage an ailing staff member to stay home to prevent the spread of illness.

- has a gastrointestinal infection with diarrhea or vomiting.

- has any of the specific conditions requiring exclusion [see Appendix 4.1, page 213]. (CPS, 2015, p. 375)*

Much of what we know about childhood infections applies also to adults, who can get the same infections. The more common childhood illnesses are discussed in Unit 4, which includes a table that summarizes the management of children's illnesses in the program (see Childhood Infections and Nuisances: Just the Basics, page 183).

---

*Source: Reprinted with permission from the Canadian Paediatric Society.

Hepatitis B is a virus that causes infection of the liver and is spread by direct contact with blood or bloody body fluid. "The incidence of HBV transmission in child care settings is extremely low, and infection is preventable through routine practices" (CPS, 2015, p. 377). The hepatitis B virus immunization is part of the routine childhood immunization schedule in Canada. And as discussed earlier, the vaccination for educators is recommended where the prevalence of hepatitis B is higher. Where that is not the case, it may be beneficial because of educators' own personal health behaviour (e.g., sexual practices). Hepatitis C, like hepatitis B, is a virus that causes infection of the liver and is spread by direct contact with blood or bloody body fluid. According to CPS (2015, p. 378), "There have been no reports of HCV infection as a result of exposure in child care." Educators are not required to disclose their HCV status (CPS, 2015, p. 378). Routine practices are always important when cleaning blood and bodily fluids (see Routine Practices, page 157).

Pregnancies are not always planned. That's one of the reasons that women in childbearing years should be aware of their overall health and lifestyle habits, such as prescription drug and alcohol use. One important way for women in childbearing years to reduce the likelihood of fetus malformation is by adding folic acid to their diet. Folate (folic acid) is a B vitamin that plays an essential role in the development of the spine, brain, and skull of the fetus during the first four weeks of pregnancy. This critical time is often before a woman knows she is pregnant. Insufficient folate puts the fetus at risk for serious birth defects known as neural tube disorders (NTDs), including spina bifida and anencephaly. Recent studies have shown that women of childbearing age may significantly reduce the incidence of neural tube defects by consuming folic acid daily (foods high in folic acid and a multivitamin) (Best Start & Health Nexus, 2011, pp. 12–13).

Working with children increases your exposure to infections. Female ECE students and educators may have peace of mind if they talk with their physician. Five infections are particularly important to pregnant women: chickenpox, rubella, measles, mumps, and cytomegalovirus (CMV) (see Table 2.3).

TABLE 2.3 Pregnancy and Five Infections of Concern

Prevention	Risk to Fetus	Susceptible and Exposed: What's Next?
Chickenpox		
Students and educators who can't recall whether they had chickenpox as children or had the chickenpox vaccine; talk with your physician about the antibody test.	Susceptible women who are infected during the first half of pregnancy can pose serious risks to the health of the fetus.	When exposed to either chickenpox or shingles, you should receive varicella-zoster immune globulin (VZIG) within 96 hours of exposure (CPS, 2015, p. 376).
Rubella (German Measles)		
If your immunization schedule is up-to-date, you will know if you received your rubella vaccine. If not, ask your physician about the antibody test.	Susceptible women who are infected during the first three months of pregnancy can pose serious risks to the health of the fetus.	Talk to your physician immediately.

(continued)

TABLE 2.3   Pregnancy and Five Infections of Concern (*continued*)

Prevention	Risk to Fetus	Susceptible and Exposed: What's Next?
Measles and Mumps		
Most of us are immune to measles and mumps because we had the diseases or have received the MMR vaccine. If you have received only one dose of the vaccine, you may be susceptible to measles and mumps. If you are not sure, ask your physician about the antibody test.	Susceptible women who are infected with • measles during the pregnancy have an increased risk of premature delivery (CPS, 2015, p. 377). • mumps in the first three months of pregnancy may increase the risk of miscarriage (CPS, 2015, p. 376).	Talk to your physician immediately.
Cytomegalovirus		
The best protection is effective hand washing, effective diapering and toileting routines, and cleaning and sanitizing surfaces that have been contaminated with body secretions (e.g., saliva, vomit, urine, or stool). The only real concern about CMV is when women who are susceptible to CMV become infected during their pregnancy.	"There is a risk that an infant will be infected in utero and approximately 10 per cent of infants with congenital CMV infection will have serious disease at birth. There is also a small risk associated with re-exposure during pregnancy. Approximately 20 per cent of all sensorineural hearing loss in children is caused by congenital CMV infection. Some infants also have developmental delay" (CPS, 2015, p. 380).	A vaccine for CMV is not available. Talk to your physician immediately.

Preventing Musculoskeletal Injuries

Lower back injury is the typical experience for early childhood educators due to excessive lifting, pulling, pushing, or carrying. The layout and design of the building, its furniture, the number of people, and available floor space all play a role in the likelihood of injury. Fortunately, many educators who injure themselves aren't going to need to leave work as a result. Typical injuries are going to be strains and sprains—such as pulling a muscle when awkwardly lifting a child or tripping over a toy on the floor. In addition, there now may be added possibility of "repetitive strains" due to typing documents such as observations, reports, and other ongoing typed administrative work at computers that may come with the job. This can contribute to carpal tunnel syndrome or, if computers are not ergonomically comfortable for the user, to neck or back pain.

Ergonomics is the science referring to the ways that the job can be altered to fit the person performing it, rather than the other way around. A survey of 258 early childhood educators in Wisconsin found that although most were aware of ergonomic interventions and were currently experiencing musculoskeletal pain while performing their jobs, they did not believe they needed to make ergonomic changes. The results of this study highlight the need for further analysis of specific child care tasks and identification of more effective methods to reduce the risk of musculoskeletal pain and injuries (King et al., 2006).

You don't have to go very far to find someone who has experienced or is experiencing back or neck pain. You may have had back or neck pain too. Not all pain is preventable, but there are ways to reduce the risk of musculoskeletal injury and to manage back or neck pain when it does occur:

- Maintain the three natural curves of your spine, to take undue pressure off your spine. In a healthy spine, the 33 vertebrae form a natural "S" curve.
- Change posture, even slightly, every few minutes because the discs, like the rest of the body, take in nutrients and get rid of waste products. When we remain in one position for too long, that process can't happen efficiently.
- Do stretching exercises regularly to increase flexibility, decrease the risk of injury, and correct posture. Stretching can fit into your workday with little effort, such as moving your neck slowly from side to side while rubbing children's backs at naptime, stretching the back and each side when standing, or making "air circles" with ankles while sitting.
- Take part in regular physical activity, which helps increase the muscles' ability to support the back.
- Use proper lifting techniques, as described in Figure 2.1.

When back pain does occur, individuals should

- consult with their family physician. Strained muscles and sprained ligaments are the most common causes of back pain and tend to heal within a few weeks.
- resume routines gradually but as soon as possible—it is now widely believed that bed rest for more than two or three days usually does more harm than good.
- pursue physiotherapy, chiropractic, acupuncture, massage, and yoga as more conservative therapy options. Surgery is not recommended as a therapeutic option in the vast majority of back problems.

In particular, improper lifting and carrying can result in back injuries, which may lead to long-term back problems, loss of wages, and even the need for a career change. Awareness of the potential problem and proper lifting techniques can help prevent back problems. Whether you are standing, walking, sitting on a chair or floor, or lifting or carrying something, your goal is to maintain the natural curves of your spine.

Some readers may think that the following list of preventive steps applies only to people who lift boxes in a warehouse, not to educators who lift infants off the floor. Granted, lifting a baby off the floor in the same way as you might bend to touch your toes may not hurt your back the first time, but using this technique repeatedly almost guarantees eventual back injury. You may lean over a table or reach down to pick up a piece of paper and then find you can't straighten up. A baby may not look as heavy as a large box or suitcase, but a nine-month-old could easily weigh 8 kilograms (18 lb.) or more. When we lift something by using our back (by bending over) rather than our legs, that 8-kilogram baby puts 82 kilograms (180 lb.) of pressure on our back. To prevent injury, follow the steps in Figure 2.1 when you are lifting infants from the floor.

FIGURE 2.1 Lifting Infants from the Floor

Infant Lifting Technique—"Tripod Lift"

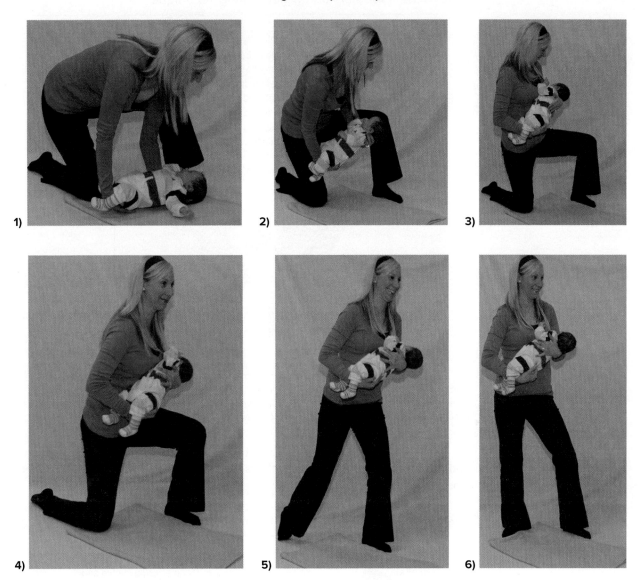

1) Put one foot next to the infant. Keep your back straight, push your buttocks out, and slowly lower yourself down onto one knee.
2) Position the infant close to your knee on the floor.
3) Slide the infant from your knee onto the floor to mid-thigh; keep your head forward, your back straight, your buttocks out; and lift the infant onto the opposite thigh.
4) Put both of your forearms under the infant with your palms facing upward and hug the infant close to you.
5) Prepare for the lift by looking forward.
6) Lift upwards following your head and shoulders. Hold the infant close to your body. Lift by extending your legs while keeping your back straight and buttocks out. Remember to breathe as you lift.

Source: Occupational Health Clinics for Ontario Workers, "Toddler and Object Lifting Technique," *Prevention through Intervention: Safe Lifting Techniques of Children*; http://www.ohcow.on.ca/uploads/Resource/General%20Handouts/Lifting%20Children%20Safely.pdf. Used with permission.

Learning how to lift children and objects properly and ensuring that you actually follow the steps each time helps prevent back injuries (see Figure 2.2).

FIGURE 2.2   Toddlers and Object Lifting Technique

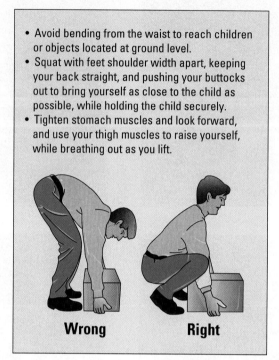

- Avoid bending from the waist to reach children or objects located at ground level.
- Squat with feet shoulder width apart, keeping your back straight, and pushing your buttocks out to bring yourself as close to the child as possible, while holding the child securely.
- Tighten stomach muscles and look forward, and use your thigh muscles to raise yourself, while breathing out as you lift.

Wrong   **Right**

Source: Used with the permission from the Occupational Health Clinics for Ontario Workers Inc. *Prevention through Intervention: Safe Lifting Techniques of Children.* http://www.ohcow.on.ca/resources/handbooks/childlift/safeliftingbrochure.pdf (July 2008).

When you are caring for toddlers, there will be many times when they need and want to be held. Figure 2.3 outlines the steps that will help protect you from a back injury.

FIGURE 2.3   Holding Small Children

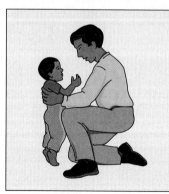

- When holding toddlers, you should avoid placing them on one hip.
- When holding or rocking children, use chairs or furniture with upper back support.
- Keep children centred on your body and use both arms to hold.
- It is also helpful to teach the children to help you lift by holding onto your body rather than leaning away from you.

Source: Used with the permission from the Occupational Health Clinics for Ontario Workers Inc. *Prevention through Intervention: Safe Lifting Techniques of Children.* http://www.ohcow.on.ca/resources/handbooks/childlift/safeliftingbrochure.pdf (July 2008).

Going hand in hand with holding children is carrying them. Keep the following dos and don'ts from the Canadian Centre for Occupational Health and Safety (CCOHS) (2013) in mind:

DOS AND DON'TS OF CARRYING A CHILD

DOS	DON'TS
• *Keep* the load (or child) close to your body. • *Face* in the direction you are travelling. • *Watch* where you're going. • *Watch* for tripping hazards. • *Walk* at an easy pace. • *Grip* under the object (or child) and use your whole hand. • *Make* more than one trip or use a cart for objects rather than try to carry too much. • *Use* the handrail as a guide and to help your balance on stairs and ramps.	• *Do not* run. • *Do not* allow the object (or child) you're carrying to obstruct your vision. • *Do not* attempt to carry heavy objects too far. If you need to rest, place the package on a solid object and rest or get assistance. • *Do not* hurry up or down stairs or ramps. • *Do not* attempt to take more than one stair at a time.

Furnishings and Layout

The physical environment's design and the actual layout of space, including the height of counters and storage shelves, contribute to our health status. The equipment and furnishings in ECLC settings are designed for children's (not adults') comfort and accessibility. Many activities happen on the floor. In addition, educators tend to put the children's safety before their own. Of course, this is necessary, but it may mean that unforeseen twists and turns are a reality. Of the many factors that create stress for educators, five relate to the physical workspace: noise, temperature, lack of rest areas, inadequate furnishings, and lack of equipment. As students, you have little or no control over the physical aspects of the space where you do placements. However, if you observe questionable or unsafe situations, you are obliged to report them to staff. Table 2.4 outlines some activities that educators are constantly involved in and provides suggestions for avoiding injury.

Courtesy of George Brown College/Richmond Adelaide Child Care Centre

TABLE 2.4 Worksite Analysis of the Child Care Work Environment

Problem	Recommendations
1. Incorrect lifting of children, toys, supplies, equipment, etc.	1. Educate staff on proper lifting and carrying techniques 2. Promote task rotation where possible 3. Encourage independence in children whenever feasible
2. Inadequate work heights (e.g., child-sized tables and chairs)	1. Create a chair that allows the staff to slide their legs under the table 2. Use sit/kneel chairs 3. Educate staff on using proper body mechanics 4. Provide the staff with adult-sized chairs for occasional use
3. Difficulty lowering and lifting infants in and out of cribs	1. Modify crib sides to enable them to slide down or modify the legs of the cribs to accommodate the staff 2. Educate staff on using proper body mechanics 3. Have step stool available in sleep room
4. Frequent sitting on the floor with back unsupported	1. When possible, have staff sit up against a wall or furniture for back support 2. Perform stretching exercises 3. Educate staff on using proper body mechanics
5. Excessive reaching above shoulder height to obtain stored supplies	1. Redesign kitchen area, placing heaviest items at waist height, lightest above 2. Reorganize snacks and supplies to simplify snack preparation procedures 3. Use step stools when retrieving items that are above cupboard height
6. Frequent lifting of infants and toddlers on and off diaper-changing tables	1. Educate staff on using proper body mechanics 2. Encourage toddlers to use steps to decrease distance staff are lifting
7. Forceful motions combined with awkward posture required to open windows	1. Use step stool to allow for better leverage and reduce awkward posture 2. Have maintenance staff improve quality of window slide
8. Carrying garbage and diaper bags to dumpster	1. Provide staff with cart to transport garbage 2. Relocate garbage cart closer to work area 3. Reduce size and weight of loads 4. Educate staff on using proper body mechanics

Source: Reprinted from *Work: A Journal of Prevention, Assessment, and Rehabilitation, 6*(1): 25–32. From article entitled "The Ergonomics of Child Care, Conducting Worksite Analyses" by Phyllis M. King, Rene Gratz, Gina Scheuer, & Ann Claffey (1996). With permission from IOS Press and the authors.

There are still programs that do not provide an adult-sized table, chair, or sofa to be used in rooms with children or adult-sized seating outside. Educators, like other employees, need to get away from their work for breaks and to do administrative work. A staff room provides an area in which educators can relax and socialize.

In the long term, ergonomic research will provide architects and early childhood licensing offices with vital information on designing settings that meet the physical needs of adults as well as children. Lack of funding and resources impedes needed improvements for adults in the early childhood environment. In the meantime, how can we improve workplace conditions? The most obvious answer is to purchase more adult-sized furniture and relatively inexpensive equipment to prevent musculoskeletal problems. For example, legless chairs are available that provide the educator with the necessary back support while sitting on the floor with the children. New tables and chairs should be light and easy to move; mats and cots should be easy for staff to store. When replacing worn equipment such as cribs, look for ones that meet Canadian Standards Association (CSA) safety standards and that have rails that can be lowered to mattress level.

Courtesy of George Brown College/Casa Loma Child Care Centre

With regard to the increasing use of computers in ECLC settings, employers should ensure what can be done ergonomically to minimize this strain. At the very least, a fully adjustable chair is the undisputable "must have" when more than one individual is using the workstation. Individual workers are responsible for their proper posture and safe behaviour but may need initial instruction and demonstration for optimal sitting posture, as is the case with bending, lifting, and carrying. CCOHS (2014) recommends the following:

- Take a 5- to 10-minute break every hour spent at a workstation to ease muscle aches, eyestrain, and stress.
- Relax your muscles, stretch, and change position.
- Maintain good posture when sitting to avoid these negative effects on your health:
  - Slouching while sitting with the back slumped against the backrest of the chair compresses your spine and can lead to low back pain.
  - Slouching puts your head in an imbalanced position, contributing to neck and shoulder problems.
  - Slouching while sitting encourages you to rest the wrists on the edge of the desk, causing your hands to either be bent up or down from your wrist. This poor wrist placement is the leading cause of carpal tunnel syndrome.

Courtesy of George Brown College Child Care Centre on Charles Street

A couch in a play area provides a comfortable spot for adults and children to sit and talk or read and for staff to bottle-feed infants. Perhaps a set of steps can be built that slide in and out under the diaper counter to give toddlers the opportunity to climb onto or down from the table rather than being lifted—an activity that most toddlers would prefer.

Educators should gather all the necessary diapering supplies before they bring the child to the change area. This eliminates the educator having to keep one hand on the child while reaching or turning to get supplies during the change.

Educators looking at their own workspace, talking about the issues, and referring to resources will undoubtedly come up with many more ideas. Directors and employers need to assess how work is organized to avoid excessive demands on staff. Work tasks should also be evaluated on the basis of physical demands. Of course, the primary obstacle in implementing improvements is accessing funds.

Courtesy of Barb Pimento, taken at the Downtown Montessori (Coatsworth) Childcare Centre

While doing a field placement with toddlers, you notice that you are starting to get lower back pain and are concerned that, as a young adult, this is already bothering you. You realize that you need to make some changes immediately in both your personal and professional practices to ensure that you prevent further back pain.

Footwear

According to CCOHS (2015, p. 1), there are two major categories of work-related foot injuries:

- Foot injuries from punctures, crushing, sprains, and lacerations, which account for 10% of all reported disabling injuries.
- Foot injuries resulting from slips, trips and falls, which account for 15% of all reported disabling injuries.

Fortunately, not every slip or fall results in a foot injury, but a lack of attention to foot safety plays an important role in the frequency of slips and falls, which in turn increases the likelihood of an injury. In child care centres, sprained or twisted ankles or fractured or broken bones can occur because of slips, trips, or falls. Common causes of these injuries are slippery floors, littered walkways, incorrect footwear, and poor lighting.

Footwear that fits poorly or is in need of repair also contributes heavily to foot discomfort. Pointed toes and high heels are particularly inappropriate for working footwear. Improper footwear can cause or aggravate existing foot problems. Unfortunately, being fashionable sometimes takes precedence over choosing well-fitting, supportive safety footwear. An ECLC program's policy on appropriate footwear goes a long way to prevent injuries in the workplace (see Appendix 2.2, page 120).

FOOT PROBLEMS: CAUSES AND PREVENTION

FOOT PROBLEMS	COMMON CAUSES	PREVENTION GUIDELINES
Severely aching feet, blisters, calluses, corns, rheumatism, arthritis, malformations of toes, fallen arches (flat feet), bunions, sprains	Long periods of standing, hard flooring, and poorly fitting footwear: • high heels • pointed shoes • lack of arch support • too loose or too tight footwear	• Give your feet a break from standing regularly • Talk to your employer about what can be done to improve comfort of flooring • Buy shoes that fit well and are practical and comfortable for the job (see Appendix 2.2, page 120)
Sweaty feet, fungal infections (athlete's foot)	Hot and humid environment, strenuous work, footwear with synthetic (non-porous) uppers Some feet sweat more than others and are more prone to athlete's foot	• Select shoes made of leather or canvas—not synthetic materials • Keep several pairs of shoes on hand and rotate shoes daily to allow them to air out • For some workers, non-coloured woollen or cotton socks may be recommended since dyes may cause or aggravate skin allergies • Foot powder may be helpful • If problems persist, see a doctor or health care specialist
Persisting ingrown toenails, calluses, corns, fungal infection, and more serious foot problems		For conditions such as flat feet and arthritis, seek the advice of your physician

Source: Adapted from Canadian Centre for Occupational Health and Safety. (2010, July 9). *Foot Comfort and Safety at Work*. Retrieved November 2017 from http://www.ccohs.ca/oshanswers/prevention/ppe/foot_com.html#_1_14

Working with Art and Cleaning Products

Art supplies and cleaning products can be hazardous to educators and children. Educators must select play materials that are nontoxic and read labels for any special handling instructions. Pay particular attention to solvents, glues, dyes, and pottery products.

Creating with clay is a desirable, ongoing experience for children. Rather than buying powdered clay, which is easily inhaled and contains silica and possibly asbestos, a talc-free, premixed clay will not produce dust. After using clay, wet mop or sponge surfaces thoroughly. If inhaled, the powder from powdered clay can harm the lungs' airways. Educators with asthma may need to avoid mixing powdered clay or wear a filter over their nose and mouth. Ventilation must always be considered if materials are being mixed.

Boric acid is a common form of boron, a naturally occurring element found in different minerals. Canadians are exposed to boric acid in their diet. Reducing exposure from other sources is recommended to avoid overexposure. The main way to minimize exposure to boric acid is to check product labels for the terms "borax," "borate," and "boric acid."

Boric acid is used in everyday products, such as cosmetics, pesticides, cleaning products, drugs, and natural health products. There are also home-made arts and crafts recipes (often available online), including putty, playdough, slimes, and modelling clay, that suggest use of boric acid. When making children's arts and crafts at home, use recipes that *do not* contain boric acid.

Children and pregnant women should minimize their exposure to boric acid as much as possible. Health Canada is monitoring products that contain boric acid and will respond quickly if a product becomes a risk to Canadians (Government of Canada, 2016).

The Canadian Child Care Federation's resource sheet on safe art materials includes a list of products to use and those to avoid (see Table 2.5).

TABLE 2.5 Safe Alternatives for Common Art Materials

Avoid	Use
Powdered clay. It is easily inhaled and contains silica and possibly asbestos. Do not sand dry clay pieces or engage in other dust-producing activities.	Talc-free, premixed clay. After using clay, wet mop or sponge surfaces thoroughly.
Ceramic glazes or copper enamels	Water-based paints instead of glazes. Adults may waterproof pieces with shellac or varnish.
Cold-water, fibre-reactive dyes or other chemical-based commercial dyes	Vegetable and plant dyes (such as onion skins or tea) as well as food dyes
Instant papier mâchés, which create inhalable dust and may contain lead or asbestos	Make papier mâché from black and white newspapers and library or white paste

(continued)

TABLE 2.5   Safe Alternatives for Common Art Materials (*continued*)

Avoid	Use
Powdered tempera paints, which create inhalable dust and may contain toxic pigments	Liquid tempera paints or paints an adult premixes
Pastels, chalks, or dry markers that create dust	Oil pastels, crayons, or dustless chalks
Solvents such as turpentine, toluene, and rubber cement thinner. Also avoid solvent-based inks, alkyd paints, and rubber cement.	Water-based products only
Aerosol sprays	Water-based paints with brushes or spatter techniques
Epoxy, instant glue, airplane glue, or other solvent-based adhesives	Water-based glues or markers only
Casting plaster. Besides creating dust, casting body parts can result in serious burns.	Adults can mix plaster in ventilated areas or outdoors for sand casting and other safe projects.

Source: Canadian Child Care Federation. (1992). *Safety in the Arts. Resource Sheet #21.* Retrieved April 2018 from http://www.cccf-fcsge .ca/wp-content/uploads/RS_21-e.pdf

In terms of cleaning products, many programs choose soap and water for cleaning surfaces and objects. Many use a dilute solution of bleach and water for disinfecting. Facilities with automatic dishwashers will use the detergent recommended for the machine. All kinds of commercial products are on the market that we can use in our homes and in programs. Many companies advertise the product's disinfecting qualities and claim that it makes things sparkling and fresh. For the most part, however, soap and water and good old elbow grease, which creates friction, remove most germs. Bleach kills any germs that may remain after cleaning. The recommended bleach dilution is strong enough to be effective yet dilute enough that it won't ruin clothes or make everything smell like bleach. It is also safe to use around children. Many public health agencies across Canada have approved non-bleach alternatives. Whichever disinfectants are used, educators need to take precautions to protect themselves and others when using products.

PRECAUTIONS TO FOLLOW WHEN USING DISINFECTANTS

- Read and follow the product's instructions (see Workplace Hazardous Materials Information System, page 92).
- Wear household rubber gloves to protect your hands from drying, if you prefer.
- Never mix two products (e.g., when ammonia and bleach are mixed, a poisonous gas is produced).
- Keep solutions in their original container and locked out of reach of children.
- Choose cleaners that are safe for our environment.

Courtesy of George Brown College/Richmond Adelaide Child Care Centre

Workplace Hazardous Materials Information System

Health Canada coordinates the administration of the **Workplace Hazardous Materials Information System (WHMIS)** and serves as the coordinator for the governance and administration of WHMIS in Canada. The legislation for WHMIS applies to all workplaces, which include ECLC settings. Employers are obliged to provide employees with information on the products they use at work. Certain controlled products have been defined as hazardous because they are compressed gas, flammable and combustible, oxidizing, poisonous, or infectious. These products must have labels that list their ingredients, their toxic effects, instructions on safe handling, and first-aid treatments. This legislation applies mainly to industries that use these types of products. Public health inspectors (PHIs) may be consulted to verify whether any of the cleaning and disinfecting products are controlled products. ECLC programs frequently buy their cleaning products at grocery stores, and products for sale there would not be controlled.

Read the label for directions and the first-aid treatment on the container (e.g., "If splashed in eyes, flush thoroughly with water. If swallowed, give water or milk. Call a physician"). The first-aid treatment also includes the name of the hazardous ingredient (e.g., "contains sodium hypochlorite"). This information will be very helpful to your poison control centre, whose number is listed in the front of your phone book, if someone ingests the product.

The Rights of the Worker

Although every province and territory has its own legislation on worker health and safety, the *Canadian Centre for Occupational Health and Safety Act* (CCOHS, 2016a, 2016b) gives every worker in Canada three important rights: the right to know, the right to participate, and the right to refuse dangerous work.

The Right to Refuse Dangerous Work. You can refuse work if you have reason to believe that the situation is unsafe to either yourself or your coworkers. This is the procedure you should follow:

- You must report to your supervisor that you are refusing to work and state why you believe that the situation is unsafe.
- You, your supervisor, and a Health and Safety Committee member or worker representative will investigate.
- You return to work if the problem is solved.
- If the problem is not resolved, a government health and safety inspector is called.
- Your supervisor may assign you reasonable alternative work.
- The inspector investigates and gives a decision.*

The Right to Participate. All employees have a right to take part in health and safety activities. For example, you can be chosen to be a health and safety representative or a member of a committee. You also have a right to report unsafe practices and conditions without worrying that you will lose your job or be reprimanded (get in trouble).**

The Right to Know. All employees have a right to know what hazards are present on the job, and how these hazards can affect them. You usually learn about the hazards during health and safety training sessions and through on-the-job instructions. Learning about chemical safety through WHMIS is also part of the "right to know" system.**

When applicable, don't be afraid to exercise your rights!

* Source: *Young Workers: What Laws Apply to You,* https://www.ccohs.ca/youngworkers/resources/whatlaws.html, Canadian Centre for Occupational Health and Safety (CCOHS), 2017. Reproduced with the permission of CCOHS, 2018.

**Source: *Young Workers: Employee Rights,* https://www.ccohs.ca/youngworkers/resources/employeeRights.html, Canadian Centre for Occupational Health and Safety (CCOHS), 2017. Reproduced with the permission of CCOHS, 2018.

Role of Public Health Agencies in Health Promotion

Public health nurses (PHNs) and PHIs work in **public health agencies**. PHNs may be available for consultation on staff illnesses, immunizations, and other concerns. PHIs conduct environmental sanitation inspections of ECLC settings. At least annually, PHIs inspect the building—its lighting, ventilation, kitchen facilities, garbage disposal, and so on. They submit a report to the licensing office (with a copy to the program) that includes any concerns and recommendations for improvement. As well, they may consult with the staff and answer questions about cleaning and disinfecting procedures and products. If the role of public health personnel in your community has been curtailed due to cutbacks, it is important for directors and staff to seek other consultants to perform this role. Keeping the physical environment up-to-date with current information and changes is essential for children's and adults' health in the ECLC program.

Workplace Environmental Issues

Comfortable environmental conditions are important for overall well-being. **Workplace environmental issues** can result in stress, fatigue, and other conditions. Heating/air conditioning, ventilation, noise, and light levels all contribute to educators' and children's emotional and physical well-being. If it's too hot inside, we get drowsy and irritable and are more prone to making mistakes. Inadequate lighting causes eyestrain and headaches. The building's architectural design should allow as much natural light into the space as possible.

A well-ventilated space helps remove indoor air contamination. Indoor air is tainted by hair sprays, perfumes, cleaning products, and dust; odours from photocopiers and computer laser printers; formaldehyde (e.g., from unsealed plywood or particleboard, urea-formaldehyde insulation, fabrics, glues, carpets); and outdoor pollutants. These pollutants are particularly irritating to people with asthma, respiratory illnesses, and contact lenses. For those with asthma or other respiratory illnesses, their breathing may be affected. For some individuals who suffer from migraines, strong scents may cause more severe headache pain, dizziness, and/or nausea. Skin irritation and eye irritation (for those with contact lenses) may be another issue.

CCOHS developed a document to outline how a company can go about incorporating a scent-free policy for the workplace if staff are affected by perfumes and other scents. (See Resource Materials.) A scent-free policy is not mandatory. For individuals whose workplace does not have such a policy, they can discuss possible accommodations with their supervisor. Also note that accommodation is required under the federal and provincial human rights acts. Contact your local human rights commission for more information if needed.

NELSONstudy

To access Resource Materials, visit NelsonStudy.

A common concern about carpet cleaners is their ingredients, which can include known human carcinogens, central nervous system toxins, and/or eye, skin, and respiratory irritants. They can also contain detergents that irritate skin, as well as ammonia and fragrances (Environmental Health Association of Nova Scotia, 2004, pp. 5–6).

Most deodorizers rely on chemicals to cover up, overpower, or deactivate odours. Some deodorizers block the nerves in people's nasal passages so that they cannot smell the odour. Instead of relying on chemicals, the key to dealing with odours is to remove the source of the odour or to dilute it.

A range of recommended less toxic alternatives to chemical carpet cleaners and deodorizers is available on the Environmental Health Association of Nova Scotia comprehensive website (see *Guide to Less Toxic Products* in Resource Materials). Homemade alternatives such as sprinkling baking soda on the carpet overnight and vacuuming it before children arrive can be effective. There are also professional carpet cleaning companies that use less toxic carpet cleaning products and processes.

NELSONstudy

To access Resource Materials, visit NelsonStudy.

Staff should suspect the quality of the air in the building when people are frequently experiencing symptoms such as headaches, fatigue, dizziness, or irritation in the eyes, nose, or throat. Temperature and relative humidity are two of several parameters that affect indoor comfort. Relative humidity levels can dry out the mucous membranes and skin, leading to chapping and irritation. Low relative humidity also increases static electricity, which can be irritating, and the static shocks can sting adults and children. High indoor humidity contributes to mould and fungus, which can cause poor indoor air quality and health problems, especially for children and adults with breathing issues, such as asthma (Government of Canada, 2015, p. 1). Approximately 50% humidity in summer and 30% in colder weather tends to be best. If needed, use a dehumidifier or air conditioner to reduce humidity levels, or a humidifier to increase humidity (e.g., when the furnace is in use). Note that anything that holds water, such as humidifiers, dehumidifiers, and air conditioners, must be cleaned regularly to prevent mould and fungus (Government of Canada, 2015, p. 3).

Ideally, there are windows in every room that staff open every day for some time, year-round. However, for programs located within larger buildings (e.g., in an office tower), the air is part of the building's ventilation system. Programs located in workplaces (e.g., in a manufacturing plant) should have a separate ventilation system to ensure that the children and staff are not breathing air from the plant. If staff or children frequently experience symptoms of illness, the ventilation system must be evaluated.

Of course, outdoor air quality can also have an effect on breathing, especially for those who have respiratory conditions such as asthma. Air Quality Index levels, on days when there is concern about smog or other airborne contaminants, can always be confirmed by checking online with Environment Canada's air quality forecasts and advisories. (See Resource Materials.) This website also offers advice on whether to exercise indoors on days with air quality issues such as high smog.

Finally, the noise level can be an issue, considering the number of children and adults in the same place for extended periods. Although the noise level is never in a range that could potentially damage someone's hearing, a constant noise level can make people feel tired and irritable. Couches, curtains, carpets, pillows, carpeted areas, acoustic ceiling tiles, dress-up clothes, etc., all absorb sounds within the room.

Educators can manage noise by

- alternating quiet and active programs;
- when staffing permits, rotating children in smaller groups outdoors and indoors;
- guiding children to use their "indoor voice" indoors;
- alternating educators who supervise the playground; and
- taking staff breaks in a separate room.

In a broader environmental perspective, as citizens and professionals, we have much to be concerned about with regard to our own health and the health of our planet. North Americans are on a binge of consumption, at a rate that is clearly unsustainable for the planet. Many individuals have recognized the importance of taking action at all health promotion levels to reduce their own feelings of powerlessness and, of course, to make a difference. In particular for women, the increase in breast cancer rates is alarming, and environmental risks must be considered. For example, among other causes, radiation, pesticides, and some plastics have been linked to breast cancer. Although radiation and pesticides have long

NELSONstudy

To access Resource Materials, visit NelsonStudy.

been issues as powerful carcinogens, there is growing concern (and controversy) about the ingredients (nonylphenols) in some plastic wraps used to cover food, added to make the wraps more flexible. Nonylphenols, known carcinogens, are not chemically bound and can leach out of the plastic fairly easily. Other ingredients in plastics (e.g., phthalates, bisphenol A) are hormone disruptors. For more information on the environment, your health, and actions you can take to lessen your exposure to potentially hazardous products, refer to resources on environmental health and safety (see Resource Materials for Units 2 and 7).

NELSONstudy

To access Resource Materials, visit NelsonStudy.

Injury Reports

When educators are injured at work, they must complete an injury report. This is also essential for students, volunteers, and even parents. It can be tempting to avoid the extra paperwork, especially if you believe that the injury is minor. However, a report is important for a number of reasons:

- to maintain adequate workplace injury records for liability
- to document any injury that seems minor at first but becomes serious later (e.g., a cut that becomes infected)
- to prevent further injuries, potentially

When staff can assess the conditions that caused or contributed to an injury, employers can implement preventive practices, review or provide training (e.g., in proper lifting), or modify the physical space to make it safer (e.g., by installing a handrail by the stairs or improving the lighting of the staff parking lot), which benefits everyone. Often the same injury report (or serious incident report) can be used for children and educators.

In addition, if an injury needs more attention, such as a visit to a physician or hospital, it is considered to be of a serious enough nature to require reporting to the provincial/territorial department of labour. Each province and territory in Canada has its own exclusive Workers' Compensation Board/Commission (WCB). The WCB will have its own injury reporting forms and requirements.

OBJECTIVES

To discuss the major role that communication at work plays in educators' psychological well-being. (LO 1, 3)

To identify possible sources of personal, professional, and societal stress and their impact on our well-being. (LO 3)

To list strategies to eliminate, reduce, or manage stress. (LO 1, 3)

To understand the role and benefits of effective communication in the workplace and networking with community professionals and agencies. (LO 5)

PROMOTING YOUR PSYCHOLOGICAL WELL-BEING

Workplaces don't present only physical risks and benefits; there are also emotional and social factors that can have positive and negative effects on employees' mental health. In general, **workplace stress** is the reaction from the combination of high demands in a job and a low level of control over the situation (CCOHS, 2012).

National Standard on Psychological Health and Safety in the Workplace

In January 2013, the Canadian Standards Association (CSA) Group and Bureau de normalisation du Québec (BNQ) published *Psychological Health and Safety in the Workplace—Prevention, Promotion, and Guidance to Staged Implementation,* marking an historic moment. (See Resource Materials.) This document is championed by the Mental Health Commission of Canada (MHCC) and was developed collaboratively by the BNQ and CSA Group.

"Psychological health comprises our ability to think, feel and behave in a manner that enables us to perform effectively in our work environments, our personal lives, and in society at large" (Centre for Applied Research in Mental Health & Addiction, 2012, p. 1).* Protecting psychological health and safety at work is the role of Canada's new national standard. Albeit voluntary at this point, standard of care and its guiding principles for psychological (also referred to as mental) health protection in the workplace have been put forward after 150 years of occupational health and safety development. By working to increase self-esteem, coping skills, social support, and well-being in all individuals and communities, psychological health promotion empowers people and communities to interact with their environments in ways that enhance psychosocial well-being (emotional, mental, social, and spiritual). It is an approach that fosters individual resilience and promotes socially supportive environments. Mental health promotion also works to challenge discrimination against those with mental health problems. Respect for culture, equity, social justice, interconnections, and personal dignity is essential for promoting mental health for everyone.

Creating a Supportive Workplace

Working with children and families is a rewarding career, as was echoed in the *You Bet We Still Care!* survey (Child Care Human Resources Sector Council, 2013b, p. 24): The survey found that 97% of directors and 94% of program staff agreed with the statement that their work is important. However, no job is without elements that can create feelings of stress for employees. By recognizing potential stress factors, students take the first step in preventing or reducing the negative impact, resulting in richer professional and personal lives.

The single most important component of high-quality ECLC, in terms of promoting healthy child development, is the nature of the daily relationship and interactions between educator and child. This relationship is, of course, affected by other quality factors. Although educators are the key component of quality, we have discussed the lack of recognition for the value of ECLC as a profession. As stated earlier, many educators are relatively poorly paid, and many have few traditional occupational benefits and may lack adequate professional development opportunities. The survey (Child Care Human Resources Sector Council, 2013b) found that for these issues to change, we need a coordinated policy approach and a new method of funding child care. These changes will take time and political will, but, in the meantime, the survey found that approximately 95% of educators and directors stated that the satisfaction of working with children and helping families keeps them in their jobs.

Educators who are content with their work conditions are much more likely to develop self-confidence and competence and are less likely to be dissatisfied and resign. Lower turnover rates mean more consistent care for children.

---

*Source: *Guarding Minds at Work*. Gilbert, Bilsker, Shain, & Samra, 2018. Reprinted with permission.

A program emphasizes the personal and professional growth of the employees. The employer (e.g., director, board of directors, agency, college, or university) provides support and access to professional development activities (e.g., conferences, workshops). However, educators need to be motivated to attend, learn, and incorporate their learning into their work with children.

Role of Directors

How can directors promote staff physical and psychological well-being? Directors' philosophies and management styles play an integral role in supporting a healthy work environment. First, directors often set the tone in the program—if they are committed to employee health and ongoing professional development, their commitment will likely have a positive effect on educators. For those working in a nonprofit agency, the board of directors is the employer, and the director who speaks on behalf of the educators is a critical link in keeping the board informed about the needs of staff. These directors will advocate for proactive employee health policies that are clearly outlined in their policy manuals. These policies may include

- an interview and selection process that assists in hiring individuals who fit their specific program;
- job descriptions for all staff members;
- an orientation program and job performance appraisals;
- well-defined lines of communication and conflict resolution;
- an immunization schedule to ensure that all staff immunizations are up-to-date;
- techniques for staff to implement that reduce the physical hazards of the work, such as proper lifting techniques, methods for safely handling potentially hazardous products, and methods for cleaning up spills of those products and bloody body fluids;
- exclusion criteria for educators and pregnant women in relation to infectious diseases;
- reporting of **workplace injuries** and compensation for illness or injury;
- opportunities for professional development and in-service training; and
- role of substitutes, students, and volunteers in the program.

Regular job evaluations (at least annually) are acknowledged as a learning tool rather than a punitive device. A health-promoting director supports educators in goal setting and in achieving those goals. She implements measures to decrease stress for staff whenever possible. She serves as an advocate for educators with the board of directors and the outside community.

Directors also have the following responsibilities for educators' health:

- They conduct regular inspections of ECLC settings.
- They ensure that educator–child ratios and group sizes are maintained throughout each day.

- They regularly review the work assignments to assess whether the work is too demanding and how tasks can be modified.

- They review and discuss work-related injuries and determine what preventive steps are required.

Probably the director's most important role in promoting educators' emotional and social well-being is to establish clear lines of communication. Most workplace factors in Table 2.6 (see page 114) are directly related to communication. Educators who receive effective administrative support, encouragement, and clear expectations tend to experience job satisfaction. Directors can also provide opportunities for educators to participate in decision making and professional growth. They recognize that leadership among employees can be demonstrated in many ways, not necessarily leadership as a director. The purpose of health promotion is to increase the amount of control that individuals and groups have over their lives. It makes sense that the more autonomy educators have at work, the more they feel in control. With the director's support, they feel free to express themselves on the job, especially when they view the director as an advocate. Directors support problem solving as issues arise, such as inadequate opportunities for regular breaks or issues about communication with a family member. A director's role is also paramount in difficult issues such as supporting educators when they report suspected child maltreatment. Educators often need to relieve feelings of stress by talking frankly with the director without fear of repercussion, even if the educator feels compelled to follow a grievance process. Effective directors expect professional confidentiality from educators and also model this behaviour.

Occupational Standards for Child Care Administrators includes a standard on managing staff, with a section on motivating staff as an essential element (Child Care Human Resources Sector Council, 2013a, p. 33). Required skills and abilities of administrators for motivating staff include the following:

a) be fair and consistent, i.e., avoid favouritism

b) establish a positive work environment

c) create work teams where individuals' skills complement one another

d) listen and respond to staff concerns

e) acknowledge and express gratitude for individual accomplishments

f) use incentives when appropriate

g) involve staff in the decision-making process, when appropriate

h) match staff skills and interests to job tasks, when possible (Child Care Human Resources Sector Council, 2013a, p. 33)

Role of Educators

Working with children has many rewards. It's probably the main reason you chose to enroll in an ECE program. You are also entering a profession that has occupational standards for educators that reflect the extensive range of skills and abilities, core knowledge, and standards of ethical practice expected of you. (See Resource Materials.)

Many educators prefer to work with a particular age group because their experience tells them that their aptitudes and interests fit best there; they usually

NELSONstudy

To access Resource Materials, visit NelsonStudy.

find the stress factors manageable. Yet some educators may work with a particular age group because they have no choice. Others may have lacked previous experience or ECE training and assumed that they would fit well but didn't. Educators who don't have a "fit" with their work or the age group may find the nature of the work overwhelming. Working with infants is quite different from working with preschoolers, which is quite different from working with school-agers. During your placements, you ideally will have opportunities to work with various age groups, gain realistic perceptions of working with children, and talk with educators about how they feel about their work and what they find rewarding and challenging (or stressful). You may have assumed, for example, that working with infants would not match your personality but, after your placement with infants, decided to begin your career working with this age group.

One thing is certain about work stress in early childhood learning and care settings: educators who develop and practise effective communication skills have lower stress levels. We have discussed the director's role in creating a supportive environment—let us not overlook the educators' attitudes, knowledge, and behaviour. Much of educators' work involves communicating with children, coworkers, and families. Educators who demonstrate collegiality with coworkers are likely to have it reciprocated. Fairness is an essential component of a healthy workplace. Recognition of each individual's rights and interests requires us to see one another as whole people rather than split us up into specific roles (e.g., director, educators).

Directors who are appreciated for their efforts find it easier to support staff. The opportunity for autonomy assumes that the educator has the ability and motivation to make responsible decisions. In other words, communication is not a one-way street! However, communication skills are complex and require work, practice, and a willingness to learn. Cross-cultural communication, for example, assumes that you recognize that your usual way of communicating is only one way, not the best way just because it's what you know.

CRITICAL THINKING

Identify an issue that you are going to find stressful when you begin your career in ECLC. List three strategies that will help reduce your apprehension and build your confidence as you begin your career.

Criteria for Respect in the Workplace

The following three criteria apply to all educators: accountability, reciprocal support, and establishing positive working relationships.

Accountability includes educators taking on their responsibilities with skill, punctuality, consistency, and ongoing professional development. All educators who take an active role in communicating respectfully with children, families, coworkers, and managers demonstrate their accountability. For example, communicating with parents regularly about the child's day helps parents trust that educators are knowledgeable and care about their child. Parents can then get to know and trust the educators who support their child's learning and development. Also, educators who demonstrate professional behaviour avoid subtle and overt insulting remarks, jokes, and other such slights so that working relationships are positive, not tainted with negative overtones.

Reciprocal support—having opportunities to talk about issues that arise and possible ways to handle them—can be helpful in managing stress and preventing problems in the workplace.

Emphasizing effective communication with the other educators reduces or avoids the "them and me" attitude. For example, male educators, who are often a minority in ECLC programs, feel added stress from female educators, managers, or parents if they are stereotyped in particular roles, such as being expected to do all the heavy lifting or repairs. Obviously, the assumption of roles or abilities on the basis of gender is inappropriate and does not contribute to positive working relationships. (For further discussion of recent research on Workplace Predictors of Educators' Health and Well-Being, see page 107.)

Courtesy of Lynn Wilson

The Juggle Struggle: Stress

Stress is a fact of life. Both positive and negative events in our lives create stress. "Hans Selye, a pioneer in studying physiological responses to challenge, defined stress as the non-specific response of the body to any demand made upon it" (Hales & Lauzon, 2018, p. 58). Stress affects the mind and emotions as well as the physical self. In moderation, stress is positive (termed "eustress" by Selye): it motivates us to learn, develop, and cope with life's frustrations. But the way that stress is perceived and managed depends on the individual and the environment (e.g., family, work, school, socioeconomic class, and community).

Coping refers to the ways that a person tries to decrease or eliminate a stress factor—a person's response to it. Stress management plays a major role in our wellness. If the individual is able to find ways to cope with stress, this has a positive impact on health. We all have had days when one thing after another goes wrong, usually minor things, and we feel "stressed out." We may stomp our feet, shout, slam a door, cry, or feel defeated or in distress. Eventually, those feelings pass. But when stress is severe or long term, the body and mind are weakened, making the person vulnerable to a number of physical and emotional conditions. This is especially true in individuals who have inadequate coping strategies or whose environment contains insurmountable barriers. These people may experience symptoms of stress overload, including headaches, insomnia, back or neck pain, repeated cold or canker sores, higher than usual susceptibility to illness, ulcers, addictions, anxiety, or depression. Stress overload is also a factor in heart disease and other chronic conditions.

Stress factors can result from a number of sources: our personal and professional lives and societal pressures.

FIGURE 2.4   Juggling Roles and Needs

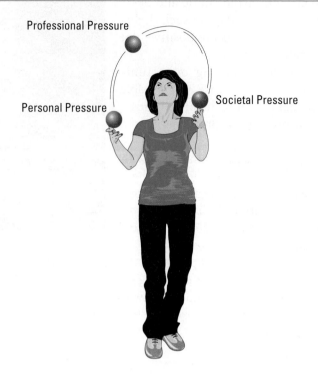

Professional Pressure

Personal Pressure

Societal Pressure

Personal Stress Factors

Personal stress factors can be short term (e.g., an argument with a family member or friend, a minor injury, a busy week). Some stress factors are longer term (e.g., separation or divorce, financial difficulties, death of a loved one). How we perceive and cope with personal stress depends on our temperament, tolerance level, and experience. Our temperament plays a part in how we perceive the stress in our lives. People who prefer (innately) stability and predictability experience change as stressful.

> The idea of moving to another city and beginning a new job is quite exciting and positive for some people. Yet for others, that change is perceived as anxiety producing and negative.

We all have individual tolerance levels for stress. When our tolerance level is reached and surpassed, we can experience feelings of distress. Past experiences with stress and the types of coping mechanisms that we have developed either help or hinder our ability to manage stress. An individual whose childhood was fraught with insecurity is likely to react differently to stressful events as an adult than a person whose childhood was happy and secure.

Our personal lifestyles can either magnify our feelings of stress or help us manage them. A **balanced lifestyle** contributes to our health; part of that lifestyle is helping our mind and body manage stress. Adequate sleep and leisure, physical activity, healthy eating, and meditation are effective body and mind defences against stress. We can help our body by avoiding certain substances that can trigger stress responses, such as caffeine and nicotine.

Professional Stress Factors

Every profession and workplace has inherent stress factors; even people working from their homes experience stress. Identifying **professional stress factors** and eliminating them, or at least reducing them, fall into the domain of occupational health. Working with children, families, and staff is not a calm and tranquil experience. Although the majority of educators express high job satisfaction while working with young children and making a difference in their lives, the following stress factors are commonly experienced by educators:

- the increasing demands on and expectations of educators
- the need for further knowledge and skills in guiding children with behaviour challenges, in culturally sensitive practice, and in inclusive care for children with special needs
- the constant attention needed to ensure the safety and security of young children
- low compensation rates and benefits such as paid sick leave and extended health care, which seem to be more available in other professions
- the lack of resources needed to maintain an optimal environment
- the isolation from other adults, particularly in family home child care
- the perceived lack of opportunities for career advancement
- communication issues with coworkers, directors, and parents, which can be stressful

Chronic stress can result in higher risks for a number of ailments. Figure 2.5 (see page 104) depicts the costs of an unhealthy workplace. Individuals may respond to chronic stress with unhealthy lifestyle habits such as overeating, smoking, drinking excessively, or being physically inactive. Also, responding to stress with anger can contribute to increased blood pressure and other negative physiological changes. These habits increase the risk of many of the conditions included in Figure 2.5.

Making changes involves identifying stress factors and, with the commitment of staff and management, working toward that change. Educators who have access to additional training, education, and professional development increase their knowledge and skills and improve the quality of care that children experience. Taking advantage of these opportunities enriches educators' work environments, confidence, recognition, and leadership skills.

Workplace stressors vary greatly, as do the ways to reduce or prevent them. For workplace stressors that are physical in nature, it is best to control stress at its source. *For example, deal with noise through control measures such as adding carpeting to a non-carpeted surface or increasing insulation.* With regard to the expectations of the job, it should be reasonably challenging, but not what could be defined as "sheer endurance." As mentioned earlier in this unit, opportunities for learning and making decisions, a future career path, and a degree of social support and recognition in the workplace are all important components to prevent burnout (CCOHS, 2012).

FIGURE 2.5   The Costs of an Unhealthy Workplace

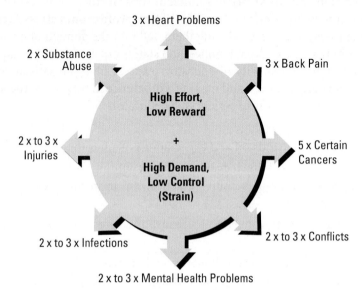

How to read the chart: For example, employees under sustained conditions of high effort/low reward and high pressure/low control are two to three times (2 x to 3 x) more likely to contract infections than other employees.

Source: © All rights reserved. *Best Advice on Stress Management in the Workplace, Part 2 of 2*. Health Canada 2008. Adapted and reproduced with permission from the Minister of Health, 2018.

PSYCHOLOGICAL HEALTH IN THE WORKPLACE

Below are some quick facts about psychological health and the workplace provided by the Mental Health Commission of Canada, as well as CCOHS (Government of Canada, 2017, p. 1):

- Psychological health issues are the leading cause of disability in Canada, with approximately 20% of Canadians experiencing them every year.
- This reality has a huge negative cost impact on the Canadian economy and decreases workplace productivity.
- Almost half of employed Canadians consider their daily work life to be most stressful, but less than one-quarter of them are comfortable communicating with their employer about a psychological health issue.

It is important to note that psychological health problems occur on a spectrum, from mild psychological difficulties on one end to severe psychological disorders on the other. The most common in the workplace are anxiety and depression. These conditions account for a large proportion of the negative impacts on employees and employers.

Psychological safety deals with the risk of injury to psychological well-being that an employee might experience. Improving the psychological safety of a work setting involves taking precautions to avert injury or danger to employee psychological health.

Psychological Health and Safety in the Workplace

The **National Standard on Psychological Health and Safety in the Workplace** is a voluntary set of guidelines, tools, and resources. There are current and emerging legal requirements in Canada for the protection of employee psychological health and safety and the promotion of civility and respect at work. Psychological health in the workplace, the way people interact with one another daily, has an impact on all workplaces and can no longer be ignored.

Guarding Minds @ Work's survey consists of 68 questions to assess 13 psychological factors that have been identified by a large body of research.

GUARDING MINDS @ WORK'S 13 PSYCHOLOGICAL FACTORS IN THE WORKPLACE

The 13 factors are:

1. Psychological Support
2. Organizational Culture
3. Clear Leadership & Expectations
4. Civility & Respect
5. Psychological Competencies & Requirements
6. Growth & Development
7. Recognition & Reward
8. Involvement & Influence
9. Workload Management
10. Engagement
11. Balance
12. Psychological Protection
13. Protection of Physical Safety

Source: *Guarding Minds at Work*. Gilbert, Bilsker, Shain, & Samra, 2018. Reprinted with permission.

Agencies across Canada, big and small, are asking their employees to complete the survey, anonymously, to help determine how each participating agency can improve their workplace environment, policies, and the way decisions are made and communicated. Workplaces with a positive approach to psychological health and safety are better able to recruit and retain competent employees, who also are more productive, creative, and innovative. Other positive impacts include reducing key workplace concerns such as conflict, grievances, turnover, disability, injury rates, absenteeism and performance, and morale problems (CSA & BNQ, 2013; Guarding Minds @ Work, 2012).

Societal Pressures

The quality of ECLC across Canada and the issues of affordability, accessibility, and comprehensiveness for parents are national concerns. Many families are affected by governments' lack of commitment to ECLC, and educators across Canada experience every day the effects of these societal attitudes. Other **societal pressures** affect everyone, educator and noneducator alike, such as the following:

- the expectation, especially for women, to have multiple roles and to perform them all well (e.g., to have two full-time jobs, one inside and one outside the home)
- issues of discrimination
- the fast-paced, ever-changing world, particularly its technology, which makes many of us feel that we are being left behind
- growing concern about violence in our communities and around the world
- serious concerns about other national and global issues, such as the economy and the environment (e.g., climate change)

Identifying sources of stress in our lives is the first step in managing them and avoiding stress overload. Some stress factors may be impossible to change. Fortunately, many can be addressed, with problem solving and commitment. There is a range of "stress busters," depending on individual needs and interests: incorporating physical activity, eating well, practising mindfulness, sharing your feelings with trusted friends, taking time for yourself, and finding ways to laugh are just some of many possibilities.

The Heart and Stroke Foundation of Canada and Canadian Mental Health Association's websites are excellent resources that provide you with numerous tools to identify stressors in your life and ways to manage them. (See Resource Materials.)

Before deciding which coping strategy to use in a situation, ensure that you have determined whether it is

- an appropriate thing to do in a situation (e.g., chanting during a stressful interaction with a family member is not advisable);
- a positive way of coping (e.g., excessive alcohol or even excessive exercise is not positive); and
- a strategy that will help in the long run (e.g., a short-term solution may not be enough).

- An ECLC program institutes a family responsibility leave for its staff, allowing educators whose own children are ill to be at home with them. This significantly reduces their overall stress level as working parents.
- All educators who belong to their provincial/territorial ECE association benefit from lower premiums for disability insurance.

Societal pressures can be complex, and we may feel that we have little or no control over them. Anxiety is often reduced through education—taking courses to enhance our understanding of issues or to build skills (e.g., computer, self-defence, yoga). Get involved in national, regional, or local organizations advocating for change in areas such as ECLC and the environment. Participating in and working for positive change, even if it seems daunting, is one of the best ways to gain a sense of control over the world around you. It also tends to reduce isolation and expand your social support when you are involved with others.

NELSONstudy

To access Resource Materials, visit NelsonStudy.

Workplace Predictors of Educators' Health and Well-Being

Recognizing and managing stress in your life are essential now and upon graduation, when you will likely be working in an ECLC program. There is growing recognition that an employee's overall health plays a significant role in job satisfaction, productivity, and turnover rates. Although much attention is given to the healthy development of children, less is known about the health and well-being of educators. Yet it is clear from the research that adult well-being has a significant influence on child well-being. Research indicates that early learning outcomes are affected by factors such as the quality of attachment with caregivers, emotional regulation, and well-being (Edwards et al., 2008). Quality of the educator–child relationship is central to the mental health and well-being of children.

To enhance the capacity of educators to develop warm, responsive, and consistent relationships with the children and families with whom they work, the well-being of the ECLC workforce must also be considered and supported. The purpose of a recent research study of Ontario registered early childhood educators (RECEs) was to document the health and well-being of full-time RECEs (Ioannone & Pimento, 2017). The data could then be applied to develop significant recommendations for improved RECE health and well-being at all three levels of a health promotion action plan (Ioannone & Pimento, 2017).

The survey link was sent to all Ontario registered early childhood educators via the College of Early Childhood Education's online college newsletter. The authors of the study (Ioannone and Pimento) acknowledged this support, which resulted in 604 surveys, completed by RECEs currently working full time (i.e., at least 30 hours weekly) in ECLC settings in Ontario. Here is a summary of the makeup of the participants:

- More than 97% female
- 65% worked in centre-based settings
- Almost 67% worked directly with children
- Unionized or Not: 56% were not unionized
- 89% worked more than 30 hours per week
- Experienced: 60% had 10 years, 18% had 11–15 years, and 43% had >15 years
- Ages: ~25% were 50+ years, >50% were between 30–49 years, and about 18% were 20–29 years
- In a relationship: 72%
- A parent: 66%
- Education: 77% had a college certificate/diploma, and 23% had a BA or higher*

Survey Responses

Health Status

"While over three-quarters of RECEs reported being in excellent or very good or good physical health, more than one in five (21.4%) RECEs reported being in fair or poor psychosocial health" (Ioannone & Pimento, 2017, p. 9). The extent to which psychosocial health must be considered an essential aspect of health and well-being is significant.

---

*Source: Reprinted by permission of Palmina Ioannone and Barb Pimento.

FIGURE 2.6   RECEs' Self-Rated Physical and Psychosocial Health

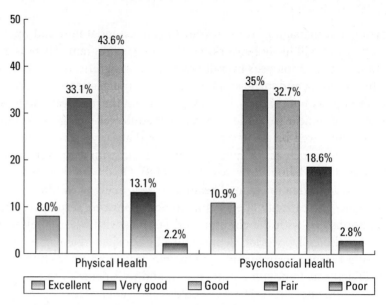

Source: Reprinted by permission of Palmina Ioannone and Barb Pimento.

Symptoms of Stress

"[One] in 5 RECEs (21.4%) reported experiencing six or more stress-related symptoms in the past three months" (Ioannone & Pimento, 2017, p. 10). There are many physical symptoms that result from stress, affecting educators' short- or long-term health and well-being. The symptoms can also have a negative impact on the educators' performance at work with the many responsibilities, especially related to children's needs.

FIGURE 2.7   Symptoms Experienced by RECEs in the Past Three Months

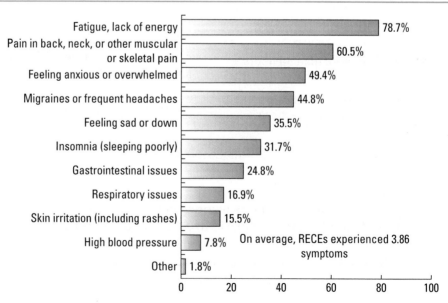

Source: Reprinted by permission of Palmina Ioannone and Barb Pimento.

Stressful Workplace

"More than one in four (26.9%) of RECEs reported being extremely stressed or very stressed from work" (Ioannone & Pimento, 2017, p. 15). Although some level of stress is everyone's reality, it is interesting to note that work-related stress affects approximately 1 in 4 RECEs, compared with approximately 1 in 10 educators who find stress outside of work more stressful.

FIGURE 2.8   Percentage of RECEs Who Report "Work" and "Outside of Work" as "Very Stressful" or "Extremely Stressful"

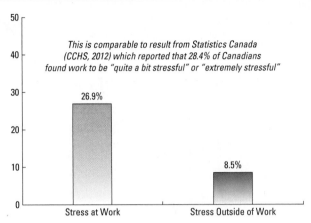

Source: Reprinted by permission of Palmina Ioannone and Barb Pimento.

Presenteeism

RECEs who regularly come to work when unwell are likely to feel exploited, adding to the stress and physical symptoms related to this situation. Top reasons for presenteeism included lack of supply staff (53.1%) and too many work responsibilities (42.6%). Several key reasons were identified as to why an RECE who is not feeling well may not take needed time off for recovery. This situation can contribute to increased stress and a longer period of time when the educator feels unwell.

FIGURE 2.9   Reasons for Presenteeism

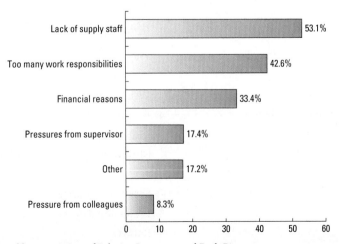

Source: Reprinted by permission of Palmina Ioannone and Barb Pimento.

Absenteeism

"Top reasons for being absent included being physically ill (56%) or a mental health issue (24.3%)" (Ioannone & Pimento, 2017, p. 12). The most common reason for absence from work identified by over half (56%) of the respondents was respiratory illness (mostly cold and flu infections). Ergonomic and injury issues together affected fewer than one-fifth (17.9%) of absentee RECEs.

FIGURE 2.10   Reasons for Absenteeism

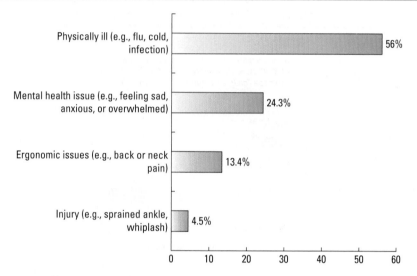

Source: Reprinted by permission of Palmina Ioannone and Barb Pimento.

Recommendations for Improving Health and Well-Being in Work Life

The participants were asked for recommendations to improve their health and well-being in their work life and what could be done provincially to improve the health and well-being in the work life of all RECEs. Here are their overall responses for each question, starting with what was identified as priorities:

ONESELF: INDIVIDUAL RECE	COLLECTIVELY: ALL RECES
1. Support (from staff and environment)	1. Wages
2. Personal well-being	2. Feeling valued/recognized/respected
3. Manageable work hours	3. Wellness initiatives from employers
4. Benefits	4. Benefits
5. Professional development	5. Reasonable expectations (documentation/paperwork/planning)
6. Supply staff	6. Colleagues
7. Other	7. Services/resources
	8. Professional development
	9. Ratios

Although each of the factors listed in Figure 2.11 are predictors in supporting health and well-being, these were the strongest two factors identified by the participants:

- psychological protection
- development, recognition, benefits, and wages (Ioannone & Pimento, 2017)

FIGURE 2.11   Best Workplace Predictors of Health and Well-Being

Team and colleague support	
Supervisor support	
Psychological support	
Psychological protection	✓
Physical environment and safety	
Development, recognition, benefits, and wages	✓
Workload	
Involvement and influence	
Engagement	

Source: Reprinted by permission of Palmina Ioannone and Barb Pimento.

Psychological Protection

Guarding Minds @ Work (2012, p. 3i) states that when employees' psychological safety is not protected, "they perceive workplace conditions as ambiguous and unpredictable." When employees are psychologically protected they have more job satisfaction, work and learn better as a team, and are less likely to suffer from stress-related illness. They have higher confidence in their abilities and in getting involved with positive changes in the program.

Development, Recognition, Benefits, and Wages

These aspects of workplace predictors of health and well-being are somewhat obvious, considering the impact of appropriate and regular salaries to support the employees' needs for adequate housing, food, and the amenities required for the health and well-being of employees and their families. Health benefits (such as dental) also contribute to healthy lives. Recognition of educators' contribution to children and families through quality care and learning is also necessary to uplift the employees' well-being. Recognition of years served, acknowledgment of milestones reached, and opportunities for continued development in their profession (e.g., conferences, workshops, courses, portfolios for submission to a professional affiliation) also contribute to RECEs' well-being.

Recommendations Linked to Health Promotion

Health promotion practice is the process of enabling people to increase control over and improve their health. It moves beyond a focus on individual behaviour toward a wide range of social and environmental interventions.

FIGURE 2.12   Promoting the Health of RECEs

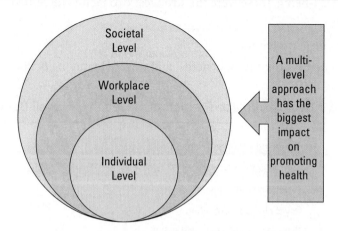

Source: Reprinted by permission of Palmina Ioannone and Barb Pimento.

Individual Problem Solving and Self-Reliance

Examples of what educators can do:

- Practise self-care (physical and mental)
- Take breaks, take your vacation time, and expend your benefits
- Aim to achieve work–life balance
- Work toward positive relationships with coworkers and supervisors
- Build current relationships with family and friends
- Increase your social support
- Become knowledgeable about the national standard

Community Action

Examples of what ECLC settings can do:

- Comply with the national standard
- Develop policies, practices, and programs that address potential harm to employees (e.g., bullying, harassment, violence)
- Link to mental health services
- Support and develop healthy living/wellness initiatives

Societal Change

Examples of what federal, provincial/territorial, and municipal laws and policies can do:

- Implement a national child care plan (federal)
- Set a mandatory workplace requirement to follow the national standard (federal)
- Improve wages (increase the minimum wage in provinces/territories)

- Collaborate with ECE advocates and professional organizations (all three levels)
- Build healthy public policy via four complementary approaches: legislation, fiscal measures, taxation, and organizational change (all three levels)

The survey authors believe that, ultimately, the well-being of the ECLC workforce must be supported at individual, community, and social policy levels of health promotion. This research supports investment in the health and well-being of the ECLC workforce beyond training and the individual level of health promotion. Investment also occurs through modifying psychosocial working conditions (i.e., increasing psychological protection, recognition, wages, and professional development) and the early childhood learning and care system, which includes relevant government policy and initiatives at all levels of government.

Early Childhood Educational Experience: Setting the Stage

The process of becoming a professional begins the day you start your early childhood education and training. You have chosen a career that requires a vast range of attitudes, knowledge, and skills. ECE students are on the road to lifelong learning that begins with recognizing their individual and social responsibilities and taking ownership of their responsibilities. Here are some examples of the professional behaviour that you can take ownership of now:

- promptness for classes and placements—behaviour that is not only expected throughout your professional life but is also appreciated in your personal life
- good personal hygiene
- communication skills that demonstrate respect for others' opinions, such as listening respectfully in class when the instructor or a classmate is speaking (as a matter not of authority but of respect) and using body language that conveys interest and learning (while recognizing a range of ways of communicating that reflect ethnocultural diversity). Communication is a lifelong learning process and is obviously a critical skill for professionals. It is important to become aware of how you, as a student, communicate and to be open to learning new skills.

CRITICAL THINKING

As a student, you are frustrated by a clique of three students who sit together and regularly disrupt the class. What do you do?

Placements in ECLC settings provide you with opportunities to observe and analyze, which help you formulate your personal philosophy of education, which, in turn, is based on an integration of theory and practice. Placements also offer the advantage of starting your professional career with some experience working with educators already behind you. This experience helps you identify some of the attitudes, knowledge, and skills that either contribute to quality care or detract from it. Some examples of human qualities that are beneficial for educators include warmth, patience, high energy, openness to new ideas, flexibility, critical thinking, and maturity. Educators who possess these qualities are positive role models for students and graduates. With every placement experience, you meet a variety of educators who have their own styles yet fulfill these criteria. However, some educators demonstrate physical and emotional exhaustion through behaviour such as impatience and sarcasm with children, tension with others at work, and apathy toward their job. Unfortunately, these educators are modelling as much for students as are their positive coworkers.

Placements allow you to experience different management styles. The working environment is created by the educators' personal styles and the levels of education, how well they work together, the types of policies, and the style of the director. Some individuals like to work in an environment that is more laid-back; others like a structure with rules clearly laid out. As a student, you probably will not see the inner workings of the organization (e.g., salaries and fringe benefits, how promotions are handled, how the program implements change). Yet you can get a sense of how staff work together, the level and effectiveness of the supervision, and staff morale. Table 2.6 identifies factors in a work setting that contribute to either a more positive or negative atmosphere in the workplace.

TABLE 2.6 Evaluating Workplace Factors: Positive and Negative Features

Positive Features	Negative Features
Clear and consistent policies and procedures	Absent or inconsistent policy and procedures
Fair and consistent application of rules for the employees	Different application of rules for different employees
Adequate resources to meet expectations	Lack of resources to meet expectations
Leadership is able to make quick decisions	Leadership has difficulty making decisions
Leadership is able to and willing to take corrective action when errors are made by leadership	Leadership is unable or unwilling to correct errors made by leadership
Errors are seen as an opportunity to learn	There is no tolerance of errors
Recognition is given and employees feel valued	There is no recognition for good work
Workers feel safe, or if conditions are unsafe, steps will be taken	Workers feel unsafe
Communication is open and issues are dealt with	Communication is limited
Issues are raised when they occur	There is an atmosphere of secrecy
There are no surprises	You never know when you might be in trouble
Environmental conditions (i.e., safety, belonging, consistency/predictability, opportunity, acceptance/love, and hope) are present	Environmental conditions (i.e., safety, belonging, consistency/predictability, opportunity, acceptance/love, and hope) are absent

(continued)

TABLE 2.6 Evaluating Workplace Factors: Positive and Negative Features *(continued)*

Positive Features	Negative Features
Peer support is built into the organizational structure and accessible	There are no opportunities (or few opportunities) to debrief with and access support from peers
Reflective practice is standard practice for the organization	Reflective practice is not entrenched into or encouraged by the organization

Source: Adapted from *When Compassion Hurts: Burnout, Vicarious Trauma and Secondary Trauma in Prenatal and Early Childhood Service Providers.* (2012), by Best Start Resource Centre. Toronto, Ontario, Canada: Author.

Among the most important training opportunities that placements offer you as a student are self-reflection and, of course, evaluation of your progress by experienced professionals. Ongoing feedback of your demonstrated skills assists you in identifying areas of strength and areas in which you need to make immediate or long-term changes. Students who view evaluation positively as a valuable learning tool can incorporate constructive criticism into their learning and make consistent progress in their skill levels. Both self-reflection and evaluation by others will be essential aspects of your career.

When you are an educator, being a reflective practitioner means thinking about what and how you are doing things now and self-evaluating to improve your mindset and your practice. Incorporating reflection into your everyday life at home and work contributes to stress reduction by recognizing what is causing some of your stress and problem solving what you can change. Take a balanced look by asking yourself questions such as "How do I treat my peers?" "Am I considering their views?" "Am I helping families feel welcome?" or "Do I help the program run more smoothly by thinking ahead?" Evaluating your own practice helps you to recognize changes that are needed of you and the agency, identify your professional development needs, and build your confidence and job satisfaction. Managers need educators' active participation and commitment to their self-reflection and motivation to continue learning.

Graduates: Starting the Job Search

Your first position in an ECLC setting will probably leave a lasting impression on you. Starting in a program where you are treated with respect by educators who remember what it's like to be the new kid on the block, and who provide you with guidance and support, helps build your confidence and self-esteem. New graduates are influenced significantly by their first director. The kind of assistance, support, opportunities, and guidance that graduates receive contributes greatly to their ability to move forward. Therefore, during job interviews, it's in your best interest to consider the qualities of the director—will they fit with yours?

Graduates often bring a breath of fresh air, new ideas, and enthusiasm into programs. Graduates who demonstrate openness to learning from others—not an "I've learned everything I need to know" attitude—will start off on the right foot with their coworkers. A commitment to lifelong learning means that you recognize that your early childhood education and training have set the stage for a career of future learning rather than being the final curtain.

REVISITING THE HEALTH PROMOTION ACTION PLAN

With reference to the health promotion action plan introduced in Unit 1, the following discussion illustrates this plan put into practice in terms of occupational health.

Individual Problem Solving and Self-Reliance

With the awareness of health issues that affect educators, each of us is able to identify our own health concerns and can be proactive in preventing or reducing the impact of our choices on our health. As a result of positive changes you make to your well-being, you're probably beginning to notice that you have more energy in working with children. You feel like a better role model. You are practising sensible lifting, bending, and carrying techniques. You are dressing appropriately for work—with footwear that includes heel support, for example. Your commitment to lifelong learning through reading and attending workshops, seminars, and conferences on health issues enhances your ability to make choices in your personal life and professionally. All education plays a role in your ability to advance in your career.

Community Action

Together, the director or principal and staff support each other, parents, and families. Staff meetings are based on the premise that you can learn from one another through sharing resources and acknowledging each educator's expertise, experiences, and contribution. Stress relief comes in part from the knowledge that you can share concerns with a coworker or director and trust his or her professional confidentiality—and this contributes to a positive working environment. Conferring with professionals and agencies with expertise in occupational health, management, communication, and other areas also helps staff reduce stress and increases educators' knowledge and skills.

Becoming involved in local organizations related to work with children and families (e.g., local breakfast clubs, joint health and safety committees) can enhance educators' understanding of issues and help effect change. As the early childhood profession is enhanced, so, too, are educators' feelings of self-worth and status as professionals.

Representatives from your workplace and a few others in the community sponsor a full-day conference on the Mental Health Works initiative with the local chapter of the Canadian Mental Health Association. The morning focuses on awareness of workplace mental health and the afternoon on issues and solutions. Workplace representatives from across the community are invited to attend, broadening the knowledge and commitment to mental health in the community. Union stewards, managers, and workers are in attendance.

Societal Change

Advocacy at the provincial/territorial and federal levels can create change that affects occupational health on a broader level, such as a national child care plan, family responsibility leave, or positive, supportive changes in legislation. The quality of the work environment in ECLC settings (including wages, benefits, working conditions, and the organization of the work) affects educators' performance and the program's quality. Everyone benefits from a national child care plan.

As educators develop skills in the process of thinking about and addressing problems, they also develop increased pride in their work and growing confidence in their ability to communicate outside the classroom. Passive acceptance of disheartening conditions in schools or programs, which leads to cynicism and burnout, can be replaced with optimistic attempts to improve situations whenever possible.

CONCLUSION

A proactive way to achieve job satisfaction and manage stress is to be aware of how well you are implementing healthy physical, emotional, and social practices. It is also important to examine your workplace—are the policies and practices contributing to staff well-being? Appendix 2.3 (see page 122) provides a checklist for this purpose. Can you identify practices that could be improved? Can you identify supports and barriers and possible solutions? Look back to the dimensions of wellness. Achieving balance in your life through setting achievable goals and action plans will contribute to your sense of control.

Where are we going in the future? The career ladder integrates education with career advancement, each a step further along in growth. Each step—based on education and training, job skills, experience, and interest—broadens your role and responsibilities. With career advancement comes increases in salary and job status.

Career advancement shouldn't mean that once you have worked with children for a certain period, the only place to go is the position of supervisor or director. Community colleges and some universities offer post-diploma certificates and degrees to ECE graduates who wish to continue their formal education. Educators may want to continue working with children and their families within a program but have more specialized skills and knowledge, such as education and care for infants and toddlers or children with special needs, child assessment, program evaluation, family resources and support, or health promotion advocacy. Here again, salaries must reflect the level of education and roles. Recognizing that educators are the key component of quality ECLC, *People, Programs and Practices: A Training Strategy for the Early Childhood Education and Care Sector in Canada* (Beach & Flanagan, n.d., p. 63) identifies the best practices and supports needed to refine mentoring and coaching approaches for new graduates as one of its strategic directions. New graduates are successful when they find ways to prevent or manage stressors that are within their control. When they feel supported in their new work environment and are members of at least one professional organization that helps them stay current and involved as advocates, they also tend to contribute to their profession.

ASSESS YOUR LEARNING

Define terms or describe concepts used in this unit.

- aerobic (cardiovascular) fitness
- balanced lifestyle
- endurance
- ergonomics
- flexibility
- National Standard on Psychological Health and Safety in the Workplace
- personal stress factors

- professional stress factors
- public health agencies
- societal pressures
- strength
- stress
- workplace environmental issues
- Workplace Hazardous Materials Information System (WHMIS)
- workplace injuries
- workplace stress

Evaluate your options in each situation.

1. A colleague buys her lunch from the nearby fast-food restaurant almost every day. You can't resist having her pick up something for you too, even though you often feel full after eating the nourishing hot lunch with the children before you have your lunch break. The fries or burger tastes great, but you feel sluggish all afternoon.

2. You and a coworker rarely agree on program-related issues. As a result, your relationship deteriorates to the point where you speak as little as possible, and the tension is felt by the other staff, children, and families.

3. You and two coworkers have been injured over the past month from pinching fingers in a cupboard door while putting things away (out of children's reach). Each of you completed a detailed injury report and submitted it to the director, yet none of you have heard anything from her about this situation.

4. You enjoy talking with family members of the children in your program but are not confident trying to communicate with individuals whose first language is not English. You feel that you are being patronizing, speaking loudly and very slowly, and making hand gestures.

5. To the best of your parents' and your own knowledge, you never had rubella as a child. You are now pregnant, and three children in your preschool program have contracted rubella.

APPENDIX 2.1

Evaluating Health Information on the Internet

Here are some specific guidelines for evaluating online health sites:

Check the creator. Websites are produced by health agencies, health-support groups, school health programs, health-product advertisers, health educators, health-education organizations, and provincial and federal governments. Read site headers and footers carefully to distinguish biased commercial advertisements from unbiased sites created by scientists and health agencies.

Look for possible bias. Websites may be attempting to provide healthful information to consumers, but they may also be attempting to sell a product. Many sites are merely disguised advertisements.

Check the date. If you are looking for the most recent research, check the date the page was created and last updated, as well as the links. Several non-working links signal that the site isn't carefully maintained.

Check the references. As with other health-education materials, Web documents should provide the reader with references. Unreferenced suggestions may be unwarranted, scientifically unsound, and possibly unsafe.

Consider the author. Is he or she recognized in the field of health education or otherwise qualified to publish a health-information Web document? Does the author list his or her occupation, experience, and education? (Hales & Lauzon, 2018, pp. 361–362)

APPENDIX 2.2

Footwear Policy for an Early Childhood Learning and Care Program

For All Staff, Students, and Volunteers

To reduce potential hazards and injury, the footwear of all adults in the ECLC program needs to contribute to their and the children's safety, both indoors and outdoors.

The following policy and guidelines are meant to be followed year-round:

1. All footwear worn at work should have a good fit and support.

2. Shoes should be comfortable, with good traction.

   The construction of shoes needs to include soles made of slip-resistant materials for good grip in the case of wet or slippery surfaces.

3. It is preferable to have closed-toe shoes.

   Closed-toe shoes minimize injuries (e.g., they provide protection from falling or rolling objects or being stepped on).

   If wearing open-toe sandals, they should have lateral (side) support.

   Freedom of movement for toes prevents aching feet, blisters, calluses, etc.

4. The footwear must grip the heel firmly.

   Footwear that is loose fitting or lacks heel support (e.g., clogs, flip-flops) can result not only in personal injury but also the unintentional injury of a child. If your foot comes out of the shoe while carrying a child, you may fall with the child in your arms or fall on the child.

   Sandals should have a heel strap.

   Flip-flops and slippers are not to be worn while working.

5. It is recommended that footwear be flat or have a low heel with a wide base.

   Higher or narrow-based heels provide for less balance and increased chance of tripping.

6. Look for the following features in shoes (including sandals) to provide support for your feet:

- The inner side of the shoe is enclosed from the heel to the top of the big toe (i.e., lateral support).

- The material (e.g., leather) that the shoe is made of provides protection to the top of the foot (metatarsal bones) and the toes to reduce injury when they are stepped or dropped on.

- The instep and outside of the shoe should be connected (e.g., laces, strap, loafer), which prevents the foot from slipping out of the shoe while walking.

  This consideration is usually unnecessary for boots, which normally cover the entire foot and ankle.

The photos below are more reflective of seasonal (summer) footwear. It is always safest (year-round) to wear footwear that has a closed toe and heel.

Not Appropriate:
Open toe and no back strap

Better, but Not Best:
Open toe, but has back strap

Best:
Closed toe, instep, and heel; strap connecting instep and outer side of shoe

APPENDIX 2.3

Health Practices:
You and Your Employer

The following checklist summarizes the aspects of occupational health and well-being discussed in this unit. How do you rate yourself and a centre where you've done a placement? You may find it enlightening to check again after you've been working in an early childhood learning and care program for a year.

DO YOU . . .	YES	NO	SOMETIMES
maintain healthy eating habits by			
being aware of your eating pattern	❏	❏	❏
setting reasonable goals to improve eating pattern (if needed)	❏	❏	❏
drinking water every day	❏	❏	❏
increasing fibre	❏	❏	❏
decreasing processed foods	❏	❏	❏
balance work, rest, and exercise by			
taking time for regular physical activity	❏	❏	❏
setting goals and keeping track of fitness progress	❏	❏	❏
ensuring you get adequate sleep	❏	❏	❏
finding ways for leisure daily	❏	❏	❏
spending time with friends and family	❏	❏	❏
prevent the spread of illness by			
keeping your immunization up-to-date	❏	❏	❏
washing your hands effectively and consistently	❏	❏	❏
implementing cleaning and sanitizing routines effectively and consistently	❏	❏	❏
prevent workplace injuries by			
using proper bending, lifting, and carrying techniques	❏	❏	❏
identifying and reporting required adjustments to workspace, equipment, and furnishings	❏	❏	❏
following products' safety recommendations	❏	❏	❏
using environmentally friendly products	❏	❏	❏
implementing the principles of WHMIS	❏	❏	❏
reporting workplace injuries	❏	❏	❏
keeping your first-aid and CPR certificates up-to-date	❏	❏	❏

(appendix continues on next page)

promote your social and emotional well-being by

- demonstrating respect for self and others through professional behaviour such as promptness and confidentiality ☐ ☐ ☐
- developing and practising effective communication skills ☐ ☐ ☐
- knowing and using designated lines of communication to share concerns ☐ ☐ ☐
- integrating ongoing reflective practice ☐ ☐ ☐
- being actively involved in your self-evaluation and evaluation by others ☐ ☐ ☐
- being flexible and open to learning new ideas ☐ ☐ ☐
- being supportive of peers who are experiencing stress ☐ ☐ ☐
- coming to work with a positive attitude ☐ ☐ ☐
- asking for help and offering help in situations of workplace abuse ☐ ☐ ☐
- reporting any incidents of workplace abuse, violence, or harassment ☐ ☐ ☐
- taking rest during designated breaks and holidays ☐ ☐ ☐
- achieving work–life balance ☐ ☐ ☐
- achieving a healthy lifestyle by eating well and exercising ☐ ☐ ☐
- identifying your stress factors and developing coping mechanisms that eliminate or reduce them ☐ ☐ ☐
- seeking further professional development ☐ ☐ ☐
- being a member of an early childhood association ☐ ☐ ☐

lower other risk factors by

- stopping smoking ☐ ☐ ☐
- conducting monthly breast or testicular self-examinations ☐ ☐ ☐
- limiting regular consumption of alcohol ☐ ☐ ☐
- practising safer sex ☐ ☐ ☐
- having checkups with a health care professional ☐ ☐ ☐
- keeping up-to-date on health issues ☐ ☐ ☐

evaluate balance in your life through awareness of wellness dimensions:

- physical ☐ ☐ ☐
- emotional ☐ ☐ ☐
- social ☐ ☐ ☐
- intellectual ☐ ☐ ☐
- occupational ☐ ☐ ☐
- spiritual ☐ ☐ ☐
- environmental ☐ ☐ ☐
- financial ☐ ☐ ☐

(appendix continues on next page)

Goal statement (specific and measurable)
Action steps: 1.
           2.
           3.
           4.
Target date:
Resources available to help you:
Barriers and how to deal with them:

DOES YOUR EMPLOYER . . .	YES	NO	SOMETIMES
support educators' healthy eating habits by			
ensuring adequate break times	❏	❏	❏
providing a relaxing place to eat and relax	❏	❏	❏
recognize the importance of staff balancing work, rest, and physical activity by			
maintaining adequate educator–child ratios	❏	❏	❏
ensuring that all staff take regular breaks each day	❏	❏	❏
enabling physical activity opportunities by identifying staff needs and matching these with reasonable employer provisions	❏	❏	❏
incorporating sufficient time in the daily schedule for program planning and documenting	❏	❏	❏
curtailing overtime and discouraging staff from taking work home	❏	❏	❏
prevent the spread of illness by			
keeping track of staff 's immunization records	❏	❏	❏
providing orientation and regular in-service updating in:			
• infection control strategy	❏	❏	❏
• food handling and preparation	❏	❏	❏
providing adequate supplies and posters for hand washing, diapering, toileting	❏	❏	❏
developing and posting cleaning and sanitizing routines	❏	❏	❏
prevent workplace injuries by			
providing orientation and regular in-service training in:			
• proper lifting techniques	❏	❏	❏
• WHMIS and product safety	❏	❏	❏
• other training, as needed	❏	❏	❏
responding to inadequacies in workspaces, equipment, and furnishings to strive toward ergonomic ideals	❏	❏	❏
purchasing environmentally friendly products	❏	❏	❏
completing workplace injury reports and responding to injuries	❏	❏	❏
requiring evidence that staff 's first-aid and CPR certificates are up-to-date and arranging for staff to renew as a group	❏	❏	❏

(appendix continues on next page)

promote staff's collegiality and emotional well-being by

	YES	NO	SOMETIMES
keeping policies current and clear and ensuring that staff are involved in collaborative decision making when possible	❏	❏	❏
providing job descriptions for each position and ensuring that all understand one another's role	❏	❏	❏
outlining clear lines of communication	❏	❏	❏
providing adequate supervision	❏	❏	❏
making reflective practice standard practice for the organization	❏	❏	❏
conducting regular performance evaluations	❏	❏	❏
organizing staff meetings and in-services on communication, conflict resolution, etc.	❏	❏	❏
providing a comprehensive employee benefit package that includes family responsibility leave	❏	❏	❏
providing time and possibly financial support for professional development	❏	❏	❏
actively participating as a centre member in a regional or national child care association	❏	❏	❏
encouraging opportunities for staff to socialize	❏	❏	❏

lower other risk factors by

	YES	NO	SOMETIMES
networking with community health resources	❏	❏	❏
providing current health literature for staff (e.g., public health pamphlets)	❏	❏	❏

CAN YOU ARTICULATE YOUR PROGRAM'S

Goal statement (specific and measurable)
Action steps: 1.
            2.
            3.
            4.
Target date:
Resources available to help you:
Barriers and how to deal with them:

DO YOUR MANAGER AND SUPERVISOR . . .

	YES	NO	SOMETIMES
clearly outline employee responsibilities	❏	❏	❏
recognize early indicators of workplace stress	❏	❏	❏
accommodate employees who need flexible work arrangements	❏	❏	❏
provide training on workplace psychological health	❏	❏	❏
recognize employee contributions	❏	❏	❏
make him- or herself accessible and actively listen to employees' concerns	❏	❏	❏
respond effectively to employee concerns or conflicts	❏	❏	❏
encourage employee participation in team-building exercises	❏	❏	❏
lead by example for respectful workplace behaviours	❏	❏	❏

(appendix continues on next page)

DOES YOUR ORGANIZATION . . .	YES	NO	SOMETIMES
keep up-to-date on psychological health policies	❏	❏	❏
involve employees in the development of workplace psychological health programs	❏	❏	❏
develop a policy statement that supports workplace psychological health and related initiatives	❏	❏	❏
assess the current workplace culture	❏	❏	❏
connect employees with resources on psychological health	❏	❏	❏
financially support workplace psychological health programs	❏	❏	❏
establish peer support and/or counselling networks	❏	❏	❏
designate one individual per organization to be the psychological health coordinator, who sits on the Policy Health and Safety Committee, and where there is no policy committee, sits on the Work Place Health and Safety Committee	❏	❏	❏
establish an incident-reporting system	❏	❏	❏
establish a conflict resolution system	❏	❏	❏
recognize employee contributions	❏	❏	❏
organize stress-reduction activities at work	❏	❏	❏
keep up-to-date on workplace psychological health research	❏	❏	❏
share health promotion strategies with other organizations	❏	❏	❏

DOES YOUR GOVERNMENT . . .	YES	NO	SOMETIMES
promote the National Standard on Psychological Health and Safety in the Workplace	❏	❏	❏
establish the protection of psychological health at work as an employee's right	❏	❏	❏
survey the state of workplace psychological health among public and private sector industries	❏	❏	❏

Illness Prevention

3

CONTENTS

Young children get sick whether they are cared for at home or in an early childhood learning and care (ECLC) program, but the estimated rates of common illnesses are two to three times higher for children enrolled in centres. You only have to talk to a parent whose child has started in an ECLC program to hear the stories of the illnesses. Typically, while children are at home, their exposure to illnesses is limited. So when they start in a program, their potential exposure increases dramatically; as a result, they get sick. However, the longer children are in a program's care, the less often they are sick, and, in fact, they aren't sick much more often than children in family daycare. This information is reassuring for parents who choose centre care.

Among the reasons for higher rates of childhood infections are the following:

- The children enrolled in an ECLC program are from different families, which increases the number of infections that could be spread. Each child may be exposed to germs or infections from his or her parents, siblings, friends, or even strangers riding on the bus in the morning. So every day, it is likely that children spread germs among themselves and staff.

- Preschool children are still learning good personal hygiene habits.

- Infants and young children are more susceptible to illness because their immune systems are still developing.

In the past, most infants, toddlers, and preschoolers remained at home with their mothers. It was not until the children were in kindergarten or Grade 1 that they frequently experienced common childhood illnesses during the first few months of starting school, for the reasons outlined above. But by the time children are five or six years old, they are better able to fight infections. Their immune system has matured, and they have almost completed their series of immunizations. Obviously, every child must eventually become part of a group, so the concerns lie in the age at which this occurs and in what can be done to reduce the number of infections that each child experiences as a result of that participation.

The opportunities for illnesses to spread are even higher among infants and toddlers than among preschoolers. Young children wear diapers, may be learning to use the toilet, require a great deal of hands-on care, crawl on the floor, and put hands, toys, and objects in their mouths and then share these wet objects with others. They are only beginning to learn how to wash their hands. They are also quite affectionate with one another (e.g., kissing, hugging, touching). Although this physical contact can contribute to the spread of respiratory infections, the emotional and social benefits of physical affection far outweigh the risk of illness. Rather than discourage this social behaviour, educators implement hygiene practices that reduce the spread of germs among infants and toddlers (e.g., hand washing, cleaning and disinfecting mouthing toys, diapering and toileting routines).

Educators' understanding of how infections are spread and the ability to implement health practices reduce the incidence of infections in children. The less often children are ill, the less often parents and staff need to manage illness. In other words, the discomfort and stress experienced by children, parents, and staff are reduced. Also, the fewer visits that children make to their physicians, the less money government is obliged to spend on physicians' fees, laboratory tests, and prescriptions, thus reducing health costs.

Most common childhood illnesses are minor and don't last more than a few days. The most typical childhood illnesses are the common cold, ear infections, other respiratory infections, and diarrhea. There are also several more serious communicable diseases that children and adults are susceptible to if they have not developed immunity either through immunizations or by having had the disease (see Immunity, page 130, and Immunization, page 139).

OUR BODY'S NATURAL DEFENCE MECHANISMS

OBJECTIVE

To identify and describe our body's natural defence mechanisms. (LO 1, 3)

Because germs are everywhere, we are fortunate that our body has a built-in defence system; otherwise, we would have some kind of infection all the time. Our skin is our body's first defence, and one of the most important defence mechanisms, against the germs that we contact every day. The oily substance excreted by glands in the walls of hair follicles is acidic; it kills germs that would otherwise grow on our skin. Normal intact skin is impermeable to germs and to fluids such as water and blood. Where the skin is nonintact (because of cuts, scrapes, sores, or burns, for example), germs can enter. Some chemical agents, such as some pesticides, can enter our body through hair follicles.

Many germs enter our body through the nose. The nasal hair that you can see and the cilia that cover the mucous membranes in our nose and throat filter and collect air particles such as dust and germs. The mucus produced by the mucous membranes traps the particles, which are then swallowed and destroyed by gastric and acidic secretions in the stomach. We also expel mucus by coughing or sneezing, which rids our body of germs. As well, the mucous membranes in the gastrointestinal and urinary tracts can inactivate or destroy germs, which the bloodstream then clears out of our body. The urine's bacteriostatic (bacteria-destroying) action keeps the urinary tract sterile. Tear secretions destroy bacteria in our eyes. Wax protects our ears.

You have probably heard the sayings "You'll catch a cold if you go outside with wet hair" and "If you sit in a draft, you'll get a cold." In fact, the only way to catch a cold is through exposure to a cold virus that infects our body. Therefore, neither saying is true. But both remind us to think about vulnerability to viruses and bacteria. *For example, when you are rundown or "running on empty," your body will be more vulnerable to a virus or bacteria.* Every day we can provide our body with the nutrients and energy to fight off an infection or to get better. Our body needs these essential elements:

- nutritious food and water and a well-balanced diet
- adequate sleep
- adequate physical activity
- fresh air
- coping strategies to keep stress under control

And, of course, we need to live in a home that provides us with the basic needs of clean water, sewage disposal, and comfortable temperature, and we need warm clothes, coats, shoes, and boots in the winter. If we were always using our energy to keep warm in the winter, our body wouldn't have energy left for everything else we must do to keep healthy.

Immunity

Immunity provides us with protection from specific infections. Each time a germ enters your body, your immunity increases. When a specific germ multiplies in your body, it produces large numbers of its specific protein (antigen), which enter the bloodstream. The immune system responds by producing specific antibodies. Even when an infection is over, your body may continue to make antibodies for long periods, sometimes even for life.

But after many infections, the antibodies disappear from your body over time. Despite this disappearance, cells in your immune system remember the germ, so that if it is contracted again, the immune system makes antibodies very rapidly. Most people who have had chickenpox have a lifelong immunity to it. It is rare to get it again, even after being exposed to a person who has it. The body has a harder time warding off the common cold, however. There are approximately 200 different viruses that cause the common cold. The same cold virus can cause a cold more than once. Our body does not build immunity to these cold viruses, which is why some of us get so many colds over our lifetime.

We develop immunity to a disease in one of two ways:

- naturally or actively
- passively (see Immune Globulin, page 143)

For the first few months of life, infants are resistant to some diseases. This naturally acquired immunity is passed on to babies from their mother before birth. Breast milk contains antibodies, which help protect infants from some bowel, ear, and respiratory infections. However, this natural immunity is short-lived. The immune systems of infants and young children mature through actively acquired immunity. Children develop different antibodies in two ways: either by actually having an infection or through immunizations (see Immunization, page 139).

HOW INFECTIONS SPREAD

OBJECTIVE

To explain how germs are spread. (LO 1, 3)

Germs are everywhere. By understanding how germs are spread, you can break the chain of transmission and ultimately reduce or stop the spread of germs that cause illness.

The chain of transmission has four links, as illustrated in Figure 3.1:

- the germ
- the host (person who is ill)
- the vehicles of transmission
- the new host (next person who becomes ill)

Table 3.2 (see page 137) summarizes the discussion on the four links of the chain.

The Germ

The term "**germ**" is used generically to include viruses, bacteria, parasites, and fungi. Although most germs can't be seen by the naked eye (they are microscopic), they are capable of causing infections that range in severity from minor to fatal. The type of germ usually determines which part of the body develops the infection. This explains why we develop different infections, such as colds, strep throat, ear or chest infections, impetigo, urinary tract (bladder) infections, or diarrhea.

FIGURE 3.1 The Links in the Chain

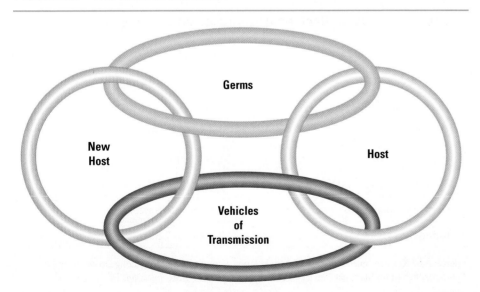

We all have germs that live in our body and play an important role in keeping us healthy. Women, for example, have small numbers of bacteria and a fungus known as *Candida* living in the intestinal tract and the vagina. Let's use this example to see how the germs normally found in the body can cause infections in the following two scenarios.

In the first scenario, women may experience vaginal yeast infections while they are taking an antibiotic for a bacterial infection. While the antibiotic is destroying the bacteria that have caused the infection, it may also destroy the bacteria normally found in the vagina. Consequently, the fungus in the vagina multiplies, causing a yeast infection, because the natural balance of the vaginal bacteria and fungus has been altered by the antibiotic. *Candida* diaper rash can develop in young children in a similar way. An antibiotic given to an infant or toddler to treat a bacterial infection may also destroy bacteria normally found in the bowel, which then permits the fungus to multiply.

In the second scenario, you don't have to have diarrhea yourself to cause someone else to get diarrhea. We all have bacteria that live in our bowels and help keep us healthy. But when those bacteria contaminate an environment and someone else comes in contact with them, that person may develop diarrhea. ***Effective hand washing is the key to preventing stool from contaminating an environment***.

Some germs, surprisingly enough, can live outside our body on countertops, toys, fabric, and other dry surfaces for several hours or even months and can still cause infection (see Table 3.1). Rotavirus and hepatitis A can live for weeks on objects such as toys, and germs that cause respiratory infections can live for several hours. This longevity contributes to the spread of infection. Germs thrive and multiply in food, causing intestinal infections that can, in rare cases, be fatal (see Through Food, page 136).

Furthermore, children and adults who have an infection are often infectious (or contagious) for a period of time, which fluctuates depending on the type of germ. Children with the common cold may be infectious for a day or two before the cold symptoms start and may remain so for the next seven days (see Appendix 4.1, page 213).

TABLE 3.1 Life of Bacteria and Viruses on Surfaces

Bacteria	Time Range
Escherichia coli (E. coli)	1.5 hours to 16 months
Haemophilus influenzae	12 days
Shigella spp.	2 days to 5 months
Virus	Time Range
Cytomegalovirus (CMV)	8 hours
Herpes simplex virus, type 1	4.5 hours to 8 weeks
Rhinovirus	2 hours to 7 days

Source: Axel Kramer, Ingeborn Schwebke, and Gunter Kampf (2006). "How Long Do Nosocomial Pathogens Persist on Inanimate Surfaces? A Systematic Review." *BMC Infectious Diseases*, 6: 130.

The Host

Health and medical professionals use the term "**host**" to describe the person with the infection. Think of the infected person as the host of a dinner party. The infected person's body provides the germs with the nourishment and warmth that they need to thrive. Germs may be spread to others during the three stages of an infection: before we know we are ill, while we are ill, and, in some cases, even after we have recovered. A "carrier" is a host who does not actually have symptoms of an infection but has the germ living dormant in his or her body. Carriers can spread germs (e.g., hepatitis B) to others, and sometimes the germs may reactivate and cause an infection (e.g., shingles) in the carrier.

The Vehicles of Transmission

Hosts have germs in their body secretions (such as stool, saliva, blood) that can be transmitted (or spread) in a number of ways. The germs contaminate our environment and are spread directly from person to person through the air or by direct contact (e.g., touching, kissing, biting) or indirectly on vehicles (e.g., toys, hands, food, objects).

Through Direct or Indirect Contact

Infections are spread directly and indirectly from one host to another. The direct spread of infection takes place when we breathe in the germs that cause infections such as colds, chickenpox, and flu. Another way we come into contact with germs that cause skin infections is by touching the host's infected skin (e.g., impetigo, cold sores, scabies, the fluid in the blisters of chickenpox, the rash of shingles). Another example is when someone becomes infested with head lice after coming in contact with head lice.

Germs are spread indirectly on contaminated **vehicles of transmission**. Vehicles can be anything around us that germs can contaminate. The vehicles in ECLC programs that we need to pay particular attention to are hands, food and food-related objects, facial tissues, diapers, potties, mouthing toys, hairbrushes, toothbrushes, and blow toys/pipes/straws used in water tables. The germs on these vehicles can easily and frequently find their way into our body. If you watch TV, it is very likely that you have seen the frequently run TV commercials for different types of disinfecting products to use around your home. *Spray your phones and door handles. Wipe down surfaces. Spray the inside of garbage cans.* Some toilet cleaners claim that they kill almost 100% of the germs way down at the curve in the pipe at the bottom of the bowl. Obviously, the toilet needs to be cleaned, but how, exactly, is disinfecting the toilet protecting us? Is residue left in the toilet water for those who have dogs that drink from them? What is the environmental impact of these unnecessary chemicals being flushed into the sewage system? The first time someone uses the toilet, there are germs in it again. We can't sterilize our homes or ECLC settings. We must remember that disinfecting an item is a temporary state. As soon as the item is used again, it becomes contaminated. This is why we assess what needs to be disinfected against its intended use and by whom. For this reason, hand washing is key: how you do it and when you do it.

Direct Contact   Indirect Contact

Source: Reprinted with permission from the Canadian Paediatric Society.

Educators of toddlers and young preschoolers are often concerned about children biting. From the standpoint of infection control, the risk of children transmitting hepatitis B or C or human immunodeficiency virus (HIV) through biting is extremely unlikely. It is unusual for a child's bite to actually break (cut) the skin and cause bleeding, and, as such, none of these diseases would be spread. When the skin is broken, the risk of transmission continues to be very low. The spread of hepatitis B has occurred in ECLC settings but is rare (American Academy of Pediatrics, 2015, p. 145). It is important to remember that when the skin is not broken, hepatitis B is not spread in the saliva (Canadian Paediatric Society [CPS], 2018). The number of children living with hepatitis C is very small. There has not been a case reported in which hepatitis C was spread from one child to another as the result of a bite (American Academy of Pediatrics, 2015, p. 147; CPS, 2018). Saliva has not been shown to spread HIV. According to CPS (2018, p. 3), "there has been no report of HIV transmission in child care.... [T]ransmission of HIV through biting incidents in the child care setting is extremely unlikely." In the rare occurrence that a bite does bleed, it is usually considered a serious incident or occurrence. Educators must follow the reporting process set out by their government licensing body, which can include a report and contacting the local public health agency. Refer to *Well Beings* (2015) for CPS's recommendations for administering first aid to the child who was bitten and the child who bit, as well as for communicating with the parents and health care providers.

Keep in mind that biting is a guidance issue for educators. Consideration may need to be given to children who are known to bite and to the pain they inflict on others in the program. Biting is usually a short-term behaviour and reaches a peak in toddlerhood, when children do not as yet have the words to voice their anger and frustration. Parents and educators will need to discuss a consistent way to manage the biting.

When a child is bitten and the skin is not broken, wash the area with soap and water and apply a cold compress to help soothe the area. When the skin is broken, CPS (2018, p. 3) recommends taking the following steps:

- The wound should be allowed to bleed gently, without squeezing.
- The wound should be cleaned carefully with soap and water, and a mild antiseptic should be applied.

- An official report should be written and filed.
- The parents of both the biter and the bitten child should be notified as soon as possible (preferably within 2 h of the incident).
- The bite should be reported to local public health authorities, who may elect to refer both the bitten child and the biter to a physician for evaluation of risk of infection and possible need for postexposure prophylaxis.
- The wound should be observed over the next few days, and if redness or swelling develops, the child's parents should be advised to consult a health professional.*

Before applying any antiseptic ointment, you need permission from the bitten child's parent. The program's director will follow how incidents such as these must be reported to the child care licensing and public health agencies. Both staff and the child's parents will watch for changes in the child's wound. The director will contact the parents if staff have concerns about the wound and recommend that the parents take their child to their family physician.

Through the Air

Young children frequently experience colds and eye, nose, and throat infections. It is easy to understand why. The germs, both viruses and bacteria that cause minor or serious infections, are in the host's saliva and nasal secretions. The germs are spread by droplets of secretions that move through the air when we cough or sneeze. We can breathe in the droplets, or they can land in our eyes, nose, or mouth. Or the droplets, saliva, or nasal discharge lands on an object or our hands and the germs find their way into our mouth.

Droplet   Airborne

Source: Reprinted with permission from the Canadian Paediatric Society.

Through Contact with Stool

Diarrhea can be caused by bacteria, parasites, or viruses found in the host's stool. As we have discussed, there are bacteria in our bowels that help keep us healthy. However, if those bacteria contaminate our environment, they can cause an intestinal infection in someone else. Whenever stool contaminates our

*Source: Reprinted with permission from the Canadian Paediatric Society.

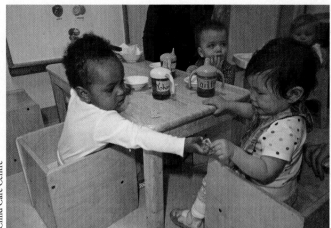

hands, food, water, cooking surfaces, toys, taps on sinks, and other objects, the germs spread very easily among us. Germs enter our mouth from our hands and from toys or through food or water. This means of transmission is also known as the fecal–oral route.

Through Food

Food is an ideal medium for germs to grow on and multiply. Typically, food is contaminated in one of two ways: germs may be in or on the food before we buy it, or we can contaminate food when we handle or prepare it. Regardless of the way germs get into food, the way we prepare, cook, serve, and store food determines whether the germs multiply or are destroyed.

Although most food will have some germs in it, you don't get sick every time you eat because your body's defence mechanisms can destroy many germs. Only when germs multiply in numbers before you eat the food can they cause mild, serious, or, rarely, fatal infections. The severity of the infection depends on the type of germ or the number of germs that have entered the body. Breaking the chain of food transmission involves several safe food-handling practices: hand washing, purchasing, storing, preparing, cooking, and serving (see Food Safety Practices, page 302).

Through Contact with Blood and Bloody Body Fluids

Two serious infections, hepatitis B and HIV, are blood-borne diseases and in most cases spread to others through direct contact with blood or semen. These viruses are spread in three ways:

- by sexual intercourse
- by sharing needles used for illegal intravenous drug use
- by an infected woman to her fetus and, in the case of HIV, during breastfeeding

Through public education and awareness, we have come to understand HIV and its transmission. For the majority of us, our anxiety has been alleviated, and we have come to accept and support people living with HIV and AIDS.

The routine screening of patients, students, employees, or children in ECLC programs, schools, and hospitals is neither warranted nor permitted under human rights legislation. Nor is it recommended or necessary under the guiding principle of routine practices in infection control. It is important to understand that someone's HIV status is confidential medical information and that it is against human rights legislation either to insist on HIV testing or to demand that someone disclose her or his HIV status to program staff or to anyone else. If parents disclose their child's HIV-positive status to an educator, that educator must maintain confidentiality by not telling her or his coworkers, the director, or other parents. This information can be shared only by the parents.

Working with children and coworkers does not put educators at risk for HIV transmission. We must focus instead on our personal lives to reduce our risks. Educators, like the general population, put themselves at risk if they participate in unprotected sexual intercourse or share needles and syringes. To learn more about HIV and hepatitis B transmission and about reducing your risk, contact your college/university resource or health centre, the public health agency, physicians, or the AIDS committee in your province or territory. (See Resource Materials.)

Hepatitis C is another blood-borne disease that has a very low infection rate among the general public. Its profile was raised, however, in recent years by those infected from tainted blood transfusions before 1989. But like HIV and hepatitis B, those at risk for the infection are intravenous drug users and those who participate in unprotected sexual intercourse.

NELSONstudy

To access Resource Materials, visit NelsonStudy.

The New Host

The term "**new host**" refers to the next person who gets the infection after the germs enter the body, whether through the mouth, eyes, or nose; an open cut; or a rash or sore on the skin or by way of the gastrointestinal or genitourinary tract. The type of germ usually determines which part of the body develops the infection. This explains why we develop different infections such as colds, strep throat, ear or chest infections, impetigo, urinary tract (bladder) infections, or diarrhea.

The incubation period begins when the germ first enters the new host's body. Then the germ multiplies in number. The body's natural defences try to destroy the germs, and if they are successful, we don't get sick. But if they are unsuccessful, we experience symptoms within hours, days, or weeks depending on the germ and how much time it needs to multiply before it causes infection. By the time you feel that cold coming on, however, you have already been spreading the cold virus among others. This is relatively common for infections, including chickenpox, which makes controlling the spread of infection very difficult. Therefore, the control of infections is an ongoing job; you don't do it just when you know someone is ill.

TABLE 3.2 Summarizing the Links of the Chain

The Germ	● viruses ● bacteria ● parasites ● fungi
The Host	● person who is ill (germs found in saliva, stool, and blood, on skin or hair, etc.)
The Vehicles of Transmission	● directly from person to person (e.g., through air, by touching, kissing, biting) ● indirectly from person to person (e.g., on hands, toys, food, objects)
The New Host	● new person who becomes ill or a carrier

To explain the role that policies and procedures play in infection control. (LO 6)

To describe the principles and recommended practices for immunization. (LO 1, 3)

To state the rationale for effective hand washing as the most important health practice in reducing the spread of infections. (LO 6)

To describe the when, what, and how of hand washing for educators and children. (LO 4, 6)

To explain the rationale behind the steps in diaper-changing and toileting routines. (LO 6)

To explain why certain items must be cleaned and disinfected before and after use or on a daily or regular schedule. (LO 6)

To state the rationale for routine practices and how to put them into practice. (LO 3, 6)

BREAKING THE CHAIN: DEVELOPING AN INFECTION CONTROL STRATEGY

Our initial defence against germs is understanding that although germs are everywhere, we neither want to, nor are we able to, produce a sterile environment (as in an operating room). ECLC environments are designed to be friendly, nurturing, interesting, and child centred. Although children do become ill, our underlying assumption is that most people are healthy most of the time. Thus, we carefully choose where to focus our energy to prevent or reduce environmental contamination and the spread of germs. Maintaining our own health and that of the children in our care prevents the germs normally found in our bodies from causing infection and in many cases helps us resist germs from other sources. Thus, a program's infection control strategy demonstrates the staff's understanding of the chain of transmission by developing and implementing specific policies and procedures. To break the chain of transmission, as illustrated in Figure 3.2, programs' policy manuals will include infection control policies and procedures on the following:

- immunization
- hand washing and other hygiene practices
- cleaning and disinfecting routines
- pets and contact with animals
- daily observation of children (see page 170)
- documentation of health observations and sharing observations with parents and physicians (see Documenting Health Observations, page 177)
- effective communication with parents
- exclusion criteria (see Excluding Children from Early Childhood Learning and Care Programs, page 180)

FIGURE 3.2 Breaking the Chain

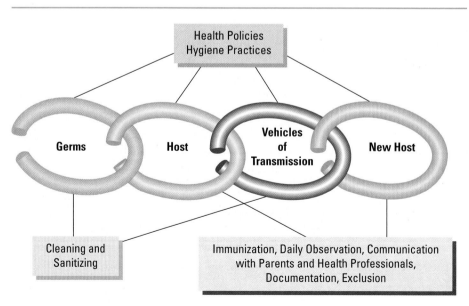

- In addition to these policies, the manual will include policies and procedures that cover the following:
  - safe food handling and storage (see Food Safety Practices, page 302)
  - control of pests (see Controlling Insect and Rodent Infestation, page 307)

Immunization

Before vaccines were developed, epidemics caused thousands of people to die or, in the case of polio, to be left physically challenged. Currently, there are over 13 serious infections—communicable diseases—that can be prevented through routine **immunization**, which can begin in infancy. The Public Health Agency of Canada (PHAC) (2017d) also has schedules for children who were not immunized during infancy. The schedules vary depending on whether the vaccination program begins before or after the child is seven years old.

"Vaccines are a cornerstone of public health and their use has significantly contributed to the prevention and control of infectious diseases in Canada and internationally" (Public Health Agency of Canada [PHAC], 2017b, p. 1).*

WHAT ARE THE OBJECTIVES OF CANADA'S IMMUNIZATION PROGRAMS?

The objectives of immunization programs are to prevent, to control, to eliminate or to eradicate vaccine-preventable diseases by directly protecting vaccine recipients and indirectly protecting vulnerable individuals who may not respond to vaccines or for whom vaccines may be contraindicated. (PHAC, 2016, p. 1)

The risk of vaccine preventable disease transmission remains and would significantly increase if vaccination were stopped. Immunization providers and the public should be aware that, with the success of childhood immunization programs, there is a tendency to underestimate the risks of vaccine-preventable diseases and overestimate the risks of vaccines. (PHAC, 2017b, p. 1)

Source: © All rights reserved. *Canadian Immunization Guide.* Public Health Agency of Canada, date modified: March 3, 2017. Adapted and reproduced with permission from the Minister of Health, 2018.

Although you may not have heard of a child in your community coming down with the measles or mumps, it does not mean that these and other serious infectious diseases don't exist in Canada and around the world. Without immunizations, children are susceptible to these infections. Canadian children are fortunate that routine vaccination costs are covered by medicare; this is not the case for millions of other children around the world. Your body responds to a vaccination by forming antibodies against specific diseases. The vaccination almost always results in lifelong immunity. In other words, the antibodies remain in your body, ready to

---

*Source: © All rights reserved. *Canadian Immunization Guide.* Public Health Agency of Canada, date modified: March 3, 2017. Adapted and reproduced with permission from the Minister of Health, 2018.

destroy the virus every time it enters, whether you know you were exposed to it or not. There are other vaccinations that do require booster shots at regular intervals to maintain this immunity (e.g., tetanus).

Some parents in Canada, however, choose not to immunize their children for personal reasons. In addition, we live in a country that welcomes people from around the world. Many children born outside Canada may not have been vaccinated and could be carrying the virus for polio or diphtheria, which could put nonimmunized persons at risk. In addition, Canadian families vacation in countries where immunization rates can be very low. As a result, these children may be exposed to serious infectious diseases and contract and spread them. As well, after reaching adulthood, these unvaccinated adults can travel and work in areas of the world where these diseases are prevalent.

In the past several years, there has been more public discussion surrounding parents' concerns over the presumed correlation between a child receiving the measles-mumps-rubella (MMR) vaccine and a child developing autism. CPS published the position statement *Autistic Spectrum Disorder: No Causal Relationship with Vaccines*, which concludes that vaccines are not the cause of autism spectrum disorder (CPS, 2016b, p. 1).

To ensure the health of Canadian children and those arriving in Canada, public health agencies must work toward 100% immunization. Here are some important facts about immunization:

- For measles, mumps, and rubella, we require two doses of each vaccine.
- For other diseases, we need a series of vaccinations to achieve immunity.
- For lifelong immunity against tetanus and diphtheria, adults require booster shots every 10 years.

  An exception is pertussis (whooping cough), whose vaccine protection wears off over time. As a result, previously immunized children and adults can develop pertussis, although the infection would not be as severe. Vaccinations against pertussis are not given to people over age seven because the risk of severe complications from pertussis is low in older children and adults. Moreover, adverse reactions from the vaccine, such as fever and pain, are common.

- A series of three doses of vaccine for hepatitis B is recommended for children in infancy or two doses for children between 9 and 13. This protects them before they might become sexually active or use intravenous drugs.
- Since 1999, Health Canada has recommended that children over 12 months of age be immunized against chickenpox.
- There are three vaccines against the three types of meningitis: *Haemophilus influenzae* type b, pneumococcal, and meningococcal.
- The polio vaccine is available in two forms: oral and injection. Other vaccines can be given as individual injections. Fortunately, they are commonly given in a combined solution, so children are given just one shot.

Immunization schedules vary between provinces and territories and are updated on a regular basis. Visit the PHAC website for the immunization schedule in your region. For more than a decade, CPS (2016c) has been calling for PHAC to develop a Canada-wide immunization schedule that would apply to all children, with the costs being covered for all families. This harmonization will have a positive impact on the health and safety of Canadian children.

"The development of effective vaccines has been called the most significant advance in human health of all time! Within the past 50 years, we have witnessed the control of tetanus, diphtheria, measles and polio, and the complete eradication of smallpox. These magnificent achievements can be attributed both to fundamental research and to national and international collaboration" (CPS, 2016c, p. 1).* For Canada's 150th birthday, Statistics Canada published an example of the positive impact immunization has had for us living in Canada.

In celebration of the country's 150th birthday, Statistics Canada is presenting snapshots from our rich statistical history.

Childhood vaccines that are part of provincial and territorial publicly funded routine vaccination programs are free to Canadian families. These programs are part of the public health landscape in developed countries. This is a change from 150 years ago, when vaccines did not yet exist.

The first routine vaccination program was implemented in 1930, with the introduction of the vaccine against diphtheria. Over the past 80 years, many vaccines have been added to publicly funded routine vaccination programs. As a result, Canada has seen the reduction and elimination of vaccine-preventable diseases which at one time resulted in widespread serious illnesses and several deaths among children.

The number of measles, mumps and rubella cases is much lower today

In Canada, routine infant immunization programs have helped to eliminate the transmission of rubella infection and to decrease the number of reported cases of measles and mumps.

Before a measles vaccine was authorized for use in Canada in 1963, an average of 53,800 cases per year was reported during the period from 1951 to 1955. In contrast, there were only 195 cases of measles reported in Canada in 2015.

Prior to the introduction of vaccines for mumps and rubella in 1969, annual averages of 32,800 cases of mumps and 11,500 cases of rubella were reported during the same period (1951–1955) in Canada. In 2015, the number of reported cases of mumps was reduced to 59 and official data indicated that rubella has been considered eliminated from Canada since 2005. No cases were reported in 2015.

Sources:

Public Health Agency of Canada, Notifiable Disease On-line, https://diseases.canada.ca/notifiable/, accessed in June 2017. (The reference period of 1951–1955 was the last five consecutive years for which data were available for all 10 provinces before the introduction of the vaccine, with the following exceptions: New Brunswick did not report on rubella in 1951, nor did Prince Edward Island in 1954.)

Source: Statistics Canada, *Childhood National Immunization Coverage Survey, 2015* (2017, June 28), page 1. Retrieved December 2017 from https://www.statcan.gc.ca/daily-quotidien/170628/dq170628a-eng.htm. Reproduced and distributed on an "as is" basis with the permission of Statistics Canada.

*Source: Reprinted with permission from the Canadian Paediatric Society.

Immunization Records

Considering the importance of immunization, you may be surprised to learn that early childhood regulations on immunization at enrollment vary across Canada. But even in regions where immunization is not mandatory in the regulations, many programs require children to be immunized on enrollment and document it in their policy manual.

Although most parents agree that immunizing their children is important, there are children whose immunization schedules are not kept up-to-date. Depending on where children live, either individual physicians or a local public health clinic is responsible for immunizing them. As a result, there is often no systematic way of notifying parents of an upcoming appointment.

At the time of enrollment, parents provide the director with a copy of their child's record. Directors compare the information on these cards with the standard immunization schedule. If any discrepancy is found, the director asks the parents to discuss it with their physician, or the director contacts the public health agency (see Children's Medical Examination at Enrollment, page 170).

Children's immunizations may not be up-to-date for many reasons, including

- families' hectic schedules,
- children of different ages in a family needing immunizations at different times, or
- the family's lack of a regular physician.

For most parents, a simple reminder that their child is due for an immunization prompts them to make an appointment with the doctor or clinic. Programs play an important role in ensuring that children are immunized at enrollment and by regularly reviewing these records to ensure that children don't miss a booster shot.

Some parents have decided not to immunize their children for religious, moral, or other reasons. Children cannot be denied access to programs if they are not immunized. In these cases, directors should have the parents provide a letter from the child's physician. If a child or educator develops a communicable disease, the public health agency then excludes all nonimmunized children and staff from the program for a certain period. This eliminates further contact with the infected child and attempts to protect nonimmunized individuals (see Appendix 4.1, page 213).

If a child develops a serious disease, all susceptible children must be identified quickly and the illness managed properly. Consequently, the director and public health staff must have immediate access to the current immunization record for every child and staff member in the program.

Adverse Reactions

Before children are immunized, the physician or public health nurse discusses the possible adverse reactions and contraindications of the vaccines with the parents. A day or two after a vaccination, children commonly experience mild side effects, ranging from redness, slight swelling, and tenderness at the injection site to a low-grade fever and irritability. Directors may suggest that parents arrange to have the vaccination appointment on a Friday. This way, children can spend the weekend getting the extra care they might need at home.

Children rarely experience serious allergic reactions following a vaccination. If one does occur, the child's physician and public health officials will determine whether the child receives further vaccinations.

Immune Globulin

Passively acquired immunity results when a susceptible individual is exposed to a certain disease and then given the immune globulin for it. Immune globulins are injections of antibodies that temporarily protect the individual from the disease or at least reduce the symptoms. In the case of chickenpox, within 96 hours of exposure, susceptible educators are given the varicella-zoster immune globulin (VZIG) (PHAC, 2017c, p. 9). Immune globulins are available for only a few diseases.

Hygiene Practices

You may initially feel overwhelmed by the number of **hygiene practices** that you are expected to perform in a program. You may wonder, for example, why so many steps are involved in changing a diaper. Over time, effective hand-washing and diapering routines become second nature. And you will see that the time spent learning these steps reduces the number of ill children and educators. Remember: Infection control is an essential component of programs' disease prevention strategies.

Now let's begin by examining the vital role **hand washing** plays in reducing the spread of infections in programs. This practice is important for everyone in the program: children, educators, and parents. The physical care of infants and toddlers poses challenges for infection control for educators. Without stringent adherence to diapering and toileting routines, outbreaks of diarrhea are inevitable.

Hand Washing

The most common and efficient way for germs to enter our body is through our mouth. Take a moment to think of everything that our hands touch each day: the number is staggering. Combine that with the number of times we put our hands or objects (e.g., pencils, toys, eating utensils) into our mouth.

Hand washing is the most important health practice that educators and children must implement to reduce the spread of infections. From the moment we wash our hands, we begin to collect germs all over again. Yet we can't spend the day with our hands in running water and soap. But if we pay particular attention to when and how we wash our hands, we accomplish the most significant practice in infection control.

When Do We Wash Our Hands?

While we care for children and carry out tasks in the program, we collect germs on our hands. By washing off germs before we begin particular activities, we greatly reduce the opportunity to spread germs to others. Washing our hands is important

- before preparing, serving, or eating food;
- before feeding infants and children;
- before giving a medication;
- before playing in the water table; and
- before carrying out first aid.

Certain activities expose our hands to large numbers of germs. To prevent contamination, it is important that we wash our hands immediately after completing the following activities. Washing our hands is important

- upon your arrival at work;

  Before we arrive at work, our hands can come into contact with a multitude of contaminated surfaces, including the hand rails on public transit, bicycle handles, and a vehicle's steering wheel, not to mention public doors that we have opened. Washing your hands before you start work helps limit the number of germs you begin to spread in the setting.

  In *Well Beings* (2015), CPS recommends that the hands of all children are washed upon arrival too. This recommendation is ideal, but some programs may find it challenging to implement. At drop-off time, parents may be rushed, and educators are greeting parents and children, supervising children in the room, communicating with parents about their child's well-being, sharing relevant information, and settling the child for the parent's departure. Implementing this recommendation for infants, toddlers, and young preschoolers will depend largely on a centre's design and easy access to hand-washing sinks during this hectic part of the day. Perhaps for these younger children, ensuring that they wash their hands at the recommended times during the day is more practical. As for older preschoolers and school-agers, washing their hands upon arrival is a great hygiene habit.

- after using the toilet or helping children at the toilet;
- after changing a diaper;
- after caring for ill children;
- after cleaning up spills of blood and body fluids;
- after wiping a child's nose (if possible);
- after cleaning or disinfecting routines, even if you wore disposable or rubber gloves;
- after preparing food;
- after handling animals;
- after playing outside or in sand tables; and
- after handling garbage.

What We Use for Effective Hand Washing

The five important components in the hand-washing routine are running water, soap, friction, drying the hands, and turning off the taps.

Running water is essential to rinse the germs off the hands and down the drain. A comfortable water temperature allows you to keep your hands in the running water for 10 to 15 seconds. Take disposable alcohol-based hand wipes or solution with you on field trips when you don't have access to running water.

Using running water may raise concerns over water conservation and our environment, but washing in a full sink or basin of water is *not* the solution. You defeat the purpose of hand washing by rinsing off the soap and germs in a pool of water. This practice recontaminates your hands with all the germs that are now in that pool of water. To conserve water, don't turn on the tap full blast.

All you need is plain, mild hand soap for hand washing, regardless of the activity you have just completed. Soaps with germ-killing ingredients are expensive and unnecessary and may kill "friendly" protective bacteria as well. Soaps with an alcohol base dry the skin. It is actually the friction that is created by rubbing hands and plain soap together that removes the germs from our skin.

Liquid hand soap is recommended for two reasons: the soap pump is convenient, and it's easier for children to use than a slippery bar of soap, which often falls on the floor. Also, germs, dirt, paint, and sand collect on the soap bar and in the soapy water at the bottom of the soap dish.

Educators wash their hands frequently, which may dry and chap their skin. Using mild soap and hand lotion helps prevent this. And, as discussed earlier, germs can enter our body through nonintact skin. As you'll see in Step 2 of the hand-washing routine (see page 147), you wet your hands before adding the soap. This reduces soap's drying effect on your skin.

You have most likely seen advertisements for **hand-sanitizing products** as an acceptable replacement for running water. Alcohol is the cleaning ingredient; the hand sanitizer must have a minimum of 60% alcohol.

> While it is true that regular soap and water does not actually kill microorganisms (they create a slippery surface that allows the organisms to 'slide off'), antibacterial soaps are typically considered to be 'overkill' for most purposes. The exception may be in a hospital where special situations are present (e.g., before invasive procedures, when caring for severely immuno-compromised patients, critical care areas, intensive care nurseries, etc.). (Canadian Centre for Occupational Health and Safety [CCOHS], 2014, p. 2)*

But are they a replacement for soap and water in an ECLC program? They are more expensive than soap, which is a consideration for programs operating on tight budgets. Although these products are used in health care facilities, they are not recommended for routine use in ECLC settings (CPS, 2015, p. 148). Due to their high percentage of alcohol, care must be taken with children as hand sanitizers can be harmful if swallowed. Also, they are flammable; these products should be kept out of children's reach. Following the instructions properly requires applying an adequate amount on the hands for 15 seconds, which is not much of a time-saver compared with the recommended hand-washing routine (see How We and Children Wash Our Hands, page 146). These products will not work when you have substances such as stool, urine, blood, or vomit on your hands either. You would need to use paper towel or a disposable moist towelette first to wipe off the visible substances before a hand sanitizer would be effective. They are convenient when activities such as field trips do not provide easy access to running water.

Soap and water are available everywhere in Canada. The single most important infection control practice and life skill that children learn is proper hand washing. During the course of the day, children observe educators washing their hands effectively. In addition, when the children's hand washing is supervised, this

---

*Source: *Hand Washing: Reducing the Risk*, http://www.ccohs.ca/oshanswers/diseases/washing_hands .html, OSH Answers, Canadian Centre for Occupational Health and Safety (CCOHS), 2014. Reproduced with the permission of CCOHS, 2018.

essential health practice is reinforced, which has a significant impact on the rates of infection in the program.

Many programs refill rather than replace empty soap pumps and hand lotion containers. Before you refill them, however, clean out the containers with soap and water and rinse them with water to remove the remnants and any germs that may have travelled down the pump during use. If the insides of the containers are not properly cleaned, these germs will contaminate the fresh liquid that is added.

Occasionally, educators' and children's fingernails need to be cleaned. Nailbrushes should not be used, for two reasons. First, the brushing action can cause very small cuts on the cuticles and under the nails, which can trap germs. Second, a communal nailbrush accumulates and transmits germs from everyone who has used it. Instead, ask parents to keep their children's nails trimmed (CPS, 2015). When there is material under your or a child's nails that won't come out with hand washing, use a disposable orange stick.

Drying our hands and turning off the taps are the final steps in hand washing. These steps can either remove further germs or recontaminate our hands before we leave the sink.

Towels can be either cloth or paper. Programs base their decision on cost, access to laundry facilities, storage space, and the number of staff and children. Rolling towel dispensers and electric hand dryers are not used in programs. We've all used rolling cloth towel dispensers that wouldn't let us pull out a clean towel or had run out of towelling, and we've all seen someone use a section of towel that someone else has used already. Electric hand dryers are not used for two reasons: they can break down, and they take a long time to dry hands thoroughly. It is not practical to expect groups of children and staff to wait in line to dry their hands.

Since we turn on taps with dirty hands, we don't want to wash and dry our hands and then turn off the taps with our clean hands. Some programs' sinks may have elbow taps, foot pedals, or sensors, which eliminate the need to use hands to turn the water on and off.

The scrubbing and rinsing during hand washing remove most of the germs. The drying action may remove even more. But reusing a wet or dry cloth towel increases the likelihood of recontaminating our hands with the germs that were left on the towel from the previous use. Single-use towels, however, whether cloth or paper, ensure that we dry our hands with a fresh towel each time. Then the towel can be used to turn off the taps before it is put into the laundry or the garbage.

Some programs may choose to use individual cloth towels, each one clearly marked with the child's or educator's name, hung to dry without touching, and changed at least daily. Individual cloth towels have disadvantages, however. They should not be used to turn off the water because the taps then contaminate the towels used throughout the day. As well, it is likely that the same towel will be used by more than one person during the day.

How We and Children Wash Our Hands

How, when, and what we use to wash our hands help ensure effective hand washing. The eight steps in the hand-washing routine ensure that as many germs as possible are removed. Remember, you are not trying to sterilize your hands, which is impossible, but rather to remove as many germs as you can.

Just as it is important for us to wash our hands, it is equally important for all children to wash their hands. Effective hand washing is one of the health habits we need to develop for a lifetime. Learning this habit begins in infancy (see Hand Washing for Infants and Toddlers, page 148).

For preschool and school-age children, the educator's role evolves from one of physically washing their hands to one of encouraging, supervising, and modelling effective hand washing. In school-age programs, children often need to be reminded to wash their hands because their attention turns easily to more exciting activities. Basically, children should wash their hands before and after the same activities that were listed for educators. But children must be encouraged to focus especially on washing their hands after they use the toilet and before they eat or handle food (see Hand Washing and Germs, page 590).

ESSENTIAL STEPS IN AN EFFECTIVE HAND-WASHING TECHNIQUE

1. Use warm running water.
2. Wet your hands and add soap.
3. Rub your hands vigorously for 10 to 15 seconds.
4. Wash all surfaces, including the backs of hands and between fingers.
5. Rinse your hands well under running water for 5 to 10 seconds.
6. Dry your hands well with a towel. Turn off the taps with a single-use towel.
7. Dispose of the cloth or paper towel.
8. Apply hand lotion as needed.

This is particularly relevant to staff.

Courtesy of George Brown College/Casa Loma Child Care Centre

STEPS TO USING A HAND-SANITIZING PRODUCT

1. Apply about 2.5 mL (1/2 tsp.) onto your palm. Rub your hands together over all surfaces—paying special attention to backs of hands, between fingers, fingernails, thumbs, and wrists—until hands are dry, usually 10 to 15 seconds.
2. For young children, dispense the rub into your own hands, then rub the surfaces of a child's hands between yours.
3. Alcohol-based hand rubs are less effective than soap and water for cleaning hands that are visibly dirty, but they still kill microorganisms, which makes them a good second choice if you don't have access to a sink. Use paper towels or disposable moist towelettes to remove as much dirt as possible, apply an alcohol-based hand rub, then use a fresh hand wipe or paper towel to remove residue.
4. Wash hands with soap and water to remove dirt as soon as possible.

Disposable moist towelettes: These can be as effective as soap and water. They're a good third choice when a sink or alcohol-based hand rub is not available or practical to use.

Source: Reprinted with permission from the Canadian Paediatric Society.

Courtesy of Barb Pimento, taken at the Downtown Montessori (Coatsworth) Childcare Centre

Monitoring Hand Washing

We have all been in public washrooms that didn't have soap or towels, have seen the tail end of the rolling towel lying on the floor, or have experienced electric hand dryers that don't blow hot air. The next time you are in a public washroom, compare the number of people who wash their hands thoroughly with the number who simply run one hand under the water or don't wash at all. How would you feel about sharing a box of popcorn at the theatre, being served at a restaurant, or having as a coworker someone who is so casual about hand washing?

Although we know the importance of the eight hand-washing steps, we may tend to skip steps or cut down on the time we spend at the sink because we are in a hurry. A poster close to the sink will act as a reminder to educators and parents. Regular monitoring of educators' hand-washing compliance is very important to maintain a high level of hygiene. Remember, this simple, inexpensive, low-tech routine is the most important health practice in the program's infection control strategy.

Hygiene Practices for Infants and Toddlers

The rate of gastrointestinal infection is highest for infants and toddlers. The responsibility for infection control rests squarely on the educators' shoulders. This section highlights the hygiene practices that should be in place to reduce the opportunity for infection.

Hand Washing for Infants and Toddlers

Have you ever wondered why babies would need to have their hands washed during the day? Watch them to see what their hands touch as they explore and you will know the answer to this question. And remember, germs can be almost anywhere. Washing babies' hands is important

- after they have a diaper change or use the toilet/potty,
- before they eat or are bottle-fed, and
- after they play outside or with materials such as sand or paint.

To wash an infant's hands, use a warm, wet, soapy, single-use towel; rinse with a second wet towel; and dry with a third. When toddlers are able to stand at a sink, with careful supervision and help, they will follow the same steps for hand washing as the older children and educators.

Caring for Children in Diapers

Before we discuss the steps involved in changing a diaper, we examine other hygiene practices related to diapers. Either cloth or disposable diapers are used in programs. To prevent stool from contaminating the environment, diapers must

- absorb the urine and stool,
- fit snugly around the thighs and waist to contain the urine and stool,
- have a waterproof cover, and
- be covered with clothing.

Courtesy of George Brown College/Casa Loma Child Care Centre

Researchers continue to compare the amount of fecal contamination in programs from disposable diapers with that from cloth diapers. Generally, disposable diapers are more absorbent and leak less than cloth diapers. However, CPS and many public health officials do not recommend one type of diaper over another in programs. Programs and parents can choose the type of diaper that best meets their needs, based on financial considerations, environmental issues, access to a commercial diaper service, and laundry facilities.

If cloth diapers are chosen, care must be taken to ensure that the diaper covers ("pants") are laundered properly to ensure that urine and stool are removed. Many programs use a fresh diaper cover at each diaper change. The use of diaper covers that are pulled up and down the legs is discouraged. Problems arise if the leg elastics have stool on them because stool contaminates the child's legs when the pants are pulled off. Instead, diaper covers that fasten at the waist permit the educator to remove the cover and diaper in one step, reducing the risk of contaminating the program's environment. Obviously, if stool has leaked out of the diaper onto the legs, it will be washed off with soap and water during the change.

Studies have shown that the amount of fecal contamination is significantly reduced when children wear clothes over their cloth or disposable diapers. Clothing is an additional barrier between the diaper, its contents, and the room. Permitting children to wear just a T-shirt and diaper, or to eat in just a diaper and bib to make cleanup easier, is not acceptable practice for infection control. Babies soon figure out how to open a diaper and will learn even more quickly when there aren't any clothes to slow them down. Sitting beside another child provides another opportunity to gain easy access into another's diaper if that other child is wearing no outer clothing.

Second in importance only to hand washing, a strict diapering routine is essential in infant and toddler programs to control the incidence of gastrointestinal infection. Regardless of the type of diaper used, the educator's actions are crucial in determining the level of fecal contamination. Children learn to use the toilet at different ages; for many, this occurs after age two. Preschool programs may have children in diapers, and, if so, the diapering routine applies to preschool staff and parents.

The diaper-changing surface, the surrounding area, and diapering supplies should always be considered contaminated. The area should never be used for anything else, including putting a baby bottle down on the counter even for a minute.

Posting a diapering routine by the changing area acts as a reminder for educators and parents. However, regular monitoring of the educator's diapering technique helps ensure that the routine is properly implemented all the time.

You may be thinking, "I've changed a lot of diapers, and it didn't take me 11 steps—or 10 minutes—to change a single diaper" or "There must be a ton of diapers to change during a day's work in an infant program!" However, if you were to write down everything you did during a diaper change, you may be surprised at just how many steps you did take. Furthermore, parents and others who change one child's diapers at home do not need to follow the same stringent guidelines because one baby at home is quite different from 8 or 12 infants and toddlers in a group setting. At home, every family member gets used to each other's germs. Older siblings are past the developmental stage at which they put everything in their mouth, and their own personal hygiene habits are improving.

STEPS TO EFFECTIVE DIAPERING

1. Assemble all the necessary supplies.
2. Place the child on the changing surface and remove the soiled diaper. Fold the soiled surface inward and set it aside. If safety pins have been used to fasten the diaper, close them and put them out of the child's reach. Never put the pins in your mouth. Note: Keep one hand on the child at all times.
3. Clean and dry the child's skin. When necessary, use a facial tissue to apply ointments or creams. Put a fresh diaper on the child.
4. Wash the child's hands. Return the child to a supervised area.
5. Dispose of the diaper and, if used, the disposable paper covering. When cloth diapers are used, bag the diaper without removing stool. The diapers are either sent home with the parents for laundry or placed in your laundry service's container.
6. Spray the disinfecting solution onto the entire surface of the changing surface. Leave on the surface for the length of time based on the product's instructions.
7. Put away all diapering supplies.
8. Wash your hands.
9. Dry the changing surface with a single-use towel. Dispose of the cloth or paper towel.
10. Wash your hands thoroughly.
11. Record skin condition and bowel movements, as necessary.

Educators' compliance depends on their understanding of the importance of and the rationale for the routine. The list below provides the rationale for several steps from the diapering routine:

Step 1: From the perspective of injury prevention, it is essential that you gather the diapering supplies before you bring the child to the diapering surface. Once you get started, you can't safely walk away from the child to retrieve supplies. It is not necessary to wash your hands before starting. We assume that educators have been washing their hands whenever necessary during the day. As well, the diapering area and supplies are always considered to be contaminated. So it doesn't make sense to wash your hands and then contaminate them immediately after taking off the soiled diaper or picking up a tube of ointment. After you take off the diaper and wash the child's skin, your hands are covered with germs.

Step 3: Using a facial tissue to scoop ointment out of the jar or to squeeze it from a tube onto the tissue has two purposes. First, the tissue provides a barrier between your hands and the ointment, which keeps the ointment in the jar or at the end of the tube from being contaminated by your hands. Second, the tissue is then used to spread the ointment onto the skin. This keeps the germs that are already on your hands off the child's washed skin. If you need more ointment, use a new tissue to get more from the jar or tube. This rule applies regardless of whether each child has her or his own jar of diaper cream or a communal container is used. From what you've read so far, you should be able to come up with the rationale for this last requirement.

The routine use of diaper creams and ointments on children's healthy skin is discouraged. Changing diapers frequently and cleaning the skin at each change prevent urine, stool, or ammonia from contacting the skin long enough to cause irritation. These preparations are also difficult to wash off thoroughly with every change, so urine and stool can be trapped under the cream and irritate the skin. When you do use these products, apply them sparingly. Do not use baby powders or talc because the infant's airways can be damaged by inhaling powder in the air when the container is shaken.

Step 4: Before children arrive at the diaper table, they may have already had their hands in their diaper. During diaper changes, children will likely touch the wet or soiled diapers, the changing surface, and the educator's hands. If children don't have their hands washed after the diaper change, they will immediately begin contaminating the environment with their hands.

Step 5: At home, parents who use cloth diapers often soak soiled diapers in the toilet, but educators must not do this in programs. The number of times the diaper is then handled increases by at least three times, and it is difficult not to splash and drip the water in the diaper over the toilet and onto the floor. The amount of fecal contamination would be excessive.

Step 8: Educators must wash their hands to prevent them from recontaminating the surface while they are drying off the disinfecting solution and remaining germs. But by drying the surface and then discarding the towel, they have now recontaminated their hands and need to wash their hands again (Step 10).

Step 9: During a diaper change, stool or urine can end up on the changing surface. Diapering surfaces need to be smooth, durable, and easy to clean, which allows educators to wipe up any visible urine or stool with toilet paper and then disinfect the surface. Cleaning first with soap and water is not necessary except in cases in which a large quantity of stool or urine is left on the diapering surface. Some programs use disposable change-table paper (the kind used in doctors' offices), which provides a barrier between the baby and the surface. Yet when urine or watery stool touches the paper, the liquid leaks through, which defeats the paper's purpose. Remember, even if the paper is still dry following a diaper change, the paper must be discarded and the surface disinfected. This, along with the cost and the extra garbage created by the paper, is why change paper is not recommended.

The routine use of disposable gloves is not recommended for changing diapers, even with stool. Gloves provide little protection in this situation beyond the natural protection of your skin. The toilet paper or facial tissue used to wipe stool off the skin and the disposable or cloth towel to wash and dry the child's skin provide the barrier between the stool and your hands. If stool gets on your hands, germs can't get into your body through your skin. If you are concerned about a cut or scrape, use a bandage and replace it when it is soiled or wet. If you have dermatitis or a cut or other broken skin and you must change diapers, use disposable gloves as a temporary means to keep stool off your open skin. Sometimes diapers are filled with loose or watery stools, which may have covered the child's front and back or run down the legs. Some educators find these diapers to be "difficult to stomach," and using disposable gloves makes them feel more comfortable.

Diaper changes provide ideal opportunities in your busy day for one-to-one interaction with the child. Wearing gloves puts plastic between your skin and the child's skin, which can't be comfortable for the child. And are we inadvertently sending children the message that bowel movements are somehow not a natural function of their body and that they are "dirty"?

The only time that disposable gloves are recommended for diaper changing is when blood is visible in the child's stool. Choosing disposable plastic gloves over latex gloves affords the program the same kind of protection without the increased cost. In addition, reducing exposure to latex (e.g., gloves and balloons) is a safer alternative for staff and children who are allergic to latex. Regardless of the reasons for wearing gloves, you must wash your hands after removing the gloves. If you don't wash your hands well after every diaper change, you contaminate objects, food, and the environment, and the germs can then enter children's and educators' bodies through the mouth.

Toileting

STEPS IN A TOILETING ROUTINE

The toileting routine is made up of the following 14 steps:

1. If the child wears a diaper, remove it. If the diaper is soiled, clean and dry the child's skin. Dispose of the cloth or disposable diaper.
2. Place the child on the toilet or potty. Stay with the child for a specific period of time. Five minutes is usually long enough.
3. Wipe the child.
4. Flush the toilet or let the child flush it. If a potty was used, empty its contents into the toilet and flush.

(continued)

5. If necessary, diaper the child and help the child get dressed.

6. Assist the child in hand washing. Return the child to a supervised area.

7. If a potty is used, rinse out and flush the water down the toilet. If any stool remains in the potty, you may want to wear disposable gloves and remove all the stool with toilet paper. Spray the disinfecting solution onto the potty. Leave on the surface for the length of time based on the product's instructions.

8. Put away all diapering supplies.

9. Wash your hands.

10. If a potty is used, dry with a single-use towel. Dispose of the cloth or paper towel.

11. Dry the diaper-changing surface with a different towel. Dispose of the cloth or paper towel.

12. Return the potty to the storage area (if used).

13. Wash your hands thoroughly.

14. Record the child's use of the toilet or potty, any bowel movements, and any skin condition, as necessary.

For many of the same reasons that apply to the diapering routine, educators need to take extra steps when cleaning a potty to prevent contamination of the surrounding area:

- Utility sinks should be available for staff to use for cleaning, including potties. The utility sink must be cleaned and disinfected after every use. Hand-washing sinks should not be used to rinse or clean potties.

- You may prefer to wear disposable gloves while you remove stool stuck to the potty. However, wearing gloves does not eliminate the need to wash your hands.

Cleaning and Disinfecting

You know that germs are everywhere. You know that germs can live on surfaces for hours, days, and even weeks. You've read about the vehicles of transmission and the important role they play in spreading infections. The rationale for the **cleaning and disinfecting routines** in programs is to have staff focus on objects and surfaces that pose the greatest risk to children and staff.

It can be overwhelming to think about all the objects and surfaces that children and staff come into contact with every day, as well as everything and everyone who has come into contact with germs that are spread through the air from coughing, sneezing, and talking. Where do I start? How often do I clean this and that? What do I clean with? How do I know that I am cleaning this object properly? These are just some of the questions that are answered in this section.

One of the infection control practices carried out by staff to break the chain of transmission is regular cleaning and disinfecting of objects, surfaces, and areas within programs. To implement this, educators need to

- identify what needs to be cleaned, disinfected, or both;
- use effective cleaning and disinfecting products and techniques; and
- understand how to protect themselves from **potentially hazardous substances**.

The purpose of *cleaning* is to remove dirt (organic material) and germs from objects and surfaces. But, as in hand washing, the cleaning solution must be combined with a scrubbing action to create the friction needed to remove dirt and germs. This is followed by rinsing with water and air-drying.

The purpose of *disinfecting* an object or surface is to ensure that as many germs as possible are eliminated. In most cases, objects and surfaces are cleaned and rinsed, then disinfected, and left to air-dry.

What Needs to Be Cleaned or Disinfected?

By establishing priorities, you can identify the items to be cleaned, disinfected, or both and how frequently. With the *Well Beings* publication, much of the organizational work has been done for program staff. Rather than repeating those recommendations, let's explore the rationale behind two of them.

Toys

Toys that have been in infants' and toddlers' mouths are obvious vehicles of germ transmission. Many toys for infants are designed to be safe for them to put in the mouth (e.g., plastic stacking rings on a cone, squeak toys, rattles). These toys are often referred to as mouthing toys. Of course, young children can put almost anything into their mouth (e.g., corners of books, puzzle pieces, plastic fruit and vegetables). For clarity, we will refer to any toy that children have chewed or sucked on as a mouthing toy. After one child has finished playing with a mouthing toy, it should be picked up by staff before a second child chews on it.

Toys that are mouthed should be cleaned and disinfected daily. Cleaning washes off organic materials, such as the children's saliva and any stool that may have been on a child's hands and transferred to the toys. Disinfecting is an added precaution that removes germs that may remain after cleaning, before the toys are air-dried and returned to the children. Plastic books can be cleaned and disinfected by hand; cloth ones can be put in the laundry.

The potential for spreading germs via toys used by preschoolers or school-agers is much lower than via mouthing toys, for three main reasons. Older children are not constantly putting their toys and hands into their mouth; they aren't touching, hugging, and kissing one another as frequently as babies and toddlers do; and their personal hygiene is improving. For these reasons, these toys can be cleaned weekly and when they are obviously soiled, but disinfecting is not necessary.

Water Tables

Although the water table is an important medium for learning, a pool of water can be easily contaminated and spread germs among the children using it. Germs enter the water from the children's hands and from everything they put in the water, such as toys, soap, and food colouring. Additional germs enter the water from blow toys and straws, as well as airborne germs that land in the water from laughing, talking, and coughing. Adding bleach or other disinfecting solutions is not necessary— saliva, soap, and sand in the water will reduce the bleach solution's effectiveness.

CPS (2015, p. 158) recommends the following hygiene practices for communal water tables:

> For preschoolers, be sure to empty and disinfect a shared water table daily and whenever you suspect contamination. If the water looks cloudy, it needs to be changed. Fill the water table with clean tap water just before use. *Do not add bleach, disinfectant or vinegar to the play water.…* Remove any water toy that comes in contact with a child's mouth during shared play, and clean, sanitize and air dry all water toys between sessions.*

In *Well Beings*, CPS (2015, p. 158) recommends five steps for cleaning a water table:

1. Empty the water and wash out the water table with detergent.
2. Rinse off the detergent with clean water.
3. Apply a sanitizing solution following the manufacturer's directions *or* use a medium strength (500 parts per million [ppm]) bleach solution.
4. Sanitize for at least 10 minutes or for whatever time the manufacturer recommends.
5. Allow the water table to air dry.*

Courtesy of George Brown College/Scotia Plaza Child Care Centre

Given how much infants and toddlers love to explore, not to mention their willingness to share toys, their affectionate nature, and their vulnerability to infections, it makes sense that infants and toddlers not use communal water tables. Instead, each child should have his or her own basin of water. The basins can be placed on the floor or on a table in a way that encourages social play. Individual basins permit children to use toys that can go between their own basin of water and their mouth and to splash and drool in the water and even drink it. In this way, the children do not share toys or come into direct contact with the contents of one another's basins. *Children must never be left alone with the basins of water*, even for a second. Children have drowned in as little as 5 centimetres (2 in.) of water.

Products

Household cleaning products and detergents that are safer for the environment are also effective cleaning products in programs. Cloth towels can be used for all cleaning and can be laundered after each use. When cleaning up blood and large amounts of stool, urine, and vomit, paper towelling is preferred because it can be safely discarded.

In the past, household bleach was the go-to disinfecting product for a number of reasons: it is highly effective, inexpensive, easy to use, readily available, and safe to use around children. Today questions are raised about chlorine in the environment, along with concerns about bleach ruining clothes, the smell left in the air, and the potential corrosive effects on equipment. When bleach is not used, programs consult their public health inspector before choosing disinfecting products. Other products are effective, and directors consider each product's cost and its safety

---

*Source: Reprinted with permission from the Canadian Paediatric Society.

around children and staff, as well as its environmental friendliness. You may find that programs limit the use of bleach to when they clean up blood. However, when using bleach, make sure to use the dilutions that are recommended by your provincial or territorial child care office in conjunction with public health inspectors.

When selecting an alternative, consult with your region's licensing agency or public health department to ensure that the product is approved for use in ECLC settings. Not all products are created equal, and as such, you want a product that is effective and safe for use around children.

Having effective cleaning and disinfecting products, cloths, and rubber gloves—and being organized—takes some of the work out of cleaning. Some objects, such as books and puzzles in infant and toddler programs, need to be disinfected only. Obviously, these and other objects are not placed in a container of the disinfecting solution. Instead, they are wiped with a cloth that has been rinsed and wrung out in the solution.

The dishwasher can be a timesaving device for cleaning and disinfecting smaller plastic toys. Make sure the toys can withstand the water temperature and the detergent.

Implementing the Routines throughout the Day

The number of times that educators wash their hands and the time spent on the routines discussed in this unit depend on the following factors: the size of the program, the number of children and staff, the ages of the children, and whether meals and snacks are prepared in the program or provided by parents.

Some programs, because of their location (e.g., workplace, office buildings, colleges, universities), have cleaning services that maintain bathrooms, floors, carpets, and so on. In these programs, staff have more time for the remaining routines. However, it is important that staff monitor the external cleaning services to ensure that the quality is satisfactory, that the cleaning is done with the recommended frequency, and that the products used are safe around children.

A day in any program is busy, and fitting in all the routines takes some finesse. But the importance of implementing routines to break the chain of transmission means that there can't be shortcuts. We must ensure that the time spent on implementing routines is protected because the work reduces the frequency of infection.

A written schedule for all routines is essential to ensure that they are implemented consistently. Programs may design a schedule based on the frequency of the routines (e.g., daily, twice a week, weekly) or by room. The schedule breaks down what can seem like an overwhelming task into more manageable routines. It includes instructions on how each item is to be cleaned or disinfected so that educators aren't left questioning the effectiveness of their work.

When there is an outbreak of an infection, a review of these written schedules can provide insight into the effectiveness of the cleaning and disinfecting routines and whether the schedule should be revised on a short- or long-term basis.

During an outbreak of diarrhea, it is advisable to close the water table. At the same time, staff's hand washing, diapering routines, and food-safety practices need to be evaluated.

Protecting Yourself from Potentially Hazardous Substances

In this section, we discuss the potential risks and steps to reduce educators' exposure to hazardous products related to infection control. These include the concept of routine practices, the safe use of cleaning and disinfecting products, and the appropriate use of gloves.

Routine Practices

Under normal conditions, when patients are admitted to a hospital, they are not routinely tested for any number of diseases. This practice would be expensive and time-consuming. In addition, such tests may not provide the hospital's infectious disease experts with reliable information. You have already read that a person can spread germs to others before she or he develops symptoms and that some of us carry infections even though we are not ill.

Routine practices constitute the fundamental principle in protecting staff from the potential risks in the workplace. Routine practices are based on the premise that blood, body fluids, secretions, excretions, nonintact (broken) skin, and soiled objects are potentially infectious. In other words, hospital staff assume that everyone has the potential to expose them to germs, so safe medical and nursing procedures are developed specifically for the task or medical technique being implemented. Routine practices, in turn, protect patients from hospital staff.

You may be wondering how anything in a hospital has any relevance to programs. Educators aren't changing bandages with blood, giving needles, routinely being exposed to blood, or caring for seriously ill patients. The fundamental principle on which hospitals build their infection control strategy is the same one as for programs. To reduce the spread of germs and to protect themselves from unnecessary exposure to potentially harmful organisms, educators must implement routine practices in their daily work with children. All the procedures covered in this unit are based on routine practices and, when implemented, protect not only the educators but also the children.

Cleaning and Disinfecting Products and Gloves

Cleaning products used in programs should be safe to use around children and staff and, preferably, be friendly to the environment. This does not eliminate the need for the products to be stored out of reach of children. Most products used in programs are household products purchased in grocery stores. It is advisable to read all product labels for safe handling directions and any first-aid information (see Workplace Hazardous Materials Information System, page 92).

Just as water and soap can dry our skin, cleaning and disinfecting products can be abrasive. Using rubber gloves while dishwashing and during cleaning and disinfecting routines helps protect our hands. Using differently coloured rubber gloves for routine tasks and writing the task near the wrists of the gloves are two ways, in addition to separate storage areas, that help staff use the right gloves for the right task. *For example, pink rubber gloves are used only in the kitchen and are hung to dry in the kitchen. Yellow rubber gloves are used for cleaning and disinfecting toys and play equipment and are hung to dry in the utility area.* Another option is to use single-use gloves for these tasks.

There are times when disposable rather than rubber gloves are preferred. In addition to occasional use during diapering and the toileting routine for toddlers, disposable (nonlatex) gloves are used when educators are at risk for exposure to blood or bloody body fluids. Once the gloves have been used, they can be disposed of carefully. Carefully remove one disposable glove at a time. While you are slowly peeling off a glove (starting at the wrist), turn the glove inside out. This method protects you from the germs on the gloves and also protects the immediate area. Wash your hands after disposing safely of the gloves.

Disposable gloves are just one way of providing a barrier between your hands and the blood. Facial tissue used to stop a nosebleed provides a barrier between your hand and the child's nose. Cotton balls or sterile gauze in first-aid kits, when used appropriately to clean cuts and scrapes, can be effective barriers between your hands and the source of the blood. It is not necessary for staff to keep disposable gloves in their pockets in case a child is injured or gets a nosebleed. Our skin's natural ability to protect us from germs—along with effective hand washing—is our best protection.

Regardless of which type of glove is used, there are two points to keep in mind:

- Gloves can provide a protective barrier against germs that cause infection. However, they offer little protection beyond that achieved by good hand washing.
- You must always wash your hands after you remove the gloves.

After all, you are not the only person to wear those gloves. Your hands had germs on them before you put on the gloves, and so did the hands of the person who used the gloves before you. Therefore, these germs may be inside the gloves and may end up on the next person's hands. In addition, you get more germs on your hands when you put on and take off the gloves.

Pets in Early Childhood Learning and Care Programs

Pets provide children with the opportunity to learn to care for living things and add "life" to an ECLC program. Whether animals are permitted in a program or not is based on your provincial or territorial regulations and your public health regulations. When they are permitted, the regulations should cover the types of animals that are permitted and not permitted, vaccination requirements, and care of the animals and cages. Some programs are opting for a fish aquarium, which provides opportunities for relaxation, enjoyment, and responsible care for the fish. As well, discussions around the cycle of life and death inevitably become part of the experience. There are fewer daily responsibilities for the staff and none of the complexities of having a centre pet that must be cared for over the weekends.

In *Well Beings* (2015), CPS recommends that pets not be part of the ECLC program; rather, family or other community member pets could be brought in for visits. Reasons cited include the following: diseases can be passed from the animals to us and can pose issues for children, parents, and staff with allergies or weakened immune systems or pregnant staff or parents. CPS does acknowledge that home-based (family daycare) programs may have family pets in the house.

CRITICAL THINKING

RECEIVING MIXED MESSAGES

On a regular basis, educators are inundated with messages and information from different agencies that come in contact with ECLC programs, including public health inspectors, public health nurses and other staff, the licensing office, health care providers, early childhood students and instructors, and newly hired graduates. In addition, TV, online, and print ads are regularly "selling" us on products that aren't necessary.

Public Health Agencies

Let's talk about "the elephant in the room." This is an English idiom, which refers to an issue so obvious that everyone notices but doesn't discuss. You may ask, "What is the elephant?" This issue refers to the inconsistencies in the hygiene requirements and recommendations for ECLC settings set by public health agencies across Canada. These expectations vary between provinces and territories, within a region, and even within larger communities when served by multiple public health inspectors. What one public health inspector requires of a centre can be quite different from what another public health inspector requires in the same city or town.

The differences in health behaviour for optimal hygiene have a direct impact on the ECLC curriculum in individual centres. *For example, centre staff have made the decision to remove indoor water play from the daily curriculum because their public health inspector's requirements were beyond what was reasonable and manageable by the staff. Some centres have been told that they are not permitted to bring leaves or other natural materials indoors.*

Within your practicum experiences, it is possible that you will see differences between the hygiene practices outlined in this textbook, recommended by CPS, and what is being done in programs. You may work in a centre where the public health requirement is that disposable gloves are worn for every diaper change. In some instances, the procedure includes using more than one set of gloves during that routine. You may be required to wash your hands before and after putting on gloves. You may work in centres where hand washing has been replaced with the routine use of hand sanitizers.

You may come back to class with experiences that are contrary to what you have read here. You are encouraged to talk about these discrepancies with your ECE instructor and your field placement supervisor. Your education, along with nationally recognized resources such as *Well Beings*, equips you to enter into conversations regarding best practices. It is always important for students and professionals to understand the rationale for requirements; in other words, why is the recommended or required policy a "best practice"? There may be reasons that, once known, help you understand the rationale for the practice, such as temporary measures due to an outbreak, or local concerns about a particular communicable pathogen. On the other hand, if the rationale remains a mystery to you and your supervisors, it is important to follow up with the public health agency for clarification.

Hand Sanitizers

There is incredible marketing surrounding the everyday use of hand sanitizers as an acceptable alternative to washing our hands with soap and water. Earlier in this unit, we discussed the occasional use of such products in ECLC settings. It has also been shown that these sanitizers do *not* offer any germ-killing advantage over soap and running water.

Yet public health agencies across the country are encouraging the use of sanitizers routinely in ECLC settings or giving the use of alcohol-based hand rubs equal status to hand washing with soap and running water. It is not uncommon to see a two- or three-year-old come to the setting with a personal-sized bottle of hand rub in a coat pocket. Some programs have been required to have the educators carry these products with them to outdoor play areas. Why? We suggest that this is an unnecessary recommendation for the following reasons:

- First, those playing outside typically will have visible sand and soil on their hands, which render the sanitizer ineffective.
- Second, when educators help children blow their nose, tissue is the barrier between their hands and the child's nasal discharge.
- Third, no children are eating or drinking while they are playing.
- Fourth, alcohol is the sanitizing agent in such products, which is drying to the skin, and in the winter, this only adds to the dryness our hands experience.
- Fifth, if you have used such a product, you'll remember the smell and possible taste left on your hands. This is not the type of residue, no matter the amount, that you want to routinely expose young children to, particularly those who frequently put their hands and objects they touch in the mouth.
- Sixth, the outside of the bottle must always be considered contaminated, so if you use the product and then put the container back in your pocket, you have just contaminated your hands. Upon their return inside, everyone is expected to wash their hands because we know that their hands have become dirty while playing.
- Seventh, and most importantly, hand washing is still required even if you have used a sanitizer out in the playground.

Staff and parents in the programs may have conflicting opinions and practices around this issue and recommendations or requirements from their local public health agency that contradict this position. Children's use of these over-the-counter products for hygiene may undermine their development of healthy life skills, such as knowing when and how to wash hands.

Disinfecting or "Sterilizing" Our Physical Environment

As mentioned in the section on vehicles of transmission (see page 133), TV and online commercials and the marketplace overwhelm us with a multitude of disinfecting products to kill every germ around the home—an unnecessary and impossible goal. These advertisements to "sterilize" our environments raise a number of questions:

- What about the residue left behind on the sprayed objects?
- What happens when the residue gets onto our hands and, in the case of a child, into the mouth? Aside from its effectiveness, another reason why a bleach solution is recommended for use in this unit is because it is safe to use around children in the dilutions recommended.
- What is the environmental impact of these unnecessary chemicals being sprayed in the air, dumped down the sink, and flushed into the sewage system?

Antibacterial Products

It seems as if the word "antibacterial" is appearing on more and more product labels. Considerable time and money are being spent on the promotion of the antibacterial ingredients in products to try to convince us that if we use the products, we will be protected from germs and, as a result, be healthier.

One such ingredient is **triclosan**, which is found in products such as soaps and cleansers. But it is also present in unexpected products, such as eye and face makeup, deodorants, toothpastes, and shaving creams. It has been reported that triclosan is added during the manufacturing process to items such as kitchen utensils, bedding, and even toys, socks, and trash bags. On the Government of Canada's website (2016, p. 1), triclosan is on the list of permitted cosmetic ingredients. Triclosan has been banned in the United States and Europe, but Canada has not instituted such a ban. Triclosan can be absorbed through our skin and can affect our hormone function. Even in very low concentrations, triclosan is toxic to aquatic plants and animals, and "has the potential to react with chlorine in drinking water to form the carcinogen chloroform" (Ecojustice, 2017, p. 3).

The Government of Canada regulates the amount of triclosan allowed in products made and sold in Canada. They do include suggestions on how you can minimize your exposure to triclosan:

- Read and follow the product instructions. For example, directions for mouthwashes that contain triclosan say to avoid swallowing the product.
- Practise correct hand washing techniques using soap and water. In most cases, antibacterial soap is not necessary for safe, effective hand hygiene.
- Read the label if you want to avoid triclosan. The label on cosmetics, over-the-counter drugs and natural health products must indicate if they contain triclosan.*

---

*Source: © All rights reserved. *Triclosan*. Health Canada 2018. Adapted and reproduced with permission from the Minister of Health, 2018.

Antibacterial products play a significant contributory role in microbes' (i.e., bacteria, viruses, and fungi) increasing resistance to **antimicrobials** used to either kill or inhibit the growth of these microorganisms. You are most familiar with antibiotics used to treat bacterial infections (see Antibiotic-Resistant Bacteria, page 193), but there are other medical applications to help us after being exposed to certain viruses. Disinfecting products fall under the antimicrobial heading.

CPS (2016a) raised the concern that children who experience more infections in the early years are less likely to develop allergies and asthma. Or said another way, the more we "sterilize" the children's environment, the more we are under-stimulating the normal maturation of children's immune system. Researchers from the University of California summarized 14 studies and concluded that the risk of developing the most common type of childhood leukemia is reduced for those children attending ECLC programs. The lowered risk, by as much as 30%, may be attributed to children's stronger immune systems from experiencing childhood infections (ScienceDaily, 2008).

The issue of **antimicrobial resistance** is not just a Canadian issue; it is a global issue. We all have a personal responsibility to limit the use of antimicrobial products. We must read the product's list of ingredients and not purchase products with ingredients of questionable or unnecessary use. *For example, we don't need an ingredient such as triclosan in our personal grooming products, clothing, and bed linens. Take a look at the products that you are already using at home. What is in your favourite brand of toothpaste? When you are at ECLC programs that include toothbrushing in their daily routine, take a look at the toothpaste used with the children.*

In ECLC settings, do the following:

- When disinfecting, we must limit the types of products used, follow the instructions, and use the products only where appropriate. Bleach is an antimicrobial product, and it is important to remember to measure the bleach and water each time you mix it and follow the recommendations for disinfecting surfaces and items in the program. Unnecessarily disinfecting items or using too strong a dilution can contribute to antimicrobial resistance.

- Manage the illnesses of children and staff responsibly (see Appendix 4.1, page 213).

PLANNING FOR A PANDEMIC

More than a decade ago, in 2003, Toronto and other cities in Canada and elsewhere were faced with an outbreak of severe acute respiratory syndrome (SARS), a severe form of pneumonia that can make people critically ill and can be fatal. This was the first large-scale outbreak of an infectious disease for many of us in our lifetime to have witnessed, at least through the extensive national news coverage. It took the cooperation of the municipal, provincial, and federal health authorities working together to coordinate the response by both health professionals and the public to curtail the spread of SARS within hospitals, personal care homes, and the general population. After the outbreak ended, Toronto was known worldwide for its response to and control of SARS.

What is a **pandemic**? The American Academy of Pediatrics defines it as the "emergence and global spread of a new influenza A virus subtype to which the population has little or no immunity and that spreads rapidly from person to person" (2015, p. 479). In 1918, perhaps as many as 50 million people died during the worldwide flu pandemic. In the 21st century, the first influenza A pandemic started in April 2009 and lasted until August 2010. Fortunately, millions didn't die from that flu, but there were still thousands who did (American Academy of Pediatrics, 2015, p. 479).

Every fall, the annual flu vaccine program is launched. Health care workers in hospitals, personal care homes, and medical clinics and emergency first responders should be vaccinated as a matter of course to lessen the spread to those they come in contact with in their work. This recommendation includes a list of others who should be immunized, including the following selection, which is more relevant to those in ECLC and families (PHAC, 2017a, pp. 12–13):

- those working in ECLC settings (centre- and home-based) in which children are less than or equal to 59 months of age are enrolled. Educators working with children who have chronic health issues should receive the flu shot regardless of the child's age.
- the household contacts of those people at high risk for the flu's complications and those expecting a newborn during flu season; parents of children under six months old
- pregnant women*

Some groups in our population are more vulnerable to the complications of the flu. These groups include the following (PHAC, 2017d, pp. 12–13):

- those living with chronic medical conditions
- residents in personal care homes and other chronic care facilities
- adults older than 65 years old
- Indigenous peoples
- all children 6 to 59 months of age*

Planning for a pandemic is a multipronged approach. Your child care licensing agency and your public health agency recommend that the programs include procedures for pandemics as part of managing a range of health-related emergencies (see Manitoba Department of Families in Resource Materials). It isn't a question of if there will be a pandemic but when.

As a result, planning for a pandemic is needed now rather than attempting to respond to it after its onset. It is not our intention to outline such a plan in this textbook. But prevention is key, year-round, not just during the annual flu season. In addition to the flu vaccine, hand washing and hygiene practices are paramount to prevent and limit the spread of infectious diseases, including the flu. When you are at your placements, ask the staff about their plan for a pandemic. Do they have a policy and procedures already in place? Are they aware of the work being done in your province or territory?

NELSONstudy

To access Resource Materials, visit NelsonStudy.

---

*Source: The National Advisory Committee on Immunization. *Canadian Immunization Guide*, 7th edition. Ottawa: Public Health Agency of Canada, 2006. http://www.phac-aspc.gc.ca/publicat/cig-gci/index.html

REVISITING THE HEALTH PROMOTION ACTION PLAN

Recall the health promotion action plan introduced in Unit 1. The following example illustrates this plan in practice in terms of preventing childhood illnesses, using immunization as the point of reference.

CRITICAL THINKING

After reading the health promotion action plan on immunization, identify an action for each of the three levels using the topic of antimicrobial resistance as the point of reference.

Individual Problem Solving and Self-Reliance

Due to the dynamic nature of immunization research, the list of diseases for which immunization is available is increasing. This reality makes it important for educators and parents to keep current through their family physician or local public health agency. As individuals, we are encouraged by public health agencies to recognize the importance of complying with recommended immunization schedules. Parents are encouraged to follow through with their children's immunization to contribute to their health and the public's health. An annual checkup with a family physician includes a review of each child's immunization history and future needs. As adults, you will want to keep track of when you are due for your diphtheria and tetanus boosters, which are recommended every 10 years. Parents who have made a decision for religious or other reasons not to follow through with immunization guidelines have an ethical responsibility to the ECLC program to submit a physician's letter for documentation. They must also follow public health guidelines in the event that these children are exposed to certain illnesses (see Appendix 4.1, page 213).

Community Action

Directors and educators can support the goal of 100% immunization by posting reminders for families on a parent bulletin board and by providing pamphlets that clarify the availability and benefits of specific immunizations. Directors need to keep immunization records up-to-date and contact parents if their child's immunization records have not yet been submitted. Directors can also help parents find a family physician by knowing which doctors in the community are taking new patients, as well as having information about community health clinics and drop-in clinics. An annual parent–staff meeting facilitated by a public health nurse could also promote awareness and education about immunization and other public health initiatives.

In promoting 100% immunization in the community, it is important to know the issues that pose challenges or barriers to full participation in immunization compliance. *For example:*

- *In some remote communities, families may not have ongoing access to family physicians.*
- *In communities where few or no infectious disease outbreaks have occurred for over a generation, families may be more complacent and not see the need for immunization.*

- *Recent immigrants who have come from countries that do not have a universal immunization program, particularly those whose first language is neither English nor French, may not have the experience or access to our immunization information in their first language.*

We all must realize that immunization plays a significant role in continuing to prevent outbreaks. It is important to respond to specific community issues through effective action that works to create better day-to-day living conditions as well as long-term change. Community engagement in their own issues increases confidence and commitment to make a difference. A community forum with access to information relevant to the participant's needs (e.g., age, language), or other plans to build broad-based education and support, may lead to effective action and change.

Societal Change

A number of public challenges may present roadblocks to attaining the goal of 100% immunization. Provinces and territories may not make all immunizations recommended in the schedule available to everyone through medicare. In these situations, some children are possibly at a disadvantage if their families cannot afford to pay or have the costs covered through extended health benefits. Another barrier may be the lack of access to family physicians in nonurban areas. Government priorities placed on prevention involve advocacy, as stated earlier in this textbook. It is hoped that changes will improve some of these realities—funds put into universally accessible preventive health care, incentives for physicians to practise in nonurban areas (and in Canada generally), and citizen advocacy groups.

CONCLUSION

One of the primary goals of high-quality ECLC programs is to maintain or improve the health status of children, which contributes to their growth and development and to their participation in the program and activities. Indicators of high quality include adequate educator–child ratios, small group sizes, staff trained in early childhood education, the provision of orientation and regular in-service training, and low staff turnover rates. These all need to be in place to control infectious diseases.

The consistent implementation of an infection control strategy is one of the best ways to prevent infections or at least reduce their spread in programs. Such a strategy includes effective hand washing as a priority for both educators and children, to break the chain of transmission. Adherence to a strict diapering and toileting policy (and procedures), regular cleaning and disinfecting, and, of course, hand washing are all essential to promote children's physical health in the ECLC setting. In addition, informal but routine daily health observations, beginning with an observation conducted when the child arrives at the program, ensures that staff connect with the child and usually the family. This initial health observation provides educators with a baseline reading of the child's health to use for comparison during the day. This process, which is discussed in more detail in Unit 4, ensures that adults take note of each child's health status so that changes in physical or behavioural status are recognized and responded to appropriately.

ASSESS YOUR LEARNING

Define terms or describe concepts used in this unit.

- antimicrobial resistance
- antimicrobials
- cleaning and disinfecting routines
- germ
- hand-sanitizing products
- hand washing
- host
- hygiene practices
- immunity
- immunization
- new host
- pandemic
- potentially hazardous substances
- routine practices
- triclosan
- vehicles of transmission

Evaluate your options in each situation.

1. One of the daily disinfecting routines in the program is to add a capful of bleach to the water table each morning. This practice saves water and time because staff empty the water only once a week.

2. While demonstrating the diaper-changing procedure, one of the educators tells you not to bother washing the infant's hands after diapering. She says it is a time-waster; instead, she wants you to ensure that the baby's hands are busy with a toy to prevent them from becoming contaminated during diapering.

3. You are in your first program placement. You are feeling nervous and, understandably, unsure of yourself. During your first few days at the program, you observe that all the educators wear disposable gloves whenever a child has stool in the diaper. When one of the educators runs through the diapering routine with you, she makes it clear that you are expected to wear gloves.

4. You believe in environmentally friendly cleaning products, so when your room partner suggests getting rid of the bleach and using vinegar and baking soda instead, you are thinking about it. After all, that's usually what you use at home to keep surfaces clean.

5. When a new child enrolls in your program, the parents let you know that he has an allergy to the program's pet guinea pig.

Stephen Coburn/Shutterstock.com

Illness Management

4

CONTENTS

OBJECTIVES

To describe the why, how, and what of daily health observations. (LO 4)

To identify the signs and symptoms of illness and describe how to proceed with concerns. (LO 3, 4)

To explain the principle of exclusion and consider the issues surrounding exclusion from the ECLC program. (LO 2, 3, 4, 6)

CHILDREN'S HEALTH CARE

This section focuses on the appropriate role that educators play in caring for children who are ill. In addition to implementing an infection control strategy, the educators' role includes

- working in partnership with parents;
- identifying possible signs and symptoms;
- implementing the early childhood learning and care (ECLC) program's policy for ill children, including
    - documenting observations in children's files and reports,
    - sharing relevant health information with parents,
    - communicating with health professionals, and
    - implementing the health care provider's recommendations (the term "health care provider" encompasses both physician and advanced practitioners); and

- helping children feel better, including
  - excluding children,
  - TLC (tender loving care), and
  - administering medication, if necessary.

Educators observe children throughout their daily activities. With experience, educators gain the expertise to differentiate between behaviour that is developmentally appropriate for children, behaviour that should be watched more closely, and behaviour that is cause for concern. If an educator is concerned about a child's behaviour or state of health, action is required on the part of educators and parents.

Educators' ability to articulate health concerns about children is an essential skill. As with any skill, experience and motivation on the part of the individual to continue learning assist educators in fine-tuning their skills for observation and documentation. The methods used for documenting health observations vary among ECLC programs. Regardless of the method, the key to effective documentation is that it is objective, systematic, and concise. Educators are trained professionals communicating with other educators, parents, and health or social service professionals in the community.

The quality of the relationships that staff have with parents in managing illness is paramount because parents are the decision makers regarding their child's health. Establishing effective relationships with a child's parents begins at the time of enrollment, not the first time educators have concerns about the child. Because children will get sick and be unable to attend the program, the enrollment interview is the time for the director and parents to discuss the following issues: information sharing, program policies on health observations, childhood illnesses, communications with their health care provider, criteria for excluding children from the program, and administration of medication.

If the program's health policies and practices are realistic, logical, practical, and based on current health information, parents will likely understand their purpose and work cooperatively with staff. If, however, policies and practices seem unrealistic or unrelated to current health information, parents may be less willing to cooperate.

- ECLC programs that take children's temperatures at the hint of a warm forehead and then use only the temperature's value to exclude children and send them to the health care provider
- ECLC programs that exclude children with colds when the nasal discharge is yellow or green in colour

Neither example above requires children to be excluded, nor do actions like these contribute to parents' viewing the program and educators positively. Partnerships with parents in managing children's illnesses mean that staff

- ensure that **exclusion** policies and practices are parent positive—respectful, realistic, and nonpunitive;

- demonstrate empathy for the parents' situation, balancing this with the needs of the ill child, other children in the group, and staff; and

- are supportive with regard to health information and resources but do *not* diagnose illness. Instead, educators document signs and symptoms that the parent can communicate to the health care provider.

Children's Medical Examination at Enrollment

Most ECLC programs in Canada require parents to have their children examined by a health care provider within a certain time period after starting in the program. These examinations result in a number of health promotion benefits:

- They provide the parents, health care provider, and educators with an overview of the child's current health status, which can be used as a measure in the future.

- They ensure that the child's immunizations are up-to-date.

- They advise health care providers that one of their patients is starting in group care, which gives health care providers the opportunity to talk with parents about the frequency of childhood illnesses.

- They include educators as participants in the care plan for children with specific health care needs by encouraging the health care provider and parents to share relevant information with the staff.

Daily Observation of Children

As educators get to know the infants and toddlers in their care, they become increasingly aware of behavioural changes and other signs and symptoms that may indicate possible infections. Preschool and school-age children are generally better

able to tell educators if they aren't feeling well and answer questions that the educator asks for clarification. This assists educators in determining whether the parents should pick up their child early or whether the child is able to participate in the activities and can remain in the program. There are times when children are excluded because of a specific infection. When it comes to observing children for possible signs of illness, educators must first acknowledge the importance of daily health observations to identify ill children. Decisions regarding the care of children are based on the educators' observations, subsequent conversations with the parents, and health care providers' diagnoses.

Courtesy of Barb Pimento, taken at the Downtown Montessori (Coatsworth) Childcare Centre

Daily Baseline Health Observations

Programs that recognize the importance of baseline (starting point) health observations schedule enough staff at the start of the day to conduct them. Educators conduct baseline health observations of each child when he or she is dropped off so that educators can talk with the child and the parent. Staff encourage parents to take a few minutes at drop-off to ensure that parent, child, and educator have enough time to talk about

- how the child felt overnight and this morning,
- whether he or she ate breakfast,
- how well she or he slept, and
- whether the parents have any concerns about their child (e.g., "She had a sore tummy when she went to bed but seems to be feeling better this morning").

These conversations with parents, and the educator's familiarity with the children, establish a daily baseline to identify behavioural changes in a particular child for the rest of the day. The most reliable indicator of possible infection in children is a change in behaviour.

During the morning, there are times when the child just doesn't seem to be herself: she wants to lie down, turns down her snack, wants to be held a lot. Educators watch her more closely, taking into account the time of day and whether other children are sick. The director calls the parent to let him know that his daughter is feeling under the weather. Jointly, they decide whether she can remain in the program for the rest of the day or whether other steps should be taken.

Physical and Behavioural Signs and Symptoms

Using a checklist to evaluate children's **signs of illness** systematically assists educators in checking children. With practice, using the checklist quickly becomes second nature. Starting at the child's head and moving down to the toes, educators will have completed a baseline health observation in just a few moments.

Observing children calls on your senses of sight, hearing, touch, and smell. Educators should look for the following physical signs:

- Face: sad, tired, angry, upset, flushed
- Eyes: eyelids are puffy, whites of the eyes are red or yellow; eyes themselves are watery and clear or show thick (pus) discharge; sores or styes are present; child rubs eyes
- Ears: child rubs or pulls at ears; drainage seen in the outer ear
- Nose: runny; red or chafed from wiping or rubbing; child sneezes
- Mouth: bleeding; cold sores
- Neck: swelling along the jawline

- Breathing and/or voice: wheezing, congestion, coughing; child sounds stuffed up (nasal) or hoarse
- Skin: rashes or patches of irritated skin; cuts, scrapes or abrasions, bruises, bumps; skin has a yellow colour; child scratches the skin; skin feels hot, cold, sweaty, clammy, etc.

It is unnecessary and inappropriate for educators to examine children physically by using a flashlight to look into children's mouths and throats or by examining the skin for rashes or marks (e.g., bruises) on parts of the body that are covered by clothing. Even if a child complains of a sore throat, you are not responsible for examining the throat to determine whether the tissue is red or swollen or for concluding that he or she should be seen by a health care provider. Medical examinations are just that—medical—and can be intrusive to patients. Keep in mind that you are not expected or trained to be a health care provider or nurse.

During the day, educators will naturally see the bodies of infants and children while changing diapers, helping them on the toilet, or helping them change into swimsuits. These occasions provide opportunities to note the presence of skin rashes, bruises, and so on.

In most situations in which a child is injured or complains of itchiness or pain, it is appropriate for the educator to look at the child's skin and proceed accordingly. An exception is with preschoolers and school-agers when the genitals or buttocks are involved. In such cases, the child's health care provider or parents examine the child. However, in cases in which sexual abuse is suspected, educators should follow their suspected child maltreatment protocol.

The baseline health observation includes assessing children's hygiene, emotional health, and growth and developmental milestones. Early childhood courses in child development thoroughly cover the observation and documentation of children's milestone achievements. Concerns about children's maltreatment are examined in Unit 8 (see page 469).

The terms "personal hygiene" and "cleanliness" are often used interchangeably. However, personal hygiene is a broader term. It includes hand washing, toileting practices, and dental care, along with the cleanliness of one's skin, hair, and clothing. In hygiene, as in many other things, there is a range of what each person finds to be an acceptable level. The food we eat (e.g., spices), the way foods are prepared (e.g., fried), the laundry products we use (e.g., scented or unscented), and whether we smoke, as well as whether we use perfumes or colognes, what shampoos or conditioners and deodorants or even incense we use, and whether we have pets—and so on—all contribute to our individual scent and the aroma in our homes. You may be aware of children's individual scents (e.g., the smell of fabric softener on a child's clothes). Some scents may be different from your own, and you may find particular scents unpleasant. In other cases, the scents may just be unfamiliar. Yet just because the scent is different doesn't mean the child is unclean. As in any other situation, educators' sensitivity to children and parents and respect for personal preferences are important to children's emotional well-being. Educators model appropriate comments and behaviour to children. There may be times when children have a distinctive odour because their skin, hair, or clothing is dirty from infrequent bathing or soiled clothes. Again, educators use their discretion in determining whether this is a common or infrequent occurrence. If it happens frequently, the child may be neglected.

If an educator observes more significant behavioural changes, the child should be seen by a health care provider as soon as possible. Parents or educators must seek medical attention for the child if the child shows any of the following behavioural changes or a combination of them:

- lethargic (or lacks energy)
- much sleepier than usual
- not alert
- uninterested in his or her environment (other children, toys, activities)
- unusually cranky, fussy, or irritable
- inconsolable
- refusing to eat or drink

Parents or educators must seek medical attention for the child if the child shows any of the following physical symptoms:

- change in breathing (rapid, shallow, or shortness of breath)
- pain or difficulty swallowing
- stiff neck
- rash with a fever
- rash with a change in behaviour

Fevers

A fever is just one of a number of signs of illness, like a runny nose, sore throat, cough, diarrhea, or vomiting. *Fever by itself is not dangerous. In fact, it is one of our body's defence mechanisms that helps us fight infection.* But when a child feels warm, many adults reach for the thermometer, give the child medication, and call the health care provider. Fever is unreliable as a sign in determining how sick a child is or whether to call the parents to pick up their child.

Even though children can be seriously ill and not have a fever, many people believe that a child with a fever is sicker than a child without a fever. But this is not necessarily the case. Children can have a very serious illness (e.g., meningitis) and have a fever of only 38.5°C (101.3°F). Very young infants can also have a temperature that is below normal even with a serious infection (Canadian Paediatric Society [CPS], 2015, p. 171). A mild viral infection can cause a fever as high as 40°C (104°F). Most infections accompanied by a fever in children are minor (e.g., upper respiratory infections [URIs]). These are often caused by a virus, and the child usually gets better without medical treatment.

Another reason why parents become concerned about their child having a fever is the possibility of a febrile seizure. About 2% to 5% of children with a fever have one febrile seizure between six months and five years old. The seizure is likely the first signal that the child has a fever, and it can seem very serious to those observing it, but, in reality, febrile seizures are not harmful to children. The involuntary movements of the child are stiffening of the body, eyes rolling upward, and jerking movements of the head and limbs. The seizure lasts from 30 seconds to 2 minutes (CPS, 2015, p. 173). There may be thrashing and drooling, which highlights the importance of ensuring that the child is in a place where he or she can be unrestricted to avoid injury. There is no treatment or preventive care for children with a history of febrile seizures. But if staff know that a child may have febrile seizures, that knowledge itself can alleviate some of the anxiety if one does occur. If a child has a seizure at the ECLC program, she or he should be seen by a doctor as soon as possible (CPS, 2015, p. 173).

A fever is not caused by teething. A number of factors cause our body temperature to rise:

- overdressing
- strenuous exercise/play
- time of day (our normal temperature varies during the day, being highest in late afternoon)
- a vaccination (within the first 24 hours after a vaccine)
- an infection

By definition, a fever is a rise in body temperature, with a thermometer reading above 38°C (100.4°F) when taken rectally or by ear, above 37.3°C (99.1°F) when taken in the armpit (axillary), and above 37.5°C (99.5°F) when taken by mouth (CPS, 2015, pp. 170–171).

Staff often feel that they are in a "Catch-22" situation—they observe a change in a child's behaviour and know that he or she is not feeling well. But when they call the parents, the parents want to know the child's temperature. And if the child does not have a fever, the parents may be reluctant or refuse to leave work. This situation causes the greatest concern. It could be dangerous to assume that because there is no fever, the child is not ill enough to be seen by a health care provider. More likely signs that a child may be running a fever are a flushed face or glassy-eyed look (CPS, 2015, p. 171).

Observing a child's behaviour is much more important than taking a child's temperature. The child's behaviour is usually a much better indicator of illness (CPS, 2015, p. 169). As educators become familiar with each child, they can identify behaviour changes. When children feel warm to the touch, you can first rule out the other possible reasons for the fever. If you think a child is ill and that is why she or he feels warm, watch closely for changes in behaviour. If the child feels warm but is playing and smiling, there is little to worry about. But if the behaviour changes, you must be concerned and take appropriate steps.

A child with any of the following behaviours or symptoms must be seen by a health care provider as soon as possible, regardless of whether the child has a fever or feels warm to the touch:

- unusual sleepiness, drowsiness
- lack of interest in toys, books, other children

- irritability, fussiness
- persistent crying, weak cry, inconsolable
- difficult or rapid breathing
- rash with a fever
- poor skin colour
- excessive drooling
- diminished appetite

The following are suggestions for managing children's fevers:

1. Share information with parents on fever and the importance of responding to children's behaviour. Encourage parents to discuss the issue of fever with their child's health care provider, or invite a health care provider or public health nurse to speak to the staff and parents.

2. Post the list of signs and symptoms of illness that staff will watch for in children at drop-off and throughout the day. Discuss this issue with each parent at the time of enrollment.

3. Taking children's temperature in ECLC programs on a regular basis is unnecessary. When staff notice a sign of fever (flushed face or glassy-eyed look), CPS (2015, p. 171) recommends that staff take temperatures. In these situations, refer to CPS's *Well Beings* (2015) for the steps for taking temperatures. Parents should understand this policy and the rationale for it. When and how educators take children's temperatures should be outlined in the program's policy manual. Guidelines will ensure that taking temperatures is done safely and correctly.

4. Note that although rectal temperatures are the most reliable, this method is *not* an appropriate method in ECLC programs.

   Develop a medication policy related specifically to fevers that includes these practices:

   - Fever medication will be administered to a child only with a written recommendation by a health care provider (see Prescription and Over-the-Counter (OTC) Medications, page 195).

   - If fever medication is administered, adhere to the following guidelines (CPS, 2015, p. 173):

     – **Don't** give acetaminophen and ibuprofen at the same time, and don't give acetaminophen to a child who is already taking an over-the-counter (OTC) medication at home. Many OTC medications already contain acetaminophen.

     – **Always** recheck the child's temperature before giving a second dose of medication.

     – **Never** exceed the recommended dose and schedule.*

---

*Source: Reprinted with permission from the Canadian Paediatric Society.

5. Parents should have children seen by a health care provider as soon as possible when educators observe any of the behaviours and symptoms listed earlier, regardless of the presence of a fever. Children who are younger than six months old and have a fever should be seen by a health care provider regardless of other symptoms or behaviours. However, when a child does have a fever and any of the following behaviours, call 911 *first* (or your seven- or ten-digit number) and then the parents (CPS, 2015, p. 174):

   - seems limp, less responsive, or much more withdrawn than usual;
   - loses consciousness;
   - breathes rapidly or with significant difficulty;
   - has poor colour (i.e., skin that is bluish, purple, greyish, or very pale);
   - has a stiff neck;
   - cries inconsolably, with high-pitched screams or cries, or cries very weakly;
   - has a quickly spreading purple or deep red rash; or
   - seems severely dehydrated (i.e., has sunken eyes or fontanelle [the soft spot on the head of children younger than 18 months], absence of tears when crying, or dry skin, mouth, and tongue).*

6. Your program's exclusion policy should include the following:

   - Children with a fever or who feel warm to the touch can continue to attend the program if they feel well enough to participate in the program.
   - Infants under six months who feel warm to the touch, look flushed, or have a fever should be seen by a health care provider as soon as possible. This should be done regardless of whether the infant shows behavioural changes.

Health Observation throughout the Day

The **health observations** made when children begin their day provide educators and parents with a baseline against which to compare children throughout the remainder of the day. This baseline is particularly important when educators note a specific sign or symptom and monitor its progress. In other words, they watch to see if the sign or symptom gets worse, is resolving itself, or remains the same. Documenting health observations also assists educators and parents in identifying patterns in types of illnesses. Educators who observe the following early signs of allergies in children can assist parents and health care providers in the diagnosis: recurring colds and ear infections, nosebleeds, headaches, stomachaches, dark circles under the eyes, and irritability (see Allergies, page 201).

---

*Source: Reprinted with permission from the Canadian Paediatric Society.

Documenting Health Observations

Educators and parents of infants and toddlers in ECLC settings keep daily written records for each child. Some programs use a form and others a journal. Regardless of the style of documentation, it ensures that the parents share relevant health information with their child's educators at the time of drop-off. Educators document throughout the day and should include both

- "anecdotal" notes that elaborate on children's activities and their overall well-being and
- "health notes" that record their daily health observations (e.g., "Beginning to sound stuffed up" or "He didn't seem to be himself after his nap this afternoon").

Parents are interested in reading this information at pickup time.

Fewer educators are working with more children in preschool and school-age programs than in infant and toddler programs. Staff may not make daily entries in each child's file because children are older and because of time constraints. If nothing unusual happens, it may be unproductive for educators to write reports for the sake of it or for parents to read what they already know.

Documentation in Children's Files

Educators' careful and accurate documentation of each child's health provides parents and, ultimately, health professionals with valuable medical information in making diagnoses.

An educator would not phone a parent and simply say, "Max is not feeling well, and you need to pick him up right away." Rather, educators formulate their thoughts about their health observations before they write in a child's file or phone the parents. Their experience and training equip them with the skills needed to ask themselves the same questions that the parents will ask them. The answers to these questions guide educators in determining what to do for the child.

- How has the child's behaviour changed to lead you to believe that the child may be ill?
- What are the signs and symptoms that the child is experiencing? Describe the symptoms as clearly as possible.

In the case of a tummyache:

- Where is the pain in the abdomen, and does the pain move? (Depending on the child's age, the child may be able to point to where the pain is.)
- What kind of pain is it (sharp, throbbing, comes and goes, etc.)? (The answer will depend on the child's verbal ability.)
- Is the child feeling nauseated? Has he or she vomited or had diarrhea?
- What has the child eaten that day? Does he or she have allergies?

- When were the signs and symptoms first noticed, and how long have they lasted?
- Have the signs and symptoms changed? If so, how? Are they getting worse? Have they stayed constant, or are they coming and going (intermittent)?
- How is the child's appetite? Is he or she experiencing difficulty urinating or having a bowel movement?
- Has the child started eating a new food, taken a medication, been immunized in the past two weeks, or recently been injured?
- Does the child have any long-term medical conditions?
- Has the child had similar symptoms before?
- What have you done for the child so far? For example, have you continued to watch the child, administered a medication, or isolated him or her from the other children?
- What time was the parent called? What was said by both parties, and what is to be done next?
- Did you call the child's health care provider or an ambulance?

If one child is ill, educators take into account what has happened in the program over the past few days to consider factors that might be relevant to this child:

- Are any other children ill in the program? What are their signs and symptoms? What was the diagnosis (if they were seen by a health care provider)?
- What activities have the children been involved in over the past couple of days? Have they been on a field trip?

Coworkers (or parents) often say that a child always seems to be sick with something. Rather than searching through daily entries to find the ones that concern illness, educators may find it useful to maintain a flow sheet that lists each child's illnesses or symptoms. It takes only a few minutes to complete and can be conveniently kept in the front of each child's file. Such a sheet enables educators and parents to review the frequency and types of illness that the child experiences or to refer back to a specific entry within the body of the child's file. Directors may also wish to include a photocopy of the child's immunization schedule.

Early Childhood Learning and Care Program's Health Record

The frequency of illnesses is of concern to educators and parents. So, in addition to maintaining the flow sheet for each child, staff are encouraged to keep an ongoing health record that includes the suspected and diagnosed illnesses of all the children in the program on one form. Staff should include the following information in each notation:

- date
- child's first and last names
- brief description of the symptoms
- health care provider's diagnosis (if the child was seen)
- whether the child was excluded and, if so, for how many days

At the very minimum, use initials on the daily attendance form to indicate trends in absenteeism. For example, use "D" for diarrhea, "URI" for respiratory illnesses, and "O" for other health reasons.

Reviewing this form provides educators with valuable information:

- the frequency of specific illnesses
- which children are ill more often
- patterns in illnesses, because similarities begin to emerge in terms of the time of year, the age group of the children, and any one group of children experiencing more illnesses than other groups

Patterns in illnesses can help staff identify factors that might contribute to the spread of illness and what they can do to reduce that spread, such as improving the children's and educators' hygiene, cleaning and disinfecting routines, and food preparation practices.

Sharing Health Information with Health Care Providers

Staff network with a variety of professionals in their community and share information verbally and in written reports. Because of the frequency of young children's illnesses, educators may regularly communicate indirectly with health care providers through the child's parents. To protect confidentiality, educators do not communicate directly with health care providers. Before they do so, parents must give the educators permission to speak with their health care provider and let the health care provider know that an educator may call.

Educators' health observations are essential to assist health care providers or other health professionals in caring for children. As professionals, educators are encouraged to document their health observations on a report form, which the parents take to their child's health care provider. For the staff, this form is a direct line of communication with the health care provider. In addition, parents benefit from this documentation because it saves them from having to remember all the details conveyed verbally by the educator.

Obviously, effective communication results when all parties share accurate information. Educators rely on the parents to share relevant medical information with them after the visit to the health care provider's office. The program can have a form that is given to the parents, which they ask the health care provider to complete. Ideally, the form includes a summary of the program's exclusion criteria. Parents return the completed form to the staff when their child returns to the program. This document provides staff with pertinent care information. Educators must keep in mind that health care professionals must act in accordance with the *Personal Health Information Act* (PHIA), and some medical information will not be shared with the educators. Providing the health care provider with the program's exclusion criteria reduces unnecessary conflicts between staff, parents, and the health care provider that can arise when the health care provider's recommendations are not consistent with those of the program.

Work experience familiarizes educators with the more common childhood illnesses. Educators may feel they know quite a bit about illness, especially if they are parents themselves. Once they have seen a few children with chickenpox or head lice, they are able to identify pox marks or lice eggs. Parents in the program, particularly those with infants or toddlers, often view individual educators as consultants on a range of topics, including their child's health. Of course, educators want to be helpful and can answer some health questions for parents. However, giving out medical information is overstepping their professional boundaries. Diagnosing illnesses and offering medical consultation are the roles of health professionals, not educators.

Excluding Children from Early Childhood Learning and Care Programs

If you ask educators to list the issues that they find to be the most challenging, ill children will probably be among the top three, perhaps even the first. If you are not a parent, you may have a hard time putting yourself into a parent's position. As discussed earlier, parents are in work or school situations and face a vast range of reactions and expectations from employers or teachers. Imagine yourself sitting in a board meeting, working on an assembly line, or writing an exam and being called away to take a phone call. Your child's educator tells you that your daughter is ill and you must pick her up as soon as possible to see the health care provider. Not only are you going to be worried about your child, but you are also faced with rescheduling your workday or class work, making a health care provider's appointment, and returning to work. As a student, are you able to concentrate on your exam when you know that your daughter may be ill?

Most employers do not provide family responsibility leave for their employees. This benefit entitles parents to paid leave to attend to a child who is ill or for other family emergencies. Currently, most parents either use their personal sick-leave benefits, if eligible, or leave work without pay. Others may risk losing their job if they leave work. Few parents have jobs that afford them the flexibility to work from home during a child's illness. Families often do not live in the same community as their extended family, who may have been able to relieve the parents in a crisis. Travelling between work and the program and then to the health care provider's office may not be convenient, especially on public transportation in the middle of a Canadian winter! On the other hand, for many of the same reasons, parents may feel pressured to bring their children to the program in the morning, even if the child is not feeling well.

CRITICAL THINKING

Use the three levels of the health promotion action plan to identify at least one action for each level that would support families in the difficult dilemma of having a child who is too ill to participate in the program for one week, although not so ill that she or he needs to stay in bed. None of the adults in the family have paid time off.

Educators and parents are responsible for establishing a clear understanding of the program's exclusion criteria at the time of enrollment. Unnecessary exclusion of children is unacceptable. With the exception of certain infections, the primary reason for excluding children is that the child does not feel well enough to participate in the program's activities. Staff–child ratios in centres are such that it is seldom possible to give a great deal of individual care to a sick child and still have enough staff to meet the needs of the other children. Also, where would you rather be when you are sick—in a program with a group of energetic children and adults or at home with someone to bring you food and beverages and to care for your needs in quiet surroundings? Obviously, most children would prefer to be at home when they are ill.

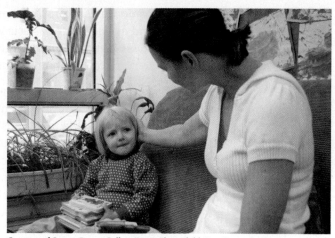

Directors evaluate each situation individually. A director will think twice before he or she calls a parent to pick up a child if the parent works in a factory and has been warned about taking time off. However, a director is expected to give equal consideration before calling a parent who has a flexible work schedule. Who are the child care staff concerned about in managing illness?

Courtesy of George Brown College/Scotia Plaza Child Care Centre

- *The ill child.* Educators and the director want to ensure that the child is comfortable while in their care.
- *Other children and staff.* Educators may be concerned that the child's illness is contagious. Another concern may be the extent of one-to-one care that the ill child needs and how this affects the quality of supervision available to other children.
- *The ill child's parents.* Educators and the director consider the effects of the child's illness on the family.

The program's exclusion policy should stipulate that if the child presents with one of the following conditions (CPS, 2015, pp. 174–175), the child will be excluded:

1. The illness prevents the child from participating comfortably in all program activities, including going outside.
2. The illness results in a greater need for care than the staff can provide without compromising the health, safety, and care of other children.
3. The illness poses a serious health risk if it spreads to other children or staff, and/or local public health authorities require exclusion. (Consult your local public health unit for a list of these infections.)* (See Appendix 4.1, page 213.)

Erik and Anastasia in the preschool room have bad colds with runny noses and coughs and are irritable and lethargic. According to the third point in the exclusion policy, excluding children with colds is not recommended (see Appendix 4.1, page 213). However, both children's behaviour is affected, so the director needs to consider the first two points of the exclusion policy. She must decide if she will

- call both sets of parents to come immediately to pick up their children or
- call the parents and discuss what is in the best interests of each child. Erik's parents will be able to leave work in an hour and drop him off with his grandfather. Anastasia's mother is a single parent who recently moved to the city to attend university. She is in the middle of exams. She is already stressed and has

---

*Source: Reprinted with permission from the Canadian Paediatric Society.

Courtesy of George Brown College/
Scotia Plaza Child Care Centre

no one to help care for her daughter. The director and mother discuss the issue and decide that Anastasia will rest in the director's office for the afternoon. If she is still feeling unwell tomorrow, the director will arrange for a volunteer to come to the program and care for her.

Each medical officer of health (MOH) in Canada is responsible for the health of children in centres within his or her geographic area. One of the responsibilities of the MOH is to establish the exclusion criteria for centres. These should be communicated to the health care providers as well. There are usually several MOHs working in one province or territory. Because they work independently of one another, centres in different regions may be provided with different exclusion criteria. In some cases, neither centres nor health care providers have received written criteria. So it is not surprising that there can be inconsistent expectations among everyone. In *Well Beings*, CPS (2015) recommends exclusion criteria that centres, MOHs, and health care providers are encouraged to implement (see Appendix 4.1, page 213).

Programs are required to have space available to isolate ill children temporarily as a strategy to try to prevent or limit the spread of infection. The director's office is often used, or a cot is set up in a quiet, separate part of the play or nap area that allows educators to supervise the resting child. The decision to keep the child in the program until the end of the day is made by the director and educators. The decision is based on issues such as

- what the educators think is wrong with the child,
- the time of day, and
- whether they feel they can care for the child.

Alternative Care Arrangements

There are times when children must be excluded from the program. For some families, this is a minor glitch in their schedule. For others, it creates chaos. Programs require every family to have backup, or alternative, care available (e.g., relative, neighbour, friend) in the event that a child is ill. For parents who have neither job flexibility nor relatives or friends available as backup, **alternative care** arrangements can be makeshift, unreliable, or inconsistent. This latter situation often puts directors in an awkward position: they know the ill child's home situation but must balance the needs of the other children and staff. In some instances, the director may decide to keep the mildly ill child at the program. In other cases, the director may have to exclude the child, and the parents must deal with this decision.

Early Childhood Learning and Care Programs and Health Services for Ill Children

The pressure experienced by parents trying to continue to work or go to school while managing the care of ill children has led to the establishment of centres and health care services specifically for ill children. These services can range from a centre that cares only for ill children to private nursing or trained educators who go into the child's home. The parents pay the cost of these services. In addition, the parents continue to pay the centre for the days that the child is excluded.

These services are relatively few, and they raise questions about the best interests of the ill child. At best, these health services are feasible only for parents who can afford them. No one disagrees that an ill child at home with a loving parent is best. But parents who can't miss work, can't afford private care, and don't have access to alternative adults may be forced to leave a child at home alone—which may raise questions about neglect.

Caring for ill children is a political issue that has not been dealt with in any substantial way. Where does this situation leave children and families?

CHILDHOOD INFECTIONS AND NUISANCES: JUST THE BASICS

Fortunately, most common childhood infections are short-lived and minor. Nuisances such as head lice and bedbugs don't carry disease, yet they are problematic. They cause challenges for the children and adults with head lice or bedbug bites as well as for those trying to get rid of or prevent further infestations in their home or ECLC setting. Children become ill regardless of the disease prevention practices implemented in programs, but these practices do reduce the spread of infection. There are far more childhood infections than we have included in this textbook. Our focus is on health promotion in children, not on cures. *As educators, your role is not to diagnose but to recognize potential signs of infection and refer children to health professionals.* Educators can refer to a number of books and resources describing childhood infections once a health care provider has made a diagnosis. *Well Beings* (CPS, 2015) is the resource manual of preference for Canadian centres. CPS's *Caring for Kids* website includes fact sheets on a variety of common childhood illnesses and infections that can be downloaded and shared with parents. (See Resource Materials.) Therefore, we have included only the common childhood infections. Understanding the basics and how to manage them addresses the needs of the ill child, parents, other children, and staff. Refer to Appendix 4.1 (see page 213) for additional information about managing illness.

The Common Cold

Children in centres can get as many as 8 to 10 **common colds** a year. It may seem that at any one time at least one child has a runny nose or cough. Cold viruses, more than 100 of them, are spread easily through the air and on contaminated hands and objects. That's why preventing colds is nearly impossible. Another reason is that we spread the cold virus a day or two before we feel a cold coming on. Typically, colds last five to seven days. Symptoms include coughing, sneezing, a runny nose, a fever, fatigue, and lack of appetite. A child's runny nose may produce a clear discharge at first and then a yellow or green one.

Q. Should children with colds be excluded from the program?
A. No, not from the point of view of infection control. Imagine the havoc that would be created both in the program and for the families if every child and educator with a cold were excluded. Instead, educators can

- wash their hands and the child's hands carefully;
- model and encourage children to cover their mouth when they cough and sneeze;

OBJECTIVE

To describe how to respond to the most common childhood infections and nuisances. (LO 2, 3, 4, 6)

NELSONstudy

To access Resource Materials, visit NelsonStudy.

- discard used tissues after use and never use the same tissue to wipe more than one child's nose, tempting as reuse might be when you are out in the playground in the winter;

- ensure that mouthing toys in infant and toddler areas are removed once a child has used them and that all of these used toys are cleaned and disinfected daily;

- observe those with colds to ensure that children are feeling well enough to take part in activities; and

- reassure parents that if their child feels well enough to be at the program, he or she is well enough to play outside, even in the winter (fresh air is good for the child).

Remember, colds are caused by viruses, which are *not* treated with antibiotics. It is inappropriate to insist that the child must be prescribed an antibiotic and have taken it for 24 hours before the child can return to the centre. You will find the following interesting:

> *Well Beings* describes a number of common infectious conditions, including detailed exclusion criteria for child care.... Many staff members and child care centres requested that antibiotics be started for symptoms consistent with a viral URTI [upper respiratory tract infection] before the child returned to care. This may be one factor contributing to the increase in antibiotic resistance seen in children who attend child care and may lead to drug side effects, such as diarrhea.... This attitude may influence parental behaviour in seeking medical advice and potentially unnecessary antibiotic use. (CPS, 2016c, p. 3)*

Courtesy of George Brown College/Richmond Adelaide Child Care Centre

Ear Infections

The eustachian tube, which runs between the middle ear and the back of the nose, is shorter and straighter in young children than in adults. The tube creates a path for fluid behind the middle ear to drain to the back of the throat. The straightness of the tube also permits fluid in the back of the throat and nose to travel into the ear. **Ear infections** often occur at the same time as colds, which seems logical because coughing, sneezing, and blowing the nose can force mucus from the nose or throat into the eustachian tube and the middle ear. The tube may become swollen, which prevents fluid from the middle ear from draining. In such cases, the trapped bacteria may cause infection. CPS (2015, pp. 178–179) estimates that "most children will have one or more [ear infections] before they are 3 years old, and these infections can occur with such frequency in child care settings that they seem to be contagious (even though they aren't)."* Children with speaking skills can tell you whether they have an earache; for infants, you'll observe a change in behaviour—they often become cranky or unhappy. Parents and educators often comment that they see infants pulling or rubbing their ears, but this can be coincidental and shouldn't be relied on as a sign of infection.

Health care providers can usually confirm ear infection by looking into the child's ear. "Children younger than 2 years of age are usually treated with antibiotics

---

*Source: Reprinted with permission from the Canadian Paediatric Society.

because this infection can lead to other, more serious complications. For older children who don't experience too much discomfort from an ear infection, the doctor may suggest a painkiller, such as acetaminophen, and then re-examine the child 2 or 3 days later to see if antibiotics are needed" (CPS, 2015, p. 179).*

Q. Should children with ear infections be excluded from the program?
A. No. The infection is in the child's middle ear. The virus or bacteria will not spread to other children or educators. Whether the child attends or not is based on how she or he is feeling and able to participate.

Gastrointestinal Infections: Diarrhea

Diarrhea is the most common symptom of gastrointestinal infection. One of the common causes of diarrhea is the rotavirus. There is a vaccine for that virus, but currently it isn't included in the routine immunization schedule, nor is the expense covered by each province and territory (see Immunization, page 139). Basically, diarrhea is a change in the consistency or frequency of an individual's bowel movements. The stool may be very loose or even watery. And—depending on the virus, bacteria, or parasite causing the infection—the stool may contain blood or mucus and be foul smelling or mushy in consistency. In addition to the diarrhea, children may have abdominal cramps, fever, nausea, vomiting, or a loss of appetite. Others may just have a few loose stools and otherwise be fine.

Educators play an important role in preventing other children or staff from getting the infection. Diarrhea spreads easily among children, and if other children do come down with it, the hygienic practices in that program must be called into question. *Effective hand washing, strict diapering and toileting routines, and food safety every day, not just when someone is ill, are essential in reducing the spread of intestinal infection.*

As educators become familiar with the infants and toddlers, they are able to notice any change in a particular child's bowel movements. Educators should follow these recommendations when caring for children with diarrhea:

- Tell the other educators that the child has had one episode of diarrhea. All the educators should be extra vigilant when hand washing and diapering to ensure that stool does not contaminate the environment. The child can remain in the program as long as he or she feels well enough to participate and the stool is contained in the diaper (or the older child is able to get to the toilet in time). Parents appreciate being called so that they are aware of this situation.

- After the second episode of diarrhea, or when the diarrhea is accompanied with a fever, vomiting, or blood in the stool, call the parents to pick up the child. The parents should have the child seen by the health care provider as soon as possible. Advise the parents to *seek immediate medical attention* if the child

  - has bloody, mucousy or black stools,

---

*Source: Reprinted with permission from the Canadian Paediatric Society.

- is vomiting and showing any sign of dehydration:
  - no tears when crying,
  - dry skin, mouth, and tongue,
  - fewer than four wet diapers in 24 hours,
  - sunken eyes or fontanelle (the soft spot on the head of children younger than 18 months),
  - grayish skin; or
  - rapid breathing. (CPS, 2015, p. 187)*

- While waiting for the parents to arrive, prevent the child from becoming dehydrated. Children, especially infants and toddlers, can become dehydrated quickly because they lose more of their body fluids in diarrhea and vomit than they are able to drink. Pediatricians recommend that programs with infants and toddlers have oral rehydration solution (ORS) available for these situations and that you have the parents' written permission to give it to the child when warranted. ORS is available in liquid or powder (e.g., Lytren, Gastrolyte, Pedialyte) and is used to replenish the child's fluid and electrolytes even when the child is vomiting. "Give small amounts often, gradually increasing intake until the child can drink normally. If a child isn't vomiting, continue to offer breast milk, formula or regular foods in small, frequent feedings. If the child vomits, you may need to stop food and drink but continue to give ORS" (CPS, 2015, p. 188).*

- Notify the public health agency if two or more children have diarrhea within 48 hours of each other. These situations are called "outbreaks," and steps must be taken to control the gastrointestinal infection, including determining the cause.

Q. Should children with two or more episodes of diarrhea be excluded from the program?
A. Initially, the child should be separated from the other children while you are waiting for the parents to arrive. After the child has seen the health care provider, the child will be excluded from your program when

- diarrheal stool cannot be contained in a diaper or a toilet-trained child cannot control bowel movements,
- there's blood or mucus in the stool (unless bacterial infection has been ruled out by a doctor),
- the child is also vomiting (unless infection has been ruled out), or
- local public health authorities require it (e.g., if it is a symptomatic, confirmed *Giardia, Escherichia coli* [*E. coli*], *Shigella*, or *Salmonella* infection). (CPS, 2015, p. 188)*

Refer to Appendix 4.1 (page 213) for the exclusion criteria that relate to the various types of gastrointestinal infections.

---

*Source: Reprinted with permission from the Canadian Paediatric Society.

Pinkeye

Pinkeye (or conjunctivitis) is another childhood infection that is easily spread among children. The causes are viruses, commonly, and bacteria, occasionally. These infect the covering of the eyeball. However, children who have allergies or have been exposed to pollutants may develop pinkeye. Watch for the following symptoms in one or both eyes:

- The whites of the eye are pink or red.
- The child rubs the eye because it is itchy.
- The eye may be tearing a lot.
- There is a clear or pus (thick or yellow) discharge from the eye; the parents may tell you that the eyelid is stuck shut after sleeping.

Pinkeye is a good example of an infection caused by germs spread by indirect contact. A child with pinkeye touches or rubs his or her eyes; the eye discharge contaminates the fingers. In the course of play, the child touches other children's hands or objects, which, in turn, become contaminated. Now those children who have the eye discharge on their fingers and who touch their own eyes will get pinkeye. Sharing towels among children is another way that pinkeye is spread. The cycle continues until it is broken.

Q. Should children with pinkeye be excluded from the program?
A. Initially, the child should be excluded until being seen by the health care provider to diagnose the infection and determine the cause. After that appointment, whether the exclusion continues depends on whether the cause is viral or bacterial. When there is pus discharge, the child may be prescribed an antibiotic (eye drops or ointment) to treat the bacteria. If this is the case, children should be excluded until they have started taking the medication. Otherwise, the child can return to the program. Regardless of the cause, educators must pay particular attention to hygiene practices to reduce the spread to other children and staff.

- Effective hand washing is critical, for both staff and the child, after wiping or touching the infected eye.
- Never share towels, facial tissues, and so on, among children, regardless of whether someone has pinkeye.

Chickenpox

"**Chickenpox**" is a word that parents dread, although most of them want all the children in their family to get the illness at the same time and be done with it. For teens and adults who did not have chickenpox as children, it's usually a much more serious infection. The good news is that for children who haven't had chickenpox, the varicella (chickenpox) vaccine has been available in Canada since 1999. CPS (2016d, p. 4) recommends that children receive the first dose between 12 and 18 months and the second between the ages of 4 and 6 years. The second dose minimizes their immunity waning in adulthood. When children begin in a program, checking whether or not they have been vaccinated is recommended. Children who did not receive the varicella vaccination can receive it at an older age and have the second dose four weeks later. But even with the vaccine available, you will most likely care for a few children who have chickenpox.

Chickenpox is common in children because the varicella-zoster virus (VZV) spreads easily through the air and by touching the liquid in the pox. By the time the red bumps appear, children may have already had a mild fever for a couple of days and have been spreading the virus through the air. Spots appear over two or three days. Gradually, the bumps turn into liquid-filled blisters (or pox) that crust over, at which time, the risk of the spread stops. Some children may be covered in pox; others may have just a few. For many children, the infection is mild, and the primary complaint is the itchiness of the pox. It takes 10 to 21 days to tell whether a susceptible person exposed to chickenpox is going to get it.

Never give the child acetylsalicylic acid (aspirin) to treat a fever or aches and pains from chickenpox. While the child is recovering, both educators and parents need to watch for signs of severe illness and seek immediate medical attention if any of the following signs are seen (CPS, 2015, p. 199):

- the child's fever lasts longer than 48 hours and is 39°C (102°F) or higher,
- the fever subsides and then returns to 39°C (102°F) or higher in a day or two,
- any chickenpox spots become enlarged, red, or very sore, or
- the child seems very ill.*

Having chickenpox once provides most people with lifelong immunity to it, although some people get chickenpox twice. The virus can remain inactive in our bodies for life, but it can become reactivated and cause shingles. Children or adults with shingles can spread the virus to those susceptible to chickenpox. Shingles is a painful rash of itchy blisters, which often develop around the trunk of the body.

Q. Should someone with chickenpox or shingles be excluded from the program?

A. "Exclusion is not a very effective way to prevent the spread of chickenpox in child care facilities, because it is contagious 1 to 2 days before the rash appears" (CPS, 2015, p. 199).* "A child with mild illness should be allowed to return to school or daycare as soon as he or she is well enough to participate normally in all activities, regardless of the state of the rash. Parents, particularly parents of immunosuppressed children, should be notified that chickenpox is in the class as well as be provided with information on the VZV incubation period and how to detect early VZV" (CPS, 2016e, p. 2).* Educators are advised to assess each child individually. What is in the best interests of this child? If the child feels well enough to take part in activities, or if you have enough staff available to provide more individualized care, the child can remain in the program.

---

*Source: Reprinted with permission from the Canadian Paediatric Society.

Head Lice

Having **head lice** does not reflect a lack of parenting ability or cleanliness, despite popular belief to the contrary. As a matter of fact, lice like warm scalps and clean hair best! Yet some adults and children still make derogatory comments about people with lice, which can be very hurtful. Children who have head lice may already feel embarrassed, fearful, or ashamed, and educators need to be sensitive to these feelings. Know the facts and effective ways to treat head lice, listen to parents' concerns, and dispel stereotypes, and you can manage an outbreak.

Head lice are tiny, greyish insects that live on human hair. Usually, they lay their eggs (or nits) on hair behind the ears, on the crown, or at the back of the head. Nits look like dandruff but stick to the hair so that you can't pick or wash them off.

You may first suspect head lice when you see a child scratching or complaining that his or her head is itchy. Check for nits on the hair, close to the scalp. However, there is a degree of expertise needed to identify head lice definitively (detection of a living louse); otherwise, head lice can frequently be misdiagnosed. The presence of nits indicates a past infestation, which may not be presently active (CPS, 2016b, p. 2). The hatched lice shy away from light, so it is unlikely that you will actually see the lice. Although you may be scratching your head just thinking about lice, they actually don't hurt, spread disease, or jump between people. *Head lice spread quickly when children have their heads together or share items such as combs, brushes, hats and scarves, headphones, and play clothes.* Staff can reduce the opportunities for head lice to spread by

- providing space for each child to store his or her outerwear and a change of clothes without coming into contact with the next child's clothes (e.g., in a cubby/locker, in bins/baskets, or on hooks);
- stuffing hats and scarves down coat sleeves, especially when coats are hung on hooks;
- having parents provide a comb or brush for their child's personal use, to be kept in the child's space; and
- laundering dress-up clothes weekly. In the event of an outbreak of head lice, the clothes and accessories should be laundered and put away until the outbreak is over. The hats and wigs that can't be washed must be sealed in a plastic bag for two weeks. Dramatic play is an important element of child care programs, and wigs, hats, scarves, and dress-up clothes should be available for children despite the chance of head lice.

Basically, head lice are a nuisance that creates work for staff and parents at home. If you find one child or educator with head lice, you must check everyone. Then educators must notify all parents, especially those whose children have the lice. Only the infected children and adults should be treated. Special shampoos and conditioners containing an insecticide are the go-to products for killing lice. There are concerns that head lice have developed resistance to the insecticide. Alternative methods that suffocate the lice, and require the manual removal of the nits, kill the resistant lice. The goal of any method is to kill lice and nits and prevent reinfestation (if nits are not destroyed, they hatch in seven days).

George Bernard/Science Photo Library

Life Cycle of Head Lice

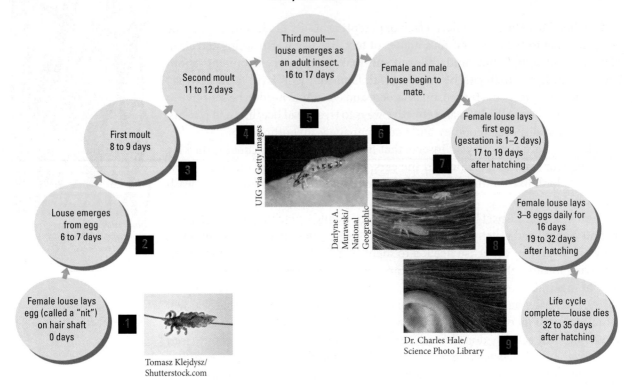

Third moult—louse emerges as an adult insect. 16 to 17 days — 5

Second moult 11 to 12 days — 4

First moult 8 to 9 days — 3

Louse emerges from egg 6 to 7 days — 2

Female louse lays egg (called a "nit") on hair shaft 0 days — 1

Tomasz Klejdysz/ Shutterstock.com

UIG via Getty Images

Darlyne A. Murawski/ National Geographic

Female and male louse begin to mate. — 6

Female louse lays first egg (gestation is 1–2 days) 17 to 19 days after hatching — 7

Female louse lays 3–8 eggs daily for 16 days 19 to 32 days after hatching — 8

Life cycle complete—louse dies 32 to 35 days after hatching — 9

Dr. Charles Hale/ Science Photo Library

Parents can check with their health care provider or pharmacist about different brands. There is a range of other treatments used by parents, including putting an oil and vinegar mixture on the head overnight (covered with a shower cap). Parents need to check every person in the household for nits but treat only those who have them.

Insecticides are chemicals that kill insects. In Canada, 2 insecticides are approved to treat head lice:

- pyrethrin (found in R&C shampoo + conditioner)
- permethrin (Nix creme rinse or Kwellada-P creme rinse)

Pyrethrin and permethrin are safe when used on humans over two months old. You do not need a prescription. Over time, head lice have become resistant to some of the chemicals used to kill them. So some products may be less effective than they used to be. (CPS, 2016a, p. 2)*

Noninsecticidal products approved for use in Canada include the following:

- isopropyl myristate/cyclomethicone (should be used only on children older than four)
- silicone oil dimeticone (NYDA) (not recommended for children under two years old)
- benzyl alcohol lotion 5% (Ulesfia) (CPS, 2016a, p. 2)

*Source: Reprinted with permission from the Canadian Paediatric Society.

For all products, carefully follow the directions. Most products require more than one treatment.

> Since lice don't live long off the scalp, there's no need for extensive cleaning. To get rid of lice or nits from specific items, like pillowcases or hats, wash them in hot water and dry them in a hot dryer. Dryclean items that cannot be washed, such as stuffed animals, or simply store them in an airtight plastic bag for 2 weeks. (CPS, 2015, p. 192)*

Q. Should someone with head lice be excluded from the program?
A. No. At the time of pickup, the parents of the infected child need to know about the treatment that should be done that day.

In the past, public health nurses were called into programs and schools to do "nit-picking" on every child. Nowadays, directors simply consult with their public health nurse and receive up-to-date information on prevention and treatment, perhaps in a number of languages. However, if a program has recurring outbreaks of head lice or a particular child's parents are not responding to the program's requests to use the treatment, the public health department should become directly involved.

Bedbugs

Bedbugs are a challenging problem in hotels, on cruise ships, on buses and trains, in movie theatres, in homes, and even in ECLC settings in Canada. You may have had firsthand experience with bedbugs or know someone who has. Like head lice, bedbugs are equal opportunity bugs. Five-star hotels in major North American cities have them. Bedbugs are similar to head lice in other ways too:

- They don't indicate uncleanliness.
- Finding them in one's home may cause embarrassment.
- They feed off humans and animals.
- "Some people do not react at all to the bites, while others may have small skin reactions. In rare cases, some people may have severe allergic reactions" (Government of Canada, 2015, p. 1).
- Getting rid of the infestation takes work as they move easily from room to room on objects.
- Thinking about having them likely makes you squirm.

Marco Uliana/Shutterstock.com

Bedbugs are wingless and red-brown in colour (blood red after feeding) and suck blood by biting. The adults can be as long as 10 mm (~ 0.4 in.), whereas the younger ones are just a smaller version, measuring around 1.5 mm (0.06 in.) in length.

Their eggs are white and so small that they are almost impossible to see. The female can lay 1 to 4 eggs each day, reaching around 200 eggs in her lifetime. The eggs are laid in cracks and crevices, hatching in 6 to 17 days (Government of Canada, 2015, p. 1). Unlike head lice, bedbugs can live from four months to more than a year when the conditions are right. The older bugs can live for more than a year without feeding (Government of Canada, 2015).

---

*Source: Reprinted with permission from the Canadian Paediatric Society.

Their flat shape allows them to hide almost anywhere, even in places you might not think of, such as under wallpaper, behind picture frames, and inside electrical outlets (Government of Canada, 2015, p. 1). Bedbugs typically hide during the day and come out to feed in the dark, and they are attracted to the carbon dioxide we exhale, just like mosquitoes. Their behaviour is where the saying "Goodnight, don't let the bedbugs bite" comes from.

The bites are typically found on the face, upper body, and arms (Government of Canada, 2015, p. 1). How we react to bedbug bites will vary. It may take as long as 14 days between the bite and the reaction to appear. There might not be any reaction; there may be small swollen or raised areas such as a welt, or, rarely, there may be a severe allergic reaction. Scratching can cause skin irritation (Government of Canada, 2015). What signs can centre staff look for to suspect bedbugs?

- unexplained bite marks or welts on children, or others, at the facility
- spots (dried blood or bedbug fecal matter) on bedding, mattresses, or box springs
- cast-off bedbug skins
- actual live or dead bedbugs
- a musty or sweet odour (usually with very large bedbug infestations) (Manitoba Early Learning and Child Care, n.d., p. 3)*

Q. Should someone with bedbug bites be excluded from the program?
A. No. At the time of pickup, the parents of the child with the marks need to be notified. The parents may want to consult with their physician depending on the child's reaction. Because the reaction can take up to 14 days to develop, where the child may have come into contact may be difficult to determine. When children from different families present marks at the same time, it may very well be that the ECLC facility has the bedbugs. All of the parents will need to be told of the infestation. Not only does this present an immediate issue for the staff, but care must also be taken to prevent the bedbugs' spread to the homes of staff and families. When the bedbugs are found in the program, the facility doesn't need to be closed unless temporarily based on the requirements of the pest control company.

Your province or territory's child care licensing agency may have information available on prevention of bedbug infestations. Manitoba Early Learning and Child Care's *Bed Bug Guide for Licensed Child Care Facilities* (n.d., p. 4) recommends the following prevention strategies:

Bed bugs will most likely enter a facility on the clothing or belongings of children or staff who come from homes with bed bugs. To prevent bed bugs from entering the child care facility:

- **Check blankets, backpacks and clothing daily** for signs of bed bugs as the children enter and leave the facility.
- **Encourage families not to send blankets or stuffed animals** with their children, if possible.
- **Carefully inspect all second-hand or donated items** for signs of bed bugs before they are brought into the facility (ex: books, stuffed animals,

Source: Healthy Child Manitoba, *Bed Bug Guide for Licensed Child Care Facilities,* http://www.gov.mb.ca/fs/childcare/pubs/bedBug_e_web.pdf. Copyright: Manitoba government. Reprinted by permission.

furniture). Where possible, smaller items can be immediately run through the dryer for 20 minutes to kill any suspected bed bugs.

- **Keep individual children's belongings separate** by storing children's coats, clothing or other personal items in individual lockers or cubby holes. (See Manitoba Child Care Regulation 62/86, Sections 12(2), 14(2) and 29(2).) Use sealed plastic bags or containers for extra clothing, bedding or other cloth items.

- **Put clean cloth items in a dryer, or wash dirty cloth items in hot water, then dry in a dryer.** Running a normal dryer load for 20 minutes on high heat should kill all stages of bed bugs.

- **Vacuum daily.** It is important to pay close attention to places bed bugs like to hide, such as along baseboards. Dispose of vacuum bags/waste in an outside garbage container immediately after vacuuming.*

ANTIBIOTIC-RESISTANT BACTERIA

OBJECTIVE

To outline the significant role educators can play in decreasing the unnecessary use of antibiotics. (LO 1)

The discovery of penicillin was a medical breakthrough. Since then, more and more antibiotics have been developed for the treatment of bacterial infections. As a result, lives have been saved and the quality of lives has improved. Ironically, pharmaceutical firms today are faced with the immediate challenge of discovering new, more potent antibiotics to be used to treat infections caused by bacteria resistant to previously effective antibiotics.

As you read earlier in this unit, bacteria live in our body and work to keep us healthy by fighting invading bacteria. When we take antibiotics, some of the beneficial bacteria are killed, which gives the disease-causing bacteria the opportunity to multiply and cause an infection. There is also the potential for the normal bacteria to become resistant to antibiotics. If conditions are right, such resistance would enable the bacteria to multiply, creating an infection that would be difficult to treat because of the resistance:

> Germs constantly adapt to their environment and have the ability to take on the characteristics of other germs. When antibiotics are used inappropriately, the weak bacteria are killed, while the stronger, more resistant ones survive and multiply. Germs that develop resistance to one antibiotic have the ability to develop resistance to another antibiotic. This is called cross-resistance. (Health Canada, 2012, p. 1)**

Viruses cause the majority of respiratory tract infections. "Viral infections can make you just as sick as infections caused by bacteria" (Government of Alberta & Alberta Health Services, 2011, p. 6). "Bacterial infections are less common than viral infections and don't spread as easily from one person to another" (Government of Alberta & Alberta Health Services, 2011, p. 6). The common upper respiratory infections are rarely caused by bacteria. Most of us with these infections do not need to be taking an antibiotic as it will not kill the virus that is causing the infection.

---

*Source: Healthy Child Manitoba, *Bed Bug Guide for Licensed Child Care Facilities*, http://www .gov.mb.ca/fs/childcare/pubs/bedBug_e_web.pdf. Copyright: Manitoba government. Reprinted by permission.

**Source: © All rights reserved. *It's Your Health: Antibiotic Resistance*. Health Canada date modified: 2017. Adapted and reproduced with permission from the Minister of Health, 2018.

Of course, antibiotics continue to be used effectively to treat many bacterial infections. But the soaring overuse of antibiotics must stop. They are often misused for nonbacterial infections (i.e., those caused by viruses) or automatically given for bacterial infections (e.g., ear infections) that may clear up on their own in a couple of days. Treating a cold with antibiotics does not work—period.

You may be asking yourself how this information relates to your work in ECLC programs. There is a direct correlation. We know

- that young children in groups are exposed to more illnesses,
- that the additional needs of ill children in attendance make it difficult for educators to provide quality care for all children in the group, and
- that the exclusion of children may prevent others from getting sick.

This last point is where educators should recognize the significant role they can play in decreasing the unnecessary use of antibiotics. These infections are common among young children; also, they are easily spread, and antibiotics are often used as a treatment for some URIs.

Appendix 4.1 (see page 213) contains a table on the management of illness that lays out clearly the exclusion criteria and conditions recommended in *Well Beings* (CPS, 2015, pp. 225–234) for a child's return to a program. As you can see, few respiratory illnesses require that a child be excluded to prevent the spread to other children. The most common reason for a child's exclusion is that she or he is too ill to participate in the centre's activities.

How do these exclusion practices affect antibiotic use? If centres require parents to take their child to the health care provider because of green nasal discharge (a common symptom of the common cold) and exclude their child from the centre, one may assume that staff will request that the child be on antibiotics before he or she can return.

> A telephone survey of child care centre workers in Ontario found that an exception to exclude children with upper respiratory tract infection (URTI) symptoms was made if they had an antibiotic prescription (69% of staff), and if the parent could not stay home from work (14% of staff). Further pressure from parents to keep their sick child with a URTI in child care was experienced by 64% of the staff. Many staff members and child care centres requested that antibiotics be started for symptoms consistent with a viral URTI before the child returned to care. This may be one factor contributing to the increase in antibiotic resistance seen in children who attend child care and may lead to drug side effects, such as diarrhea. In a qualitative survey of Australian child care workers, some responders believed that it was difficult to maintain healthy staff when "parents constantly bring their sick and highly contagious child to day care." This attitude may influence parental behaviour in seeking medical advice and potentially unnecessary antibiotic use. (CPS, 2016c, p. 3)*

There are other practices—in addition to having educators understand the principles behind exclusion—that staff can implement in the centre to reduce infections:

- proper hand washing
- proper diaper-changing routine

---

*Source: Reprinted with permission from the Canadian Paediatric Society.

- proper food-handling practices. These include washing off bacterial and possible antibiotic residue from fruit and vegetables.
- the observation of children's behaviour as a key indicator of illness
- practising the principles of routine practices
- the purchase and use of cleaning and hand-washing products that are not advertised to be antibacterial (see Antibacterial Products, page 161)
- striving to consume organic food and meat products

> Links have also been made between giving drugs to animals and the development of resistance in humans. Drugs are often given to food-producing animals to treat and prevent infections in the agri-food industry and to promote growth. Products are also sprayed on fruit trees to prevent or control disease. These can then be transferred to humans in meat, milk, fruit, or drinking water, adding to the resistance problem. An example of this is drug-resistant Salmonella, which can be transferred from animals to humans through the food chain. (Health Canada, 2012, p. 2)*

We all need to understand when antibiotics are necessary and when they are not. When prescribed an antibiotic, follow the instructions and take the entire prescription. Do not stop taking a prescription once you start feeling better and then save the medication for later use, either by yourself or someone else.

ADMINISTERING MEDICATION

OBJECTIVE

To describe the safe administration of medication to children. (LO 6)

Fortunately, most healthy children need medication rarely or not at all. Moreover, most of the common childhood infections are caused by viruses (e.g., colds, other URIs, diarrhea) that are not cured by antibiotics. Strep throat and sometimes ear infections and pinkeye may be caused by bacteria that are treated with antibiotics. Occasionally, educators administer medication to children in programs. Educators have a legal and professional responsibility to be familiar with their child care regulations on administering medication. You must know which medications educators are permitted to give, what type of parental consent is required, and how medications are stored, administered, and documented. A program's medication policy should be accompanied by a list of procedures that all educators follow.

As an early childhood education student, you cannot administer medication to children when you are in program placements; that remains a staff responsibility. After graduation, you will eventually be assigned this role, however, so you need to be familiar with the fundamental principles of a medication policy and the rationale behind it.

Prescription and Over-the-Counter (OTC) Medications

What is the difference between prescription medication and OTC medication? We are all familiar with health care providers writing **prescriptions** for medication when we have a short-term illness (e.g., urinary tract infection, yeast infection, strep throat). Anyone with a particular medical condition, such as asthma, diabetes, cystic fibrosis, or a seizure disorder, is prescribed medication that is taken

---

*Source: © All rights reserved. *It's Your Health: Antibiotic Resistance.* Health Canada date modified: 2017. Adapted and reproduced with permission from the Minister of Health, 2018.

at specific times each day. **OTC medication**, however, is purchased off a shelf in a pharmacy. These medications include cough and cold remedies, painkillers, fever medication, Ovol for flatulence in infants, and medicated creams and ointments.

> It is estimated that more than one-half of children younger than 12 years of age use one or more medicinal products in a given week; over-the-counter (OTC) products, mostly cough and cold medications (CCMs) account for the majority of medication exposures.... The effectiveness of most CCMs has not been proven in children. (CPS, 2016f, p. 1)*

Some government child care regulations may include sunscreens, insect repellents, and diaper creams in their definition of medication and require that the child's health care provider recommend their use in writing. However, this is the exception rather than the rule across Canada.

Is it recommended that OTC drugs come with the health care provider's recommendation in writing before they are administered in ECLC programs? OTC medications are medications nonetheless, despite their easy availability, and should not be treated casually. Whenever you take more than one medication at the same time, you put yourself at risk for side effects because the ingredients from the different medications may interact. Drug interactions may influence the effectiveness of the medications. Also, the multiple medications may contain the same active ingredients, which increases the amount of active ingredients given at the same time.

Vitamins, including chewable ones, are medications. Eating well-balanced, nutritious food provides children with their daily requirement of essential nutrients. Health care providers discourage the routine use of vitamins; they are prescribed only when a child has a vitamin or mineral deficiency. Prescribed vitamins can be given at home by parents. Educators do not have to administer the vitamins during the day.

Naturopathic medicine and homeopathic medicine have been practised for centuries in many cultures and are gaining popularity in Canada (see Natural Health Products, page 20). Herbal medicines, nutrition, vitamins, ointments, acupuncture, and hydro- and physical therapies are used to treat various maladies. Herbal medicines consist of different combinations of herbs and plants that are available OTC or prescribed by naturopaths. As with any medication, they must be taken with care and knowledge. Across Canada, how prescriptions are seen to be medically necessary varies based on whether they are written by health care providers and dentists, versus naturopathic doctors. Consequently, parents who use herbal medicines for their children may be asked to give them to their children at home and not in the program.

OTC Medications: Effective?

"Don't give 'over-the-counter' (OTC) cough and cold medicines to children in your care. There is no proof that they work, and some side effects can make a child feel worse" (CPS, 2015, p. 176; 2016f, p. 1). Colds and coughs have to run their course. Children benefit from extra fluids, rest, and care but not from many of the OTC medications. Keep in mind that colds are caused by viruses and are not treated by antibiotics.

Over a two-year period in the United States, more than 1500 children under two years old were treated in emergency rooms for adverse reactions to cold or cough

---

*Source: Reprinted with permission from the Canadian Paediatric Society.

medications. In 2005, three children under six months old died after taking nasal decongestants. Tests showed that these three infants had drug levels 14 times higher than the recommended dose for children starting at two years old (CBC News, 2007).

CPS (2016f, p. 2) outlines a number of contributing factors that can result in fatalities when children take OTC cough and cold medications:

- age younger than two years
- use of the medication for sedation
- use in a daycare setting
- combining two or more medications with the same ingredient
- failure to use a measuring device
- product misidentification
- use of products intended for adults*

We also wonder whether children who are given an OTC medication for every sniffle, cough, ache, or pain could potentially develop a lifelong reliance on medication. These medications treat symptoms, not the cause of the illness. We should focus instead on preventive strategies and, when we are ill with a viral infection, let the illness run its course.

Acetaminophen (e.g., Tylenol, Tempra) is an analgesic (or painkiller) and may be recommended by health care providers for treating children's aches and pains from a cold and cough. Programs with infants and toddlers still commonly give acetaminophen whenever the child's temperature rises to a certain degree, although this practice is not routinely recommended. In these programs, parents are asked to sign a medication consent form, which is kept in the child's file and referred to each time the child's temperature is elevated. It is unlikely that each child's health care provider has provided the parents and educators with such a written recommendation. This practice shows how grey the interpretation of a specific child care regulation can be (see Fevers, page 173).

Ensuring the Safe Administration of Medication

Whether the medication is prescribed or recommended by the child's health care provider, the steps in its administration are identical to eliminate the chance of medication error. For an extensive discussion on medication administration, refer to Appendix 9.1: Administering Medication in *Well Beings* (CPS, 2015, pp. 220–221). The general principles and rationale for the administration of medication in programs are as follows:

- Obtain the parents' written consent to administer any medication. A medication consent form must be completed for each medication, both prescribed and health care provider recommended. Consent forms should include at least the following information:
  - name of the child and date
  - name of the medication
  - reason why it is needed (e.g., strep throat)

---

*Source: Reprinted with permission from the Canadian Paediatric Society.

- amount to be given (dosage)
- time(s) it is to be given during the day
- time and date of the last dose in the program, which helps ensure that children don't continue to get medication longer than recommended by the health care provider and is particularly relevant to OTC medication (the bottle usually holds more medication than required for two or three days)
- parent's signature

- Before starting the medication at the program, ask parents whether the child has taken it at home for the past 24 hours. This period allows parents to watch for side effects or signs of allergic reaction to the medication, for the child to get used to the way it tastes or feels (e.g., eye ointment), and for the medication to begin its work. Parents may have a helpful hint or two to share.

- Keep all medication in a locked container out of reach of children. Liquid medications usually require refrigeration, which won't harm capsules, tablets, or creams either. All can be kept in a locked container in the fridge. Sunscreens, insect repellents, and diaper creams do not have to be kept locked but must be out of reach of children. Diaper creams are kept in the change area.

- Know who is responsible for giving the medication during the day. Programs usually assign this responsibility either to one educator, who gives all the medications, or to a number of educators, who give medication to specific children. Any confusion over this responsibility can lead to a child either getting a double dose or missing the medication altogether.

- Compare the information on the medication label with the information the parent filled in on the consent form. Discrepancies must be verified and corrected.

- All medication, both prescription and OTC, must be kept in the original containers. It is not acceptable, for example, for a parent to put medication into a glass jar and label it with masking tape. When the medication must be administered while the child is at the program, encourage the parents to have the pharmacist split the medication into two containers so that one stays at home and the other at the program. This also eliminates parents forgetting to bring the container with them each morning. Prescription labels must include
  - the child's name (not a sibling's),
  - the name of the medication,
  - the dose (amount),
  - the number of times it is given each day, and
  - the route (oral, nasal, rectal, eye, ear).

  Sometimes pharmacists place stickers on the container with additional information: "Shake well," "Take with meals," "May cause a photosensitive reaction."

- Follow the steps provided in the program's medication policy for preparing, giving, and recording medication. Know the procedure for reporting and responding to medication errors.

- When children have allergies to medicine, post the children's names and pictures and the names of the drugs at the place where medication is stored and prepared.

- For children who are prescribed an epinephrine auto-injector to treat allergic reactions, always have the medication in the same general area as the child. Epinephrine is the exception to the rule about keeping all medication in a locked container. Although it should be out of reach of children—perhaps in the first-aid kit in the play area—educators must be able to access and administer this medication on a moment's notice. If a child has a severe allergy to insect stings or other allergens found outside, you must take medication to the playground, on walks, and so on. For children with severe food allergies, take the medication outside only if the child might eat something there (e.g., a picnic lunch or snack, on a field trip). All educators must know how to use the auto-injector. It is an emergency when a child needs epinephrine, so educators don't have time to look for the educator responsible for giving medication. Ask the pharmacist for the manufacturer's poster that shows how to give the injection, to display it in the centre. Educators may also be required by child care regulations to receive training on injections from a health professional or the parents. In any case, auto-injectors are simple to use (see Allergies, page 201). The same practice holds true for children who are prescribed an inhaler as a reliever medication during an asthma episode. The medication needs to move with the child.

- Remember the following tips when you give medication to a child:

  - Be honest with the child (e.g., if you don't know how the medication tastes, admit it).

  - Especially for young children, the child who receives the medication should know and be comfortable with the educator administering it.

  - Explain to the child what you are going to do and how he or she can cooperate.

  - Never call medicine "candy." Medicines are potentially hazardous products, and children must learn how to take medications safely.

  - Give the child the medication away from the other children.

Preventing Medication Errors

Medication errors—such as giving medication to a child who wasn't prescribed a drug, mixing up medications among children, giving an incorrect dosage, or putting ear drops in the wrong ear—can occur for a number of reasons. The consequences of such errors range from minor to very serious. However, you can go through your child care career without making any medication errors.

Medication errors result when one or more of the **"five rights" for administering medication** have not been verified:

- right child,
- right medication,
- right dose (amount),
- right time, or
- right route (oral, nasal, rectal, eye, ear, injection).

Courtesy of George Brown College/Scotia Plaza Child Care Centre

Safeguards:

- Always use a measuring spoon, dropper, or cup that is designed for medication.
- Check the sheet you use to record the administration of medication to ensure that no one has already given the drug to the child.
- Read the prescription label three times:

1. when you take the medication out of the storage space,
2. before you pour the medication from the bottle, and
3. after you pour it and are putting the bottle back in storage.

During the three checks, compare the prescription label to the parents' medication consent form. Verify that all of the "five rights" are correct.

- If a child tells you that someone else has already given him or her the drug, or that he or she is no longer taking the medication, double-check with the other educators. Another educator could have given the drug and not recorded it, or the drug may have been stopped and the parent may have forgotten to tell you.
- Immediately record that you gave the medication on the parents' medication consent form.
- Document and report every medication error as soon as you are aware of it.

CRITICAL THINKING

During school hours, school-agers with asthma or life-threatening allergies are encouraged to be responsible for their own puffer or adrenaline kit and to carry it with them. However, while they are in the school-age program, educators are responsible for these medications. How do we help school-agers understand that expectations differ for them between the school and the child care program? And how do educators in school-age programs advocate for change in child care regulations to bring these programs into line with the school, to create the "seamless day"?

Parents should be encouraged to tell educators when their children are taking medication at home, even when staff don't need to give the drug during the day. Educators may notice that the child is experiencing side effects such as dizziness or fatigue and can notify the parents, who can then talk with their health care provider.

ALLERGIES AND ASTHMA

Perhaps you have allergies or asthma. Many of us do. In fact, experts estimate that about three million Canadians have asthma, which includes 600,000 children (Asthma Canada, 2017, p. 1).

The number of children and adults with allergies and asthma is increasing. Environmental pollutants, particularly air pollutants, and sick-building syndrome are playing a significant role in this increase. We can assume that every program has at least one child with allergies or asthma. As such, educators must be aware of these health conditions, know how to avoid factors that trigger reactions, and know how to handle reactions when they occur. Depending on their age, children with allergies or asthma may wish to talk with other children about the condition, about how they feel when they get sick, about what they do to make themselves feel better, or about their hospital experiences. These opportunities are wonderful and natural times for children to learn about health.

Allergies

Basically, **allergies** are the result of our body's hypersensitivity to a substance. These **allergic substances** are not usually harmful to most people (e.g., pollen, peanuts, feathers, animal fur, perfume, latex), but for those with allergies, they can cause mild to severe allergic reactions.

Fortunately, most allergies are not life threatening. The substances that cause allergies, called allergens, enter our body through breathing, eating, touching, or being stung or bitten. Once the allergen is in the body, our immune system responds by producing antibodies that attack it. These antibodies remain in our body to protect us the next time we are exposed to that allergen, providing immunity. But for people with allergies, repeated exposure to an allergen results in their immune systems becoming overly sensitive to that particular allergen. An allergic reaction results when the person is exposed to the allergen and the body produces chemicals such as histamines, which cause various physical symptoms (or reactions), such as sneezing, a runny nose, vomiting, tightness in the chest, or hives. Table 4.1 lists allergens that are responsible for allergic reactions.

Allergic reactions can cause feelings of fear, discomfort, or anxiety in children and their parents. The goal should be to maintain as normal a lifestyle as possible. It is important to balance supporting a child's awareness of his or her allergens with

---

TABLE 4.1 Common Allergic Substances and Reactions

Common Allergic Substances	Typical Reactions
Environmental dust, dust mites, mould, pollen	runny and itchy nose, itchy eyes or skin, red rash, breathing difficulties, coughing, wheezing, chest tightness
Pets pet dander, skin flakes, saliva, and urine	itchy eyes and nose, runny nose
Insects stings from bees and wasps	wheezing, dizziness, hives, swelling of upper airway with difficulty breathing and, in extreme cases, swelling of face and anaphylactic shock
Foods eggs, peanuts and tree nuts, sesame seeds, soy, seafood (shellfish, crustaceans, fish), sulphites, milk, and wheat and other cereal products containing gluten (the latter two are common causes of infant allergies)	flushed face, hives or a rash, red and itchy skin; swelling of the eyes, face, lips, throat, and tongue; difficulty breathing, speaking, or swallowing; anxiety; cramps; diarrhea; vomiting; and, in extreme cases, anaphylactic shock
Drugs commonly seen with antibiotics such as penicillin and with aspirin and anti-inflammatory drugs	range from mild to severe skin rashes, swelling, difficulty breathing, and, in extreme cases, anaphylactic shock

(continued)

TABLE 4.1 Common Allergic Substances and Reactions (*continued*)

Common Allergic Substances	Typical Reactions
Latex balloons, rubber toys, baby-bottle nipples, pacifiers, bandages, erasers, craft supplies, cleaning gloves, medical gloves, fabrics with elastic, rubber ducks, sports equipment (e.g., soccer balls), condoms, dental dams, rubber mats, and carpet backing	itchy, watery eyes; sneezing or runny nose; coughing; rash or hives; chest tightness; shortness of breath; and, in extreme cases, anaphylactic shock
Scents strong odours found in products such as perfumes, hair spray, lotions, cosmetics, deodorants, soaps (laundry, dish, hand), fabric softeners, air fresheners, cleaning products	irritation of the nose and lungs

Sources: Allergy/Asthma Information Association (2004, 2006, n.d.); Canadian Allergy, Asthma and Immunology Foundation (n.d.); Government of Canada (2017).

knowing what to do if the child is exposed and avoiding overwhelming fear and excessive limits on the child's activities.

Most of the symptoms listed in Table 4.1 are from four of the body systems: upper and lower respiratory tract, skin, eyes, and gastrointestinal tract. The more body systems that are affected by an allergen, the more severe the allergic reaction. Severe allergic reactions are most commonly caused by peanuts, which are actually legumes, and tree nuts; eggs; shellfish; bee and wasp stings; penicillin; and aspirin. In a severe allergy to bee sting, for example, the first sting results in a significant reaction. Any subsequent sting, however, could be fatal. When children are diagnosed with severe allergies, the health care provider prescribes epinephrine (e.g., EpiPen® [epinephrine] Auto-Injector) to be administered in the event of a severe allergic reaction. In these instances, parents are required to provide the program with an adrenaline kit.

The most severe allergic reaction is called **anaphylactic shock**, which affects the entire body. *This reaction happens quickly.* Within seconds, the child's eyes, lips, and face begin to swell; he or she may get a headache; hives may appear all over the body; the throat may swell and cut off the breathing; and he or she may vomit and have diarrhea. Eventually, the child becomes unconscious. All of this can happen in less than 10 minutes. Educators must identify these symptoms immediately, administer the child's epinephrine, and call an ambulance. *To save the child's life, further emergency medical care is needed.* Even if you aren't sure about the child's allergic symptoms, always give epinephrine to the child and call an ambulance. Parents should be encouraged to obtain a medical alert bracelet for any child who has been diagnosed with severe allergies. The bracelet must be worn at all times. There is no cure for allergies. We try to prevent reactions by eliminating exposure to allergens whenever possible (e.g., peanuts, shellfish, animals) or at least limiting exposure to allergens (e.g., smoke, dust, pollen). The only treatment for allergies is to alleviate or reduce the effect of the symptoms (e.g., runny nose, itchy red eyes, nasal and sinus congestion) with medications such as antihistamines and decongestants. During hay fever season, children with hay fever may be more comfortable playing outside in the afternoon because most plants pollinate in the morning.

CRITICAL THINKING

Preventing Allergic Reactions

First, effective communication is essential between educators and parents to prevent allergic reactions. At the time of enrollment, parents must be asked for the following information about their children's allergies: the name of the allergen(s) and the specific symptoms, steps to prevent exposure to the allergen, what actions the educators should take when a child has symptoms, and what medication the health care provider has prescribed or recommended. Educators and parents can then develop an allergy care plan that meets the child's needs.

The program's policy and preventive practices on allergies should include all of the following:

- a medical form completed by the child's health care provider outlining the management of the allergies, what educators need to be aware of, and any instructions on handling emergency situations

- the sharing of allergy information with all staff members by

  - posting a list of children with their allergies in the kitchen and eating areas. Adding photos of each child to the list ensures that children are not exposed to known allergens, especially when volunteers, students, and substitute educators enter the program. This is particularly important when the children are younger and when there are children with the same first names. There have been educators who raise concerns around medical confidentiality and the posting of such information. However, the health risk of not sharing this vital information surpasses any such concern and assists staff and volunteers in providing a safe environment for the children.

  - including the pertinent allergy information with the emergency information cards kept in the first-aid kits.

  - attaching an allergy list to the top of the first-aid kit used outdoors (i.e., on the playground, field trips, walks) that focuses on children who are allergic to substances found outside, such as bees, wasps, animal hair, and feathers. Educators can quickly refer to this list to prevent or respond to allergic reactions. Educators can also refer to the list before they leave, to make sure they take the epinephrine auto-injector outside for those children who have been prescribed one. The epinephrine auto-injector must always be in the same general area as the child. Educators do not have time to go back to the program and then return to the playground to give the injection. Remember, anaphylactic shock happens very quickly, and educators must administer the adrenaline immediately (see Ensuring the Safe Administration of Medication, page 197).

ALLERGY/FOOD RESTRICTIONS LIST: October
INFANT ROOM

Nicholas: NO sesame (tahini etc.), peanuts, pistachios, cashews **Nicholas has an EpiPen**

Aaryan: NO beef (family preference)

TODDLER ROOM

Ruth: Vegetarian (family preference)

PRESCHOOL ROOM

Zimri: NO tofu (sensitivity)

Evelyn: Allergy to Drugs: Suprax/Cefixime (hives)

Olivia: Vegetarian (family preference)

Aarzaya: Lactose Intolerant (sensitivity)

Emilio: NO cow's milk, cheese, or yogurt (sensitivity)—has goat's milk from home

SENIOR PRESCHOOL ROOM

Hayden: NO peanuts, hummus, sesame seeds **Hayden has an EpiPen**

Landon: NO nuts **Landon has an Epipen**

NO PEANUTS OR TREE NUTS PERMITTED IN CENTRE

Source: Reprinted by permission of Suzanne Feltoe

- an awareness of how food is purchased, prepared, and served. The cooks or educators responsible for snacks and meals must know which children have food allergies, read all the ingredients on labels, and so on. New food labelling regulations came into effect in 2003. Processed food labels now clearly list the ingredients so consumers can avoid foods that provoke allergic reactions. With time, there will be further legislative changes to support the education of consumers in understanding what foods they are eating.
  - Use extreme caution for children with allergies to peanuts and peanut products. Educators must take parents' concerns very seriously because for some children, even the smell of peanuts or a trace of grated nuts in a cookie can cause anaphylactic shock. Some ECLC programs have voluntarily banned peanut butter and nut products from their programs. In the province of Manitoba, for example, in the Child Care Regulations a guideline in Section 16(3) states that "no foods containing known peanut products are to be served to children under three years of age" (Province of Manitoba, 2018, p. 36). Obviously, this regulation does not prevent parents from sending nut products in their child's meals, but educators strongly discourage parents from doing so.
- the posting of menus so parents can make substitutions for foods or food ingredients to which their child is allergic. When the program provides substitute foods, choose foods that look similar to those the other children are having. This can help normalize eating experiences for children with food allergies.
- the documenting of all allergic reactions in the child's file. The child's parents must be contacted.

Eighty percent of allergies develop before the age of five. To ensure children's safety, programs need to

- require all parents to give their children prescribed or OTC medication for 24 hours before educators administer it in the program so parents can determine whether their child has any side effects or allergic symptoms;
- outline how new foods are introduced to promote early awareness of allergies, which is particularly important for infants (see The Process of Introducing Semisolid Foods, page 284); and
- as a general practice, use unscented laundry and cleaning products and encourage staff not to wear perfumes and colognes, to which many people are sensitive.

Asthma

When someone has **asthma,** the mucous membrane that lines the airways is chronically inflamed, which narrows the airways (or bronchial tubes). The membranes produce more mucus, which is stickier than normal, resulting in less space in the airways for air to pass through. The cause of the tissue's chronic inflammation is not known.

Asthma varies in severity and is diagnosed when children have recurring episodes of wheezing, coughing, or shortness of breath. Wheezing has been considered the classic asthma symptom. Some people with asthma have a chronic dry cough rather than a wheeze, so their asthma may go undiagnosed because the wheezing can't be heard over the coughing. Severe asthma episodes can be life threatening because the airway closes completely and no air can get to the lungs.

The mucous membranes are more sensitive to allergens (e.g., dust mites, pollen, mould, grass, trees, and weed pollens), substances (e.g., air pollution, perfume, cologne, paint fumes, chemicals, tobacco smoke), cold weather, strenuous exercise (episodes in this connection are referred to as exercise-induced asthma [EIA]), URI, colds, emotional upset, sudden changes in the atmosphere or weather, and food additives and preservatives. Any of these **triggers** may irritate the mucous membranes and trigger an asthma episode. The child has to work hard at breathing because the muscles around the airway tighten, and the lining swells further and produces more sticky mucus. The child may cough frequently, wheeze, breathe at a faster rate, complain that the chest feels tight, and have behaviour changes (e.g., tiredness, restlessness, irritability).

"Six out of ten people with asthma do not have control of their disease. Their poorly controlled asthma may lead to a severe, life-threatening asthma attack and permanent lung damage" (Asthma Canada, n.d.-b, p. 1). Approximately 250 people per year die of asthma in Canada. "It is estimated that more than 80 per cent of asthma deaths could be prevented with proper asthma education" (Asthma Canada, n.d.-a, p. 1).

IS YOUR ASTHMA WELL MANAGED?

If you have asthma and experience one or more of these symptoms, see your doctor—your asthma may not be under control.

ANYTIME:

- Coughing, wheezing, chest tightness (occurs three or more times a week)
- Need to use your blue inhaler frequently (more than three times a week, not including once per day for exercise)

WHEN SLEEPING:

- Awakened due to breathing difficulties (occurs once or more per week)

AT WORK OR SCHOOL:

- Cannot attend due to asthma-related symptoms (in the past three months)

WHEN EXERCISING:

- Feel you need to stop your workout due to your asthma (in the past three months)

Source: Adapted from "30 Second Asthma Test." Retrieved December 2017 from http://pert.ucalgary.ca/asthma/30%20Second%20Test%20for%20Control.pdf

Identifying and managing the triggers of the child's asthma episodes are the first line of prevention. Educators can work with the children's parents to identify triggers, to remove or at least reduce exposure to allergens, and to administer prescribed medications. Three of the most common allergens for children are dust mites' feces, pollen, and cat dander. For some children, even being around another child who comes to the program or school with cat or dog hair on his or her clothes can irritate the airways. Dust mites thrive in warm, humid places, live off human skin scales, and can be found on pillows and mattresses, carpets, cloth-covered furniture, and soft toys. Educators can reduce the number of dust mites in programs by regularly dusting, vacuuming, and laundering cloth toys. Many allergens and irritants are found outdoors (e.g., pollens, fumes, tobacco smoke) and in public places and are more difficult to reduce or alleviate.

Two types of medications can be prescribed for children to treat the two aspects of asthma. The controller (or preventer) medications reduce the inflammation in one's airway, keep the airway clear, and prevent redness, mucus, and swelling. These medications are taken daily regardless of experiencing symptoms and may be in the form of an inhaler (e.g., Pulmicort®, Flovent®) or pill (e.g., PediaPred®, Decadron®). Like the name, the reliever (rescue) medications are taken to relieve the symptoms during an asthma attack, when breathing is difficult, and sometimes before exercising. These medications are often administered in an aerosol inhaler (or puffer) (e.g., Ventolin®, Airomir®) (Asthma Canada, n.d.-a, p. 1; The Lung Association, 2015, pp. 1–3, 5–6). Figure 4.1 provides examples of the range of inhalers that children may use to take their medication.

FIGURE 4.1 Types of Asthma Inhalers

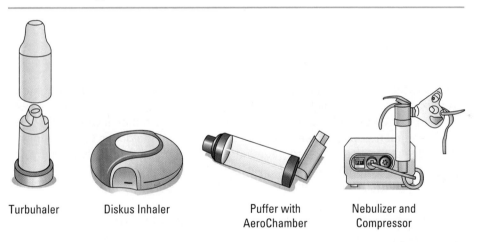

Turbuhaler   Diskus Inhaler   Puffer with   Nebulizer and
                                             AeroChamber   Compressor

Younger children often use an AeroChamber because they are not yet able to use a puffer, which requires exhaling completely, pumping the puffer once, and inhaling the puff of medication in one breath. Most individuals are prescribed two or three puffs.

At one end of the AeroChamber is the hole where the mouthpiece of the puffer is inserted; the face mask is on the other end. The mask is placed over the child's mouth and nose, one puff of the medication is pumped into the chamber, and the child breathes in the medication over at least six breaths. Before the second puff, the child

Courtesy of George Brown College/Casa Loma Child Care Centre

needs to wait one minute to allow the medication to travel through the air passages. This wait between puffs applies to all ages and all types of inhalers.

The program's policy and practices for the care of children with asthma should include

- providing parents with a medical form for the child's health care provider to complete, which outlines the management of the asthma, what educators must be aware of, and any instructions on medication and emergency situations. Have parents provide you with a copy of the child's asthma action plan.
- parents sharing this medical information and instruction/demonstration of administering medication with the child's educators.
- observing the child during strenuous play and in cold weather. If the child starts wheezing or coughing or is short of breath, stop the activity. If the weather is cold or damp, bring the child inside. Have the child sit down to use the bronchodilator. Regular exercise is just as important for children with asthma as it is for other children; however, it is important to discuss the child's specific needs for exercise or being outside in the winter or in very hot weather.
- documenting all asthmatic episodes in the child's file and contacting the child's parents. If an episode doesn't subside after two consecutive treatments of the bronchodilator medicine, the child should be seen by a health care provider as soon as possible.

CRITICAL THINKING

The dad tells you in the morning that he was up with his four-year-old daughter, Amanda, much of the night because the wheezing from her asthma woke her up often. She has had this nighttime wheezing for more than a week now. You suggest that he doesn't need to worry because Amanda doesn't have asthma episodes at the child care program during the day. Is this good advice? Why or why not? If not, what would you say instead?

REVISITING THE HEALTH PROMOTION ACTION PLAN

Recall the health promotion action plan introduced in Unit 1. The following two examples illustrate this plan in practice in terms of preventing and managing childhood illnesses or head lice and bedbug infestations.

Example 1

Individual Problem Solving and Self-Reliance

Each day, educators have the opportunity to influence individual children's health positively by implementing the program's infection control strategy. Granted, children get sick, and even if they are ill for only a few days, the whole family's schedule can be disrupted. Health policies and practices should be supportive, empathetic, and respectful of parents' situations and should take into account the program's responsibility for the health of the other children. We often forget that programs are also employers, and as such, the program's board can demonstrate a commitment to employees' families by providing family responsibility leave for staff and permitting staff to bank overtime hours.

Community Action
Directors can benefit from developing a pool of substitute educators and/or volunteers who can be called on when

- a child is mildly ill but stays at the program and needs extra attention;
- an educator is absent due to illness;
- a program needs extra adults (volunteers or paid), who come in for a few hours each day to cover busier times (e.g., meals, staff break times); or
- a field trip is planned or an activity needs additional supervisors.

Ideally, volunteers and substitutes are in the program often enough that the children and the adults get to know one another. When they are approached by staff, these trusted adults may be interested in providing care for the mildly ill child in the family's home or in their own home when the need arises. For parents who don't have access to alternative (or backup) care, this service could be extremely valuable. In communities where there is a cluster of programs in close proximity, directors could work collaboratively to support families and their staff.

Staff have identified the need for a community service that provides care for mildly ill children. Either on an individual basis or with a collective of programs, educators could advocate to a local agency to develop such a service (e.g., Victorian Order of Nurses [VON]). In communities with only one or two main employers, most, if not all, of the parents who use the program work for the same company. The program's board could meet with the company's management to discuss establishing family responsibility leave for their employees. Perhaps the local public health agency would work cooperatively with the program and the company.

Societal Change
Provincial/territorial and national child care associations (e.g., Saskatchewan Child Care Association, Canadian Child Care Federation) lobby the government to legislate employers to provide family responsibility leave. These associations are made up of members like you. Individual educators can exercise their democratic right (and responsibility) to vote for political candidates who are committed to child care and the family.

Example 2

Bedbugs are a nuisance. They cause a lot of discomfort to children, families, staff, ECE students, and volunteers who experience their bites! Bedbugs have made a "comeback" around the globe. In several Canadian cities, bedbug infestations have become a public health issue, which requires much collaboration by individuals, communities, and governmental agencies to confront. Much has been and needs to continue being done in order to prevent further physical and psychological stress, costs to replace furniture, and social isolation of persons living with bedbugs (Shum et al., 2012, p. 399). A study conducted with Winnipeg's inner-city residents found that bedbugs negatively impacted their ability to lead healthy lives (Comack & Lyons, 2010). The following discussion offers examples of how all levels of health promotion action can reduce the occurrences of bedbug infestations and ultimately contribute to health promotion in ECLC environments and the wider community.

Individual Problem Solving and Self-Reliance

Staff, parents, and older children need to know the basic information about bedbugs, signs of their presence, and what bites look like. Information can be available and shared through bulletin boards, newsletters, and other, more direct ways of communication. There are many strategies that staff and parents can practise to reduce or eliminate the spread of bedbugs, including but not limited to those outlined earlier in the unit (see Bedbugs, page 191).

Community Action

Education is one of the keys to control infestations. This is true for communities as well as for individuals. To successfully tackle infestations, the community, which includes the child care centre, other organizations, the neighbourhood, and the broader community, needs to be engaged in meeting with its "members," as well as in consultation with experts such as public health officials. A mutually accepted plan of action calls for widespread communication to ensure that everyone involved is "on the same page." Face-to-face conversations and written updates via a newsletter, email, or an agency website are possible methods for communicating and gathering information. Whatever methods are best, touching base regularly is essential to the success of managing and preventing further bedbug infestation.

Toronto Public Health established the Toronto Bed Bug Project in 2008. The project includes working groups of landlords, tenants, pest control firms, social housing and shelter managers, community agencies, and others. It supports education and outreach, creation of legislative tools, and development of best control practices. The project relies heavily on partnerships and donations to continue the project (Shum et al., 2012, p. 400).

In Winnipeg, grants are provided for community-based organizations and individuals to support their education and prevention efforts and include the provision of bedbug prevention materials, such as mattress covers, insect monitors, and laundry bags, and assistance with treatment (e.g., furniture removal, vacuuming, heat treatments) (Shum et al., 2012, p. 400).

Societal Change

Municipal and provincial/territorial governments are becoming more aware of the need for permanent, sustainable funding to make broader strides in this issue. For example:

- Municipal: A Montreal municipal bylaw on sanitation and maintenance of dwelling units is designed to ensure that apartments and residential buildings are safe, sanitary, and properly maintained. Recently, the city implemented a bylaw that requires pest control operators to submit a bedbug control plan (Shum et al., 2012, p. 400).

- Provincial: Section 13 of the Ontario *Health Promotion and Protection Act* indicates that medical officers of health can order both landlords and tenants to manage bedbugs (Shum et al., 2012, p. 400).

Public health agencies are recognized as key players in bedbug management across Canada. They are often demonstrating their role as facilitators in collaboration with all levels of government and nongovernmental agencies involved. In addition, their roles in education, outreach, and support are helping to reduce the spread of bedbugs and decrease the stigma, which is encouraging affected persons to report and resolve problems earlier.

CONCLUSION

Even when an ECLC program implements the infection control strategies covered in Unit 3, children do get sick. Fortunately, most of the illnesses are mild and short-lived, and nuisances such as head lice and bedbugs don't spread disease. Most do not require exclusion or prescriptions. In cooperation with families, educators address the needs of the child who is ill or impacted by nuisances while considering the best interests of the other children and staff.

ASSESS YOUR LEARNING

Define terms or describe concepts used in this unit.

- allergic substances
- allergies
- alternative care
- anaphylactic shock
- asthma
- bedbugs
- chickenpox
- common colds
- diarrhea
- ear infections
- exclusion
- "five rights" for administering medication
- head lice
- health observations
- over-the-counter (OTC) medication
- pinkeye
- prescriptions
- signs of illness
- triggers (asthma)

Evaluate your options in each situation.

1. One of the two-year-olds is listless and unhappy today. He is unable to participate in the program and needs to be held and comforted. When the director calls his mother, she asks that you take his temperature. You do so, and because the child does not have a fever, the mother refuses to pick him up early.

2. A preschooler has a number of food allergies, so she is often offered other foods at lunch and snack. She cries and says she wants only what the other children eat. Meanwhile, some of the other children only want to eat the same food she eats.

3. One of the families goes to a naturopath as their health practitioner. You also believe that naturopaths have a lot to offer in promoting health. The parents ask you to administer the homeopathic (i.e., not prescribed by a medical doctor or advanced practitioner) medicine to their child daily. They are willing to sign the medication form. Are you able to administer this medication?

4. One of the preschoolers who has asthma often needs her rescue medication (Ventolin® inhaler) to treat severe episodes. Today you are going on a field trip away from the centre but didn't notice until you are ready to leave that the inhaler is empty. The parent has already left for work. What do you do?

APPENDIX 4.1

Management of Illness

Requirements for reporting vary across Canada. Find out which infections are reportable in your province/territory by contacting your local public health unit. All page numbers cited below refer to *Well Beings: A Guide to Health in Child Care.*

ILLNESS	TRANSMISSION	SIGNS/SYMPTOMS	INFECTIOUS PERIOD	EXCLUSION	REPORTING AND NOTIFICATION
Viral respiratory infections					
Viruses include respiratory syncytial virus, parainfluenza virus, influenza, adenovirus, rhino-virus, coronavirus, metapneumovirus. See page 175 for additional information.	Viruses in the nose and throat spread by **direct contact** with respiratory secretions or contaminated hands, **indirect contact** with toys, tissues, or other objects contaminated with respiratory secretions, or **droplets** from coughs and sneezes.	**Common cold:** Runny nose, cough, sneezing, sore throat, headache, possibly fever. **Bronchiolitis:** Cough, laboured breathing, wheezing, fever. **Croup:** Hoarseness, barking cough, rapid, laboured or noisy breathing, fever. **Influenza:** Fever, chills, cough, headache, and muscle pains. **Pneumonia:** Fever, cough, rapid or laboured breathing, poor skin colour.	Depends on the virus but usually 3 to 8 days (longer for children with a weakened immune system). Most infectious while symptoms are present.	**Common cold:** No, unless the child is too ill to participate in all program activities. **Bronchiolitis, croup, influenza, pneumonia:** Yes, until the child is well enough to partici-pate in all program activities.	No. No, unless you suspect an outbreak.

(appendix continues on next page)

ILLNESS	TRANSMISSION	SIGNS/SYMPTOMS	INFECTIOUS PERIOD	EXCLUSION	REPORTING AND NOTIFICATION
Bacterial pneumonia See pages 206, 209 for additional information.	Bacteria usually present in the nose and throat and can cause disease if they get into the lungs.	Fever, cough, rapid or laboured breathing, poor skin colour.	Usually not considered contagious.	Yes, until the child is well enough to participate in all program activities.	No, unless pneumococcus or *Haemophilus influenzae* type B is isolated during blood testing.

Gastrointestinal infections

ILLNESS	TRANSMISSION	SIGNS/SYMPTOMS	INFECTIOUS PERIOD	EXCLUSION	REPORTING AND NOTIFICATION
Can be viral or bacterial. See page 186 for additional information.	Germs in stool spread by **direct contact** (hand to mouth) or **indirect contact** with toys, other objects, or surfaces contaminated with stool				
Campylobacter	Bacteria usually ingested in contaminated **food** (e.g., improperly cooked poultry, unpasteurized milk) or water. Person-to-person spread by **direct or indirect contact with stool** can occur, especially among young children.	Fever, diarrhea (often with blood and/or mucus in stool), cramps.	Bacteria excreted in stool for 2 to 3 weeks. Most contagious during the acute illness.	Yes, if a child's diarrhea can't be contained in a diaper or a toilet-trained child can't control his bowel movements.	Yes, by the testing laboratory. Contact your local public health unit if a child at your facility is diagnosed with *Campylobacter* gastroenteritis.
Clostridium difficile (C. difficile)	Bacteria are normally found in soil and in the intestinal tract. Antibiotic treatment permits overgrowth of C. *difficile* in the gut and may trigger disease. Person-to-person spread by **direct or indirect contact with stool** can occur.	Diarrhea (sometimes with blood and/or mucus in stool), cramps, fever. Most children under 1 year of age have no symptoms, and most older children have a very mild illness.	Infectious as long as diarrhea lasts.	Yes, if a child's diarrhea can't be contained in a diaper or a toilet-trained child can't control his bowel movements.	No.

(appendix continues on next page)

Escherichia coli 0157 (*E. coli*)	Bacteria usually ingested in contaminated **food** (e.g., poultry, beef, milk, unpasteurized apple juice, raw vegetables), or **water contaminated with animal or human feces.** Also spread from person to person by **direct or indirect contact with stool.**	Starts as non-bloody diarrhea, usually progressing to visibly bloody stools, with severe abdominal pain.	Bacteria excreted in stool for about a week. Infectious as long as diarrhea lasts.	Yes, until diarrhea subsides **and** 2 stool cultures (taken when the child is no longer receiving antibiotics) test negative.	Yes, by the testing laboratory. Contact your local public health unit if a child in your facility is diagnosed with *E. coli* 0157 gastroenteritis.
Giardia See page 187 for additional information.	Parasites in the stool are spread from person to person by direct or **indirect contact with stool** or are ingested in **contaminated food or water.**	Watery diarrhea, recurrent abdominal pain. Some children experience chronic diarrhea with foul-smelling stools, a distended stomach, and weight loss. Many infected children have no symptoms.	Infectious as long as cysts are in the stool, which can be for months.	Yes, until diarrhea subsides.	Yes, by the testing laboratory. Contact your local public health unit if a child at your facility is diagnosed with *Giardia* gastroenteritis. In the case of an outbreak, authorities may screen and/or treat all children and staff, with or without symptoms.
Rotavirus See page 186 for additional information.	Viruses in the stool spread easily from person to person by: **Direct or indirect contact with stool and contaminated objects/surfaces.**	High fever, vomiting, followed within 12 to 24 hours by profuse, watery diarrhea.	Infectious just before onset of symptoms and as long as 3 weeks later.	Yes, if a child's diarrhea can't be contained in a diaper or toilet-trained child can't control her bowel movements.	No. Contact your local public health unit if you suspect an outbreak (i.e., 2 to 3 or more children have diarrhea within 48 hours).

(appendix continues on next page)

ILLNESS	TRANSMISSION	SIGNS/SYMPTOMS	INFECTIOUS PERIOD	EXCLUSION	REPORTING AND NOTIFICATION
Salmonella typhi (gastroenteritis or typhoid fever)	Bacteria in the stool are spread from person to person by **direct or indirect contact with stool**, or are ingested in **contaminated food**.	Diarrhea, cramps, fever.	Infectious as long as bacteria are in the stool, which can be many weeks.	Yes, until diarrhea subsides **and** 3 stool cultures (taken when the child is no longer receiving antibiotics) test negative.	Yes, by the treating physician and testing laboratory. Inform your local public health unit **immediately** if a child or adult at your facility is diagnosed with *S. typhi* infection. Stool cultures for other children and staff may be required.
Salmonella gastroenteritis (non-typhi)	Bacteria are usually ingested in **contaminated food** (e.g., meat, poultry, eggs, unpasteurized dairy products, vegetables and fruit). Person-to-person spread **may occur from direct or indirect contact with stool**. **Reptiles and amphibians** are also sources of infection.	Diarrhea, cramps, fever.	Infectious as long as bacteria are in the stool, which can be many weeks.	Yes, until the child is well enough to participate in all program activities.	Yes, by the testing laboratory. Contact your local public health unit if a child at your facility is diagnosed with *Salmonella* gastroenteritis.
Shigella gastroenteritis	Bacteria in stool spread from person to person by **direct or indirect contact with stool**.	Watery diarrhea, with or without blood and/or mucus, fever, cramps.	Infectious as long as bacteria are in the stool, which can be up to 4 weeks.	Yes, until diarrhea subsides **and** 2 stool cultures (taken when the child is no longer receiving antibiotics) test negative.	Yes, by the testing laboratory. Contact your local public health unit if a child at your facility is diagnosed with *Shigella* gastroenteritis. Other children, staff or household contacts with symptoms may need testing.

(appendix continues on next page)

Illness	Cause/Spread	Symptoms	Infectious period	Exclude from care?	Notify public health?
Yersinia gastroenteritis For more information and important requirements, see pages 198–199 and 375.	Bacteria are ingested in **contaminated food** (e.g., raw or undercooked pork, unpasteurized milk) or **water.** Person-to-person spread is rare.	Fever, diarrhea (often with blood and/or mucus in stool).	Infectious as long as bacteria are in the stool, which can be up to 2 to 3 weeks.	Yes, if a child's diarrhea can't be contained in a diaper, or toilet-trained child can't control his bowel movements.	Yes, by the testing laboratory. Contact your public health unit if a child at your facility is diagnosed with *Yersinia* gastroenteritis.

Other Illnesses

Illness	Cause/Spread	Symptoms	Infectious period	Exclude from care?	Notify public health?
Chickenpox (varicella) See page 193 for additional information.	Viruses in the throat and from skin lesions spread easily from person to person **through the air**, and can travel large distances. Viruses in skin lesions spread **by contact with fluid from blisters.** Virus persists in the body for life and may recur as shingles. **Viruses can spread by contact with shingles if lesions are not covered.**	Fever and itchy rash. Crops of small red spots turn into fluid-filled blisters that crust over within a few days and become itchy.	Infectious for 2 days before rash starts until all blisters have crusted over and dried (usually about 5 days after start of rash).	No. Children with mild chickenpox can attend child care regardless of their rash, as long as they feel well enough to participate in all program activities.	Yes, in some jurisdictions, by the treating physician and testing laboratory. Contact your local public health unit if there is an outbreak at your facility. Non-immune children and staff may need to see a doctor right away. Preventive treatment (vaccine or immune globulin) may be needed. **Notify all parents and staff immediately.**
Cold sores (herpes simplex type 1 virus)	Viruses spread from person to person by **direct contact** of mucous membranes (mouth, nose, eyes) with cold sores or saliva. Virus persists in the body for life and infections may recur.	Range from no symptoms to a simple cold sore or many painful ulcers in mouth and a high fever.	Infectious for at least a week during the first infection. Recurrences are less contagious for a shorter time.	No, for a child with simple cold sores. Yes, for a child with mouth ulcers who is drooling, until she is well enough to eat and participate comfortably in all program activities.	No.

(appendix continues on next page)

ILLNESS	TRANSMISSION	SIGNS/SYMPTOMS	INFECTIOUS PERIOD	EXCLUSION	REPORTING AND NOTIFICATION
Conjunctivitis (pinkeye) See page 180 for additional information.	Bacterial or viral. Germs spread easily by: **direct or indirect contact with eye secretions**, or **droplets** from coughs and sneezes when associated with a respiratory virus. It can also be caused by an allergy or eye irritation, which usually does not cause discharge.	Scratchy, painful or itchy red eyes, light sensitivity, tearing with purulent (pus) or mucousy discharge.	**Bacterial:** Infectious until 24 hours of appropriate antibiotic treatment received. **Viral:** Infectious as long as there is eye discharge.	Yes, until seen by a doctor. If bacteria, child can return to the program after starting appropriate antibiotic treatment. If viral, child can return with doctor's approval. No need to exclude if there is no eye discharge, unless there is an outbreak.	No. Contact your local public health unit if you suspect an outbreak (2 or more children in one room have red eyes with watery discharge).
Cytomegalovirus (CMV infection) See pages 184 and 380 for additional information.	Viruses in saliva and urine spread by **direct contact.** Virus persists in the body for life and infections may recur.	Children usually have no symptoms. Can infect a fetus if the mother is infected or re-exposed during pregnancy.	Infectious as long as virus is in the urine and saliva, which can be for months in many healthy infants.	No.	No.

(appendix continues on next page)

Disease		Infectious period	Can child return?	Action required
Group A Streptococcus (GAS) invasive diseases (e.g., toxic shock syndrome, necrotizing fasciitis [flesh-eating disease]) For more information and important requirements, see page 211.	Some strains of GAS cause invasive disease. Bacteria spread from person to person by: **direct contact with skin lesions**, or **respiratory droplets**. Children are at highest risk of infection within 2 weeks of having chickenpox. **Toxic shock syndrome:** Fever, dizziness, confusion, and abdominal pain. **Necrotizing fasciitis:** Fever, severe, painful localized swelling, and a rapidly spreading red rash.	Infectious until 24 hours of appropriate antibiotic treatment received.	Yes. A child can return to the program once she has received **at least 24 hours** of appropriate antibiotic therapy, and a doctor has determined she is recovered and well enough to participate in all program activities.	Yes, by the treating physician and testing laboratory. **Notify your local public health unit immediately if a child or adult at your facility is diagnosed with invasive GAS.** Antibiotic treatment may be required for all exposed contacts, especially if chickenpox is also present. Inform public health authorities if a child or staff member in your program has had a non-invasive GAS infection (e.g., impetigo or pharyngitis) or chickenpox within the previous 2 weeks.
Haemophilus influenzae type b (Hib) disease For more information and important requirements, see page 206.	Bacteria in mouth and nose are spread by **direct contact** and respiratory droplets. Does not spread easily, and requires prolonged close contact. Causes fever and pneumonia, meningitis, epiglottitis, blood, bone and joint infections. Symptoms develop rapidly.	Infectious until **at least** 24 hours of appropriate antibiotic therapy received.	Yes. A child can return to the program once she has received at least 24 hours of appropriate antibiotic therapy and a doctor has determined she is well enough to participate in all program activities.	Yes, by the treating physician and testing laboratory. **Inform your local public health unit immediately if a child at your centre is diagnosed with a Hib infection.** Antibiotic treatment or vaccine may be required for exposed children. Notify all parents.

(appendix continues on next page)

ILLNESS	TRANSMISSION	SIGNS/SYMPTOMS	INFECTIOUS PERIOD	EXCLUSION	REPORTING AND NOTIFICATION
Hand-foot-and-mouth disease See page 200 for additional information.	Intestinal viruses spread from person to person by: **direct or indirect contact with stool or saliva.**	Fever, headache, sore throat, small, painful mouth ulcers and a rash (small red spots or small blisters), usually on the hands and feet.	Virus in saliva for a few days only but can remain in stool for 4 weeks after onset of illness.	No. Children can attend child care as long as they feel well enough to participate in all program activities.	No.
Head lice See pages 191–192 for additional information.	Spread from person to person by: **direct contact** (head to head), or **indirect contact** (e.g., shared hats, hairbrushes, headphones).	Itchy scalp.	Infectious as long as left untreated.	No. Exclusion is ineffective and unnecessary.	Contact your local public health unit for guidance if an outbreak cannot be controlled.
Hepatitis A virus (HAV) For more information and important requirements, see pages 189–190 and 380–381.	Virus in stool spreads from person to person by: **direct or indirect contact with stool,** or **contaminated food or water.**	Tea-coloured urine, jaundice and fever. Most young children do not get sick but can still spread the virus to others. Older children and adults are more likely to have symptoms.	Most infectious 1 to 2 weeks before onset of illness until 1 week after onset of jaundice.	Yes, for 1 week after onset of illness (unless all other children and staff have received preventive treatment).	Yes, by the treating physician and testing laboratory. **Inform your local public health unit immediately if a child or adult at your facility is diagnosed with HAV.** Contacts may need vaccine and/or immune globulin. **Notify all parents and staff.**

(appendix continues on next page)

Hepatitis B virus (HBV) For more information and important requirements, see pages 212–214 and 377–378.	Virus in blood and other body fluids (e.g., saliva, genital secretions). Mainly transmitted through sexual intercourse, from mother to newborn, by sharing contaminated injection equipment, or by transfusion of unscreened blood. May be transmitted if an open cut or the mucous membranes (eyes or mouth) are exposed to blood.	Young children almost always have no symptoms. Older children and adults may have fever, fatigue, jaundice.	Infectious as long as the virus is in the blood and body fluids. May persist for life, especially in infants infected at birth.	No. A child with HBV can participate in all program activities, unless there are medical or behavioural risk factors (e.g., biting).	Yes, by the treating physician and testing laboratory. Contact your local public health unit about **any** bite that breaks the skin. Blood tests may be required.
Hepatitis C virus (HCV) For more information and important requirements, see pages 216 and 378.	Virus in blood. Mainly transmitted from mother to newborn. Also by sharing contaminated injection equipment or by transfusion of unscreened blood. May be transmitted if an open cut or mucous membranes (eyes or mouth) are exposed to blood.	Young children almost always have no symptoms. Older children and adults may have fever, fatigue, jaundice.	Infectious as long as the virus is in the blood. May persist for life.	No. A child with HCV can participate in all program activities.	Yes, by the treating physician and testing laboratory. Contact your local public health unit about **any** bite that breaks the skin. Blood tests may be required.

(appendix continues on next page)

ILLNESS	TRANSMISSION	SIGNS/SYMPTOMS	INFECTIOUS PERIOD	EXCLUSION	REPORTING AND NOTIFICATION
Human immunodeficiency virus (HIV) For more information and important requirements, see pages 215–216 and 378–379.	Virus in blood, genital secretions, and breast milk. Children usually acquire HIV from mothers before, during, or after birth (by breastfeeding). Otherwise, transmitted through sexual intercourse, by sharing contaminated injection equipment or by transfusion of unscreened blood. May be transmitted if an open cut or the mucous membranes (eyes, nose or mouth) are exposed to a large amount of blood.	Children usually have no symptoms. If AIDS develops, they may have persistent thrush, *Candida* dermatitis, chronic diarrhea, and be unable to gain weight.	Infectious as long as the virus is in the blood and body fluids, presumably for life.	No. A child with HIV can participate in all program activities.	Yes, by the treating physician and testing laboratory. Contact your local public health unit about **any** bite that breaks the skin. Blood tests may be required.
Impetigo For more information and important requirements, see pages 194–195.	Caused by Group A *Streptococcus* or *Staphylococcus aureus* bacteria. Both spread from person to person by: **direct contact** (e.g., by touching skin lesions), or **indirect contact** (e.g., via contaminated bed linens or clothing).	Fluid-filled blisters, usually around the mouth or nose, but may occur elsewhere. Blisters break, ooze, and form a honey-coloured crust.	Infectious until lesions have dried up. If Group A *Streptococcus*, until 24 hours after first dose of an appropriate antibiotic.	Yes, if draining lesions cannot be kept covered. For Group A *Streptococcus* infections, until 24 hours of appropriate antibiotic treatment received.	No (but community-associated methicillin-resistant S. *aureus* [CA-MRSA] is reportable by the testing laboratory in some jurisdictions). Contact your local public health unit for advice if you suspect an outbreak (e.g., more than one child in the same room has impetigo within a month).

(appendix continues on next page)

Illness	How it is spread	Signs and symptoms	How long it is infectious	Can the child return to care?	Reporting requirements
Measles For more information and important requirements, see pages 200–201 and 377.	Viruses in respiratory secretions **spread easily from person to person through the air.**	High fever, cough, runny nose and red eyes 2 to 4 days before a rash appears, first on the face, then over entire body.	Highly infectious from 3 to 5 days before and up to 4 days after the rash appears.	Yes. A child with measles cannot return to child care until **at least** 4 days after onset of rash. Non-immune children and staff must be excluded for 2 weeks after the onset of rash in the child diagnosed with measles, unless they have been vaccinated within 72 hours of first exposure.	Yes, by the treating physician and testing laboratory. **Measles exposure is a medical emergency.** **Notify your local public health unit immediately if a child or adult at your facility is diagnosed with measles.** Exposed susceptible children and staff may require vaccine within 72 hours of the first contact or immune globulin within 6 days of exposure. **Notify all staff and parents immediately.**
Meningitis (bacterial or enteroviral) For more information and important requirements, see pages 204–206.	Not all forms of meningitis are contagious. **Bacterial:** See Meningococcal disease and *Haemophilus influenzae* type b disease. **Enteroviruses** are found in saliva for only a few days but can remain in stool for 4 weeks after onset of illness.	**Bacterial:** Fever, lethargy, headache, extreme irritability, vomiting, stiff neck, seizures, a bulging fontanel in babies under 18 months old. Usually progresses rapidly. Child may have a rapidly spreading, bruise-like rash. **Viral:** Usually milder, often fever and irritability only.	**Bacterial** meningitis is infectious until after 24 hours of appropriate antibiotic therapy received. **Enteroviruses** in saliva and stool are spread by **direct or indirect contact.**	Yes. A child can return to the program once she has received **at least** 24 hours of appropriate antibiotic therapy, and a doctor has determined she has recovered and feels well enough to participate in all program activities.	Bacterial meningitis: Yes, by the treating physician and testing laboratory. **Notify your local public health unit immediately if a child or adult at your facility is diagnosed with bacterial meningitis.** Antibiotic treatment or vaccine may be mandated for some or all exposed children and staff. **Notify all parents and staff immediately.**

(appendix continues on next page)

ILLNESS	TRANSMISSION	SIGNS/SYMPTOMS	INFECTIOUS PERIOD	EXCLUSION	REPORTING AND NOTIFICATION
Meningococcal disease For more information and important requirements, see pages 207–209.	Meningococcus is a bacterium found in the mouth and respiratory secretions. Does not spread easily but can be transmitted by: **close, direct contact** (e.g., with saliva), or **respiratory droplets.**	Usually causes sepsis or meningitis, with high fever and rapid progression to shock (decreased responsiveness, poor skin colour). Child may have a distinctive rash that starts as small red spots but rapidly progresses to large red-purple bruises.	Infectious until after 24 hours of appropriate antibiotic treatment received.	Yes. A child can return to child care once he has received **at least 24 hours of** appropriate antibiotic therapy and a doctor has determined he has recovered and feels well enough to participate in all program activities.	Yes, by the treating physician and testing laboratory. **Inform your local public health unit immediately if a child or adult at your facility is diagnosed with meningococcal disease.** Public health authorities may mandate antibiotic treatment and/or vaccination for exposed children and staff. **Notify all parents and staff immediately.**
Molluscum contagiosum See page 197 for additional information.	Virus spreads from person to person by **direct (skin-to-skin) contact with lesions** or **indirect contact (e.g., with bed linens contaminated with material from the lesions).**	Smooth, shiny pinkish-white bumps with a dip in the middle and a cheesy material inside, anywhere on the body.	Unknown. Molluscum disappears after several months without treatment.	No.	No.
Mumps For more information and important requirements, see pages 184 and 376–377.	Virus in saliva and respiratory secretions spreads easily from person to person by: **direct contact** (e.g., kissing) or **respiratory droplets.**	Fever, swollen glands at the jawline or on the face, headache.	Infectious from 2 days before onset of swelling until 9 days after.	Yes, for 5 days after onset of swelling. Public health authorities may exclude non-immune children or staff for at least 26 days after symptom onset in the last person with mumps in a child care setting.	Yes, by treating physician and testing laboratory. **Notify your local public health unit immediately if a child or adult at your facility is diagnosed with mumps.** The authorities may mandate vaccination for non-immune contacts.

(appendix continues on next page)

Illness	Cause / Transmission	Contagious Period	Exclusion	Reporting / Notification
Otitis media (middle ear infections) See page 178 for additional information.	Viral or bacterial, usually a complication of the common cold. Non-contagious.	Non-contagious.	No, unless child is too ill to participate in program activities.	No.
Parvovirus B19 infection (fifth disease, erythema infectiosum, or "slapped cheek" syndrome) For more information and important requirements, see pages 201–202 and 379–380.	Virus in respiratory secretions spreads by: **direct contact**, and (possibly) **respiratory droplets.** Can also be transmitted from mother to child before birth.	Infectious for several days before the rash, and non-infectious once rash appears.	No. Once rash appears, a child is no longer contagious.	No. Notify all parents and staff. Advise exposed pregnant staff and parents to contact their doctor.
	Red rash on the cheeks followed by a lace-like rash on the torso and arms that spreads to the rest of the body. Sometimes preceded by a low fever or cold symptoms 7 to 10 days before rash appears.			
Pertussis (whooping cough) For more information and important requirements, see pages 182–183 and 379.	Bacteria in respiratory secretions spread easily from person to person by **droplets from coughs and sneezes.** Runny nose, frequent and severe coughing spells, sometimes followed by a whooping sound, gagging or vomiting. Babies may have serious difficulty breathing.	Infectious for up to 3 weeks from onset of illness if not treated and for 5 days if appropriate antibiotic treatment is received.	Not routine but exclusion may be mandated by public health authorities, especially if people at high-risk are present. Exclude until 5 days of appropriate antibiotic treatment received or for 3 weeks from onset of illness, if not treated.	Yes, by the treating physician and testing laboratory. **Inform your local public health unit immediately if a child or adult at your facility is diagnosed with pertussis.** Antibiotic treatment and/or vaccination may be mandated. **Notify all parents and staff immediately.**

(appendix continues on next page)

ILLNESS	TRANSMISSION	SIGNS/SYMPTOMS	INFECTIOUS PERIOD	EXCLUSION	REPORTING AND NOTIFICATION
Pinworms See pages 190–191 for additional information.	Worm eggs spread by **direct contact** (e.g., contaminated fingers), or **indirect contact** (e.g., contaminated bed linens, clothing, toys).	Anal itching, disturbed sleep, irritability.	Infectious as long as eggs are being laid on skin. Eggs are infective for 2 to 3 weeks indoors.	No.	Contact your local public health unit if an infestation persists. Treating all household members and close contacts may be needed.
Pneumococcal disease See pages 209–210 for additional information.	Bacteria are normally found in the nose and throat and usually do not cause infection. Possible person-to-person spread by **close, direct contact with mouth secretions** (e.g., kissing), or **respiratory droplets.**	Usually an ear or sinus infection following a cold. Invasive infections include fever and pneumonia, meningitis, blood, bone and joint infections. Symptoms develop rapidly.	Not usually considered infectious. Probably not transmissible after 24 hours of appropriate antibiotic therapy.	No, for minor illness (e.g., otitis, sinusitis). A child with serious illness can return to child care once a doctor has determined he is well enough to participate in all program activities.	Yes (for invasive pneumococcal infections **only**), by the treating physician and testing laboratory.
Ringworm See pages 195–196 for additional information.	Fungus spreads from person to person by: **direct contact** (skin-to-skin) and **indirect contact** (e.g., shared combs, unwashed clothes, or shower or pool surfaces). Also acquired from **pets, especially cats.**	Ring-shaped itchy, scaly lesions on scalp, body or feet (athlete's foot). Bald spots on the scalp.	Transmissible as long as rash is untreated and/or uncovered.	Yes, until the first treatment has been applied.	No.
Roseola See page 203 for additional information.	Virus probably spreads from person to person by **direct contact with saliva.** Often found in saliva of people with no symptoms.	High fever and crankiness for 3 to 5 days. When the fever subsides, a rash of small red spots appears on the face and body, lasting a few hours to 2 days.	Infectious while symptoms are present.	No. A child with roseola can continue to attend child care as long as she is well enough to participate in all program activities.	No.

(appendix continues on next page)

Illness	How it spreads	Symptoms	Infectious period	Should child be excluded?	Does the local public health unit need to be notified?
Rubella (German measles) For more information and important requirements, see pages 203–204 and 376.	Virus spreads from person to person by: **direct contact with nose/mouth secretions** or **respiratory droplets.**	Mild in children, with low fever, swollen glands in the neck and behind the ears, and a rash with small red spots. More severe in adults. If acquired in pregnancy, may seriously affect the fetus.	Infectious from 7 days before to 7 days after the rash appears.	Yes, for 7 days after the rash is first noticed.	Yes, by the treating physician and testing laboratory. **Rubella exposure is a medical emergency. Notify your local public health unit immediately if a child or adult at your facility is diagnosed with rubella.** Non-immune children and staff may need immunization. **Notify all parents and staff immediately.** Advise pregnant staff and parents who aren't sure of their immune status to see their doctor.
Scabies See pages 192–193 for additional information.	Mites spread from person to person by **direct (prolonged, close and intimate) contact.**	Itchy red rash, usually between fingers and toes, or the wrists or in the groin, with thread-like lines and scratch marks. May be elsewhere on the body in children under 2 years of age.	Transmissible as long as infestation is untreated.	Yes, until the first treatment has been applied.	No. Contact your local public health unit for guidance if an outbreak cannot be controlled.

(appendix continues on next page)

ILLNESS	TRANSMISSION	SIGNS/SYMPTOMS	INFECTIOUS PERIOD	EXCLUSION	REPORTING AND NOTIFICATION
Streptococcal pharyngitis (strep throat) and scarlet fever See pages 181–182 for additional information.	Bacteria in throat spread from person to person by: **direct contact with saliva, or respiratory droplets.**	Sore throat, fever, swollen tender neck glands. Scarlet fever is reportable by the treating physician in some jurisdictions.	Infectious from onset of illness until 24 hours of appropriate antibiotic treatment received.	Yes. A child can return to the program once he has received at least 24 hours of appropriate antibiotic treatment, and the child is well enough to participate in all program activities.	Scarlet fever is strep throat with a red sunburn-like rash covering the entire body. Contact your public health unit if you suspect an outbreak at your facility (more than 2 cases in a month).
Thrush and *Candida* diaper rash See pages 196–197 for additional information.	Fungus is normally present in the body without causing illness, and rarely spreads from person to person. Thrush can be transmitted to an infant by contact with contaminated bottle nipples or soothers.	Thrush presents as whitish-gray patches on the inside of the cheek or on the tongue. *Candida* diaper rash is a painful bright-red rash in the deepest creases of a baby's groin, on the buttocks or in moist neck folds.	Usually not spread from person to person.	No.	No. Make sure bottle nipples and soothers aren't shared between children.
Tuberculosis (TB) For more information and important requirements, see pages 210–211 and 381.	Bacteria from the lungs **spread through the air in particles produced by coughing.**	For infectious TB: fever, cough, difficulty breathing. Young children rarely have infectious TB.	If infectious TB: As long as bacteria are in the respiratory secretions.	If infectious TB: Yes, for at least 2 weeks after starting appropriate antibiotic treatment and until the treating physician or local public health unit states that the child is no longer infectious.	Yes, by the treating physician and testing laboratory. **Notify your local public health unit immediately if a child or adult at your facility is diagnosed with TB.** Exposed children and adults may need testing and antibiotic treatment. **Notify all parents and staff immediately.**

Source: Reprinted with permission from the Canadian Paediatric Society.

alice-photo/Shutterstock.com

Nutrition

5

CONTENTS

Nutrition is the science of food and how it is used by the body. Discussion of nutrition includes these facts:

- Food has different meanings for each individual.
- Eating patterns are shaped by interrelated factors in our lives.

Nutritious food is essential for all dimensions of our health. This key factor is the cornerstone of developing and evolving nutrition programs for young children. Educators' motivation plays an essential role in promoting children's well-being. It is important to balance children's rights to have control over what and how much food they consume with adults' responsibility to provide

- enough food,
- a variety of wholesome foods, and
- an eating environment that promotes healthy eating.

When we recognize that healthy eating habits developed early tend to have lifelong benefits, the influence that early childhood educators have in supporting eating habits cannot be understated.

FACTORS THAT SHAPE EATING HABITS

For most people, food usually means more than just relieving hunger and providing nourishment. The meaning that food carries can be positive and healthy and associated with celebrations, including special foods, holidays, social time with family and friends, and religious or ethnocultural events. Other meanings may be negative and not conducive to health or well-being; these may result in eating for the wrong reasons (see Emotional, page 233).

Think about how you view food generally, the food choices you make, and how you feel before, during, and after eating. Awareness of our emotions, attitudes, and behaviour toward food and eating is necessary to foster healthy eating

To list and discuss six factors that shape our eating habits. (LO 1, 6)

To acknowledge food insecurity in Canada. (LO 1, 6)

habits in children. If we perpetuate myths or model poor eating habits—such as a focus on dieting—we are giving negative messages to children and may unwittingly influence lifelong eating problems.

Several Factors That Affect Eating Habits

Several factors must be considered when we look at nutrition: physical, emotional, social, cultural, body image, and economics. The interaction of these factors and others results in complex dynamics that educators need to be aware of to promote healthy attitudes toward nutrition and eating.

Physical

The first factor that comes to mind is our physical need for food. Nutrients in food provide the building blocks for cell and tissue growth, the regulators for many of the body's functions, and fuel for energy. Each nutrient can play a specific role or multiple roles. The way nutrients interact with the other factors is very complex. Nutrition affects a child's thinking and learning capacities, for example. A child who is weak from poor nutrition will have little energy to learn or socialize. Canadian nutritional guidelines have been established for the intake of nutrients (vitamins, minerals, proteins, fat, and carbohydrates) for children and adults. The guidelines take into account that variations exist in the requirements for nutrients among individuals. Growth rates and body types vary because we all differ in our genetic makeup, even from our siblings. The human body's need for energy varies with age, body size, growth patterns, gender, level of physical activity, and basal metabolic rate (the rate at which your body uses energy for essential bodily functions).

Wendy Riseborough/Shutterstock.com

Physical Activity

We know that physical activity goes hand in hand with nutrition as part of an active, healthy lifestyle, which is discussed in Unit 6. Individuals of all ages who maintain a moderate level of daily activity help their bodies work more efficiently, often by increasing their basal metabolic rate and bone density. It is hoped that children enjoy physical activity just for the fun of it, but it also supports their physical fitness, brain development (Ratey, 2013), and positive self-image.

Sensory Experiences

Eating is a truly sensory experience. When you watch young children eat, they see, smell, taste, and touch the food. They hear the crispy, crunchy, and squishy sounds that food makes. From infancy, we begin to develop taste preferences. Several studies have shown that newborn babies innately prefer sweet tastes. This preference, however, may be altered early on by introducing other tastes. Older infants and young children often prefer a saltier taste. Children's love of dill pickles and salty broth sometimes surprises adults. There is interest in, but no conclusions on, some of the genetic links between taste preferences. Young children also react to texture, generally preferring soft, fluffy foods (e.g., pudding) and crisp vegetables. Meats are not favoured generally because they are difficult to chew with primary teeth.

Families' ethnocultural food habits are powerful, especially for children's developing tastes. In infancy, there may be regular introduction to a variety of foods that start with little flavour, but with repetition, the food is more and more accepted. In Mexico, for example, it is very common that young children are given food that includes chili pepper. More chili pepper is gradually added as the child's tolerance increases. Preference for tastes connect to previous experience, developmental stage, and genetics (Mennella et al., 2005, p. 3). Using this approach, broccoli should be easy!

Emotional

The emotional component of nutrition is related to individual likes and dislikes. It may simply be a matter of taste differentiation or a desire for or aversion to food associated with a positive or negative experience. *For example, a child who is forced, rather than gently encouraged, to eat yams may develop an aversion to yams.* Table 5.1 shows ways in which children can develop positive or negative associations with food and how these can affect their eating habits. Sadly, it is rare to hear of vegetables and dip as a preferred "reward" or "comfort" food. Emotional eating patterns, based on craving high-fat, high-sugar, or salty foods, can be challenging but possible to "unlearn."

Children enter early childhood learning and care (ECLC) programs with their repertoire of familiar foods based mostly on what their families serve and the emotional and social status that these foods hold. Children quickly pick up messages that may make them more or less responsive to a new food.

If a two-year-old's parent has told her to eat all her vegetables before she can have dessert, it is no mystery that she will give the dessert a higher status than the vegetables, reinforcing her preference for dessert.

Social and Cultural

The social and cultural aspects of eating have a significant influence on our lives and are linked with physical and emotional forces; food often has deep personal meaning. It would be rare not to see food playing a significant role in any social gathering. Some foods are more likely to be served in certain social situations—such as hot dogs at ball games and popcorn at movies. Many food traditions in social gatherings are related to particular ethnocultural or religious holidays.

Cabbage rolls as one of the 12 meatless dishes prepared at Ukrainians' Christmas Eve. Chinese cake at Chinese New Year. Special baked goods at Passover or Easter. Turkey at Thanksgiving. Iftar (breaking fast) during Ramadan is often done as a community, starting with eating sweet dates.

TABLE 5.1 What Food Can Mean

Positive and Negative Associations with Food	
Security	When an infant cries from hunger, someone feeds and cuddles him or her, which contributes to a sense of security.
Insecurity	When a family is unable to provide enough food regularly (food insecurity), the child's ability to predict events may be jeopardized.
Pacifier	A child who is always given food whenever he or she cries, regardless of whether the child is hungry, views food as a pacifier rather than a means of nourishment.
Learning	A young child learns about the world by experiencing food through the five senses.
Punishment	Parents withdraw food, often dessert, because of inappropriate behaviour or may send the child to bed hungry.
Reward	Children are offered food, usually sweets, as a reward for success or "good" behaviour.
Individuality	A child uses food as a way to express individuality (i.e., food likes and dislikes).
Love	The child learns to give and eat food to show love (e.g., chocolates on Valentine's Day or a mother saying, "Don't you like mommy's dinner?" which equates rejection of the food with rejection of her).
Comforter	Food is used to relieve boredom or loneliness or to handle anxiety or disappointment (e.g., following rejection by a friend or a fall from a bicycle, a child is comforted with cookies or candy). The child learns to use food as a coping mechanism.
Fear	An unpleasant experience with food (e.g., choking) causes a child to fear eating that food in the future.
Approval	A child tries to win approval and acceptance through food by eating and refusing the same foods that his or her peers eat and refuse (e.g., a school-age child rejects foods from home that had been readily accepted until the child's friends commented negatively on it). Another example of approval may be a child "cleaning off his plate" for daddy or mommy.
Weapon	A child with little control over his or her environment uses food for revenge or to get attention (e.g., by refusing to eat, demanding food, throwing food).

Dragon Images/Shutterstock.com

Eating with other people tends to be viewed as a more enjoyable experience than eating alone. Do you, or someone you know who lives alone, eat in front of the television for company? Eating together can promote positive values, such as awareness of your needs and desires as well as those of others, sharing, learning respectful rhythms of talking and listening, and celebrating as a community (see Creating a Positive Eating Environment, page 275).

Children sitting at the table with encouraging adult role modelling tend to eat better than those who have no or only negative adult involvement. Research has shown that children who eat with parents who enjoy their vegetables and fruit are more likely to meet daily recommended servings for these foods. Healthy parental role modelling in a positive environment is one strategy that can increase children's intakes of these foods (Draxten et al., 2014, p. 1).

The way foods are viewed by others in our midst affects the status of the food. If parents and educators treat all nutritious foods with equal respect, children are more likely to try a variety of them. If certain foods are given lower status, children are liable to share that view.

Traditional ethnocultural preferences for food are often strongest in families that have recently come to Canada. When ethnicity is an important aspect of family life, parents often continue to prepare traditional foods and perhaps combine them with contemporary foods of North America. We often associate North American foods with the highly processed, high-fat, and refined-sugar foods that are not as rich in nutrients as many of the more traditional, ethnocultural foods. *Eating Well with Canada's Food Guide* encourages Canadians to reduce their intake of highly processed, refined foods (Health Canada, 2011a). A study of body mass index (BMI) from almost 130 million people worldwide who were over five years old found that obesity multiplied over 10 times globally. Specifically, the number grew from 11 million in 1975 to 124 million in 2016 (World Health Organization [WHO], 2017, p. 1).

Chronic lifestyle diseases are the result of a myriad of factors, but they are undeniably linked to the energy-dense diets high in animal fat that are replacing traditional plant-based diets in much of the world. Educators should try to be aware of and reinforce traditional, ethnocultural food preferences, particularly those higher in nutrients (e.g., vegetables and fruit) and less refined (i.e., whole grains).

We are bombarded daily with information and pressure from the media. Young children are unable developmentally to discriminate between the commercial and the television show, which makes them vulnerable to advertisements for non-nutritious foods. Also, children notice that many shows depict "cool" children and adolescents regularly eating low-nutritive snack foods such as chips and cookies or complaining when they eat vegetables. Furthermore, the significant amount of sedentary screen time that children could be spending in physically challenging activities does not contribute to optimal health. Watching television is also associated with snacking on high-fat and high-sugar foods (see Impact of Screen Time on Healthy Active Living, page 364).

Parents, educators, and other adults in children's lives can have a significant influence on their acceptance of a variety of foods. The more someone experiences different foods, the more likely that child is to develop a taste for them. Children who have had less exposure to new foods are more likely to be labelled as "picky eaters" and to be unwilling to try new foods, which creates a vicious circle (Carruth et al., 2004).

Body Image

Maintaining weight within a normal range is conducive to health. However, the range that has been considered normal, particularly for women (although it is becoming more of an issue for men), has been narrowly defined by the fashion industry, the media, and some factions of the dance and sport domains. Society continues to focus too much on body weight. This preoccupation has, in fact, contributed to the dramatic overall rise in obesity (obesity in Canadian children has doubled in the past 20 years) and eating disorders in our society over the past few decades. How? Dieting can be the first step in the development of **disordered eating** (the behaviour) and **eating disorders** (a diagnosed illness) (National Eating Disorder Information Centre [NEDIC], 2014).

Dieting by restricting calories or food groups will almost certainly cause problems that are counterproductive:

- The metabolism will slow down as the body tries to fight the starvation process.
- The weight will return in a short time.
- A lowered sense of self-worth or depression is common due to feelings of failure.

The process and philosophy of dieting ignore the fact that healthy people come in all shapes and sizes and, instead, tie personal worth to physical thinness. Natural body weights, based on genetic predisposition and managed when we treat our bodies with respect through healthy eating and regular physical activity, do not come close to those of the runway models for the vast majority of women and men. The ideal **body image** is often portrayed as the unattainable "perfect" body (usually associated with thinness). Children, especially girls, from a very young age can become obsessed with their weight if they are surrounded by these dangerous messages. Early on, families and educators need to support young children to have a healthy lifestyle, become media literate, develop positive life skills such as assertiveness and problem solving, and learn how to handle harassment or teasing based on appearance (NEDIC, 2014). A study in 1961 in which fifth- and sixth-grade children ranked pictures of other children in order of how well they "liked" each child was replicated 40 years later (Latner & Stunkard, 2003). The prevalence of obesity had more than doubled between 1961 and 2001. The picture of the obese child was liked significantly less (by 40.8%) in the present study than in 1961—a disturbing conclusion that the stigmatization of obesity seems to have increased over the past 40 years (see Concerns about Childhood Obesity, page 322). Women receive ubiquitous messages from the fashion, media, and diet industries that they are never good enough and that they must deprive themselves to continually fight the natural size of their body. Young men are also expected to have muscular "six-pack" bodies. In addition, the "fear of fat" that pervades our society results in social prejudice and discrimination against individuals who weigh more than what is deemed acceptable. This can damage their feelings of self-worth and result in extreme dieting, creating a vicious circle. Another study (Latner et al., 2007) that assessed how much time 10- to 13-year-olds spent weekly reading magazines, watching TV, and playing video games revealed that a greater dislike of obese children was associated with spending more time in these activities, especially magazine reading. In other words, mass media sources, especially magazines, may lead children to stigmatize peers (or themselves) who are "overweight" according to media standards. Children gain some fat prior to puberty as part of the normal growth process. This gain often coincides with an increased concern with body image, and the cycle of dieting may begin.

The National Initiative for Eating Disorders (2017) reported the following:

- "The prevalence rate of eating disorders is between 2% and 3%" (p. 1). To put that into numbers, "an estimated 725,800 to 1,088,700 Canadians will meet the diagnostic criteria for an eating disorder" (p. 1).

- "In a Southern Ontario series of studies with a community sample of approximately 2,000 students: 30% of females and 25% of males between the ages of 10 and 14 years of age reported dieting to lose weight" (p. 3). The majority of these children were in a healthy weight range consistent with body mass index (BMI) (p. 3).

Many young children are eating less than the recommended amount of food and calories and are showing low muscle mass. This evidence suggests that lack of physical activity plays a role in their weight gain. The tendency in our society to diet adds to the problem rather than helps because lowering food intake tends to slow our metabolism rather than make it run more efficiently. *Eating Well with Canada's Food Guide*, on the other hand, focuses on the message of eating well and being active today and every day (Health Canada, 2011a).

This issue is important in ECLC because educators, like everyone else, are profoundly influenced by media messages. Remember the great impact you have on children and how they look up to you. It is important to be sensitive to the subtle messages (e.g., you are constantly on a diet) and the overt ones (e.g., you comment to a child that he or she is chubby or skinny) that you send to children.

Economics

In Canada, an exciting range of foods is available in many urban communities. However, this is not the case in all Canadian communities. Even when a vast range of foods is available, they may not be used due to cost or perhaps because many people are unsure of how to prepare them.

Family incomes and parents' awareness of nutrition directly influence the quality of the family's dietary intake. That is, higher levels of family incomes and parents who are knowledgeable about nutrition and cooking contribute to better dietary intake. Families with higher incomes can afford and prepare a wider variety of wholesome foods. Families with lower incomes not only have less money in their food budget but also may lack adequate transportation, which limits their access to bulk purchases, sales, or lower priced but more nutritious foods. Small neighbourhood convenience stores, for example, may not carry a variety of fresh fruit and vegetables or may charge higher prices.

Parents may choose to spend part of their food budget eating in restaurants. Eating out shapes eating habits because restaurant menus limit food choices and affect how foods are prepared. Even so, many families with young children eat in fast-food places that serve mainly high-fat, high-sodium fried food. Children's choices are influenced by marketing of children's "meal deals," comprising a hamburger, fries, pop, and a toy. Some of these fast-food restaurants offer to increase the portion sizes for a small increase in price, thus encouraging individuals to eat larger portions because they see the deal as a bargain (see Supporting Healthy Eating Habits, page 355).

Food Insecurity

Food is one of the most basic needs of every human being. However, in Canada and around the world, people do not have equal access to food. **Food insecurity** is defined by the Canadian government as "the inability to acquire or consume an adequate diet quality or sufficient quantity of food in socially acceptable ways, or the uncertainty that one will be able to do so" (Government of Canada, 2012, p. 1).

Generally, food insecurity is determined by financial insecurity. However, it can also be caused by much more complex realities. This is true for many people living in remote environments, most notably First Nations on reserve. Acquiring food without reliable or affordable transportation is only one of many challenges that they face.

When a family does not have the financial means to afford all the necessities of a healthy life, their food and nutrition intake suffer. Fixed payments such as rent and power bills make it likely that the more "flexible" grocery budget is what bears a large burden of poverty. McIntyre et al.'s 2012 study used the National Longitudinal Survey of Children and Youth data restricted to households with children age two to nine years. Between 1997 and 2007, the food-insecure households seemed to rely more on internal coping strategies. These strategies included (2012, p. 431)

- eating cheaper foods (46%),
- skipping meals or eating less (28%), and
- receiving food from charity (22%).

As a result, those families also reported a lot less food variety, which can also compromise nutrition. "Utilization of food banks and other community resources as a method of coping with child hunger remained static despite an increase in national food banks/affiliated agencies in Canada (2,141 in 1998 to 3,540 in 2007)" (McIntyre et al., 2012, p. 428). The authors concluded that internal coping strategies may indicate that food insecurity, specifically child hunger, is more and more regarded as a private matter that stays within family boundaries. This study strongly suggests that broader public supports, most notably employment opportunities, are key to affording sufficient, nutritious food, thereby increasing family autonomy and reducing child hunger.

Peter Bernik/Shutterstock.com

Food banks are "band-aid" solutions to the poverty and food insecurity experienced by families in Canada. Food banks and targeted, short-term nutrition support programs were meant to be stop-gap measures, but they have instead become an institution in Canada. Families whose breadwinners work at low-paying jobs or depend on social assistance and who can't manage the cost of food on top of rent, utilities, clothing, and transportation rely on food banks. Many children are hungry day in and day out, which affects their short- and long-term physical, emotional, and social well-being. In a country as rich as Canada, it is atrocious that so many children and families go hungry. Poverty is a complex social issue that must be addressed with commitment at all levels of government and communities across Canada.

Food costs have also been rising worldwide, partly due to changing fuel prices and commodity costs, weather concerns such as droughts, and other reasons, affecting long-term costs in the food industry. In the news, there are reports of families in Canada buying rice in large quantities in grocery stores and shipping it to their families living in developing countries where there is a rice shortage and what is available is very costly.

CRITICAL THINKING

After having read the six factors that have an influence on our eating habits, identify one that is most relevant to you. Eating habits are not pure science; a lot of subjectivity is involved. How do you think the factor you have chosen affects your work with young children? Consider the positive influence it can have on promoting healthy active living in your career with children and families.

Bangkok happiness/Shutterstock.com

NUTS AND BOLTS OF NUTRITION

Understanding the basics of nutrition enables us to understand the important role that eating healthy food plays in promoting health.

Role of Nutrients

Nutrients are substances found in food. They are divided into seven categories: carbohydrates, proteins, fats, vitamins, minerals, fibre, and water (see Table 5.2).

OBJECTIVES

To list the seven categories of nutrients and describe their main functions. (LO 1, 6)

To describe the digestive process. (LO 1)

To explain the important aspects of *Eating Well with Canada's Food Guide* that relate to children. (LO 1, 4, 6)

TABLE 5.2 Functions of Nutrients

Categories	Functions
Carbohydrates	primary nutrients for providing calories (or energy) needed for work and physical activity
Proteins	support bodily functions (e.g., proteins are needed for cell growth and repair); part of various enzymes, hormones, and antibodies; provide energy
Fats	all cell membranes are made of lipids (fats), including cells of the nervous system; omega-3 and -6 fats are essential for brain and nerve function and healthy skin; transport fat-soluble vitamins; provide energy

(continued)

TABLE 5.2 Functions of Nutrients *(continued)*

Categories	Functions
Vitamins	organic substances (i.e., contain carbon) essential for helping the body regulate its functions (e.g., water-soluble vitamin C is an antioxidant that protects cells from damage and helps the body absorb iron, a mineral, from nonmeat sources as it is transported through the body)
Minerals	inorganic substances essential in differing amounts to help the body function properly and stay strong (e.g., magnesium is one of the minerals needed in the formation and maintenance of strong bones and teeth); transmission of nerve impulses; release of energy
Fibre	regular functioning of intestines and bowel; feeds the bacteria in the colon to sustain colonic health
Water	necessary to maintain normal hydration, blood pressure, and fluid balance; water makes up between 45 and 75% of body weight in humans; toddlers are generally around 70% water

Appendix 5.1 (see page 315) expands on the description of **nutrients**, what foods they are found in, and their **functions**. All nutrients needed by the body are found in food. In addition to the seven categories listed above, hundreds of other chemicals are found in foods (e.g., phytochemicals found in fruit and vegetables). There is no such thing as the perfect food. Eating a varied diet usually provides our body with all the vitamins and minerals we need.

There are some exceptions; for example, women who could become or are pregnant should take a multivitamin containing 0.4 mg (400 µg) of folic acid every day. Folic acid is required to reduce the risk of neural tube defects in developing babies (see Appendix 5.1, page 315).

There are other situations in which people in particular life stages or who have certain lifestyles or a health condition that requires higher needs for specific nutrients should be under the care of a physician or a dietitian to monitor needs for added supplements.

However, parents who give their children daily vitamin or mineral supplements "for their health" should evaluate the short- and long-term safety of this practice and follow the directions of their health care professional, such as a physician or a dietitian. Keep in mind that supplements are not a substitute for food. The body absorbs nutrients best from foods, and, in addition to vitamins and minerals, foods contain many valuable substances, such as antioxidants and phytochemicals (see Increase the Consumption of Vegetables and Fruit, page 242). Plant-based foods contain fibre, which is needed in proper quantity to support good digestive health.

Strict vegetarians may need a supplement containing vitamin B12, vitamin D, iron, calcium, and zinc if not consuming any animal products (e.g., milk, meats, eggs, cheeses). Or individuals with specific food allergies may need a supplement; for example, someone with lactose intolerance may need a calcium supplement. Many nutrients work best when combined with one or more other nutrients.

Remember the following points about nutrients:

- Food provides all the nutrients our bodies need.

  Our body absorbs iron better in the presence of vitamin C, and calcium needs phosphorus, magnesium, and vitamin D to build bones and teeth.

- Many foods are not simply a carbohydrate, protein, or fat but are a combination of two or three nutrients.

  The yolk of an egg is high in fat, but the white is high in protein. Most cheeses and meats are a combination of protein and fat. The energy from whole-grain bread comes mostly from carbohydrates, with a little from protein and fat.

- We all need the same nutrients, but how much we need of each nutrient varies with age, size, activity level, and other factors.

  Children need more calcium because of bone and tooth formation. A very physically active teenager needs more food energy than a less active one.

- The quality of nutrients is affected by how food is grown, harvested, stored, and prepared.

  Broccoli provides more vitamin C and the B vitamins, especially folate, when it is raw than when it is boiled until soft because most of the B and C vitamins are lost in the water—they are water soluble.

- Rinsing fresh fruit and vegetables under running water removes soil and pesticide residue. Although peeling produce (e.g., apples, cucumbers) results in a loss of fibre, vitamins, and minerals, peeling may be advisable if there is concern about pesticide use. Other ways to avoid vitamin and mineral loss are to

  - cut, tear, or chop produce just before use to reduce the loss of vitamin C;

  - microwave, pressure cook, steam, or stir-fry vegetables just until tender;

  - avoid boiling vegetables; and

  - save cooking water for soups or stews.

- Eating too much or too little of any nutrient can contribute to or cause disease. Reduce the amount of fat, sugar, and salt you eat by using less or none at all in cooking and at the table. The taste for salt is learned, and the excess salt (sodium) intake of Canadians is of concern.

Research shows that sodium causes high blood pressure and damage to blood vessels even in children, setting them up for an increased risk of stroke and heart disease (Kirkey, 2007). (See Appendix 5.1, page 315.)

According to the Heart and Stroke Foundation of Canada, most Canadians consume considerably more sodium per day than is needed for health. "About six million, or roughly 20% of adult Canadians have high blood pressure (hypertension), the leading risk for death in the world, the number one risk factor for stroke, and a major risk factor for heart disease" (2014, p. 1). "Most of the sodium Canadians consume (77%) comes from processed foods sold in grocery stores and food service outlets" (2014, p. 1). The goal of a federally appointed working group is to bring dietary sodium to healthy levels by 2020. The level of sodium in processed foods is of most concern and may mean that targeted legislation may be necessary (Kirkey, 2007) (see Health Promotion Action Plan, page 48). If children become more familiar with herbs and spices as interesting alternatives to processed foods and the salt shaker when they are developing their tastes and eating habits, their lifelong health will benefit.

Increase the Consumption of Vegetables and Fruit

The Canadian Community Health Survey (Shields, 2006) reported that children and adolescents who eat vegetables and fruit five or more times a day are substantially less likely to be overweight than are those whose vegetable and fruit consumption is less frequent. One of the important aspects of the vegetable and fruit argument is that obesity has been linked repeatedly to consumption of low-cost foods. Refined grains and added sugars and fats tend to be less expensive, taste good to many children, and are convenient. The fact that low-nutritive foods tend to cost less than high-nutritive foods such as vegetables and fruit makes for a difficult ongoing scenario for families who are on a very limited budget. "Socioeconomic disparities in diet quality may be explained by the higher cost of healthy diets. Identifying food patterns that are nutrient rich, affordable, and appealing should be a priority to fight social inequalities in nutrition and health" (Darmon & Drewnowski, 2015, p. 1).*

We all know that vegetables and fruit are rich in vitamins, minerals, and fibre, but they also offer **phytochemicals**, which are the compounds that give vegetables and fruit their colour. Scientists are still discovering specific phytochemicals and the roles they play, such as

- the role that beta-carotene in yellow and orange vegetables plays as an antioxidant and
- the roles that flavonoids play in apples, beans, and red grapes to protect against cancer and in lowering cholesterol.

Phytochemicals help promote good health by working with the other nutrients occurring naturally in the fruit or vegetable. There are likely other aspects of plant foods that contribute to health. For example, Ratey (2013, p. 239) states that small amounts of toxins in many vegetables and fruit that are meant to keep insects away also serve to trigger a beneficial stress response.

It seems odd to think of oxidants as something negative, considering we need oxygen for life! However, oxidants, usually referred to as free radicals, are basically molecules missing an electron. When a molecule loses an electron attached to it, it is unstable and tries to take an electron from the closest molecule and restabilize itself. The molecule being attacked then becomes a free radical, which is the beginning of a chain reaction; as the process continues, damage to cells also continues. This process is known to damage biological material such as DNA and protein, contributing to degenerative diseases, such as obesity, diabetes, cardiovascular disease, and cancers.

Eating vegetables and fruits daily is connected to lowered risk for many chronic diseases. Antioxidant phytochemicals in plant foods are believed to

---

*Source: Darmon N & Drewnowski A, "Contribution of Food Prices and Diet Cost to Socioeconomic Disparities in Diet Quality and Health: A Systematic Review and Analysis," *Nutrition Reviews* 2015, 73 (10): 643–660, doi:10.1093/nutrit/nuv027. Reproduced by permission of Oxford University Press on behalf of the International Life Sciences Institute.

contribute substantially to disease prevention through attacking oxidation (Zhang et al., 2015, p. 21138).

Encourage eating a rainbow of colours daily for maximum benefits. *Eating Well with Canada's Food Guide* recommends at least four vegetables and fruit a day for children from 2 to 3 years old, at least five for children 4 to 8 years old, and six for children 9 to 13 years old. The Vegetables and Fruit food group is the most prominent arc in the rainbow in *Eating Well with Canada's Food Guide*, emphasizing the important role these foods play in a healthy eating pattern (Health Canada, 2011a). Optimally, they are offered at all meals and snacks. This is a concern when we note that the NutriSTEP study found that more than half of the almost 300 preschoolers weren't getting enough grains and fruit, and 45% weren't getting enough vegetables (Simpson et al., 2007). Advocating for a variety of daily vegetable and fruit servings in our ECLC settings and finding child-friendly ways to offer them are important roles for educators and food service personnel involved in our programs. Vegetables and fruit provide fibre. If possible, eliminate juice and offer water instead, and provide vegetables and fruit to eat. They can help people feel full and satisfied, which may help reduce the risk of obesity (Health Canada, 2011a). In the case of young children, of course, one caution is to balance their fibre needs with their need to take in enough calories. Young children need higher-energy foods to sustain their energy levels, so a homemade cheese sauce with broccoli and a hummus dip with raw vegetables are ideal combinations.

Involve children as much as possible in the preparation of vegetables and fruit. Neighbourhood, municipal, or even provincial policies can promote more vegetables and fruit in early childhood agencies and schools. Review Table 5.3 (page 244) to answer this question: Can you identify vegetables and fruit that are not included in this table, especially ones that reflect the cultural food patterns of the families in your placement or ECLC setting? Try to find ways to incorporate new vegetables and fruit reflecting a range of colours. Find ways to promote vegetable and fruit eating at home.

Courtesy of Barb Pimento, taken at the Downtown Montessori (Coatsworth) Childcare Centre

Have a "Fave Family Vegetable or Fruit of the Week" (or month), with each family member having a turn to share his or her favourite. When children enjoy a variety of vegetables and fruit daily and learn more about their origins and different ways to serve them, this essential food group becomes integrated into their lifelong eating pattern, one important way to help prevent obesity.

TABLE 5.3 Vegetables and Fruits Come in a Variety of Colours: Here Are Some Examples

Green	Red	Yellow/Orange	Blue/Purple	White/Tan/Brown
avocados	cherries	cantaloupes	blackberries	pears
green grapes	cranberries	lemons	blueberries	cauliflower
kiwis	raspberries	mangoes	figs	garlic
bok choy	red apples	nectarines	plums	ginger
broccoli	watermelons	pineapples	purple grapes	lychees
green peppers	beets	carrots	eggplants	mushrooms
kale/collards	radishes	sweet potatoes	purple asparagus	onions
peas	red tomatoes	yellow squash	purple endive	turnips

Fats: Unsaturated and Saturated

In addition to the main functions of fats (see Table 5.2, page 239), it is important to know the difference between unsaturated and saturated fats to make healthy choices.

Have you heard the terms "good" and "bad" cholesterol (Government of Canada, 2016a, pp. 2–4)?

- Good cholesterol is high-density lipoprotein (HDL), which is found in **unsaturated fats**. There are two types of unsaturated fats:
  - monounsaturated, found in avocados, nuts, seeds, and vegetable oil (such as olive, sunflower, peanut, and sesame)
  - polyunsaturated, found in nuts, seeds, fatty fish (such as salmon and trout), and vegetable oil (such as canola, corn, flaxseed, and soybean)

  These types of oils are usually liquid at room temperature.
- Bad cholesterol is low-density lipoprotein (LDL), which is found in **saturated fats**. Saturated fats are generally from animals (e.g., butter, lard, and animal fat) and tropical oils (e.g., coconut and palm), and are usually solid at room temperature (e.g., cheese and fatty cuts of meat).

We all have good (HDL) and bad (LDL) cholesterol in our blood. We want more of the HDL so that it moves the LDL from our arteries to our liver, which removes it from our bodies. This is why when health care providers test our cholesterol levels, they are very pleased when we have high HDL and low LDL.

Unsaturated fats should make up the majority of fats in the diet, in order to help lower cholesterol levels and reduce the risk of heart disease. The Government of Canada (2016a, p. 4) notes that 23 to 45 mL (2 to 3 tbsp.) of unsaturated fats a day is recommended. Limiting intake of saturated fats is helpful in reducing the risk of high cholesterol and heart disease.

Although not all fats are equal when it comes to our health, the total amount of all fats is important to consider because all are equally high in calories. Currently, most Canadians get more than they need of their daily calories (or energy) from fats. Although fat is important for body functions such as providing essential fatty acids and carrying fat-soluble vitamins through the body, research into links between fat intake and disease has resulted in recommendations regarding the type and amount of fat we consume. Do keep in mind that young children's needs for fat differ from those of older children and adults.

Highlighting Fats in Our Daily Food Consumption

The following summary outlines the general suggestions made by the Government of Canada (2016a), but keep in mind that ongoing research may result in future adjusted recommendations:

- "Omega-3 fat helps prevent blood from sticking and clotting and helps lower triglycerides. This fat is found in fatty fish such as salmon, mackerel, herring and sardines as well as in flax and some newer products such as omega-3 liquid eggs" (Heart and Stroke Foundation of Canada, 2017, p. 3).
- "Omega-6 fat helps lower LDL-cholesterol ('bad' cholesterol), but when eaten in large amounts is thought to lower high density lipoprotein (HDL) cholesterol ('good' cholesterol)" (Heart and Stroke Foundation of Canada, 2017, p. 3).*

Joshua Resnick/Shutterstock.com

Omega-3 Fatty Acids: Fish Is a Source of Omega-3

Omega-3 fatty acids are essential components of all cells in the body, especially brain cells. We need to ensure that we consume foods high in omega-3. If that isn't possible, carefully choose an omega-3 supplement suited to your needs. Fish is high in omega-3, which is good for the heart and brain, making it an excellent choice for healthy eating two to five times a week.

However, one caution is that some fish, which are higher up the food chain and, as a result, live longer, contain methyl mercury. Mercury that is released into the environment may be deposited into water, where microorganisms can convert it to methyl mercury, a highly toxic form of mercury that can build up in living tissue (Health Canada, 2007).

Jacek Chabraszewski/Shutterstock.com

---

*Source: Heart and Stroke, 2017. *Position Statement: Trans Fatty Acids ('Trans Fat') and Heart Disease and Stroke*, http://www.heartandstroke.ca/-/media/pdf-files/canada/2017-position-statements/transfatty-acids-ps-eng.ashx?la=en&hash=1462D8CF328665A124340833F1362C3AE633B7D4. Reprinted by permission of the Heart and Stroke Foundation of Canada.

Fish may not be part of someone's diet if that person dislikes the taste of fish, has a fish allergy, or is a vegetarian. Other ways to get those important sources of omega-3 fatty acids may include fish oil or vegan DHA capsules and plant-based omega-3 fatty acids, including crushed flax and walnut.

FISH AND MERCURY ADVISORIES

Health Canada's recommendation to limit certain fish is particularly important for pregnant and breastfeeding women, babies, and children. Mercury can damage a growing brain. "Predatory fish such as shark, swordfish, fresh and frozen tuna, escolar, marlin and orange roughy have higher levels of mercury and should be consumed only occasionally" (Health Canada, 2009a, p. 3). Although canned white albacore tuna is a concern, canned light tuna (skipjack, yellowfin, tongol) is safe. Check the Health Canada website for current mercury advisories. Health Canada's standards for mercury in fish are some of the most stringent and protective in the world. Consult your provincial or territorial government for any sport fish advice if fish that is caught from local waters is consumed.

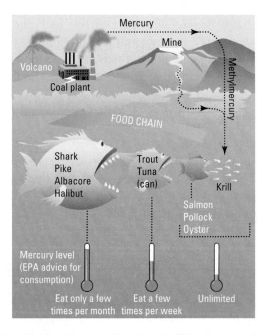

Source: Ground Truth Trekking, "How Does Mercury End Up in Your Food?" http://www.groundtruthtrekking.org/Graphics/MercuryFoodChain.html. Reprinted with permission.

Ban on Trans Fats

It is common knowledge that the types and amount of fats we take in have a substantial impact on our long-term health. In 1960, **trans fats** became very popular, and in the 1990s, Canadians had one of the highest intakes of trans fats in the world. It was also in the 1990s that research discovered that trans fats raised our LDL (bad) cholesterol and reduced our HDL (good) cholesterol. Trans fats were also recognized as a cause of heart attacks and a greater risk of type 2 diabetes.

Canada was the first country to identify trans fats on nutrition labels of food products sold in Canada. Trans fats are known to be unhealthy for all. Back in 2006, the federal government, regrettably, did not follow through with its plan to ban trans fats in food production. Health advocacy and consumer groups successfully lobbied for healthy public policy on this issue. The Heart and Stroke Foundation was a lead advocate, stating that the ban would reduce the number of heart attacks in Canada and save lives (CBC News, 2017, pp. 1–3). Thankfully, on September 15, 2018, the Government of Canada banned trans fats. Before the federal ban, some provincial school nutrition policies had banned foods containing trans fats from being food sold on their premises, including some baked goods, packaged snack foods, and deep-fried foods, among others.

Although the small amounts of trans fats (conjugated linoleic acids) occurring naturally in some foods, such as dairy products, beef, and lamb, are of no concern and have potential benefits, Canadians took in far greater amounts in processed foods made with partially hydrogenated oils, which produce trans fats. Trans fats form during a process called hydrogenation, when an oil is converted into a more stable liquid or semisolid form by pumping hydrogen into the oil—in other words, making a liquid oil into a solid fat.

Trans fats benefited the food industry by producing the pleasing textures and flavours that make bakery products and other food products so tempting and adding shelf life to food. With food being transported globally from large food-processing plants, a longer shelf life is a definite advantage, especially for foods such as bakery items. Many restaurants, including, but not exclusively, fast-food restaurants, used hydrogenated oils in their breaded seafood, chicken, and other meats; French fries; and desserts. Companies and food manufacturers, in Canada and globally, must now replace trans fats with healthier oil alternatives in order to be able to use food products or import them to Canada. The healthier replacements include monounsaturated and polyunsaturated fats, which can have a positive effect on your health when eaten in moderation.

With regard to children, especially preschoolers, we must keep in mind that they need more fat and energy in their diet for brain development and rapid growth (Health Canada, 2011b). Foods such as eggs, lean meat, nut butters (if not allergic), milk, cheese, and other dairy or soy products that are not skim are beneficial for young children because they provide a concentrated source of calories, other than those found in junk foods. Children need to eat small amounts of food throughout the day because their small stomachs tend to fill up quickly. Therefore, most young children, unless vegan, do tend to take in more saturated fat until school age. Over time, the variations in the amount a child eats usually average out to provide the calories and nutrients needed. This is especially true if the child is encouraged to eat healthy foods when hungry and to stop eating when full (Health Canada, 2011b, p. 39).

Digestion: The Basics

What happens to the food we eat? You may know how the digestive system works from a biology or physiology course or simply remember it as general knowledge. Figure 5.1 (see page 248) and Table 5.4 (see page 249) provide a peek into the digestive process, as a *basic* introduction or quick review of what you know happens

FIGURE 5.1 Gastrointestinal Tract

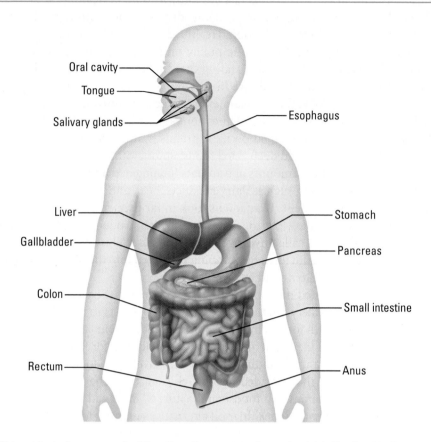

The GI tract includes any part of the digestive system through which the food being processed can pass. This diagram is a visual representation of the

- primary digestive system organs (i.e., mouth [oral cavity], esophagus, stomach, small intestine, colon [large intestine], rectum, and anus); and
- accessory organs, which include all organs needed in the digestive system although not situated in the GI tract, including the tongue, salivary glands, liver, gallbladder, and pancreas.

when food enters your body. You are encouraged to learn more about nutrition as it will benefit your own understanding and your ability to respond with age-appropriate answers to children's questions. As well, it is likely that some children in your care will be identified with a mild acute or possibly chronic condition of the gastrointestinal (GI) tract, such as constipation, diarrhea, lactose or gluten intolerance, celiac disease, or other conditions.

The main functions of the digestive system are digesting food, breaking it down into molecules small enough for the body to absorb as nutrients, and eliminating what is not needed. The digestive tract starts at your mouth when you take a bite of food and ends at the anus when you have a bowel movement. The organs work together to break down food and turn it into nutrient molecules to be used for energy and to help the body work, grow, and repair. The vast majority of **digestion** and absorption of nutrients by the blood is completed in the small intestine; nutrients from the food (fatty acids, amino acids, sugars) are released to be absorbed and circulated around your body in the bloodstream. Most vitamins and minerals are absorbed into the epithelial cells that line the mouth, esophagus, stomach, and intestines and then into the bloodstream. Because of this absorption, they are not considered to be part of the digestive system. In the large intestine, water is absorbed from indigestible or other waste unusable for bodily functions. The feces (formed stool) produced in the large intestine is passed on to the rectum, and the anal sphincter controls when the feces is passed out of the body.

TABLE 5.4 The Digestive Process: From Top to Bottom

Primary Digestive System Organs	Accessory Organs	Chemical Secretions (Enzymes/Acids)	Functions
Mouth (Oral Cavity)	Tongue		Mechanical digestion of the food as the teeth and jaws chop, grind, and chew food
			Mechanical digestion helps mix food with saliva, tongue moves food around in the mouth, assists in swallowing
	Salivary Glands	Produces saliva (which contains the enzyme amylase)	Chemical amylase in saliva starts to digest the carbohydrates
Esophagus		Produces mucus, which keeps the passageway moist and helps swallowing	Mechanical digestion as the food passes from the mouth down the esophagus to the stomach
Stomach		Produces • gastric juice that contains hydrochloric acid (HCL), pepsinogen, and other digestive enzymes • mucus	Mechanical digestion of the food by churning it against the stomach walls The pyloric sphincter at the base of the stomach opens and closes, letting some of the food pass into the small intestine, a little at a time Chemical digestion includes • gastric juice containing enzymes that – start to break down the proteins – destroy various germs – neutralize acid-base levels in the stomach • excreting mucus that shields the stomach lining from the damaging effects of the gastric juice

(*continued*)

TABLE 5.4 The Digestive Process: From Top to Bottom (*continued*)

Primary Digestive System Organs	Accessory Organs	Chemical Secretions (Enzymes/Acids)	Functions
Small Intestine (the vast majority of digestion and absorption of nutrients by the blood is completed here)		Produces intestinal juice and mucus	Chemical digestion: • Carbohydrates, proteins, and lipids continue to be digested, and chemical digestion is completed with the introduction of the bile (see below; bile from liver, pancreatic juice from pancreas) • Small, soluble nutrients (sugars, amino acids, fatty acids) are absorbed • Secretions cause the chemical breakdown of proteins, fats (lipids), and carbohydrates • Mucus protects and lubricates the intestine's lining
	Liver	Produces bile	Chemical digestion uses the bile, blends with fats (lipids)
	Gallbladder		Stores bile, then releases into small intestine
	Pancreas	Produces pancreatic juice, which is a mixture of digestive enzymes	Chemical digestion: • Pancreatic juice in the small intestine assists in completion of the digestion of proteins, fats, and carbohydrates • Pancreas helps release nutrients
Large Intestine			Water and minerals are reabsorbed back into the blood Unusable, indigestible wastes (feces) move to the rectum
Rectum			Feces are temporarily stored
Anus			Mechanical digestion with the anal sphincter controlling the movement of the feces out of the body

The Foundation for Healthy Eating: *Eating Well with Canada's Food Guide*

The Revision of Canada's Food Guide

From 2013 to 2015, Health Canada conducted a review of the current version (2007) of Canada's Food Guide (CFG). The review identified challenges that the public has in using the current food guide format to plan healthy meals and snacks.

An example is that some audiences want more specific information while others want less. On a positive note, the 2007 guide is mostly consistent with scientific evidence.

Health Canada has been in a multiyear process of revising the CFG. Their goals include reinforcing healthy eating recommendations, building upon top scientific evidence on nutrition and health, and incorporating feedback from the reviews and consultations. Until this revision is completed, the 2007 CFG can continue to be your reference on healthy eating (Health Canada, 2018, p. 2).

In 2016, Health Canada communicated with stakeholders and Canadians to make sure that the new food guide and resources will be useful, understood, and easy to put into practice. That consultation, with almost 20,000 responses, offered feedback about the needs and hopes for revisions. In 2017, consultations resulted in a range of information, including proposed healthy eating recommendations, which are expected to promote health and reduce the risk of nutrition-related chronic disease. Guiding principles and recommendations for the upcoming CFG are available online. (See Resource Materials.)

Health Canada is expected to release the new dietary guidance policy report in two parts:

NELSONstudy

To access Resource Materials, visit NelsonStudy.

- Part 1, in 2018, for *health professionals and policymakers*, consisting of general healthy eating recommendations and key messages and resources for Canadians
- Part 2, in 2019, for *Canadians and Indigenous peoples*, consisting of recommendations for healthy eating patterns (amounts and types of foods), as well as resources. For the first time, there will be resources and tools developed specifically for Indigenous peoples' traditional dietary practices and sources of foods and game meat (Health Canada, 2018, p. 3).

Health Canada's poster *Let's Eat Healthy Canada!* (Health Canada, 2017b) addresses the concerns about how many of us

- *do not eat enough vegetables and fruit;*
- *eat too much saturated fats, sugar, and salt; and*
- *do not eat enough plant-based protein.*

The poster is available online. (See Resource Materials.)

Health Canada's 2007 ***Eating Well with Canada's Food Guide*** is based on two principles of healthy living: eating well and being active every day for everyone two years of age and older (Health Canada, 2011a). *Eating Well with Canada's Food Guide*'s recommendations for the amounts and types of food support meeting the daily requirements of vitamins, minerals, and other nutrients. Healthy eating contributes to your overall health and vitality and helps reduce your risk of medical conditions such as obesity, certain types of cancer, heart disease, type 2 diabetes, and osteoporosis (Health Canada, 2011a). The four **food groups** have a range of recommended daily servings based on the different ages and stages of individuals (see Table 5.5, page 252). Table 5.6 (see page 252) lists the **key nutrients** in each food group and highlights the importance of eating a variety of foods to obtain the daily recommended nutrients.

NELSONstudy

To access Resource Materials, visit NelsonStudy.

TABLE 5.5   Recommended Daily Servings

AGES IN YEARS	2–3	4–8	9–13	14–18		19–50		51+	
Sex	Girls and Boys			Females	Males	Females	Males	Females	Males
Vegetables and Fruit	4	5	6	7	8	7–8	8–10	7	7
Grain Products	3	4	6	6	7	6–7	8	6	7
Milk and Alternatives	2	2	3–4	3–4	3–4	2	2	3	3
Meat and Alternatives	1	1	1–2	2	3	2	3	2	3

Eating Well with Canada's Food Guide recommends making food choices that are healthier and limiting foods and beverages that have few nutrients and are usually high in fat, salt, or sugar or a combination thereof. Examples include cakes and pastries, chocolate and candies, cookies and granola bars, ice cream and frozen desserts, doughnuts and muffins, French fries, potato chips, nachos and other salty snacks, fruit-flavoured drinks, soft drinks, and sweetened hot or cold drinks. In ECLC programs, nutrition policies and practices that minimize the use of "less healthy foods" can contribute to children's interest in more nutritious foods.

Canadians are urged to continue to increase their intake of foods composed of complex carbohydrates (i.e., breads, cereals, vegetables, fruit) to replace the energy derived from the fat in meat and alternatives and particularly in high-fat, low-nutritive, or junk foods such as potato chips, chocolate bars, and doughnuts. In response to this research, *Eating Well with Canada's Food Guide* emphasizes eating grain products, vegetables, and fruit (Health Canada, 2011a). For anyone ready to improve his or her eating habits, these two strategies are good places to start. However, Health Canada (2011a) reminds us that too much fibre can be a problem for growing children, whose small stomachs must be able to contain enough calories for growth. Serving raw vegetables with a dip made with a dairy product, for example, is a good way to both promote fibre and provide enough food energy.

TABLE 5.6   Key Nutrients in *Eating Well with Canada's Food Guide*

SOME IMPORTANT NUTRIENTS IN THE FOOD GROUPS				
Key Nutrient	Vegetables and Fruit	Grain Products	Milk and Alternatives	Meat and Alternatives
Protein			✓	✓
Fat			✓	✓
Carbohydrate		✓	✓	
Fibre	✓	✓		

(continued)

TABLE 5.6 Key Nutrients in *Eating Well with Canada's Food Guide* (*continued*)

SOME IMPORTANT NUTRIENTS IN THE FOOD GROUPS

Key Nutrient	Vegetables and Fruit	Grain Products	Milk and Alternatives	Meat and Alternatives
Thiamin		✓		✓
Riboflavin		✓	✓	✓
Niacin		✓		✓
Folate	✓	✓		
Vitamin B$_6$	✓			✓
Vitamin B$_{12}$			✓	✓
Vitamin C	✓			
Vitamin A	✓		✓	
Vitamin D			✓	
Calcium			✓	
Iron		✓		✓
Zinc		✓	✓	✓
Magnesium	✓	✓	✓	✓
Potassium	✓	✓	✓	✓

Source: © All rights reserved. *Eating Well with Canada's Food Guide*. Health Canada, 2011. Adapted and reproduced with permission from the Minister of Health, 2018.

Relating *Eating Well with Canada's Food Guide* to Children

During the first two years of life, children undergo a period of rapid growth and development, including brain development. At no other time in your life does your body need a diet as high in fat—approximately 50% of the total daily calories—to provide you with adequate energy and fatty acids. This is the primary reason why children under two are not included in Canada's food guidelines. A second reason is that the gradual introduction of solid foods over the first two years does not relate to *Eating Well with Canada's Food Guide*. According to this guide, the amount of fat should not be restricted other than to exclude trans fats. But since its publication in 2007, the Government of Canada has banned trans fats. What about children over two years old? Health Canada's (2011a) *Eating Well with Canada's Food Guide* includes preschoolers.

Milk Products

In the second year of life, most infants make a transition from breast milk or **formula** to cow's milk. Between 12 and 24 months, children should drink homogenized milk. Children at that age need the fat from whole milk for brain development. Toddlers are not yet eating the variety and quantity of food to provide them with the daily dietary requirement for fat, so milk products remain the primary source of fat.

Some parents and even some doctors start the one-year-old on lower-fat milk (skim, 1%, 2%) if they believe the baby is too chubby—although there is little or no correlation between body fat in infancy and later childhood. This example illustrates society's fear of fat. In fact, if the one- to two-year-old drinks lower-fat milk, he or she may be hungry and tend to eat more food. Whole milk not only provides babies with essential fats but also contributes to their sense of fullness.

Partially skimmed milk (1% and 2%) can be offered to children between two and five years old as they usually eat a number of foods that are higher in fat, supplying them with the essential fatty acids. By the time children are five years old, they can be offered skim milk. Although they still need the calcium and other nutrients that milk provides, they don't need the same percentage of dietary fat and are usually eating adult-sized servings (Canadian Paediatric Society [CPS], 2015).

Although cow's milk is commonly considered one of the staples of the Milk and Alternatives food group, it is important to acknowledge that other foods or beverages can provide the key nutrients supplied by cow's milk (see Table 5.6, page 252). A prime example of one of the key nutrients found in the Milk and Alternatives group is the mineral calcium. In childhood, calcium is necessary to build strong bones to support a growing body and help prevent osteoporosis later in life.

> During childhood and adolescence, much more bone is deposited than withdrawn, so the skeleton grows in both size and density. Up to 90 percent of peak bone mass is acquired by age 18 in girls and by age 20 in boys, which makes youth the best time to 'invest' in one's bone health. (National Institutes of Health, 2015, p. 1)

Here are the daily calcium recommendations for children (Health Canada, 2009b, p. 9):

- 1 to 3 years old is 500 mg,
- 4 to 8 years old is 800 mg, and
- 9 to 18 years old is 1300 mg.

One of the concerns about children drinking carbonated and other low-nutritive drinks is that they then drink less of any calcium-rich beverages (see Reduce the Consumption of Carbonated Beverages and Low-Nutritive Foods, page 361). However, there are several other reasons why children may not drink cow's or goat's milk, including cultural or religious reasons, allergies, or taste dislike. Lactose intolerance can usually be reconciled with several options, such as lactose-free products. For children who don't regularly consume cow's or goat's milk, Table 5.7 lists foods and beverages that contain calcium to compare with *Eating Well with Canada's Food Guide* recommendations.

What Is a Child-Sized Serving?

To determine developmentally appropriate serving sizes, look at the recommendations in *Eating Well with Canada's Food Guide* and cut the quantity by approximately

- two-thirds to three-quarters for toddlers,
- one-quarter to half for preschoolers, and
- one-quarter or nil for school-agers.

TABLE 5.7 Amounts of Calcium in Foods and Beverages

Food or Beverage	Child Serving Sizes	Amount of Calcium
Calcium-fortified orange juice	125 mL, 4 oz.	185 mg
Cheddar cheese	25 g, 3/4 oz.	180 mg
Firm tofu, set with calcium	87 mL, 3/8 cup, 3 oz.	174 mg
Cow's milk (chocolate, lactose free, or buttermilk)	125 mL, 4 oz.	173 mg
Fortified soy or rice beverage	125 mL, 4 oz.	160 mg
Goat's milk	125 mL, 4 oz.	150 mg
Sardines, Atlantic, with bones	3 fish, 38 g, 1¼ oz.	138 mg
Fruit yogurt, nonfat	87 mL, 3/8 cup, 3 oz.	133 mg
Canned salmon, with bones	38 g, 1/4 cup, 1¼ oz.	93 mg
Spinach, boiled	62 mL, 1/4 cup, 2 oz.	65 mg
Toasted almonds	30 mL, 1/8 cup, 1 oz.	50 mg
Bok choy, Swiss chard, kale, okra, cooked	62 mL, 1/4 cup, 2 oz.	25–42 mg
Cooked beans (e.g., navy beans, kidney beans, chickpeas)	87 mL, 3/8 cup, 3 oz.	20–45 mg
Edamame	62 mL, 1/4 cup, 2 oz.	26 mg
Broccoli, cooked	62 mL, 1/4 cup, 2 oz.	17 mg
Dried figs	1 fig, 8 g	14 mg
Tahini	15 mL, 1 tbsp., 1/2 oz.	10 g

Source: Adapted with permission from Toronto Public Health: Getting Enough Calcium Without the Cow, PH0802SS038 http://www.toronto.ca/health/pdf/nm_calcium.pdf

See also Table 5.8 (page 256). But remember that every child is an individual. Her or his appetite can vary greatly with age, gender, activity level, and other factors. A child's appetite will also fluctuate based on growth spurts. When she or he is going through a growth spurt, the child is likely to be hungrier and to desire more food.

Multicultural Foods and *Eating Well with Canada's Food Guide*

Often educators caring for children from various ethnocultural backgrounds are unfamiliar with the foods that they commonly eat at home. Educators may wonder whether the foods fit into the four food groups. *Eating Well with Canada's Food Guide* is designed to be flexible enough to include most foods. Obviously, many foods are eaten by almost all cultures, where available. Often the style of cooking and the spices used differ between cultures. Chicken, for example, may be fried, baked, boiled,

TABLE 5.8   Serving Sizes

What is a "preschooler-sized" serving?

A Food Guide Serving is used as a reference amount. In some cases, the serving size listed in the Food Guide will be close to what a two- or three-year-old child would eat at a sitting (e.g., one slice of bread or 250 mL of milk), but in other cases, it may not (e.g., 75 g of meat).

Preschoolers have small stomachs that fill up quickly, and so they generally need to eat small amounts of food more often throughout the day.

One Food Guide Serving can be divided into smaller amounts served throughout the day. For example, the Food Guide recommends that a two- or three-year-old child eat four Food Guide Servings of Vegetables and Fruit. This may translate into a meal schedule that looks like the following:

- Breakfast: ½ banana (½ *Serving*)

- Morning snack: 125 mL vegetables with dip (1 *Serving*)

- Lunch: 60 mL cooked carrots (½ *Serving*)

- Afternoon snack: small nectarine (1 *Serving*)

- Dinner: 60 mL tomato-based spaghetti sauce (½ *Serving*)

- Evening snack: 125 mL applesauce or avocado (½ *Serving*). For children who are having additional snacks, even smaller amounts (e.g., ¼ *Serving*) can also add up to the recommended total.

What about mixed dishes?

- Mixed dishes contain ingredients from more than one food group, such as chicken spring rolls, vegetarian samosas, or rice pudding.

- Count only the main ingredients toward the servings. For example, for rice pudding, count the milk and rice but not the few raisins. If the ingredient makes up only a small amount of the food (e.g., less than ¼ Food Guide Serving), don't use it as a serving measurement.

- Remember that the servings only tell us what we should offer preschoolers. Let them decide which foods and how much to eat.

Source: Developed by the team of Registered Dietitians at Dairy Farmers of Canada. www.goodbeginnings.ca

roasted, or cooked with different spices, batters, and sauces depending on preferences and the availability of ingredients. A Mexican chicken dish that is prepared with chocolate tastes quite different from chicken Kiev, chicken parmesan, or stir-fried chicken with vegetables. Table 5.9 shows an assortment of foods that are commonly used in a variety of cultures, to help you identify the foods commonly associated with particular ethnocultural backgrounds. *Eating Well with Canada's Food Guide* is available in not only English and French but 10 additional languages: Arabic, Chinese, Farsi (Persian), Korean, Punjabi, Russian, Spanish, Tagalog, Tamil, and Urdu. There is also a guide for First Nations, Inuit, and Métis. All have culturally familiar foods and recommendations and are available on the Health Canada website to download, as pdf files, or to order copies.

TABLE 5.9 Variety of Foods

Food Groups	Food Ideas
Grain products	pita, bagel, bannock, roti, tortilla, chapati, naan, baguette, pretzel, challah, pasta, couscous, bulgur (e.g., in tabouli salad), buckwheat, millet, quinoa, basmati rice, rice cake, dumpling wrapper, cassava bread
Vegetables and fruit	okra, guava, mango, papaya, star fruit, breadfruit, soursop, plantain, coconut, wild berries such as huckleberries and thimbleberries, Asian pear, cassava (a root vegetable), akee, lychee, bok choy, mushroom, collard greens, dandelion and beet greens, water chestnut, fern root, vegetable marrow, mustard greens, bamboo shoots, soybean sprouts, summer squash, longan, cactus fruit, chayote, taro root (see also Table 5.3, page 244)
Milk products or calcium-rich foods	goat's milk, evaporated milk, feta cheese, tofu made with calcium, yogurt, fish or animal bones used in soups and stews, almonds (see also Table 5.7, page 255)
Meat and alternatives	moose; venison; beaver; wild game; chickpeas or garbanzo beans (e.g., in falafels, hummus); soybean (e.g., in soymilk, tofu); peas and rice; black-eyed peas; legumes (e.g., kidney beans, peas, navy beans, lentils, peanuts); organ meats such as kidney, heart, and liver; chorizo (a hot sausage); squid; shellfish; cockles; mussels

Kidney and pinto beans are common in Latin American dishes; tofu is often used in Chinese dishes; roti, chapati, and naan are breads used in many Southeast Asian dishes; and wild berries are commonly used by nonurban Indigenous peoples.

Some cultural beliefs and religions restrict eating some meats or advocate vegetarianism. For example, Hindus and Sikhs can eat goat, fish, and pork but not beef. Muslims can eat goat, beef, and chicken but not pork, and all meat must be prepared according to Muslim dietary law. Similarly, many Jews can eat fish, beef, chicken, and lamb but not shellfish or pork, and meat must be prepared according to Jewish dietary law. Many cultures use meat sparingly, as a complement to the meal rather than the main focus. This may at times be due to the higher cost of meat, but it is becoming apparent that less rather than more meat is an effective way to reduce fat in the diet.

Religion is significant when it comes to food preparation and consumption. Islam, Judaism, Buddhism, Sikhism, Hinduism, and Christianity all have teachings regarding food, some on daily food preparation and consumption and others relating to special times of religious observances such as Lent or Ramadan. As with all communication with families, it is important to avoid assumptions and obtain specific information from the families themselves. Table 5.10 outlines some basic differences between halal (Muslim) and kosher (Jewish) dietary rules. There are few rules prohibiting vegetables and fruit in either halal or kosher diets, so the table focuses on meat, fish, and dairy rules. This table is not meant to be a complete list; as with all religions, ethnocultures, and lifestyles (e.g., vegetarians), there are degrees of beliefs, traditions, and adherence that fall on a continuum of practices. However, a beginning awareness is important for all and a reminder that when children in your care have specific dietary needs, it is the responsibility of the educators to learn more about the specifics and how best to respect and support the children's and families' needs.

TABLE 5.10 Halal and Kosher: An Introduction to Dietary Differences

	Halal	Kosher
Blessing of Animals	Blessing on each animal while slaughtering	Blessing before entering slaughtering area, not on each animal
Preparation of Meat	Blood is drained during slaughtering	Soaked and salted to drain all blood. No special preparation.
Pork/Swine and its byproducts	Not permitted	Not permitted
Gelatin (the main protein in animal connective tissue)		
• Dry bones	From halal bones only (halal slaughtered animal)	From kosher animals
• Skin and bones	From halal slaughtered animals only	From kosher animals
• Fish	From any fish	From kosher fish only
Fish and Other Seafood	All seafood is halal. Animals that live both in the water and on land are not halal (e.g., frogs).	Permitted except fish that do not have fins and scales (e.g., catfish, eels, rays, sharks, swordfish).
Shellfish (e.g., oyster, clam), crustaceans (e.g., crab, lobster), and mollusks (e.g., scallops).	Mostly thought to be not halal	Not permitted
Combining Dairy and Meat Products	Permitted	Not permitted
Special Occasions	Same rules apply all the time	Additional restrictions during Passover

Sources: Rich, Tracey. *Judaism 101* (last updated August 1, 2012). Retrieved February 2018 from http://www.jewfaq.org/kashrut.htm#Rules; Islamic Food and Nutrition Council of America, *What Is in Our Food?* Retrieved February 2018 from http://www.ifanca.org/cms/wpages/detail/4c74f711-5ecc-4392-9d7a-22321b830f0c

Vegetarianism

Vegetarianism means different things to different people. Generally, it means choosing a plant-based way of eating. It is hard to determine how many people in Canada are currently vegetarian, but at least reducing the percentage of animal foods we eat seems to be a growing practice and may reduce the risk of obesity and some chronic conditions such as diabetes and heart disease. Many vegetarians have based their decision on personal health reasons, religion or cultural tradition, animal rights, or cost. Others are concerned about world hunger and the environmental toll of a meat-based diet over a plant-based diet. Still others are not vegetarian but have decided to eliminate some meat, such as red meat, from their diet. The term "**flexitarians**" has been coined for this growing number of Canadians seeking to lower cholesterol or fat intake or reduce meat for any of the reasons listed above, sometimes as a transition to vegetarianism.

Vegetarians are classified according to the foods that they include in their diet:

- Lacto-ovo vegetarians, who make up the vast majority of vegetarians in Canada, do not eat animal flesh but do eat animal products such as milk and eggs.
- Pesco vegetarians eat fish in addition to foods of plant origin.
- Lacto vegetarians eat milk and alternatives but not eggs.
- Ovo vegetarians eat eggs but not milk.
- Vegans eat only foods of plant origin.

It is important to remember that any family, vegetarian or not, can have adequate or poor nutrition. Vegetarians need to ensure that they find alternative ways to obtain adequate amounts of complete protein and minerals (e.g., iron, zinc) and vitamins (e.g., B_{12}) that are found in meat. The building blocks of protein are amino acids; we get eight essential amino acids from foods. Animal flesh and its products include all of these simultaneously, whereas most plant foods have fewer. A few exceptions are soy, quinoa, and buckwheat, which are complete protein plant foods. Simply eating a lot of vegetables, grains, and fruit without complete protein is not healthy eating. Learning how to complement protein is easy. Some critics of vegetarianism believe that growing children cannot get the key nutrients they need, such as calcium, without eating meat. This concern is unfounded, particularly for lacto-ovo vegetarians, who consume milk products. As is true with any way of eating, vegetarians enjoy health benefits when their diet is balanced and varied and meets energy and nutrient needs. Parents who raise their children on a vegan diet must ensure that the children get enough of the nutrients they need to grow and develop. For all infants, exclusive breastfeeding is the best source of nutrition for at least the first six months of life.

The following are some examples of **complementary proteins**, along with the country or region known for them:

- Combining grains and legumes:
  - bread and split pea soup (Canada)
  - crackers and lentil soup (Middle East)
  - rice, kimchi, and tofu (Korea)
  - cornmeal tortillas and vegetarian chili (Mexico)
  - chapatis and dahl (India)
  - pita bread and falafel (Middle East)
  - pita bread and hummus (Greece and Middle East)
  - sticky bun with black bean sauce (China)

- Combining grains and nuts:
  - granola or muesli with nuts (Switzerland)
  - pasta with pine nuts (Italy)
  - rice with cashew-vegetable stir-fry (China)

Are vegetarian diets healthy for infants and children? That is a common question. Children need many nutrients, in the right amount, to grow and develop. Like any diet that doesn't include certain foods, some vegetarian diets make it harder to get enough energy, protein, and certain nutrients.

Some nutrients—such as vitamin B_{12}—are found only in animal sources, such as cow's milk. Iron, which is very important for babies and children, is more easily absorbed by the body when it comes from meat. So if a child's diet excludes animal foods, these nutrients come from other sources. CPS's (2017) *Caring for Kids* website provides information for parents raising vegetarian children and teens (see Table 5.11).

TABLE 5.11 What's Included in a Healthy Vegetarian Diet

Energy (calories)	
	• Vegetarian diets may have fewer calories than diets that include meat and dairy products. If your child is eating a well-balanced vegetarian diet, is gaining a healthy amount of weight, and has lots of energy, then he is probably getting enough calories. Vegans might need extra sources of energy. Foods that are high in energy include soy products, avocado, soy and canola oils, and nuts and nut butters. • Small, frequent meals and snacks for toddlers may help increase the amount of calories they get.
Protein	
	• Protein helps to build, maintain, and repair tissues in the body. Your child is probably getting enough protein if her diet has enough calories and includes many different kinds of plant foods. Foods such as legumes, cereals, and nuts and seeds and their butters are rich in proteins that will your help your child better digest foods.
Fibre	
	• Fibre is a nutrient found in all plants. It helps with digestion and blood circulation. Pay close attention to the amount of fibre your child is eating. It's possible to eat too much fibre, which will fill him up so that he doesn't eat enough calories overall, and it can affect the amount of calcium, iron, or zinc the body absorbs.
Minerals	
Iron	• Babies and children need iron to make enough red blood cells and for their brains to develop normally. Some vegetables are a source of iron, but iron from plant foods isn't absorbed as well as iron from meat foods. Cereals with added iron, grain products, and dried beans and peas are good sources of iron. Talk to your doctor to see if your child needs an iron supplement.

(continued)

TABLE 5.11 What's Included in a Healthy Vegetarian Diet *(continued)*

Minerals *(continued)*	
Calcium	• Calcium is important for the growth and development of strong bones and teeth. Vegetables that have calcium include broccoli, sweet potatoes, great northern and navy beans, and leafy greens. You can also offer soy milk or orange juice that is fortified with extra calcium.
Zinc	• Zinc is an important mineral, especially for adolescents. It helps with growth and brain and sexual development. The best sources of the mineral zinc are meat, poultry, fish, and yogurt. Some foods have zinc added to them, such as whole grains, wheat germ, brown rice, legumes, and spinach. Ask your doctor whether your child should take a supplement.

Fat and Fatty Acids	
	• Fat is an important part of a healthy diet. It helps the brain and nervous system develop correctly. Some vegetarian children eat less fat. Vegans can lack essential fatty acids because they are found mainly in fish and eggs. Fatty acids are important for brain and vision development. You can find them in canola oil, flaxseed oil, and many nuts.

Vitamins	
Vitamin D	• Babies need vitamin D for healthy growth and development. It helps them build strong, healthy bones and teeth. Babies who are exclusively breastfed, or who do not have vitamin D in their diets, need a supplement. Products that are fortified with vitamin D include cow's milk, margarine, infant formula, and most soy milk beverages.
Vitamin B_{12}	• Vitamin B_{12} is only found in animal foods, including dairy products and eggs. Offer your child foods that have the vitamin added such as cereals, breads, and soy and rice drinks.

Source: Reprinted with permission from the Canadian Paediatric Society (2017).

It is more challenging for vegans to get all the nutrients they need, but if they understand and practise good nutrition principles, they will ensure that their nutrient needs are met. In vegan families, it is important that pregnant women's and children's increased need for protein, fat, calcium, iron, vitamin B_{12}, and other nutrients be considered.

Macrobiotic diets, which are very restrictive vegan diets, are of particular concern for children. Milks made from grains, beans, and seeds, for example, are inadequate for infants and young children. CPS (2017) suggests that vegan parents talk to a registered dietitian for advice on meal planning and preparation.

Educators who have concerns about a child's nutritional intake, regardless of the type of diet, should talk with the parents and recommend that they consult with the child's physician or a dietitian. If you still have questions or need clarification, you may wish to consult with a dietitian.

To identify the type of information found on food labels and describe how this information helps consumers evaluate its nutritive value. (LO 6)

To state the function of pesticides and how this relates to organic foods. (LO 3)

To describe what food additives are, and their functions. (LO 6)

To describe how being an informed consumer influences choices around selecting and eating foods with questionable additives, fortified and enriched food sweeteners, and genetically modified and irradiated foods. (LO 3)

NUTRITION LABELS AND GROWING AND PROCESSING FOODS

Labels on food products can increase our understanding of healthy eating, enabling us to make informed decisions about choosing foods that are nutritious and fresh (check the expiry date on the label) and suit individual needs, such as allergy concerns or special dietary needs or restrictions.

A number of processes are included in the general definition of **food processing**, including curing meat (e.g., bacon, ham), increasing the length of time for storage or shelf life (e.g., canned fruit, vegetables), or combining a number of ingredients to make a food (e.g., hot dogs, bread). With few exceptions, the more processed the food, the more additives are used. Food biotechnology includes other processes, such as genetic modification and irradiation.

Nutrition Labels

We can learn a lot about foods and make informed choices by reading labels. In 2007, Health Canada's New Nutrition Labelling Policy, which had standardized the **Nutrition Facts table** on all prepackaged foods, became mandatory. In 2017, the Government of Canada updated the table (Government of Canada, 2017) (see Figure 5.2). The Nutrition Facts table is easy to read, is consistent in design, and includes information across almost all prepackaged products. Exemptions include fresh fruit and vegetables; raw meat, poultry, and seafood; food products made and packaged on site; and products with little or no nutritive value (e.g., coffee beans, spices).

What information is included in a Nutrition Facts table? The table lists calories and 13 core nutrients for a specific amount of food (a serving). The nutrients are mostly given in weights such as grams or milligrams and then translated into a percentage of recommended daily value. Vitamins and minerals are given as percentages of daily value. Since 2007, saturated and trans fats were listed separately, but since the federal government banned trans fats in 2018, saturated fats should be listed as the only fats on the label because unsaturated fats are considered healthy and therefore not an issue of concern. With regard to carbohydrates, the label identifies both fibre and sugars. The consistent format helps the consumer learn to use it quickly and evaluate whether this food has enough of the nutrients he or she needs or wants.

In addition to the Nutrition Facts table, other nutrition information can be found on food labels, including the ingredient list and nutrition claims. Ingredients are listed from most to least in weight. Nutrition claims are now regulated by Health Canada criteria, specifying the wording to be used to prevent misleading claims, which had been a problem in the past. Permitted nutrient content claims such as "low calorie" are defined and the exact conditions specified by Health Canada. These conditions are based on recognized health and scientific information.

FIGURE 5.2   Nutrition Facts Table: A Sample

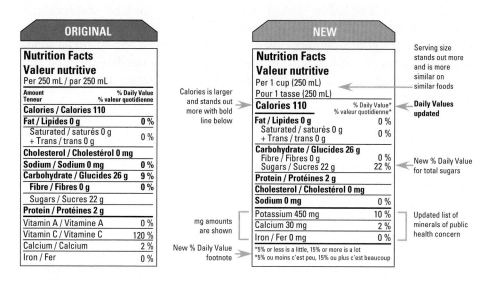

"A health claim is optional for a food. However, when it is made, it must be truthful and not misleading according to Subsection 5(1) of the Food and Drugs Act (FDA). This means that manufacturers and importers must have scientific evidence to substantiate a food health claim prior to its use" (Government of Canada, 2016e, p. 2). The list of acceptable health claims has and will continue to change based on research. Here are a few of the claims that you may have seen attached to products:

- Barley, psyllium, unsaturated fats, and oats may lower blood cholesterol.
- Calcium may reduce the risk of osteoporosis.
- Lower sodium intake may reduce the risk of high blood pressure.
- Fruit and vegetables may reduce the risk of some cancers.

For individuals with food allergies (e.g., to peanuts, milk solids, soy, wheat, dehydrated eggs), the ingredient list on packaging is essential because it names ingredients to be avoided. It is also useful for people on special diets (e.g., gluten-free, diabetic). Other information you may find on food labels includes statements related to allergens (e.g., "may contain traces of peanut"), food biotechnology information (e.g., regarding genetically modified organisms [GMOs]), organic certification, irradiation processes, and the "best before" date.

Due to the ongoing concerns about unhealthy eating habits of many Canadians, Health Canada has been developing strategies to encourage people to pay more attention to sodium, saturated fat, and sugars in their diet. *For example, an online consultation was conducted from February to April 2018 to gather opinions on front-of-package (FOP) labelling: a symbol to quickly identify foods high in saturated fat and/or sugars and/or sodium (Health Canada, 2017a, p. 1).*

An expiry or "best before" date or code is stamped on the label or somewhere on the package (e.g., the bottom or top of the cereal box) to indicate when the contents may spoil or lose nutrients or taste. A date must appear on all foods that spoil within 90 days, except for meats, which show the date the food was packaged. Actual calendar dates are useful to both the consumer and the store manager.

Pesticides

Pesticides are commonly used in farming, except in organic farming, to kill organisms (or pests) on vegetables, fruit, and grains during the growing season. Pesticides are an example of unintentional additives because some chemicals remain in or on the food after harvest. As a general rule, all of us should try to minimize our exposure to pesticides due to short- and long-term concerns about health (see Pesticides, page 455). Agriculture Canada approves all pesticides before use. Relative to most countries, Canada uses fewer pesticides in agriculture. However, imported produce may have higher concentrations of pesticides, including those that are banned in Canada.

There are particular concerns about the potential effects of pesticides on children, often termed "neurotoxins" because they affect the developing nervous system. Children tend to eat a lot of fruit. What can we do to reduce the amount of pesticides we eat? Washing produce and peeling fruit and vegetables are two ways (see Safe Food Handling, page 304). Lobbying policymakers to reduce both the commercial and the residential use of pesticides is another way to promote everyone's health. Some municipalities have successfully done so, and others are in the process of reducing the use of pesticides.

Organic Foods

Organic foods are grown under strict farming requirements. Organic foods are grown without chemicals and are not genetically modified or irradiated. What do we know about organic foods? Organic farming is not 100% pesticide free; some pesticides are approved for both organic and conventional farming. Organic foods tend to be more expensive; perhaps this may change if buying locally becomes a more widespread practice and with additional government support for organic farming. However, buying organic foods is not currently recommended as a healthier way to eat (Dietitians of Canada, 2014, p. 1). Instead, the recommendation by the Dietitians of Canada and many other national groups is the increased intake of vegetables and fruit along with milk and alternatives. Whether these food choices are organic remains a personal preference.

Food Additives

According to the Government of Canada (2016b, p. 1),

> A food additive is any chemical substance that is added to food during preparation or storage and either becomes a part of the food or affects its characteristics

for the purpose of achieving a particular technical effect. Substances that are used in food to maintain its nutritive quality, enhance its keeping quality, make it attractive or to aid in its processing, packaging or storage are all considered to be food additives…. Examples of food additives include colouring agents that give foods an appetizing appearance, anticaking agents that keep powders such as salt free-running, preservatives that prevent or delay undesirable spoilage in food, and certain sweeteners that are used to sweeten foods without appreciably adding to the caloric value of the foods.*

Substances that one might think are additives but are not include salt, sugar, vitamins, minerals, and spices (Government of Canada, 2016b).

Food additives are listed toward the end of a product's ingredient list as they are present in very low levels in foods. Research shows that most additives do not pose a threat to our short- or long-term health. However, some additives may be of concern when used regularly for long periods.

Many children favour meats that are highly processed, such as hot dogs, ham, bacon, bologna, salami, and other luncheon meats. They are easy to chew and taste salty, the result of food processing with numerous additives. If children eat these meats regularly, they often learn to choose processed meats over other meat and alternatives. This raises concerns because processed meats are usually high in saturated fat and salt and often contain the preservatives nitrates and nitrites. These preservatives are known carcinogens and have been of concern for many years.

On the other hand, it is now possible, by reading labels or asking at deli counters, to purchase nitrite- and nitrate-free processed meats. In addition, soy or other plant-based products, which resemble meat and provide protein, are readily available. Many are easy to use in foods such as pasta, rice sauces, chili, and lasagna and are an inexpensive way to get protein without saturated fat or nitrates. We are exposed to hundreds of chemicals daily, many of them necessary and harmless. When we have a choice of ingesting some that may not be in our best interests, why not choose the healthier alternative?

Dietitians and other health professionals are also on the lookout for food reactions from some additives. Although studies are limited to date, some research shows that food additives may play a role in behavioural issues. In particular, chemical preservatives called "benzoates," which have been used for a hundred years as preservatives in foods and beverages, as well as specific artificial colours (tartrazine, sunset yellow, and ponceau), may trigger hyperactive behaviour. A British study of three-year-olds and eight- and nine-year-olds found that it wasn't just children with attention deficit hyperactivity disorder (ADHD) who were affected by the artificial food colours and additives; all the children had trouble with inattention, impulsivity, and overactivity (McCann et al., 2007). There is concern in many countries regarding the use of specific

---

*Source: © All rights reserved. *Food Additives*. Health Canada, modified 2016. Adapted and reproduced with permission from the Minister of Health, 2018.

artificial colours. Some examples of bans in particular countries include the following (Dunedin, 2014, pp. 3–4):

- Tartrazine is prohibited in Norway and Austria.
- Sunset yellow is prohibited in Norway and Finland.
- Ponceau is prohibited in Norway and the United States.
- E 128 Red 2G (red dye) is prohibited in all European Union member countries, Switzerland, Norway, the United States, Canada, Japan, and Australia.

Too much sugar in children's diets is often blamed for a range of behaviour. However, eating sugar actually makes someone feel sleepy as it stimulates the production of serotonin, a sleep chemical in the brain. Foods that contain large amounts of sugar, such as soft drinks, candies, and other sweet foods, also contain artificial colours and preservatives, which, rather than the sugar, may be contributing to these behavioural changes seen in some children. The low-nutritive processed foods targeted at children often use colours for a bright colour effect, to look like popular cartoon characters. This is not to suggest that artificial food colours are the only contributing factor in behaviour changes. However, offering children foods that are high in key nutrients and do not contain additives such as benzoates and artificial colours is a healthier alternative.

We must also consider the concept of synergy. Synergism is the interaction of two or more agents or forces so that their combined effect is greater than the sum of their individual effects. All additives undergo rigorous testing and many are deemed safe, but the quantities and combinations may have unknown risks.

Food additives allow manufacturers to provide a wide variety of convenient and enjoyable foods. However, if you want to limit additives in your diet, follow these steps:

- Eat fresh foods.

  Generally speaking, eating fresh fruit and vegetables, eggs, and milk will reduce the amount of food additives you eat compared to eating processed foods.

- Learn more.

  Read the labels on food products and find out what is in the foods you buy. In Canada, most prepackaged foods have to carry a list of ingredients, including food additives. In general, the list must show the ingredients in descending order of proportion by weight so that the major ingredients are found at the beginning of the list. However, some ingredients, including food additives (which are often present in food in much smaller amounts), spices, flavours, vitamins, and minerals, are allowed to appear at the end of the list in any order, regardless of their proportion.

- Make your views known.

  Although the food and drug regulations specify which food additives are allowed in Canada, it is up to food manufacturers to decide whether or not to use them. If you are concerned about what is in the foods you eat, contact the manufacturer or grocery retailer to let them know your views.*

Fortified and Enriched Foods

Fortified or enriched food refers to the adding of nutrients to foods, such as milk fortified (or enriched) with vitamins A and D. Why are foods fortified in Canada? First, fortifying foods is a way to replace nutrients lost during the manufacturing process. Second, fortification can help prevent certain chronic diseases. Fortifying foods with calcium and vitamin D, for example, helps build strong bones and prevent osteoporosis. For those concerned about their intake of omega-3 fatty acids, omega-3-enriched eggs (produced by feeding the chickens flaxseed) are a popular choice. There is promising preliminary evidence that omega-3 fatty acids can help reduce the risk of coronary heart disease and possibly Alzheimer's disease.

Health Canada sets specific limits on what nutrients can be added to food, how much of an individual vitamin or mineral can be added, and which foods cannot be fortified at the discretion of manufacturers. The majority of foods are not fortified or enriched. For persons with a food allergy, a food intolerance, or a medical condition, fortified foods may be advantageous. Consider those who can't get their calcium from dairy due to lactose intolerance; they can find a helpful option in calcium-enriched orange juice.

Canadians should not base all their food choices on whether foods are fortified or enriched, just as children and adults cannot depend on a multivitamin as a substitute for healthy eating. The recommendation to eat a variety of foods continues to be very important.

Sweeteners

A number of sweeteners other than sugar (sucrose) are permitted for use in Canada. These include both nutritive sweeteners (other sugars such as honey and sugar alcohols, which include xylitol and maltitol) and non-nutritive or noncaloric sweeteners (e.g., aspartame, agave, sucralose, and stevia). Stevia is a relatively recent sweetener that comes from the leaves of the stevia plant. There are two types of stevia (Eat Right Ontario, 2017a, pp. 2–3):

- purified stevia extract, which is approved and regulated by Health Canada as a food additive (sweetener)
- unrefined stevia extracts, leaves, and powders, which are not considered safe

Non-nutritive sweeteners are being added to many foods, beverages, and snack products. Definitions, permitted uses, and labelling requirements by Health Canada consider all available scientific information on the effectiveness and safety of sweeteners. Regulations are then developed to identify how they should be used and the allowable amounts. A recommended daily intake (RDI) based on body weight has been set by the Canadian government for most sweeteners. Current evidence suggests that with normal use, the concentrations of artificial sweeteners are not a health risk. There are many adults and children (e.g., diabetics) who may regularly use these sweeteners due to necessity. However, others choose to consume products with non-caloric sweeteners such as gelatin desserts, yogurt, puddings, beverages, and gum. Some parents encourage their children to eat these products because they are concerned about children eating too much sugar.

Concern about high-sugar foods replacing more nutritious foods can also apply to foods containing aspartame or other non-nutritive sweeteners. If children are filling up on high-sugar, low-nutritive foods, they should be encouraged to eat fewer sweet foods rather than substitute with sweet foods containing non-caloric sweeteners. The use of non-nutritive sweeteners does not prevent or combat obesity (see Reduce the Consumption of Carbonated Beverages and Low-Nutritive Foods, page 361).

In ECLC programs, staff should provide foods that are as natural as possible and have been processed as little as possible. Non-nutritive sweeteners do not comply with this recommendation. Replacing high-sugar foods with foods containing sweeteners continues to promote a "sweet tooth," a habitual desire for sweets, rather than a focus on the natural sweetness of foods such as fruit and some vegetables.

Food Biotechnology

Genetically Modified Organisms and Foods

The term "**genetically modified**" (**GM**) refers to altering genetic material. A genetically modified organism (GMO) "is a plant-based organism, like a seed, that has its genes (DNA) altered to act in a way that does not happen naturally and/or contains genes from another plant-based organism" (Eat Right Ontario, 2017b, p. 1). Put simply, the genes of one organism have been "cut out" and then "pasted" into another organism. For hundreds of years, farmers have performed genetic engineering on their plants and animals by breeding them selectively to possess superior qualities, such as corn that is much larger and sweeter than its original wild ancestor. *For example, one bacterium was given the ability to make the enzyme rennin, needed to produce cheese. The gene for making rennin was snipped from a calf's DNA cell and transferred to a bacterial cell, which reproduced itself into mass production to be used in making cheese (Sizer & Whitney, 2012, p. 540).*

Modern genetic engineering holds the power to change even the most basic patterns of life by manipulating DNA material. Genetic engineering is much more far-reaching than simple food technology, as demonstrated by the controversies in animal and human cloning. The potential for both positive and negative outcomes is awesome. This powerful science will likely have a definite impact on our food supply. Two food technologies that are receiving attention and consumer concern are GMOs and food irradiation.

Canada's food and drug regulations consider genetically modified foods to be "novel foods" (Government of Canada, 2016d, p. 1):

- foods resulting from a process not previously used for food
- products that do not have a history of safe use as a food
- foods that have been modified by genetic manipulation, also known as genetically modified foods, GM foods, genetically engineered foods, or biotechnology-derived foods

Canada's *Food and Drugs Act* definition of a GMO has contributed to much debate in Canada over the development of labelling for GMO products, particularly because of the transfer of genetic material from one species to another, which concerns many consumers and environmental groups. Although some GM crops are produced in Canada, the majority are sold and exported. Canada's GM foods are believed to be safe for our consumption.

Most developed nations (except Canada and the United States) have mandatory labelling of GM foods, and some have issued bans on GM food production and imports. As with all foods in Canada, labelling of genetically modified foods is mandatory when there is a health or safety issue. When the nutritional value or composition of the food has been changed, or when an allergen is present in the food, that food must be labelled as such to alert consumers or susceptible groups in the population.

Since 1994, there has been approval for about 85 GM foods to be sold in Canada, including those grown in Canada and others imported from other countries. In Canada, the four main GM crops currently grown are canola, soybean, corn, and sugar beet, which are primarily exported to other countries (Eat Right Ontario, 2017b, p. 1). The potential benefits of GMOs include

- the ability to feed many more people with increasing demands for foods; and
- shrinking farmland and affordable, easy-to-prepare foods that are nutritious and safe and taste good.

However, the full extent of human health risks is not known, with the possibility of allergic reactions, nutritional changes, and the creation of toxins.

Virtually all nations are concerned about finding ways to build food systems to improve food security now and into the future. Growing genetically modified crops is one option, considered a top-down approach because of its focus on economic growth in a competitive global economy. This option may conflict with efforts to reduce environmental damage and not address the economic plights of farmers. Another option explored is a bottom-up approach, which is an agro-ecological method using and building on resources already available: local people; their knowledge, needs, and aspirations; and indigenous natural resources. The bottom-up approach also involves the public in decision making. This approach, the local food movement, is becoming increasingly strong in its advocates across Canada (European Environment Agency, 2013, p. 29).

The debate will continue.

Food Irradiation

Another process that the Government of Canada (2016c, p. 1) uses to improve food safety is **irradiation**, exposing food to gamma rays for the following purposes:

- To reduce microbial load on spices and dehydrated seasoning preparations, meaning it destroys bacteria, molds and yeast which cause food to spoil.

- To control insects in wheat, flour and whole wheat flour.

- To increase shelf life by preventing sprouting or germination in potatoes and onions.*

---

*Source: Canadian Food Inspection Agency (2018). Food Irradiation, http://www.inspection.gc.ca/food/information-for-consumers/fact-sheets-and-infographics/irradiation/eng/1332358607968/1332358680017. Reproduced with the permission of the Canadian Food Inspection Agency, 2018.

Proponents of irradiation believe that this process helps protect the public through more thorough food safety procedures. They also claim it is safer than spraying food with chemical pest-control products to protect them from spoilage caused by bugs and moulds. Although most of the radiation passes through the food, a small amount is absorbed and remains in the food. Irradiation does not make food radioactive.

Critics point out that although the process eliminates the use of some chemicals, most pesticides are applied before harvest, while plants are still growing. Irradiation does not cut down on the use of chemical pesticides by farmers. There are concerns that irradiation kills bacteria, but not necessarily the toxins that the bacteria produced in the food before they were killed. Foods that look and smell fine may be contaminated with dangerous toxins that lead to food poisoning. Like the labelling of GMOs, the issue of food irradiation will continue to be debated in Canada over the coming years.

Spices are the most commonly irradiated food worldwide. Canadian law requires all food products intended for human use that have been irradiated to be labelled with this logo. Note that spices sold in bulk or retail, as well as herbs or ingredients that have been irradiated, must be labelled with the Radura logo.

> Spices can be treated with radiation to reduce the microbial load. Products composed wholly or partially of irradiated spices must be properly labelled.
>
> - Products treated with radiation must be labelled as "treated with radiation," "treated with irradiation," "irradiated" or a similar statement, in close proximity to the Radura symbol (B.01.035, FDR).
>
> - Spices treated with radiation that make up 10% or more of a final product must be labelled as "irradiated" in the list of ingredients [B.01.035(6), FDR].
>
> - Once a product has reached the maximum permitted absorbed dose (10 kGy), the shipping container is marked with "Do not irradiate again" [B.01.035(7), FDR].*

Being Informed Consumers

Nutrition labels help us select foods for healthy eating. If you're not in the habit of reading product labels, you will probably be overwhelmed by a list of unpronounceable and obscure ingredients. You may also find that it is a time-consuming process at first, especially if you are comparing your favourite brand with its competitors. No one expects you to remember the names of all the ingredients, what they are and do, and which should be avoided or at least limited in consumption. But by reading the labels of products used in the home or ECLC program, you will soon compile a list of acceptable and unacceptable products for the shopping list. This will considerably reduce the time that is needed to shop.

Whether you are at home or at work, when you are trying to reduce the amount of fat, sugar, salt, and additives, here are a few tips for reading labels to evaluate products for healthy eating:

---

*Source: Canadian Food Inspection Agency (2018). *Food Safety Practices Guidance for Spice Manufacturers*, http://www.inspection.gc.ca/food/safe-food-production-systems/haccp-generic-models-and-guidance-documents/guidance-spices/eng/1366340448103/1366340494598?chap=0#s2c5. Reproduced with the permission of the Canadian Food Inspection Agency, 2018.

Fat:

- Remember when buying foods for children that moderate fat, not "fat free," is important for healthy growth and development.
- Use equal serving sizes when comparing two products for fat content.
- Choose milk, yogurt, or cottage cheese with 2% fat rather than whole milk for children over two years of age. For school-age children and adults, the fat content can be reduced to 1% or skim if their needs for fat are being met with other healthy foods.
- Choose cheeses with 15% milk fat (m.f.) or less.
- Select meats that are lower in fat (e.g., poultry, fish), and when selecting red meats, choose leaner cuts (e.g., lean ground beef).
- Look for canned fish packed in water or vegetable broth.
- Read the product's label for the content of saturated fats. Remember that daily values of saturated fats should not exceed 20 g.

Note: If you are wondering why the grams of saturated fats on the Nutrition Facts table does not equal the Total Fats (e.g., Saturated = 1.5 g, Fat = 4 g), the reason is that the 2.5 g fat unaccounted for is either monounsaturated and/or polyunsaturated fats, which are the healthier fats.

Sugar:

Note that ingredients ending in "ose" are types of sugar—glucose, maltose, lactose, dextrose, fructose. You may be familiar with the obvious types of sugar, such as granulated and icing sugar, brown sugar, honey, corn syrup, and molasses. Compare the amount of sugar and fibre in the carbohydrate section of the Nutrition Facts table on the label. Remember to choose foods higher in fibre and lower in sugar. Be aware of the added sugar content in beverages (e.g., pop and drinks with fruit juice) and foods.

Salt:

The word "sodium" in the Nutrition Facts table alerts you to the presence of salt. If the word "salt" does not appear on the list of ingredients, salt may still be in the product. There may be a number of sodium additives, such as monosodium glutamate, sodium bicarbonate, sodium metabisulphite, and disodium guanylate. As stated earlier, the amount of salt Canadians, including children, consume is often more than recommended daily amounts, especially when eating a range of highly processed or fast foods.

HEALTHY EATING HABITS

The foundation for supporting the development of healthy eating habits in the ECLC program starts with a philosophy of trust rather than control. In children's early childhood, they are developing eating habits that can last a lifetime. This fact can work to either their advantage or their detriment. Educators have great opportunities to promote good eating habits. Positive nutrition policies and practices recognize and respect children's ability to respond to their own bodily needs and learn to eat for the right reasons.

Mealtime situations can affect children's relationships with educators and parents when tensions and frustrations run high. Insisting that a child finish eating what is on her plate after she has indicated that she is full can result in several scenarios that contribute to future eating issues such as

- anxiety about mealtime;
- eating more than she needs, contributing to future overweight; or
- asserting herself and not eating.

As with all best practices in ECLC programs, children's trust in the adults who care for them and trust in the environment are key to optimal development and learning.

Ellyn Satter, a dietitian, family therapist, and author of *Child of Mine: Feeding with Love and Good Sense* (n.d.), is well known by educators, dietitians, nutritionists, and parents. Satter's philosophy for the **division of responsibility** on feeding was first introduced in 1990. It is a standard principle for successful feeding. According to Satter's child care feeding policy (available at https://www.ellynsatterinstitute .org/), the parent or caregiver is responsible for *what* the child eats, and the infant is responsible for *how much* will be eaten (and everything else). The adult helps the infant be calm and organized and feed smoothly, paying attention to information coming from the infant about timing, tempo, frequency, and amounts (Satter, 2006).

- Adults are responsible for what, when, and where:
  - We follow Canada's food guidelines to plan meals and snacks.
  - We provide nutritious, regularly scheduled meals and snacks that are an important part of our program day.
  - We take time to help children relax and prepare to eat.
  - We sit down to eat with children and have enjoyable times where there is respect for ourselves and each other.
- Children are responsible for how much and whether they eat:
  - We trust children to manage their own eating.
  - Children pick and choose from the food we make available.
  - Children will eat, they will eat what they need, and they will learn to eat the new foods that we offer, without coercion or forcing.
  - Children eat as little or as much of the food as they want. Some days children eat a lot, but other days, not as much. But they know how much they need.

Children's growth and development, as well as their family's cultural eating patterns, play key roles in determining their readiness for food and their interests in food and socializing. By accommodating children's development, educators ensure that individual nutritional needs are met and that eating environments are designed to promote positive eating habits.

Table 5.12 lists the developmental characteristics related to eating. Learning to recognize these characteristics will help you make sure that children are receiving the food and nutrition they need.

TABLE 5.12 Developmental Characteristics Related to Eating

Age	Physical	Social/Personal
Birth to 4 months	<ul><li>turns mouth toward nipple that touches cheek</li><li>sucks and swallows</li></ul>	<ul><li>recognizes breast or bottle as the source of food at around 10 weeks</li><li>excited by sight of food (e.g., breast, bottle)</li></ul>
4 to 6 months	<ul><li>increasing sucking strength</li><li>begins a chewing motion</li><li>uses tongue to move food in mouth</li><li>begins to finger-feed</li></ul>	<ul><li>excited by sight of food</li></ul>
6 to 9 months	<ul><li>grips a bottle (if applicable)</li><li>drinks from a cup held by adult</li><li>begins to use rotary chewing</li><li>more tongue movement, which allows for better control of food</li></ul>	<ul><li>starts to show likes and dislikes for specific foods</li></ul>
9 to 12 months	<ul><li>attempts to use spoon</li><li>chews up and down</li><li>finger-feeds with an established grasp</li></ul>	<ul><li>aware of what others do and imitates their actions</li></ul>
12 to 18 months	<ul><li>grasps and releases food with fingers</li><li>uses spoon awkwardly</li><li>rotates spoon in mouth</li><li>uses cup, but release may not yet be mastered</li></ul>	<ul><li>desires food others are eating</li><li>enjoys performing</li></ul>
18 to 24 months	<ul><li>appetite decreases</li><li>likes eating with hands</li><li>notices differences in food textures</li></ul>	<ul><li>rituals are important (e.g., has to have milk in red cup)</li><li>shows food preferences</li><li>is easily distracted</li></ul>
2 to 3 years	<ul><li>holds cup in hand and releases on table</li><li>puts spoon straight into mouth</li><li>spills sometimes or often</li><li>may show interest in pouring milk from small pitcher</li><li>chews before swallowing more often, but choking still a hazard</li></ul>	<ul><li>has definite food preferences and dislikes</li><li>insists on doing it "myself"</li><li>dawdles (eats slowly)</li><li>has food jags (e.g., refuses to eat anything but crackers and cheese)</li><li>demands foods in certain shapes or only whole foods, or dislikes mixed foods on plate</li><li>likes to help (e.g., setting table, scraping food from bowl)</li></ul>

(continued)

TABLE 5.12 Developmental Characteristics Related to Eating (*continued*)

Age	Physical	Social/Personal
3 to 4 years	• holds handle on cup • pours from small pitcher to cup or bowl • uses fork • chews most food	• increased appetite and interest in new foods • favourite foods requested • likes shapes, colours, ABCs • can choose between two different foods (e.g., cracker or bread, banana or apple) • persuaded by TV commercials • likes to copy food preparer
4 to 5 years	• uses knife and fork • confident use of cup • independent in self-feeding	• would rather talk than eat • food jags may continue • likes to help in set-up, clean-up • interested in nature of foods and where they come from (e.g., milk from cow, vegetables growing as plants in fields) • peer influence increasing
5 to 6 years	• feeds self at all times, including confidence with utensils	• generally conforms to table rules • less suspicious of mixtures but still tends to prefer separate foods • social influence outside home increasing (awareness and may be powerful influence) • food is seen as important part of special occasions
6 to 8 years	• developed small motor skills and eye–hand coordination (allow for more ease in using simple kitchen equipment such as a can opener, vegetable peeler, toaster) • high energy level	• shares and takes turns • table manners improving • often eager to please • significant peer pressure (e.g., may be less willing to try new foods if peers won't) • can follow steps for simple recipes almost independently • developing sense of humour (e.g., creating funny names for recipes) • can delay gratification for a short time
8 to 11 years	• more coordinated (can usually use most kitchen equipment, e.g., knives, microwaves; can opener; may need supervision with stove) • physical competence important for status with peers and own self-confidence • responsible and independent for most self-care	• can set standards for own behaviour • often conforms to rules set by peers (e.g., commercially high-status foods, trading lunch foods) • enjoys choosing and preparing foods, connecting nutrition and food preparation with everyday life

Creating a Positive Eating Environment

A **positive eating environment** for children has a lot to do with the expectations of the adults involved, in addition to the physical environment in which children eat. The environment can either promote or hinder healthy eating, and it can meet or inhibit children's social and emotional needs. Nutritious foods are of no value to children if they don't eat them. On the other hand, we know that any form of force-feeding or pressuring children does not work, especially for the long term. A positive environment is a much better option, regardless of the age group.

According to Ellyn Satter (2006, p. 1),

> Children are naturally skeptical about new food and cautious about eating it. *New* can be a food they haven't seen before, a familiar food prepared in a different way, or *someone they don't know doing the cooking*. But life is full of new situations. Children challenge themselves to meet them. The same holds true for eating. Children will work to master new foods and new eating skills, the same as they work to master other skills. Children learn to like new foods by having them served repeatedly, by seeing their friends eat them, and by tasting them many times and by having someone they trust eat the same food with them.*

When meals or snack times become negative experiences, with unhappy children or educators, review the checklist in Table 5.13 (see page 276) and identify which criteria have not been met.

*Source: Satter, E. (2006). *Helping Children Be Good Eaters: Provider Guidelines*, p. 1. Retrieved September 2018 from https://www.ellynsatterinstitute.org/wp-content/uploads/2016/11/Handout-HelpingChildrenBeGoodEaters-Child-Care-2013.pdf.

TRYING NEW FOODS

Encourage children to try new foods. Here are a few suggestions:

- Present one new food at a time.
- Introduce the food when children are most hungry (e.g., at the beginning of a meal as an appetizer). You may be surprised at how excited preschoolers get when they hear you mention the word "appetizer" and how much they enjoy eating raw vegetables and dip when they are hungry.
- Serve the new foods with familiar ones.
- Offer small amounts.
- Talk about the colour, texture, taste, shape, and smell of the food.
- Encourage the children to help you prepare the new food.

(continued)

- Encourage but don't insist that children taste the new food. If they reject it or say "I don't like it," accept their comments and offer it again in a week or two. The more often they see the new food, the more familiar it becomes, and the more willing they will be to accept it.

- Ask children what they didn't like about the new food. Maybe you need only change the way the food is prepared. If this food is familiar to families in the program, ask the parents for ideas about preparing it for or with the children.

Remember that if children see educators enjoying or at least trying the new food, they may be encouraged to try it too. However, you aren't expected to force yourself to eat something you dislike. Besides, if you have it in your mouth, but your body language says "It's disgusting" and your comments are negative, the children will know your true feelings.

TABLE 5.13 Positive Eating Environment: Checklist

	Yes	No
The atmosphere is relaxed. For example, if children are expected to come in from outdoor play and immediately wash their hands to eat, their difficulty in relaxing at the meal is not surprising. Educators need to think about sequence and transition needs for children.		
Distractions are at a minimum, and children are encouraged to focus on what they eat. Balance this with a warm social environment in which children can talk calmly while sitting.		
Children's rights are respected (e.g., not forced to eat foods they don't like or teased for not being skilled with spoons or forks).		
Individual food likes and dislikes are acknowledged, promoting the child's sense of self.		
Children are guided (by adult modelling) to observe certain behaviour while eating, developing a sense of self-respect and respect for others. Educators eat meals with children and model positive eating attitudes and behaviour. Adult supervision is also necessary to prevent or respond to choking risks.		
Children are encouraged to develop their five senses in enjoying a variety of foods.		
Children are not forced to conform to rigid rules or expected to have perfect table manners. For example, positively reinforcing children's use of "please" and "thank you" is far more effective than demanding that every time a child wants or receives something at the table she must use these words (e.g., repeatedly asking children, "What's the magic word?"—which is not only patronizing but misleading since we don't always get what we want). Again, adult role modelling is important in fostering table manners.		
Food, beverages, and desserts are not used as bribes or punishments. Depriving children of food is never acceptable. When unacceptable behaviour does not relate to eating (e.g., arguments over toys at playtime), there should never be any association made with food as a punishment or as a reward if he or she stops (e.g., "If you keep fighting, you won't have a snack" or "If you stop doing that, you can have dessert").		

(continued)

TABLE 5.13 Positive Eating Environment: Checklist (*continued*)

	Yes	No
Children are provided with developmentally appropriate opportunities to be involved in serving themselves. Children can start with giving themselves small servings and can have more if they would like, giving them control over the amount of food on their plate. Toddlers have some opportunity for independent serving; preschoolers and school-agers serve themselves as often as possible. ● Snacks are set out where two or three children can serve themselves at a table. ● Milk is served in small pitchers so children can pour their own. ● Family-style serving dishes are used at the table.		
Individual children's rate of eating is considered. For example, a child who eats slowly is not rushed; the child is given enough notice if reasonable time has lapsed and the child needs to move to the next routine.		
A child who eats more quickly than peers, although encouraged to take time to eat, is not expected to stay at the table until everyone else has finished.		
Adults recognize accidental spills as a natural part of mealtime and demonstrate patience. Children are encouraged to help clean up their spills (appropriate to their developmental skills) with a clean cloth available.		
There are well-maintained chairs, tables, plates, and utensils suited to the children's size and development.		
The table is made as attractive as possible (e.g., by laminating placemats that children make). Children are involved whenever possible in setting the table.		
Foods served for celebrations and holidays are nutritious and fun.		
Children are encouraged to share food experiences from their own ethnocultural or regional backgrounds and are introduced to foods from around the world as part of the regular menu.		
Families are encouraged to ● comment on and ask nutritional questions about the program's and their child's nutrition, ● contribute nutritional foods and snacks for special occasions (when the program permits) and are invited to participate, and ● provide favourite ethnocultural recipes.		

Infant Nutrition

At no other time in our lives is there as dramatic a rate in our growth and development as during the prenatal period and infancy. Infants usually double their birth weight by five months of age and triple it within the year. In the same year, they will be 1½ times as long as they were at birth (e.g., 51 cm, or 20 in., at birth and 76 cm, or 30 in., at 12 months). Infants' brains continue to grow, and they quickly develop motor skills. As well, infants move from being able only to suck and swallow to finger-feeding in 12 months (see Table 5.12, page 273). During the first year of life, one of infants' fundamental needs is to have their nutritional requirements met by their parents and caregivers. Without all the essential nutrients, infants' growth, development, learning, and play will be negatively affected.

Parents and educators must communicate effectively—meaning daily written and verbal communication—so that consistency of care between home and the program can be provided.

In 2012, the Infant Feeding Joint Working Group (Health Canada, CPS, Dietitians of Canada, and Breastfeeding Committee for Canada) published the recommendations for healthy-term infant nutrition. The following is a selection from the recommendation for children from birth to six months old (Government of Canada, 2015, pp. 1–2):

- Breastfeeding is the normal and unequalled method of feeding infants.

  Recommend exclusive breastfeeding for the first six months.

- Breastfeeding initiation and duration rates increase with active protection, support, and promotion.

  Implement the policies and practices of the Baby-Friendly Initiative (BFI) for hospitals and community health services.

- Supplemental vitamin D is recommended for breastfed infants.

  Recommend a daily vitamin D supplement of 10 µg (40 IU) for breastfed infants.

- First complementary foods should be iron rich.

  Recommend meat, meat alternatives, and iron-fortified cereal as an infant's first complementary foods.

- Routine growth monitoring is important to assess infant health and nutrition.

  Use WHO Growth Charts for Canada for optimal monitoring of infant growth.

For the complete list of recommendations, see *Nutrition for Healthy Term Infants: Recommendations from Birth to Six Months* on the Government of Canada website.

Breast Milk and Infant Formula

The best nutritional choice for infants is breast milk, for a multitude of reasons. Here are some of the **advantages of breast milk**:

- Human milk is perfectly suited to infants. It is species specific. Feeding from the breast also makes infant-led feeding (also known as "on-cue" feeding) possible. Canada's Infant Feeding Joint Working Group's recommendations emphasize that to establish good breast milk production and flow, infants need to feed on-cue. The goal in infant-led feeding is for the mother to recognize and respond to the infant's appetite, hunger, and fullness cues. "Infants fed directly at the breast have better self-regulation, which in turn could mediate the relationship between breastfeeding and childhood obesity" (Li et al., 2010, p. e1392).

- It contains the ideal quantities and quality of the three energy-producing nutrients (carbohydrate, fat, protein). The concentration of these nutrients adjusts to the needs of the baby, both daily and over time.

- The essential fatty acids promote the best possible nerve and brain development.

- The large amount of lactose (sugar), compared with the milk of other species, helps in the development of the central nervous system.

- Breastfeeding has been associated with enhanced cognitive development in a number of studies. One compelling study (Kramer et al., 2008) was based on a large number of healthy breastfeeding infants, of whom 81.5% were followed up at 6.5 years old. A variety of accredited tests and evaluations were conducted with the children, and the results provide strong evidence that prolonged and exclusive breastfeeding improves children's cognitive development.

- The Infant Feeding Joint Working Group (Government of Canada, 2015) has also cited research providing evidence that breastfeeding protects babies from gastrointestinal infections, acute otitis media (ear infections), respiratory tract infections, and sudden infant death syndrome.

- Breast milk contains the right balance of most essential vitamins and minerals. Because breast milk does not contain vitamin D, the Infant Feeding Joint Working Group (Government of Canada, 2015) strongly recommends that breastfeeding infants need a supplement of 10 µg (400 IU) of vitamin D3 daily (see Vitamin D in Appendix 5.1, page 315). The protein in breast milk is easily digested in comparison with proteins from other foods. Protein is the most difficult nutrient for us to digest. Cow's milk, peanuts, and eggs are some of the most highly allergenic foods because they are high in protein (see Table 4.1, page 201).

- Breast milk contains antibodies that provide infants with immunity against some infections during breastfeeding, whereas infant formula does not offer that benefit.

- Breastfed infants are less likely to develop allergies. Infants may react to certain foods that their mother has recently eaten (e.g., after she eats broccoli, the infant may experience flatulence).

There are also benefits for the mother:

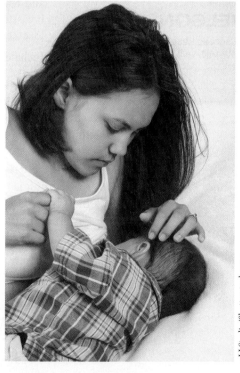

- Breastfeeding helps to nurture attachment between mother and baby. The bond that develops between the breastfeeding infant and mother leads to better emotional development and stability. The skin-to-skin contact and infant sucking at the breast release the hormones serotonin and oxytocin in both mother and infant, building a strong emotional bond between them (Oddy et al., 2012).

- The mother's body uses calories to produce milk, so breastfeeding can help the mother gradually lose weight gained during pregnancy. Exclusive breastfeeding may also delay the return of menstruation for at least a little while.

Many mothers who breastfeed need support in making the transition from home to work. ECLC programs can play a vital role in supporting and facilitating parents in their decision to breastfeed successfully and for as long as possible. When babies are breastfed exclusively (without added complementary foods) for the first six months of life, and longer with complementary foods, there are optimal benefits for the child and the mother.

oLJ Studio/Shutterstock.com

Breastfeeding Friendly

ANYTIME. **ANYWHERE.**

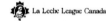

Health Canada   Santé Canada   La Leche League Canada

NELSONstudy

To access Resource Materials, visit NelsonStudy.

Supporting Breastfeeding

Infants who are offered expressed breast milk or formula at the ECLC program will usually have been introduced to a bottle or cup at home first. Infants who are used to receiving their nourishment from the breast may have a difficult time with this transition or may accept the bottle or cup readily.

A mother may want to continue nursing after her infant is enrolled in the ECLC program. Those women whose workplace is located close to the program may be able to come during the day to nurse their infant. Other mothers may bring in expressed breast milk and may breastfeed the infant at drop-off and pick-up. Find ways to be flexible so that the infant's needs are met and to encourage continued breastfeeding. Many mothers nurse at home and provide formula for the child during the day. There are also mothers who wean their infants before returning to work, so the child has infant formula exclusively. If the policies and educators have made the breastfeeding-friendly environment known, mothers may be encouraged to continue breastfeeding upon returning to work rather than weaning the infant. ECLC settings can be breastfeeding-friendly environments in a number of ways (CPS, 2015, p. 29):

- Have a written policy on how breastfeeding is supported in your program and include it in the information package.

- Provide a comfortable place on site for mothers to breastfeed and express milk.

- Promote breastfeeding on site with wall posters and free brochures.

- Encourage staff members to discuss breastfeeding with current and prospective parents and to refer them to breastfeeding community supports and resources. Your local public health agency can also help, and for peer breastfeeding support, call La Leche League of Canada's referral service. [See Resource Materials.]

- Include fathers in breastfeeding discussions.*

All the baby bottles need to be labelled with the children's first name and possibly the surname's first letter when more than one child has the same name. The breast milk must also be stored in a refrigerator or freezer and kept at optimal temperatures until preparation for feeding to the child, within the appropriate time frame.

CPS (2015, p. 30) states strongly the importance that educators ensure the breast milk is fed to the correct baby to avoid the small, but dangerous, risk of a blood-borne virus being transmitted to the baby. If there is an error, the ECLC program should have a policy whereby "both the mother who produced the breast milk and the parents of the baby who was given the wrong milk must be advised if an error occurs, and public health authorities contacted without delay. Blood tests may be required and the baby who received the milk may need immunization against hepatitis B" (CPS, 2015, p. 30).

Expressed breast milk does not present risks when it comes in contact with someone's skin (e.g., it has been spit up or during a test of the milk's temperature

---

*Source: Reprinted with permission from the Canadian Paediatric Society.

on the top of your hand). Discouraging mothers from providing expressed breast milk for their infants in programs is not an acceptable response to the issue of HIV. High-quality ECLC programs already implement the practices that prevent the spread of HIV in children. For further information on storing and handling breast milk, refer to the Nutrition chapter in *Well Beings* (CPS, 2015).

For babies who are not breastfed, commercial formula is essential for the first 9 to 12 months of life. Most formulas are made of modified cow's milk and include the infant's needs for water, fatty acids, carbohydrate (lactose), protein, and vitamins and minerals. Iron-fortified formulas are highly recommended for the first 9 to 12 months to prevent iron-deficiency anemia, rather than treat it, because anemia is a risk factor for possible irreversible developmental delays (Government of Canada, 2015, p. 13). Commercial formulas are designed to be as similar to breast milk as possible. When a formula-feeding infant is allergic to cow's milk, there are many soy protein–based formulas on the market. The Infant Feeding Joint Working Group has identified some concerns and requests that physicians consider "limiting the use of soy-based formulas to those infants with galactosemia or those who cannot consume dairy-based products for cultural or religious reasons" (CPS, 2016a, p. 3). Galactosemia is a disorder that affects how the body processes a simple sugar called galactose. Soy-based formulas are also not recommended for premature infants or infants with congenital hypothyroidism (CPS, 2016a, p. 2).

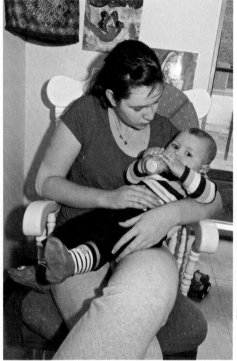

Courtesy of George Brown College/Casa Loma Child Care Centre

Even in breastfeeding-friendly ECLC programs, it is essential for educators to be supportive and positive with all families, whatever their choice. If, for some reason, you have a concern, it is important to bring it to the supervisor's attention so that she or he may follow up with the family to ensure that it has been approved by the doctor or a dietitian. *For example, the child is under nine months old and is being fed evaporated cow's milk rather than regulated infant formula.*

Bottle-Feeding

Bottle-feeding is an ideal time for educators to hold and cuddle infants. It is not a time to be rushed. The practice of bottle propping is absolutely unacceptable because of the risk of choking and dental caries (tooth decay). Feeding is one of the important daily care routines; it helps infants develop safe, secure, and trusting relationships with their educators. At this time in the child's life, the division of responsibility around feeding is very simple: the parent or caregiver is responsible for *what* the child eats, and the infant is responsible for *how much* will be eaten (and everything else). The adult helps the infant be calm and organized and feed smoothly, paying attention to information coming from the infant about timing, tempo, frequency, and amounts (Satter, 2006).

Older infants who can sit without support and, especially, toddlers may prefer to sit and drink their bottle independently. Educators discourage toddlers from walking around with a bottle in their mouth by helping them identify where they can sit comfortably, and possibly sit nearby. Obviously, the child must never be left unsupervised.

In many infant programs, parents bring in one bottle for each feeding during the day. Each bottle is filled with approximately the amount of expressed breast milk or formula that the infant drinks in one feeding. There could be four bottles, each with 90 mL (3 oz.) of milk. After the child has drunk from the bottle, do not give him or her leftovers at the next feeding. Milk is the perfect medium for the growth of germs, and during sucking, germs enter the bottle. Therefore, leftovers must be discarded (see Food Safety Practices, page 302).

Some ECLC programs are in the practice of having educators prepare the formula, when used, for each infant every day. The parents provide cans of their infant's specific brand. However, considering the amount of care and interaction that infants and toddlers need from their educators, a policy of parents bringing in the formula ready to serve in bottles is best, unless circumstances warrant preparation by the educators. As well, the logistics of clearly identifying all the individual bottles and nipples; sterilizing water, containers, measuring equipment, (unlined) bottles, and nipples; and ensuring the sterility of the formula add increased risk of foodborne illness. For information on safe handling, preparation, and storage of commercial formula, refer to the Nutrition chapter in *Well Beings* (CPS, 2015).

First Foods

Before six months of age, children's bodies are not fully ready for complementary food. Breast milk or formula provides all the essential nutrients. Early introduction of **semisolid foods** is not the best practice in promoting optimal nutrition. At around six months of age, most infants are ready to try chewing and swallowing some semisolid foods and require additional iron. At this time, offering iron-rich foods is a good way to start.

If a young infant who is not yet ready is fed semisolid food, most of it will be found undigested in the stool. Infants' digestive and renal systems are too immature to cope with anything other than breast milk or formula. Infants don't produce enough saliva or digestive enzymes, and their kidneys cannot yet filter much protein.

Parents may believe that their infants need to eat solid foods as early as two or three months of age because the child seems more hungry or is waking up more often during the night. Many parents interpret this to mean that the breast milk or formula isn't satiating the child. In fact, infants simply go through growth spurts and need extra nutrients; all they need is extra breast milk or formula for a week or two to get through the spurt. It is a myth that very young babies sleep better at night when they are fed infant cereal. In reality, "prolonged sleep reflects the baby's total neurological development and has very little to do with the food she eats, colic being one exception" (Lambert-Lagacé, 2003, p. 126).

Understandably, parents want the best for their baby and are concerned about why she or he seems hungry. Relatives and friends may also have assumed that adding solid foods early was good practice and may be encouraging (or pressuring) parents to do the same. They may suggest, for example, adding infant cereal to the formula in the bottle. There is no evidence to indicate that this practice helps infants sleep through the night, and it also can pose a choking risk.

Ideally, parents consult their infant's physician to determine on an individual basis when to introduce semisolid foods. This decision will be based somewhat on increased nutrient needs and on whether the infant has at least doubled his or her birth weight, although motor abilities and interest in other family members' foods or peers' food in the ECLC program can also influence the decision. In turn, parents and educators work together in the feeding process.

The introduction of semisolid foods should be a slow process and follow each infant's lead. This respects the infants' nutritional and emotional needs so that eating food is a positive experience rather than a process that infants can fail at or experience negative feelings about because it happened too early or too quickly. Infants should have as much control as possible in the feeding process, including some self-feeding. Watch for the following signs of infants' readiness to start with semisolids:

Courtesy of George Brown College/Casa Loma Child Care Centre

- around six months of age
- better able to sit up
- move their head back to indicate fullness or lack of interest
- move their head forward to indicate hunger or interest
- open mouth wide when offered food on a spoon
- close lips over the spoon; keep food in the mouth and swallow it instead of pushing it out
- can hold a spoon, although it will be months before they use it effectively
- have shown interest in putting food on their hands, and some food has eventually reached their mouth

Developmentally, infants need sensory experiences, including food experiences, to begin to understand their world. Some babies need and enjoy this type of sensory exploration more than others. Don't be surprised if some parents are concerned about seeing their infants with their hands in the food—perhaps feeling that educators are encouraging their infants to play with their food. Once again, effective communication between parents and educators is important in negotiating compromise. One obvious difference in feeding practices has to do with fundamental values in cultures.

Your program's goal is to encourage infant and toddler independence. You encourage the infant to use a spoon while you have a second spoon for feeding. However, the parents' philosophy may emphasize the importance of interdependence—connection with the family is a priority; the feeling of being connected is much more important than self-sufficiency. Feeding with interdependence in mind means that the adult feeds the infant, perhaps into the preschool years, as part of this value. This is not an issue of right or wrong but of two different views. With discussion, a compromise will be reached.

The Process of Introducing Semisolid Foods

Even though infants are now ready for semisolid foods, they are not ready to have the food replace the nutrients in the breast milk or formula. Remember that young infants' primary nutrition comes from the breast milk or formula until they are eating a variety of foods and in enough quantity to ensure they are getting the essential nutrients, usually around nine months of age.

According to CPS's (2016b) position statement on dietary exposures and allergy prevention in high-risk infants, there is a shift in evidence-based practice to prevent food allergy in high-risk infants. An infant who is at high risk for developing allergy usually has a close relative (parent or sibling) with a food allergy, asthma, or allergic rhinitis. Current evidence in several countries suggests that delaying the introduction of certain "trigger" or "high-risk allergy" foods may not have the protective effect on preventing food allergies that was thought. Recommendations from CPS (2016b) include the following:

- Do not delay the introduction of any specific solid food beyond six months of age. Later introduction of peanut, fish or egg does not prevent, and may even increase, the risk of developing food allergy.
- Current research on immunological responses appears to suggest that the regular ingestion of newly introduced foods (e.g., several times per week and with a soft mashed consistency to prevent choking) is important to maintain tolerance.*

Parents should introduce each food at home several times before it is offered in the early childhood program. Parents know their child best and will recognize any allergic reaction to the new food. Parents should wait three to five days before trying the next new food to observe any reaction the child may have, such as undigested food in the stool, gas, rashes, vomiting, breathing difficulties, or any other sign that the child may be sensitive or allergic to the food (see Allergies, page 201). Parents often introduce cereals first, or possibly meat and alternatives. Both options are high in iron, which is important to supplement around six months to prevent anemia. If the physician is concerned about anemia, meat or alternatives will likely be suggested first as iron from these sources is better absorbed.

All foods need to have a puréed texture when they are introduced and become less puréed and more lumpy as the infant is better able to chew and may have some teeth. Changing texture is important to support infants' abilities as they learn to chew. Generally, from 6 to 12 months, the texture offered to babies undergoes ongoing change from purée to choppy to regular table food, for the most part. Infants who eat puréed foods too long may be less willing to eat more textured foods. As infants develop a repertoire of foods and can chew more effectively, fewer table foods need to be restricted from them, except foods that are a concern for choking. By one year of age, the infant should be eating a variety of foods from each food group and drinking liquids from a cup.

Cereals

Typically, infants start with single-grain cereals such as rice, barley, oats, and wheat before mixed-grain cereals are introduced. Commercially prepared infant cereals are best suited to infants because they are a good source of iron in a form that can

---

*Source: Reprinted with permission from the Canadian Paediatric Society.

be absorbed. Their other nutrients, including protein, carbohydrates, and fats, are easily digested. The introduction of cereals takes three weeks to a month if these foods are introduced gradually. The dry cereal is mixed with breast milk or formula, with a thin consistency at first and less liquid for a thicker consistency as the infant is ready. Here are a few more tips about cereal (Best Start Resource Centre and Nutrition Resource Centre, 2012, p. 5):

- Choose plain infant cereals. Cereals with added fruits have extra sugar.
- Choose cereals without infant formula added. Read the labels.
- Do not give adult cereals.
- Always feed cereal from a spoon. Never add cereal to a bottle.

Meat and Alternatives

Meat and alternatives are high in iron and other minerals, protein, and some fat. Iron from meat sources is better absorbed than iron from nonmeat sources. The foods in this group include meats, fish, poultry, cooked egg yolks, and alternatives such as tofu and well-cooked legumes. Infants in vegetarian families will receive plant proteins, such as legumes, tofu, and meat-like products made from vegetable protein. Lacto-ovo vegetarian families will also introduce cheeses and eggs.

Suggestions from the Best Start Resource Centre and Nutrition Resource Centre (2012, p. 5) include the following regarding meats and alternatives:

- Keep meats and alternatives moist so they are easy to swallow. Add extra water or broth to meats and cooked beans. Use silken (soft) tofu. Cook egg white and yolk well.
- Do not give your baby deli meats such as ham, wieners, bologna, salami, or sausages. These are high in fat and salt.
- Give your baby fish such as white fish, salmon, and light canned tuna. Swordfish, shark, fresh or frozen tuna steak, canned albacore tuna, marlin, orange roughy, and escolar are often high in mercury. Do not give your baby these fish more than once a month.

*After your baby has started eating iron-rich foods, she needs other foods like vegetables and fruit.**

Here are a few more points to remember:

- White meats such as chicken, turkey, and fish tend to be easier to digest and therefore are often introduced before meats such as beef, veal, liver, or lamb.
- As with all new foods, introduce one new meat (or alternative) every three to five days.
- At first, serve only 5 mL (1 tsp.) alone, not mixed with vegetables, and offer this food group at the midday meal. Gradually increase this serving to a maximum of 90 mL (6 tbsp.) daily by the end of the first year. Added salt is unnecessary and may contribute to long-term concerns about overconsumption of salt.

---

*Source: Best Start: Ontario's Maternal Newborn and Early Child Development Resource Centre and Nutrition Resource Centre. (2012). *Feeding Your Baby from Six Months to One Year.* Toronto: Ontario Prevention Clearinghouse. Retrieved February 2018 from https://www.beststart.org/resources/nutrition/pdf/feeding_baby_rev2012_LR.pdf

Vegetables and Fruit

After the infant is regularly eating iron-rich foods such as infant cereals or meat and alternatives, introduce vegetables and fruit. Again, these foods should be introduced one at a time, with three to five days before starting another new food to ensure that there is no allergy to the food. Here are some points to keep in mind when feeding infants:

- Foods that are helpful for teething infants include dry toast and soft pieces of fruit or vegetables (e.g., a ring of green pepper). Most store-bought teething biscuits contain sugar and are not recommended.

- Wash and peel fresh vegetables and fruit before using. Use fresh or frozen as often as possible. Minimize the use of canned foods (see Environmental Contaminants, page 444).

- Start with mild-tasting foods such as squash, carrots, sweet potatoes, green or yellow beans, apples, peaches, pears, apricots, plums, avocados, and bananas.

- Carrots, squash, sweet potatoes, asparagus, green peas, cauliflower, and broccoli need to be cooked and puréed at first. Cooking continues to be required, but the texture of these vegetables will change as infants' teeth come in and chewing increases (e.g., whole peas, small pieces of cooked carrot).

- Ripe fresh fruit such as bananas, mangoes, and papayas can be mashed. Apples, pears, peaches, and plums need to be peeled, cooked, and puréed at first and then mashed until the child is ready for small chopped pieces.

- If fruit juice is offered, ensure that it is 100% fruit juice, pasteurized, and without added sugar. If an infant is drinking fruit juice, it needs to be limited to no more than 120 mL (4 oz.) daily (CPS, 2015, p. 36). Consumption of juice can contribute to inadequate intake of other nutrients and energy, poor weight gain, and possibly diarrhea. Infants who are able to eat puréed fruits and vegetables, and then small chopped pieces, are consuming all the nutrients that fruit offers.

- Children may drink juice at home. Educators can minimize offering juice by

  - serving fruit,

  - providing water to drink (avoid mineral water and carbonated water), and

  - having a policy that states that, if offered occasionally, juice will be served in cups only. Juice in bottles encourages children to drink far more than the limit of 120 mL (4 oz.) and contributes to dental caries (see Oral Health Education, page 583).

For children from 9 to 12 months old, refer to Table 5.14 for tips on foods.

CRITICAL THINKING

The parents of an eight-month-old girl haven't yet introduced semisolid foods, not even infant cereal. Marie's source of nutrition is her mother's breast milk. Marie is interested in what the other children are eating. She is hungry half an hour after you feed her a bottle of expressed breast milk. However, when you mention this to her mother, she assures you that she will be starting Marie on infant cereal soon. That was three weeks ago, and Marie's mother hasn't followed through. What are the issues of concern for educators? How should you proceed?

TABLE 5.14 Tips for Feeding Children from Nine Months to One Year

Food Group	Tips
Vegetables and fruit	• Offer soft, cooked vegetables cut in bite-sized pieces. • Give pieces of soft, ripe fruit such as bananas, peaches, kiwi, and cantaloupe.
Grain products	• Continue to give your baby infant cereal. It is a good source of iron. If your baby refuses to eat it, mix it with fruit or other healthy foods. • Offer finger foods such as pieces of bagel, dry toast strips, rice, roti, noodles, cooked pasta, flat bread, and unsalted crackers.
Milk and alternatives	• Breast milk is still the most important food. Continue to breastfeed until your baby is two years old or more. • In addition to breast milk, when your baby is eating a variety of foods every day, you can offer your baby homogenized cow's milk (3.25% milk fat). She should be between nine months and one year old. Give milk in a cup. • Do not give skim, 1%, 2%, or low-fat milk products. Babies need the fat to grow. • Do not give soy, rice, or other vegetarian beverages. They do not have enough fat and may not have vitamin D added to them. • Never give unpasteurized milk. • Offer yogurt, cottage cheese, and small cubes of soft cheese or shredded cheese.
Meat and alternatives	• Give bite-sized pieces of tender meat, fish, cooked beans, and tofu. • If your baby refuses meat, try mixing fish, beans, or tofu in sweet potatoes or squash to enhance flavour and texture. Be sure your baby has tried each new food on its own first. • Give cooked egg (yolk or white). • Thinly spread peanut butter or other nut butters on toast or crackers.*

By one year old, your baby should be eating a variety of foods from each food group and drinking liquids** from a cup. Babies can go directly from breastfeeding to drinking from a cup.

* Served at home, not in ECLC programs where peanut and nut butters are banned due to possible allergies.
**Drinking milk and water.

Source: Best Start: Ontario's Maternal Newborn and Early Child Development Resource Centre and Nutrition Resource Centre. (2012). *Feeding Your Baby from Six Months to One Year.* Toronto: Ontario Prevention Clearinghouse. Retrieved February 2018 from https://www .beststart.org/resources/nutrition/pdf/feeding_baby_rev2012_LR.pdf

Toddler Nutrition

Toddlers are at a stage when they are developing a sense of autonomy (a sense of independence) and balancing that need with the need to feel connected to their parents, families, and peers. As a result, parents and educators have the challenging role of respecting toddlers' need for autonomy but setting limits to promote trust and security (see Table 5.12, page 273).

Toddlers' growth slows to a rate of only half to one-third of what it was in the first 12 months, but exploration speeds up. Except during growth spurts, toddlers won't be as hungry as when they were younger and may eat less overall. Educators often find that this is less true in the ECLC program than at home as many children eat more consistently when surrounded by peers. Their appetite can be inconsistent. Many toddlers can override any desire to eat when they are overexcited, overtired, or angry with their parents or educators. Some parents and educators become concerned about this natural change in eating habits and pressure toddlers to eat. This is not appropriate practice at any age but is a big mistake with toddlers, who will assert their independence. When an adult and a toddler get into a power struggle, nobody wins!

Poor eating habits now can pave the way for eating problems that last a lifetime. Toddlers can become anxious about mealtimes, or refuse to eat, or have temper tantrums because of frustration. Parents and educators need to remember that most young children will eat when they are hungry and when they are offered a variety of nourishing foods. It is a toddler's job to assert his or her independence, and it is the trusted adult's job to confirm the toddler's security by providing firm but reasonable limits.

Here are some things to keep in mind when toddlers are eating:

- Remember the division of responsibility described on page 272:
  - Educators have indirect control of feeding (i.e., for *what*, *when*, and *where*):
    - selecting and presenting nutritious foods
    - setting routine times for snacks and meals
    - creating a pleasant atmosphere
    - maintaining developmentally appropriate standards of behaviour at the table
    - helping the children attend to their eating
  - Children have direct control of eating (i.e., how much and whether they eat).
- Some enjoy or need adult assistance with feeding.
- Many have a hard time sitting long enough to eat a whole meal if it is holding them back from doing other things.
- Toddlers typically dawdle over food. Rather than focus on the dawdling and the inconvenience this brings to the flow of the program, it is more effective to give reasonable but firm limits, such as "You have 10 more minutes for lunch," and, after the allotted time, calmly remove the child's plate without commenting on how much the child ate.
  - Practical hints:
  - Use child-sized unbreakable plates, bowls, and utensils (BPA free). (See Plastics, page 456.)
  - Toddlers often eat very small serving sizes (sometimes one-quarter of an adult's serving size). Avoid dishing out large amounts of food; they may seem overwhelming to a toddler. This may turn the child off his or her food.
  - Provide finger foods so that toddlers are not always expected to use utensils, which is an emerging skill and not always an easy one to master.
  - Serve soup thin enough to drink or thick enough to eat with a spoon.
  - Cut foods into bite-sized pieces.

Alexlukin/Shutterstock.com

Martial Red/
Shutterstock.com

- Avoid serving very chewy foods.
- Children need to sit down to eat.
- Take special care to avoid foods that may cause choking (see Reducing the Risk of Choking, page 301).

- Toddlers are often afraid to try new things (neophobic) and so tend to be afraid of new foods. The more familiar toddlers are with foods, the more they like them. Coaxing toddlers to try new foods tends to make them resist the idea more. But if they see a new food offered with no outside pressure several times, they will eventually try it, and the food becomes less and less an aversion. Expect toddlers to refuse a new food and avoid thinking, "Oh, they didn't like it, so we won't make it again!"

- Toddlers learn to like most foods that they originally rejected. However, in the process, they may do things such as spit out the food if its texture, flavour, temperature, or other aspect is unusual to them. This is a learning process that should not be discouraged because it usually leads to more openness toward food. If their behaviour (e.g., spitting out) is not tolerated, toddlers are less likely to risk trying new foods again. You may argue that permitting this behaviour wastes food or encourages poor table manners. Throwing away a piece of vegetable a few times is worth the long-term benefit when the children decide that they like that vegetable after all. In terms of manners, if you expect toddlers to demonstrate proper etiquette, you will be disappointed! Table manners are learned over time, and they should not be a priority for toddlers at mealtime.

Tusia/Shutterstock.com

- Toddlers may have **food jags**, which means that they refuse all but one or two favourite foods for a period. This, too, is part of normal development and should be handled casually. Continue to offer a variety of foods at meals and snack times, and most children will eventually start accepting other foods again.

- Toddlers should be offered a frequent, nutritious variety of foods, including energy-dense foods from the different food groups, to meet nutrient and energy needs.

Preschool Nutrition

During the preschool years, children gain only about 2.5 to 2.75 kg (5 to 6 lbs) per year. However, between the ages of two and five, children's head and body shapes change dramatically—a five-year-old no longer looks like a baby. Most preschoolers come through the toddler stage feeling that they have some power and autonomy, and most have an awareness that others have rights too. Preschoolers take increasing initiative as they become better at everything they do. With more language, they learn to express themselves in social ways and to work things out with other people. Food jags, dawdling, fear of new foods, and other toddler nutrition issues tend to diminish and are fairly uncommon by four years of age, especially if adults have not given these issues undue attention when they were toddlers. Children in this age group tend to be interested in their body and keen to learn about how foods affect their body, where foods come from, cooking, and advertising (see Table 5.12, page 273; and Nutrition Education, page 577).

Here are some things to keep in mind when preschoolers are eating:

- Children are individuals, and their appetites and interest in food fluctuate. As their body changes from toddlerhood, body fat naturally decreases, and they may have an inconsistent appetite from one day to the next. If parents seem concerned about their child eating little one day but more interested in food the next, suggest that they consider their child's intake over a week's period rather than day to day.

- Establish clear expectations for mealtime behaviour. Preschoolers are capable of understanding what is and isn't appropriate behaviour, as well as logical consequences (e.g., Carlos spills milk on the floor and understands that he will help clean it up, or Emily throws the second piece of her sandwich on the floor and understands from your earlier comments that now she is finished eating and needs to leave the table).

- Children have a genuine interest in learning about others, so this is an opportune time for them to begin to learn about other cultures, foods, and ways of cooking (see Cooking with Children, page 578).

- When introducing a new food, do not pressure a child to try it. Always remember the division of responsibility around feeding.

- Children's internal cues of hunger and fullness need to be respected. The opportunity for preschoolers to serve themselves rather than be served by adults was highlighted in a study of five- and six-year-olds (Fisher et al., 2007). When the main dish was served to the children at lunch, it was a larger serving size than recommended for the age group. The children, on average, consumed 76% more calories from that larger serving. These results support the perspective that large portions of high-calorie foods foster eating behaviour among young children by promoting higher calorie intake at meals. Serving preschoolers rather than letting them serve themselves does not offer the children as much opportunity to regulate their own food intake based on their internal cues, an important factor in developing healthy eating habits.

Courtesy of Sister Celeste—Fort Norman

School-Age Nutrition

This stage in a child's life brings many developmental changes, but in terms of actual physical change, most children do not go through dramatic growth until early adolescence. School-agers vary in height and body shape and are aware of these differences. Concerns about dieting and the fear of fat may heighten in later school-age years, particularly in girls but also with boys. Children make the transition from a primary focus on their families to increasing influence from peers and other outside influences (e.g., media). Concerns about sedentary lifestyles can be an issue at any age, but there seem to be obvious differences in energy level during the school-age years. Supporting and promoting healthy active living both with families and in our programs will provide children with the tools they need to make healthy choices a natural part of their lives when it comes to nutrition, physical activity, and balancing screen time (see Unit 6, page 320).

An important component of Satter's philosophy (1990) is that fundamental to parents' and educators' roles is trusting children to decide *how much* and *whether* to eat. If parents do their jobs with *feeding*, children will do their jobs with *eating*.

> Most school-age children who are involved in physical activity with friends have a high energy level. Others who spend long periods of time sitting in front of a television or computer screen will likely be lethargic and lack motivation to be active.

Children who have not been introduced to a variety of foods may be more judgmental about peers' food choices that are different from their own.

> A vegetarian child who brings a tofu and quinoa burger for lunch may be asked to share it by one child who is open to new foods but teased by another child for eating something unfamiliar to him.

School-agers need to understand the reasons for what they are doing. They are concerned with mastery and accomplishment as part of their self-esteem. For this reason, preparing food is popular with this age group. Learning basic skills such as where food comes from and how to cook simple, healthy meals are building blocks to children's knowledge for healthy eating. If a program can provide opportunities for learning to make breakfast, the children may be proud to do so at home. Through learning processes such as this, we promote their need to experience success that is recognized by self and others. Educators should optimize the children's interests and developing skills by incorporating regular food experiences into the curriculum. They could also participate in growing and harvesting herbs indoors or in a small outdoor vegetable garden. School-age children who learn to prepare simple but nutritious snacks or meals may continue these life skills. This also increases the opportunity for them to prepare more nutritious snacks at home rather than consuming highly processed snack foods. School-age nutrition education can include the relationships between food production and consumption, recycling and composting, food wastage and packaging, and the environment (see Table 5.12, page 273; and Cooking with Children, page 578).

Older school-agers may find it stigmatizing to be separated from other children (some of their friends) while eating lunch at school just because they participate in the program's lunch program. Children who bring lunches may do a lot of trading of foods among themselves, which may not be a problem unless some children bring in high-status, low-nutritive foods for snacks or desserts and encourage other children to bring candy or chips to trade. A study of Canadian children and adolescents' after-school snack intake found that children who had a high-nutrient, low-calorie (1 to 99 kcal.) snack (e.g., fruit or vegetables) had lower total daily energy intake than those who chose snacks such as chips, chocolate bars, or high-energy drinks (Gilbert et al., 2012). This healthy habitual behaviour can be associated with less likelihood of obesity (see Concern about Amounts of Food Eaten, page 357).

To outline ways in which foods can be provided in an ECLC program. (LO 6)

To explain rotation menus and list the steps in writing menus. (LO 6)

PROVIDING FOODS AND MENU PLANNING

Food is provided in ECLC programs in a number of ways. The most common arrangements are

- having the food prepared somewhere else and brought to the program (e.g., by a caterer, restaurant, or community kitchen). Often programs choose this option when they do not have complete kitchens.
- preparing food in the program, with an on-site kitchen and cook.
- requiring the families to bring food for their children.
- combining two of the above (e.g., an infant and toddler program provides the snacks and the parents supply their child's lunch and formula or breast milk, or a preschool program prepares the snacks and meals are catered).
- having agency nutrition programs, often sponsored by government or foundations, conduct breakfast or lunch programs.

Understanding the basics of **menu planning** helps you not only as a student but also after you graduate. The menu is basically the culmination of the program's nutrition program put into practice.

Providing Food in the Early Childhood Learning and Care Program

Regardless of how the food is provided, educators are responsible for ensuring that children have access to adequate nutrition each day. This must be clearly stated in a nutrition policy, outlining the provincial or territorial legislative requirements as a minimum but reflecting best practices beyond those requirements. As with all policies relevant to children and families, it should be written in positive language and communicated to parents before enrollment and on an ongoing basis. The nutrition policy will include additional information, such as

- foods, if any, that can be brought in by families and visitors and
- where menus are posted and how often they are revised.

ECLC programs that prepare food on the premises or bring in catered food usually offer one or two snacks and lunch, supper, or both depending on the hours of operation and their early childhood regulations. As part of the conditions for a program's licence, public health inspectors usually review the food preparation, equipment, and storage and serving facilities annually.

Financial constraints or limited kitchen facilities are often the reason why parents bring in some or all of the food. Programs need a refrigerator to store food and a stove, hot plate, or microwave oven to warm food. In some cases, the program provides milk.

This job is simpler when food is prepared in-house or is catered because staff develop the menus and establish the list of acceptable foods and beverages to be served to the children based on the program's nutrition policy. And, of course, enough food is available to provide children with second helpings. You may think that when families bring food for children, educators can relax and focus on other aspects of the program. However, since the educators are responsible for ensuring adequate nutrition for the children during the day, the nutrition policies in place cover

- the food and/or beverages that the program provides;
- the times for snacks and meals;
- the parents' responsibilities;
- a list of acceptable or unacceptable foods and beverages for parents to use as a guideline in providing the food, taking care to respect families' food preferences; and
- recommendations for environmentally friendly food containers and packaging.

Even in these programs, supplementary food will be on hand. There may be times when someone forgets a lunch at home or in the car, a child is still hungry after finishing her or his snack or lunch, a parent does not send or cannot afford to send enough food, or a parent consistently sends foods that are high in fat, sugar, or salt but low in other nutrients. So it can be more of a challenge for staff when the families provide food and/or beverages for the children.

> Putting a basket of fruit or other nutritious finger foods out at lunch makes sense. Hungry children can help themselves. This reduces the stigma associated with the children having to ask educators for food.

Educators and families want children to have adequate nutrition and to become knowledgeable about food choices. Nutrition education is an ongoing part of the program and is based on developmental and cultural appropriateness. As with any issue that educators have about children, they need to be sensitive in their approach, handle the issue discreetly, and maintain confidentiality. Food and eating habits are personal aspects of someone's identity, upbringing, and ethnicity and can be closely connected to feelings of self-worth. Making disparaging comments about a child's lunch and, even worse, throwing part or all of the lunch away are unacceptable and disrespectful practices. These practices will not make families receptive to talking with educators.

Before approaching families, educators must ask themselves a few questions:

- How frequent is the problem, and how long has it been happening?
- Has the parent experienced a recent emotional or financial setback that may temporarily affect the family's everyday life?
- Are the food products familiar to the educators? If not, find out more about the food and its preparation. It may be nutritious after all, and it can be an opportunity for new foods to be integrated into the program.

Sonali follows a vegan, plant-based diet, and her lunches don't have milk or meat. Because you are unfamiliar with the principles of veganism, you assume that she isn't getting the protein or calcium she needs. Some plant sources of calcium (e.g., almonds, figs) may be part of Sonali's daily mainstay. You want to educate yourself about veganism; asking her parents to explain their family's diet helps you do this. As for the parents, you have demonstrated an interest in their child, and they are pleased that they have knowledge and skills to share with you. They may also have religious or cultural reasons for their dietary needs that will contribute to your responsiveness to Sonali.

Ways to Provide Enough Nutritious Food

Children and adults need to eat breakfast to obtain the food energy to work, learn, and play. Many young children go to bed between 7:30 and 9:30 p.m. With the exception of infants, who wake up for a bottle or nursing, children wake up in the morning having fasted for 10 to 12 hours. The demands that rapid growth, development, and everyday activities place on children make it important that they eat enough nutrients to fuel growth and activity for several hours.

Provincial regulations and occupational guidelines specify what food must be offered and how often depending on a child's age and the number of hours spent in care. Here's a basic routine to follow regardless of the age of children in your care (CPS, 2015, p. 37):

- For 2- to 4-hour sessions (either morning or afternoon), provide a snack 1½ to 2 hours before the next planned meal.
- For 4- to 6-hour sessions, provide one meal and one snack.
- For 7- to 8-hour sessions, provide one meal and two snacks.
- For 9- to 10-hour sessions, provide two meals and two snacks.*

Try to offer a snack between 1½ and 2 hours before the next meal.

Morning Snacks

Many programs offer a flexible time for morning snack. They recognize that offering the snack at a designated time for all children cannot meet the individual nutritional needs of children.

Christopher gets out of bed as early as 6:00 a.m., eats breakfast, and leaves for the program. He is usually ready for his morning snack before or by 9:30 a.m.

Regular snacks provide a necessary and positive contribution to a child's food intake. Morning snacks that include foods from three of the four food groups provide the essential nutrients. They should be acceptable for dental health too. The snack could be available for a set period—for example, from 7:30 to 9:30 a.m.—rather than offered as a group snack. Children then have control over when to eat and can respond to their body rather than to a time imposed by the program. Because they have a smaller stomach, growing children need the opportunity to

---

*Source: Reprinted with permission from the Canadian Paediatric Society.

refuel (if they choose to) every two to three hours. It is also helpful for relatively stable blood sugar levels rather than ones that drop low ("I'm starved") and then soar high ("I'm stuffed") due to ravenous eating.

Dietitians are sometimes concerned that if there aren't set times for eating, children will develop grazing habits—eating constantly with no awareness of body signals for hunger. Having a flexible morning snack enables children to eat when they are hungry (and not ravenous) and adequately addresses dietitians' concerns. Obviously, the snack would not be available between 9:30 and 11:30 a.m. or noon, when lunch is served.

Keeping in mind that children have individual body rhythms, just as adults do, there are those who do not eat breakfast, for a variety of reasons:

- Some children may not enjoy eating or drinking as soon as they get up in the morning.
- There may be no time to eat during the morning rush to get out of the house and drop everyone off. Time pressure on families is a significant reason for children being hungry in the morning.
- Children who have not had a good night's sleep may not have an appetite for several hours after they wake up.
- Some children will have eaten only part of their breakfast at home or on their way to the program. And they will need to finish it or have the morning snack to supplement it when they arrive at the program. Other children may have eaten a doughnut or danish on the way to the program, which provides some quick energy but none of the nutrients needed for a morning's activity.
- Some families just don't have the food available for breakfast every day. The problem may be more acute at the end of the month, when there is little or no money left in the budget.
- Some parents who don't eat breakfast themselves may not see the importance of providing breakfast for their children. Or because of the parents' modelling, the child refuses to eat breakfast.

Morning snacks can be simple yet nourishing. Children who eat a nourishing breakfast at home will probably want less of each food or fewer of the items.

Here are a few simple snack ideas that include three of the four food groups. These snacks are easy to prepare even in programs with limited kitchen facilities:

- cold or hot low-sugar cereal, milk, and fruit (fresh or canned in its own juice)
- pita bread with hummus and fruit or vegetables
- cottage cheese with fruit and whole-grain crackers
- melted cheese and tomato or avocado on unbuttered whole-grain toast
- banana egg pancakes (blend one ripe banana with two eggs and grill the small pancakes on a nonstick griddle) and milk

Courtesy of Barb Pimento

- blender drinks (e.g., milk or yogurt and fruit or juice; eggs must not be used in blender drinks because of the risk of *Salmonella* food poisoning)
- scrambled tofu (soybean curd) on whole-grain toast with fruit
- egg salad on crackers with fruit
- yogurt with fruit and wheat germ

Child Nutrition Programs

It may be surprising to you that Canada is the only G8 country without a federal policy for a national child nutrition program. There is a piecemeal approach to child nutrition, with some local and provincial funding from a range of sources. On a positive note, many creative programs have emerged to respond to the food insecurity of children, sponsored by government, nongovernmental agencies, nonprofit organizations, and business. Many elementary schools have developed responsive programs because children were arriving at school hungry and unable to concentrate on their work and

have included ECLC programs in their mandate so that younger children benefit as well. Communities are recognizing the contribution of nourishing food to children's everyday well-being. Child nutrition programs are responsive to the communities served since they may be delivered in a variety of ways and may be part of an overall plan involving community kitchens or gardens, lunch salad bars, healthy snacks, or breakfasts, contributing to nutrition education that will benefit the child and family in the long term.

FoodShare's Coalition for Student Nutrition, an Ontario-wide network of individuals and agencies committed to better nutrition for children, developed eight guiding principles for a child nutrition program. The following principles have now been mandated as policy for funding proposals:

- The program supplies nutritious and safe food, regardless of family income.
- The program is accessible and non-stigmatizing, so it is universal and flexible and does not replace welfare reform.
- The program is community based and administered in a way that respects the individuality of the community and addresses its unique needs.
- The program is culturally appropriate, so it is sensitive to and respects individual and community diversity.
- The program empowers children and families, so parents are not made to feel that their role in the raising of their child is being taken away from them.
- The program creates a nurturing, warm, caring environment in which children can participate freely.

- The program has enough financial stability to ensure continual funding.
- The program provides public education about creative ways to nourish children adequately and properly, both in school and at home.*

Menu Planning

Menus may be written in ECLC programs by

- the director,
- the educators, or
- the cook.

A dietitian may be available for ECLC programs to review menus and offer recommendations.

Each of these options brings strengths and challenges:

- The expertise of a dietitian is a definite asset. However, if the same menu is used in a number of programs, there may be less opportunity to respond to individual aspects of the community in which each program is located.
- A knowledgeable cook can get immediate feedback from the children on how they feel about the food. A cook can be creative with the menu and see what works and what doesn't.
- When meals are catered, the menu plan is probably written by the caterers, with input from the ECLC director. The input should result in menus that include alternatives for children's food allergies.

Effective menus reflect a variety of foods that are developmentally appropriate, take into account ethnocultural dishes, have little repetition of recipes during the four- to eight-week rotation, and introduce new foods and recipes regularly, including foods that children are learning to prepare and eat. Educators' ability to read and develop menus is beneficial for a number of reasons:

- Educators identify the menus that are adequate in terms of nutrition, appeal, and variety.
- They know how menus can be corrected, improved, or made more creative, especially when younger children turn away from their food and older ones comment, "Not that again!"
- They suggest the appropriate substitutions for foods when a child is allergic. Serving foods as similar as possible to those that the other children eat is ideal to normalize children with allergies.
- They work within the nutrition budget and identify food wastage or unnecessary spending.

Advantages of Rotation Menus

Menus are planned on a rotational basis for periods of four, six, or eight weeks. Four weeks is a short period of time, which means that on every fifth Monday, the cycle starts again. Children are likely to become bored with the lack of variety in this case. Longer rotation cycles offer greater variety in foods, and no one has to eat

---

*Source: Adapted from Coalition for Student Nutrition, FoodShare, Toronto.

Courtesy of Barb Pimento, taken at the Downtown Montessori (Coatsworth) Childcare Centre

the same recipe more than a few times every six or eight weeks. Not many of us could say that about our cooking at home!

Developing four six-week rotation menus, one for each season, has several advantages:

- You can take advantage of the fresh produce that is available in season at its lowest prices and, in the summer, food that is grown locally or regionally. Perhaps some vegetables can be grown by the children (depending on your geography and growing season).

- The six-week menu would be rotated only once because each season lasts three months.

- You can serve foods that are more popular in certain seasons, such as soups in winter and cold plates in summer. Of course, favourite dishes (e.g., spaghetti) can be part of every rotating menu—once or twice in six weeks for the favourite foods is not too often!

- The six-week menu provides a vehicle for introducing new foods to children. It is in the children's best interests to plan a balance of familiar foods and new foods.

Getting Down to Writing Menus

The prospect of facing a page of blank squares and knowing that you must fill those and five more pages with exciting recipes can be somewhat daunting. Like other skills, planning menus takes experience to develop. A good place to start is by critiquing menus that you find in books or ECLC programs during your placements (see Appendix 5.2, page 319). As an educator, even if you are not responsible for menu planning, critiquing menus is an important skill as part of a team that consistently supports healthy and interesting food options for children. In menu planning, consider the following suggestions:

1. *Begin with a number of resources at your fingertips.* The most important one is *Eating Well with Canada's Food Guide*, followed by any guidelines for healthy snacks, simple recipes, and lists of different vegetables, fruit, juices, breads, and so on, to which the program has access.

2. *Know the number of snacks and meals that are served each day.* Programs that are six hours per day or longer should offer foods that constitute at least 50% of the daily requirements of *Eating Well with Canada's Food Guide*. As a rule, the two snacks and one meal combined consist of three servings from grain products, three servings from the vegetables and fruit group, one to two servings from milk products, and one serving from meat and alternatives.

3. *A menu-planning format applies to children over 12 months of age.* As a student, you will gain a fundamental understanding of menu planning, which provides you with the basis for adapting menus to the age group with which you will be working.

There may be concerns about foods that can cause choking in younger children. Educators working with children under 12 months of age work directly with the parents to ensure that the nutritional needs of the infants are met, including the introduction of semisolid foods.

Suggested Steps to Follow for Each Week's Menu

- Begin by choosing foods for the five lunches:

  1. Select the meat and alternatives.
  2. Select the grain products that would complement the meat and alternatives.
  3. Select the vegetables and fruit.
  4. Add the milk or alternative.

- Next, choose foods for the morning snacks:

  5. Select foods from three of the four food groups (see Morning Snacks, page 294).

- Then choose foods for the afternoon snacks:

  6. Select foods from two of the four food groups. (Children's nutritional requirements are usually lower in the afternoon than in the morning.)

- Evaluate your week's menu with the menu-planning checklist (see Table 5.15).
- Finally, because you are developing a rotational menu, the four, six, or eight weeks of menu plans should be checked for repetition of recipes, for the introduction of at least one new food or recipe a week, and the food budget.

TABLE 5.15 Menu-Planning Checklist

Nutritional Requirements: Daily ECLC menu

- vegetables and fruit—at least three servings
- grain products—at least three servings
- milk and alternatives—at least one serving
- meat and alternatives—at least one serving
- drinking water—availability at all times is encouraged

Menus are varied, interesting, and creative (e.g., variety of colours, shapes, textures, tastes). Natural colours of fruit and vegetables, especially when raw, are appealing; a single colour on a plate is not appetizing. Meals should have a variety of shapes and textures to appeal to children's sense of sight, taste, and hearing. Experimenting with new foods, ethnocultural recipes, and different herbs and spices encourages children to explore a variety of flavours. Be careful not to serve two strong-tasting foods together.

- "Make at least half of your grain products whole grain each day. Eat a variety of whole grains such as barley, brown rice, oats, quinoa and wild rice. Enjoy whole grain breads, oatmeal or whole wheat pasta" (Government of Canada, 2007, p. 1).

- "Have meat alternatives such as beans, lentils and tofu often" (Government of Canada, 2007, p. 1).

- "Drink skim, 1% or 2% milk each day. Have 500 mL (2 cups) of milk everyday for adequate vitamin D. Drink fortified soy beverages if you don't drink milk" (Government of Canada, 2007, p. 1).

- As stated earlier, unsweetened fruit juices are not recommended on a regular basis. Fruit rather than fruit juice is a much better option. Of course, fruit drinks with added sugar or sweetener are not recommended at any time.

(continued)

TABLE 5.15 Menu-Planning Checklist (*continued*)

- Desserts, if provided, are a nutritional part of the meal (e.g., fruit, yogurt, homemade puddings).

- Snacks are low in sugar and are nutritionally acceptable.

- Menus are planned and served with children in mind (e.g., some finger foods, child-sized servings, age-appropriate dishes and utensils). Preschoolers and school-agers have opportunities to serve themselves. Toddlers are encouraged to begin this process.

- Foods that have been through a number of food processes or have several additives are not served (e.g., instant potatoes, pudding mixes, processed meats such as hot dogs, pepperoni sticks, bacon, corn dogs, sausages, luncheon meats, fish sticks, and chicken nuggets).

- Foods served for celebrations and holidays are nutritious and fun.

- All allergies have been considered while planning menus and at the time of serving meals and snacks.

- Menus are posted in an obvious place for parents to read.

- The posted menu corresponds with what is actually served. Whenever there is a need for a substitute menu item, it is indicated on the posted menu so that family members are aware.

CRITICAL THINKING

When viewing the week-long summer menu in Appendix 5.2 (page 319), focus on the lunches. You know that several of the children do not drink cow's milk, for a variety of reasons. In addition to having other milk substitutions available for those who require it (e.g., goat, soya, and almond), list one good calcium, non-dairy-based food to incorporate into each of the five lunches. Refer to Table 5.7 (page 255) for substitution ideas.

FOOD SAFETY

This section includes three safety issues relevant to food and children: choking, foodborne illnesses, and microwave ovens. Children are at risk for choking on food because pieces of food are too large or they are not concentrating on what they are doing (e.g., talking while they have food in their mouth, eating while running). The safety of Canada's food supply is a shared responsibility among all levels of government, industry, and consumers. We depend on government policies and regulations to set high standards to ensure a safe food supply and inspection at all levels to maintain it. In an ECLC program, providing nutritious food for children goes beyond purchasing it and menu planning. It is of the utmost importance that food is safely stored, handled, prepared, and served. Because the immune system of young children is not yet mature, they are even more vulnerable to foodborne illnesses than are adults. Microwave ovens are great timesavers in ECLC programs. Although using a microwave in an ECLC setting is basically the same as using one at home, extra care must be taken.

Reducing the Risk of Choking

As children grow and develop, they improve their ability to eat a variety of foods. They start with liquids and move to foods that are puréed and then to minced or chopped foods, and, finally, they are able to bite off and chew solid pieces of food. The **risk of choking** is high whenever children are given foods that are not developmentally appropriate. All children must be supervised when they are eating. Children can choke on food when they have food in their mouth while laughing or crying or when they put pieces in their mouth that are too big. Other behaviour that should be monitored while eating includes proper posture while seated, proper chewing, eating too quickly, or eating and drinking at the same time. Educators should be formally trained in handling emergencies, including choking.

Educators can follow simple guidelines in food preparation to reduce the risk to children significantly. Hard, small, and round foods, whether smooth or sticky, can block a young child's airway. Adults should avoid serving the following foods to children under four years of age:

- popcorn (lower-risk grain products include pretzels or whole-grain dry cereals)
- hard candy or gum
- whole grapes or raisins
- foods with pits or seeds
- whole peanuts and other nuts
- foods on toothpicks or wooden sticks
- fish with bones

CPS (2015, p. 37) makes the following suggestions to make food safer:

- grating raw vegetables to aid chewing;
- slicing grapes into quarters or halves;
- removing pits or seeds;
- gently cooking or steaming hard vegetables to soften them;
- spreading sticky foods, such as nut butters, thinly on pieces of cracker or toast rather than on sliced bread;
- chopping or scraping stringy meat and adding broth to moisten it;
- deboning fish; and
- cutting wieners lengthwise, in small pieces.*

With regard to nut butters, never permit children to eat them straight from a spoon or finger. For many children under four, thin nut butter with juice or milk. Many programs are now "peanut-free" environments, due to life-threatening allergies, but they possibly allow other nut butters (e.g., cashew, almond, or nut-free, usually legume-based, butters that have the same consistency) (see Preventing Allergic Reactions, page 203; and Table 7.4, page 389).

---

*Source: Reprinted with permission from the Canadian Paediatric Society.

Food Safety Practices

"Food poisoning (also known as **foodborne illness** or food-related illness) is caused by eating food that has been contaminated by bacteria, viruses or parasites. Food can become contaminated by these microorganisms at any time before you eat it, including at home during:

- handling
- storing
- cooking" (Health Canada, 2015, p. 1).

Most types of foodborne illnesses cause nausea, vomiting, diarrhea, stomach cramps, fever, or chills. One or more of these symptoms can begin soon after eating, or not until days later, maybe even weeks. Full recovery can happen quickly, but there may be severe complications for those more at risk, such as children aged five and under and elderly adults (Health Canada, 2015, p. 1).

Some types of foodborne illnesses are very serious (e.g., *Clostridium botulinum*, or botulism, which is rare but can be deadly), whereas others (e.g., *Clostridium perfringens*) produce symptoms that usually last a day or less. What we may assume is a 24-hour "flu" may actually be food poisoning. Infants and young children are vulnerable to foodborne illness for many reasons, including body size and immature systems. Honey is a risk factor for infant botulism and should not be fed to infants under 12 months old. Staff have been directed to avoid raw eggs and foods containing them because of the risk of salmonellosis (caused by bacteria transmitted from hen to eggshell). Never serve unpasteurized milk or cheeses or any home-canned or preserved foods.

Health Canada and the Canadian Food Inspection Agency alert and protect the public in the case of outbreaks of food poisoning from bacteria or toxins in foods on the market. *For example, "Since 1996, raw alfalfa sprouts and mung bean sprouts contaminated with* Salmonella *have been linked to a number of outbreaks in British Columbia, Quebec, Ontario, Saskatchewan and Alberta, as well as in the United States. The largest outbreak in Canada was in the fall of 2005, when more than 648 cases of salmonellosis were reported in Ontario" (Health Canada, 2011c, p. 1). The risk of serious health effects is greater for young children, seniors, and people with weak immune systems. Health Canada recommends that these groups avoid eating raw sprouts (Health Canada, 2011c, p. 2).*

Because the food we eat isn't sterile, some bacteria are always present. Food provides an ideal environment for bacteria to multiply or produce toxins. Bacteria thrive in warm and moist environments and need something to eat. Given enough time to multiply or produce toxins, bacteria occur in food in numbers large enough to cause food poisoning. Certain foods present a higher risk of foodborne illnesses:

- most of the high-protein foods, such as meat, fish, and eggs
- custards and cream fillings, whipped cream, and other milk products
- salads with mayonnaise
- gravies and sauces

It is not surprising that summer picnics with sandwiches that have meat or egg fillings or devilled eggs, combined with poor refrigeration or cooling and the warm sun, can cause food poisoning. The bacteria are in their glory—absolutely perfect conditions for them to thrive!

Food becomes unsafe to eat when we do one or more of the following things:

- practise inadequate personal hygiene
- use dirty equipment or cooking surfaces (e.g., counters, playroom tables)
- handle and prepare food improperly
- serve food that has spoiled
- store food improperly
- do not control infestations of insects or rodents

The following is only a preliminary discussion of **food safety**, although it includes the essentials of what students and new graduates need to know when working in programs. However, educators who are responsible for cooking or persons who are hired as cooks should take a formal food-safety course. Information about these courses is available through any public health agency. In accordance with public health inspectors' food protection guidelines, programs must develop and implement safe kitchen and food-handling practices.

Personal Hygiene

Effective hand washing is essential both before and after handling food in any way, as well as during food preparation when handling different types of food (e.g., after handling raw meat, wash your hands before you touch any other food). In addition, follow these hygiene practices:

- Keep your hair clean and, if it is long, tie it back.
- Avoid chewing gum because saliva easily falls on the food or cooking surfaces.
- Wear an apron to prevent bacteria from your clothes getting into food.
- Do not prepare or serve food to children when you know you have an infectious illness.
- If possible, avoid kitchen duties and feeding children if you are also responsible for changing diapers that day.

Cooking Equipment and Surfaces

Used bowls, utensils, cutting boards, and counters have bacteria on them. If they are not cleaned and disinfected properly, the bacteria remain on the surfaces and get into food. How can we prevent this cross-contamination?

- Post cleaning and disinfecting procedures. Daily and weekly schedules include all food contact surfaces, utensils, dishes, pots, and equipment (e.g., mixer, fridge, microwave oven).

Courtesy of George Brown College/Casa Loma Child Care Centre

- Clean and disinfect counters and food preparation areas before and after preparing food.
- Clean and disinfect tables that are used for playing and eating before and after eating.
- Follow the dishwashing routine to ensure clean dishes and utensils.
- Discard cracked dishes, cups, and glasses because cracks trap bacteria. If a utensil, plate, or cup drops to the floor, place it with the dirty dishes.

Clean and disinfect cutting boards and knives that have been used for raw meat or poultry immediately after use. Assume that all raw meat and poultry have bacteria present (e.g., *Salmonella* in chicken and raw eggs), which will be killed with thorough cooking. Cleaning and disinfecting prevent the cross-contamination of food that comes in contact with the contaminated board or knife. What might happen is that the bacteria land in a food that doesn't need to be cooked, and the food is left at the danger-zone temperature range that allows the bacteria to multiply and cause food poisoning. Separate cutting boards should be used—one for raw meat, another for everything else—and thrown out when they appear rugged and after regular use for a few months.

Safe Food Handling

The way we handle food affects its safety. One of the most important factors in handling food is its temperature. The general rule is "keep hot foods hot and cold foods cold." In other words, foods that are either piping hot (above 60°C, or 140°F) or refrigerator cold (below 4°C, or 40°F) are out of the danger zone. This zone is the temperature range in which bacteria thrive, and it includes our normal room temperature. High-risk foods should never be kept at room temperature for long and should be discarded if left out of the fridge for more than two hours (Government of Canada, 2011, p.1).

It may seem like a waste to throw out food when you are unsure that it is still safe to eat, but the risk you take in serving it is too great. If children or adults eat contaminated food, they may experience discomfort, mild or serious illness, or even death. Clearly, summer outings and picnics must be well planned with food safety in mind.

Using an insulated container and ice packs to transport food and freezing the sandwiches so that they are thawed but not lukewarm by lunch time are safe strategies. Select foods that are low risk.

Thawing meat or poultry must be done carefully by ensuring that the food does not reach room temperature if possible. All frozen food should defrost in the refrigerator unless the microwave oven is used. Keep the thawed meat in the fridge until you are ready to cook it. This cold temperature prevents the bacteria from multiplying quickly.

Organize preparation times so that all the foods are ready at approximately the same time. This way, you avoid situations in which some foods are starting to cool, whereas others haven't finished heating. Because children don't like their foods really hot, programs often have all the food ready 10 to 15 minutes before serving the children. This period is long enough to let the food cool a bit but short enough to prevent bacteria from multiplying. For infants and toddlers, cool the food quickly by stirring. Other important suggestions follow:

Courtesy of George Brown College/Casa Loma Child Care Centre

- Use a meat thermometer when roasting poultry and meat to ensure that the internal temperature reaches the specified cooking temperature. When the outside of meat is cooked, the inside may still be harbouring live bacteria.

- Keep your fingers on the outside of clean cups and bowls and hold clean utensils by the handles.

- Rinse fruit and vegetables thoroughly under cold running water before using them. This should be done even if they are to be peeled (e.g., melon) to prevent cross-contamination from the outside of the food. If you suspect the use of pesticides or waxes, scrub under warm water (you may want to use a little dish soap with water or a diluted mixture of water and vinegar or lemon juice) or peel off the skin. Although you will lose some fibre and vitamins by peeling fruit and vegetables, you will reduce your exposure to pesticides (see Pesticides, page 455). Pay particular attention to leafy greens such as lettuce and spinach by discarding the outer leaves and washing the greens thoroughly, even those that say they have been "prewashed" on the packaging.

- Wipe the tops of cans before you open them.

- Taste food with a spoon that you have not used for stirring and use a clean one if you taste again.

- Never transfer food from one child's plate to another's, and ensure that children are eating from their own plate or bowl and are not sharing utensils.

- Cover all food from the kitchen until ready to serve.

- Use serving utensils whenever possible, but don't go overboard by using tongs to pass out crackers and slices of bread.

- Discard food left on children's plates and liquid left in their cups as soon as possible.

- Separate large amounts of leftovers into small, shallow containers for quicker cooling in the refrigerator. Cover or wrap leftovers and transfer them to the refrigerator promptly.

- Serve leftovers the next day.

- If children bring their lunches, ensure that they are kept in the refrigerator.

- Baby bottles need only be warmed to room temperature. Placing the infant's bottle in a container of hot tap water or an electric bottle warmer is more than sufficient to do the job. Ensure that the bottle is warmed just before feeding as room temperature allows bacteria to multiply quickly. *Never use the microwave to warm milk bottles* (CPS, 2015).

Food Spoilage

We've all turned our nose away from a container that smells of sour milk. We can feel the green slime in the bottom of the bag of lettuce or see mould growing on food left at the back of a fridge. Yet we can't always tell when food has spoiled, and often food that causes food poisoning looks, tastes, and smells fresh. Beyond cooking and serving food safely, other preventive practices can be considered to ensure that no one eats spoiled food:

- Buy food from a reputable store or supplier.
- Don't buy or accept foods that are rotting or have passed the expiry date on the label. Avoid cans with large dents that could have broken the seal and cans that leak or have bulging ends.
- Never use home-canned foods in programs, even if you eat them at home. Home canning (in Mason jars) of vegetables or meat can be a source of botulism poisoning.
- Never use unpasteurized milk, even for cooking.
- Never give raw eggs in any form (e.g., eggnog, raw cookie dough, Caesar salad dressing) to children to eat because of the risk of *Salmonella* (see Appendix 4.1, page 216). Avoid cracked eggs.

Courtesy of Barb Pimento, taken at the Downtown Montessori (Coatsworth) Childcare Centre

- When in doubt, throw it out—whenever you are unsure about whether to use or serve a food.
- *E. coli* (see Appendix 4.1, page 215) bacterial infection can cause an upset stomach for a few days but can also be life threatening if a strong strain. *E. coli* can be found in poultry, beef, milk, raw vegetables, and other food or water contaminated with feces. There have even been outbreaks from eating raw flour (e.g., eating cookie dough, uncooked playdough). If making playdough for the children, ensure that you use a recipe that requires cooking.

Safe Food Storage

Safely storing uncooked foods and leftovers is one more way to prevent bacteria from multiplying quickly. Here are the basic guidelines for food storage:

- Regularly check the thermometer (which programs are required to have) in the fridge to ensure that it is set at the right temperature.
- Store meat and poultry in containers to prevent blood or juice from leaking onto other foods.
- Write the date on leftovers and use them within three days or discard.

- Store nonperishable foods in clean, airtight metal, glass, or hard plastic containers with a label and the date they were filled. Keep containers at least 15 cm (6 in.) off the floor and in a well-ventilated space that is cool, about 18°C (64°F), and dry.
- In the cupboards and the fridge, place newer containers of food behind the older ones, ensuring that you use older foods first.

CRITICAL THINKING

You notice a pot of spaghetti meat sauce sitting on the kitchen counter early one afternoon (spaghetti is on the menu for tomorrow). You ask the cook whether it should be in the fridge. She answers, "I'm letting the sauce cool down first because it has to be at room temperature before it goes into the fridge. Otherwise, it will go bad." Is it safe? Why or why not? How would you handle the sauce to ensure its food safety?

Controlling Insect and Rodent Infestation

Insects (e.g., flies, cockroaches, ants) and rodents (e.g., mice, rats) carry germs and spread them wherever they go. An infestation of insects in food (e.g., ants in a container of flour) means the food is spoiled and must be discarded. Few ECLC programs have rodent problems, but those that do must consult with their local public health inspector and an exterminator to eliminate the problem immediately. Insects, however, are a constant concern. Flies and ants are widespread. In some areas, cockroaches commonly inhabit buildings. Controlling insects inside buildings presents a challenge because insecticides, although they get rid of insects, also have the potential to contaminate food, surfaces, toys, and so on. However, alternatives are available that are not as dangerous to humans. Public health inspectors advise staff on types of products and may suggest a "people-friendly" insecticide first.

Rather than having to deal with insect or rodent infestations once they are under way, staff can take the following preventive steps to make the building less attractive for pests in the first place:

- Store food properly (i.e., in airtight containers, dry places).
- Don't leave food on counters or tables.
- Clean and disinfect cooking and eating surfaces so that crumbs and spills are removed.
- Sweep the floor after children eat (cockroaches eat dust and food particles).
- Avoid storing food under a sink.
- Check boxes and other containers that are brought into the building—cockroaches like to travel!
- Maintain screens and other barriers that insects might try to get through.
- Close off spaces around pipes under sinks and close cracks and holes in doors and walls to the outside.

- Act quickly when you notice the first few insects.
- Rinse out recyclables before they are placed in the blue box.
- Compost appropriate kitchen scraps outdoors, if possible.
- Properly store and empty garbage both inside and outside the building. Keep the area around garbage cans free of litter and spills.
- Line all garbage cans with plastic bags and use snug-fitting lids. Preferably, indoor containers should open with a foot pedal. Open wastebaskets should be kept out of children's reach. Containers should be emptied at least once a day—more often if there are problems with odours (e.g., in the diapering area).

Microwave Oven Safety

Microwave ovens are commonplace in homes, staff rooms in workplaces, cafeterias, and ECLC settings. Although they are convenient and easy to use, they can be hazardous if used improperly. To ensure the safe preparation of foods, the following guidelines are recommended:

- Use only microwave-safe containers, preferably nonplastic containers. Plastic food wraps, which are made with nonylphenols, are of concern when heated. In addition, chemicals used to make plastics can be hazardous to long-term health. Remember that Health Canada responded quickly to ban bisphenol A from use in baby bottles in 2008, mostly due to the concern that when heated, the chemical leaches into the contents (e.g., baby formula) and is then ingested. Although now removed from baby bottles, this example highlights the need for caution with the use of plastic in microwaves. (See Plastics, page 456.)
- Use conventional methods, such as a baby bottle warmer, to heat baby formula. With these methods, you can use the warmth of the bottle to measure the temperature of the inner liquid more accurately. Be sure to shake the contents and test the temperature of the formula on your own skin before you go ahead with feeding the baby.

To Prevent Burns Using a Microwave

- All food should be covered while being heated.
- Use a low or medium heat for short time periods and test each food separately for even heating.
- Stir and test all food coming out of the microwave oven to prevent scalds and burns.
- Food heats unevenly, resulting in hot spots in the food. As well, the food can be very hot, whereas the container remains cool.
- "'Superheated' liquids: These liquids are at or above the boiling point but look harmless and show no sign (such as bubbling) that the liquid has boiled. When you remove superheated liquids from the microwave oven, they can erupt suddenly and cause serious skin burns" (Baby Food Safety, 2009, p. 9).

- "Heat transfer from food to containers: Many microwave-safe containers and dishware are not heated directly by microwave energy. However, parts of these containers may become very hot due to heat transfer from the food being cooked" (Baby Food Safety, 2009, p. 9).

- "Heating formula in baby bottles: When you heat baby formula in a microwave oven, the outer container (or baby bottle) may feel cool to the touch even though the formula inside is very hot. This can pose a risk of serious burns to the baby" (Baby Food Safety, 2009, p. 9).

- Make sure the plastic wraps and containers you use are labelled as microwave-safe.

- As a general safety precaution, always supervise children when they use the microwave oven (or any other cooking appliance).

To Prevent Foodborne Illness Using a Microwave

- Keep the microwave clean of spills and splatters. This practice prevents germs from growing on the food splatters.

- Government of Canada (2013, p. 2) offers these suggestions:
  - "Cut food into small pieces. Smaller pieces cook more evenly."
  - "Defrost food completely before cooking it in a microwave. Having frozen and thawed portions in the same food can lead to uneven cooking."
  - "Cook food immediately after defrosting."
  - "Rotate and stir food several times during cooking to ensure that the heat is distributed evenly."
  - Use a microwave-safe lid or plastic to cover the food to trap the steam.
  - Follow any directions to let the food stand after cooking is finished. The standing time allows the heat to continue spreading through the food.

For the full list, refer to *Food Safety Tips for Microwaves* (Government of Canada, 2013). (See Resource Materials.)

NELSONstudy
To access Resource Materials, visit NelsonStudy.

REVISITING THE HEALTH PROMOTION ACTION PLAN

With reference to the health promotion action plan introduced in Unit 1, the following are examples of possible actions relating to our food system. Keep in mind that because of the necessity of fresh, healthy food for optimal health, and its cultural and social importance, food is a powerful reason and tool for action.

Example 1

Many Canadians are consuming more sodium (salt) than is recommended for optimal health and for reducing the risks of heart disease and stroke. As stated earlier in the Role of Nutrients (see page 239), health concerns regarding high sodium intake by Canadians are an issue that needs ongoing attention to promote health at all ages in the life span. Note the following examples of action at each level of the health promotion action plan:

Individual Problem Solving and Self-Reliance
The following suggestions are adapted from the Heart and Stroke Foundation of Canada (2014, p. 2):

- Eat more freshly prepared food at home and less packaged food.
- Add little or no salt to foods when cooking (including food for children); avoid having a salt shaker at the table.
- Limit eating at restaurants and fast-food outlets; ask for nutrition information when dining out to make lower-sodium choices.
- Choose lower-sodium foods, meaning those that contain no more than 5% of the percentage daily value (DV) for sodium. (High-sodium foods contain 15% or more of the percentage DV.) The percentage daily value of vitamins and minerals can be found on the Nutrition Facts panel on most food packaging.
- Find out more about how salt affects your health and what you can do to reduce your risk of high blood pressure, heart disease, and stroke.

Community Action
The ECLC managers/directors, staff, board of directors, and families commit to eliminating unnecessary sodium in foods available at the centre as well as increasing overall healthy eating focus by upgrading their nutrition policy and practices.

The following suggestions are adapted from the Heart and Stroke Foundation of Canada (2014, pp. 3–4):

- The food industry
    - takes a leadership role to voluntarily continue to reduce sodium additives to foods during processing and preparation of all foods sold in Canada and make nutritional information, including the sodium content, readily available on overhead menu boards and table menus, for all foods sold in food service outlets
    - supports efforts to educate Canadians about the health benefits of consuming foods that are low in sodium
- Researchers continue to design and carry out studies to increase public and government knowledge that may affect future public policy change. Examples of relevant studies could include identifying
    - the health and economic impacts of sodium reduction in the Canadian food supply
    - the influence of sodium intake during infancy and childhood on blood pressure later in life

Societal Change

The federal government should implement the recommendations of the Sodium Working Group to benefit all Canadians, including the following (Heart and Stroke Foundation of Canada, 2014, pp. 2–3):

- Conduct public awareness and education campaigns on reducing our consumption of sodium.
- Actively monitor and report on positive developments that demonstrate the commitment of companies to achieve the government's sodium reduction targets.
- Mandate standard serving sizes on the Nutrition Facts table on package foods.
- Support food literacy among Canadians, including children.
- Support and improve the Nutrition North Canada program.

Example 2

Unreliable access to healthy foods (e.g., cost, location) is an obstacle for, or even prevents, many families from meeting recommended dietary guidelines for good health, such as eating fruit and vegetables and unsaturated fat foods. Even when cost and access are not factors, there are many families who can improve their eating habits, particularly by increasing daily intake of fruit and vegetables while decreasing intake of processed foods.

Individual Problem Solving and Self-Reliance

- Buy produce and other foods grown in Canada and locally whenever possible (e.g., local farmers' market).
- Respect food and avoid food wastage.
- Learn how to read food labels. Use Health Canada's regulated Nutrition Facts table to make healthy choices when you're food shopping.
- Handle and store food safely.
- Buy foods with a minimum of packaging.
- Routinely involve children in nutrition experiences and in building a basic understanding of how food is grown.

Community Action

- Create or use a garden at the ECLC centre. Agency/school gardens can be sources of local fruit and vegetables. They also provide the children with opportunities to learn valuable food skills by growing and harvesting healthy food. Preparing food from the garden, including herbs, or even knowing that some of the food served at lunch or snack is from their garden is empowering and encourages long-term interest in food sources.
- Get involved in a neighbourhood food cooperative, community kitchen, or other option to work and learn with others to prepare and provide food. You

may find ways that children and families can be involved as well. Discuss nutrition and food distribution issues in the staff room to broaden everyone's awareness. As a collective, you may be interested in joining a local or national food security initiative.

- Invite a local dietitian or public health nutritionist for parents and educators, with the goal of continued nutrition improvement for the children at home and in the program.
- Advocate for improvements at local supermarkets (e.g., to sell locally grown and sustainably sourced foods, a term defined as a way of raising food that is healthy for consumers and animals, does not harm the environment, provides a fair wage to farmers, and supports and enhances communities).
- Support community student nutrition programs. These programs are created and managed locally by parents, educators, public health departments, and local governments to meet the specific needs of local children and families. Many of the programs are based on a sustainable community-building principle, whereby the families who use the program are also meaningfully involved.
- Ask community groups and urban or rural planners to evaluate existing transportation routes and improve coordination of bus routes, bus stops, and schedules or shuttles to improve access for all residents to grocery stores and farmers' markets.

Societal Change

- Canada is one of the few developed countries without a nationally funded child nutrition program. This requires our federal government's commitment to making nutritious food programs available to any child in Canada. A cost-shared arrangement with other levels of government in whatever ways and locations the communities consider most appropriate is required for this vision. Of course, communities would be able to build on their existing infrastructure and organizations.
- Families in Canada would also benefit from a federal law protecting children from junk-food marketing messages that encourage poor nutrition habits.
- Provincial and territorial governments should examine existing initiatives in their own jurisdiction or elsewhere in the country, or outside Canada, to identify what makes some programs successful and move forward with support. For example, the BC Healthy Living Alliance has been taking a comprehensive approach for over a decade that has resulted in many positive changes through community engagement. (See Resource Materials.)

NELSONstudy

To access Resource Materials, visit NelsonStudy.

CONCLUSION

Although parents and educators cannot ensure that individual children develop good eating habits for a lifetime, they can provide children with

- an adequate variety of nutritious foods that are safe to eat,
- an environment that fosters or encourages healthy attitudes toward food and eating, and
- a model for healthy eating habits.

From infancy on, the right of children to decide how much to eat and what foods to eat in an emotionally respectful environment takes priority in ECLC programs. *Eating well with Canada's Food Guide* encourages us to eat well and lead physically active lives. Children's minds and bodies, now and into their future, are very much influenced by healthy eating and physical activity. These themes are continued and expanded on in Unit 6.

ASSESS YOUR LEARNING

Define terms or describe concepts used in this unit.

- advantages of breast milk
- body image
- complementary proteins
- digestion
- disordered eating
- division of responsibility
- eating disorders
- *Eating Well with Canada's Food Guide*
- flexitarians
- foodborne illness
- food groups
- food insecurity
- food jags
- food processing
- food safety
- formula
- fortified or enriched
- genetically modified (GM)
- irradiation
- key nutrients
- menu planning
- nutrients and functions
- nutrition
- Nutrition Facts table
- nutrition labels
- phytochemicals
- positive eating environments
- risk of choking
- saturated fat
- semisolid foods
- trans fats
- unsaturated fat
- vegetarianism

Evaluate your options in each situation.

1. The practice at your program placement is for the educators to serve food and to insist that the preschoolers eat everything. There have been a number of power struggles lately, and lunch time has become an unpleasant experience for everyone. The staff have asked you for suggestions.

2. Although the preschoolers eat in small groups at tables, there are a number of groups in the room. The noise level can get high, creating a less-than-calm eating environment, especially for children who are easily distracted.

3. An 18-month-old who has been in the program for three months will eat only jarred or puréed baby food that his parents provide. He refuses the more textured food that the program serves. Related to this, educators are concerned that his language development is being affected. The parents are worried that if they don't provide puréed food, their son will go hungry.

4. You are working in the school-age program at a local school and have decided to volunteer in the breakfast child nutrition program. You notice that most of the children in your after-school program who would benefit most from a nutritious breakfast do not get to school until the bell rings and therefore are not able to take advantage of this opportunity. One of the other volunteers has stated that they are not getting the number of children they expected in the program. The two of you have talked about proposing other options than breakfast to the coordinator.

5. You're planning a half-day summer trip to a park with toddlers and preschoolers. Your responsibility is to make arrangements for the food and beverages and write a list of important food safety considerations for handling the food.

APPENDIX 5.1

Nutrients: Their Functions and Food Sources

ENERGY PROVIDERS	ROLE	FOUND IN
Carbohydrates[1]	supply the body's main source of energy; assist in utilization of fats, spare protein so it can be used for tissue formation	breads, cereals, pasta, potatoes, rice, couscous, legumes and lentils, fruit and vegetables and their juices, milk and alternatives, sugar
Proteins[2]	build and repair body tissues, including muscles, bones, blood; manufacture antibodies necessary to fight infection; growth increases protein requirement for new muscles and other cells	meat, fish, poultry, milk and alternatives, eggs, legumes and lentils, tofu, nuts and seeds and their spreads (e.g., peanut butter), breads and cereals in combination with other protein sources (i.e., to include all 8 essential amino acids)
Fats[3]	provide the most concentrated source of energy, carry fat-soluble vitamins, provide essential fatty acids necessary for all cell membranes; the omega-3 and -6 fats are essential for brain and nerve function and healthy skin	foods high in saturated fats: animal products such as butter, cheese, and cream and coconut, palm, and palm kernel oils; foods high in monounsaturated fats: olive oil, avocado, nuts (macadamia, peanuts, almonds, pecans, pistachios); foods high in omega-3 (docosahexaenoic acid): cold-water fish (salmon, herring, mackerel), sardines, flaxseed; foods high in omega-6: vegetable oils (corn, sunflower, sesame, soybean, safflower), margarine

(appendix continues on next page)

FAT-SOLUBLE VITAMINS	ROLE	FOUND IN
Vitamin A[4]	forms healthy skin and membranes, assists in bone growth and tooth development, promotes good night vision, repairs tissues	yellow or orange fruit and vegetables, such as carrots, red peppers, sweet potatoes; dark-green leafy vegetables such as spinach and broccoli; egg yolk, cheese, milk, butter, and margarine
Vitamin D	needed to absorb calcium and phosphorus and regulates the movement of both in and out of the skeleton and teeth to ensure strength	fortified fluid, evaporated or powdered milk, margarine, tuna, salmon, sardines. Vitamin D is the "sunshine vitamin" available through exposure to ultraviolet rays outside in the summer.
Vitamin E	prevents oxidation of fat in tissues, especially important in red blood cell membranes and lungs	vegetable oils, margarine, whole-grain cereals, wheat germ, bean sprouts, nuts and seeds and their spreads
Vitamin K	clots blood	mainly produced by bacteria in the large bowel; food sources are green leafy vegetables and broccoli

WATER-SOLUBLE VITAMINS	ROLE	FOUND IN
Vitamin B_1 (thiamin)	helps release energy from carbohydrates; enables growth and repair of tissues, especially nerve and muscle; aids in maintaining normal appetite	whole-grain or enriched breads, cereals, and pasta; milk and alternatives; pork; nuts and seeds and their spreads
Vitamin B_2 (riboflavin)	assists in release of energy, aids cell division and promotes growth and repair of tissues, maintains healthy skin and eyes	milk, yogurt, cottage cheese, whole-grain or enriched breads, meat and poultry
Vitamin B_3 (niacin)	helps release energy from carbohydrates, protein, and fats; assists in the synthesis of fat; maintains healthy skin, gut, and nervous system	whole-grain and enriched bread, cereals, and pasta; peanut butter; meat; fish; poultry; legumes; milk; cheese
Vitamin B_6 (pyridoxine)	assists in protein, carbohydrate, and fat metabolism; promotes normal functioning of central nervous system	chicken, fish, whole-grain breads and cereals, egg yolk, bananas, avocados
Folate (folic acid)	aids red blood cell formation and protein metabolism; all women of childbearing age need folic acid every day to help prevent birth defects of the spine and brain	dark-green leafy vegetables, broccoli, Brussels sprouts, oranges and orange juice, bananas, milk and alternatives, wheat germ, cereals enriched with folate
Vitamin B_{12} (cobalamin)	promotes normal blood formation, maintains healthy nervous tissue, aids in protein synthesis	meat, fish, poultry, milk and alternatives, eggs

(appendix continues on next page)

Vitamin C (ascorbic acid)	antioxidant that strengthens connective tissue, bones, skin, muscles, teeth, blood vessels; promotes normal nerve function; helps absorption of iron from nonmeat sources (e.g., orange-spinach salad); strengthens immune function; aids in wound healing	citrus fruit, vitaminized apple juice, dark-green leafy vegetables, green and red peppers, tomatoes, broccoli, potatoes, strawberries, kiwi
MACROMINERALS	**ROLE**	**FOUND IN**
Calcium	builds and maintains strong bones and teeth, promotes normal blood clotting and healthy nerve function	milk and alternatives, salmon and sardines with bones, calcium-fortified orange juice, fortified soy or rice beverages, tofu, dark-green leafy vegetables, broccoli, bok choy, edamame
Phosphorus	aids in formation and maintenance of strong bones and teeth, transportation of nutrients, and regulation of energy balance; helps maintain body's acid balance	meat, fish, poultry, eggs, milk and alternatives, soy milk, tofu, whole-grain breads and cereals; richest source is milk; present in most other foods
Magnesium	helps in formation and maintenance of strong bones and teeth, protein production, transmission of nerve impulses, and release of energy	dark-green leafy vegetables, legumes, seafood, milk and alternatives, whole-grain cereals; also in meat, eggs, dhal, lentils, hummus, potatoes, some vegetables
Potassium	important for fluid balance, muscle contraction, and nerve conduction	milk, vegetables, potatoes; bananas, dried apricots, prunes, dates, and kiwi are also good sources
MICROMINERALS	**ROLE**	**FOUND IN**
Iron	combines with protein to form hemoglobin, the part of red blood cells that transports oxygen and carbon dioxide, and also myoglobin, which provides oxygen to cells; involved in energy metabolism and the immune system	red meats, fish, and poultry (e.g., chicken legs and thighs); whole-grain or enriched breads, cereal, and pasta; iron-fortified infant cereal; dark-green leafy vegetables; dried fruits such as raisins; legumes such as lentils and chickpeas (e.g., hummus)
Fluoride	strengthens tooth enamel and helps prevent tooth decay	fluoride-containing water and foods prepared in it, toothpaste
Zinc	functions as part of several enzymes involved in many diverse metabolic roles necessary for growth, development, and energy release; structural role in growth hormone and insulin	meat, poultry, fish, shellfish, eggs, whole-grain breads and cereals, legumes, lentils, nuts and their spreads
Iodine	aids in production of thyroid hormones, which regulate energy metabolism and growth rate	iodized table salt, seafood, vegetables depending on regional iodine content of soil and water

(appendix continues on next page)

DIETARY FIBRE[5]	ROLE	FOUND IN
	indigestible material, which promotes normal elimination of waste from the colon; normal functioning of intestines and bowel; may have other physiological effects	whole-grain breads and cereals, legumes, fruit, and vegetables

PHYTOCHEMICALS[6]	ROLE	FOUND IN
	important antioxidants; play a part in immune function; provide some protection against cancer and heart disease	all fruit and vegetables, especially brightly coloured (5 servings of fruit and vegetables per day will ensure adequate intake), cocoa and chocolate

WATER	ROLE	FOUND IN
	the main constituent of the body; needed for transporting nutrients, promoting metabolic processes, regulating body temperature, eliminating body waste, maintaining blood pressure and fluid balance	tap water, beverages such as milk and juices, soups, and a wide variety of foods, especially fruit and vegetables

[1] May be "simple" sugars, such as sucrose and glucose, or "complex," such as starches and some fibre. Fructose is the sugar in fruit and honey. Lactose is the sugar in milk.

[2] Made of peptides and amino acids.

[3] Made up of fatty acids (saturated, monounsaturated, polyunsaturated fats, including omega-3 and omega-6 fatty acids, or complex fats [e.g., cholesterol]).

[4] Retinol and beta-carotene.

[5] Fibre includes nondigestible carbohydrates, mostly derived from plant material, which are fermented in the colon, and prebiotics, which are nondigestible food ingredients that benefit us by stimulating the growth or activity of a limited number of bacteria in the colon.

[6] Substances in plants. Also called flavonoids, flavanols, and isoflavones (e.g., lycopene and lutein, which are carotenoids found in vegetables such as tomatoes and broccoli with strong antioxidant properties and great potential as battling agents of degenerative disease).

Source: Adapted from D. Gillis (1989), *Promoting Nutritional Health during the Preschool Years: Canadian Guidelines*. Ottawa: Network of the Federal/Provincial/Territorial Group on Nutrition and National Institute of Nutrition, 29–32; Infant & Toddler Forum. (2006, July). *Nutrients: Functions, Sources & Requirements: Toddler Factsheet 1.1i* (ITF1 10), July 2006. http://www.infantandtoddlerforum.org/objects/pdf/fact_sheet3.pdf (June 2008).

APPENDIX 5.2

Summer Menu

	Monday	Tuesday	Wednesday	Thursday	Friday
S **N** **A** **C** **K**	Cheesy Mini Quiche Cucumber Slices	Blueberry Wheatgerm Pancakes Mango Slices	Multigrain Toasted Bagels Tuna Salad Orange Wedges	Apple-Ginger Granola Yogurt	Whole-Wheat French Toast Orange Wedges
L **U** **N** **C** **H**	Chicken & Vegetable Stir-Fry (Carrot, Yam, Broccoli, Corn, Peas) Brown Rice Orange Wedges Milk	Vegetarian Chili with Kidney Beans, Quinoa Baby Carrots Yogurt & Strawberries Milk	Build-Your-Own Tacos (Corn Tortillas, Refried Beans, Cheddar Cheese, Red & Green Pepper Strips, Black Olives, Salsa) Cucumber Rounds Cantaloupe Milk	Kale-Mushroom Pasta Topped with Boiled Egg, Red Pepper, Zucchini, & Tomato Wedges Pear Slices Milk	Lentil and Vegetable Rice Soup Havarti Cheese Cubes Multigrain Crackers Green & Red Seedless Grapes Milk
S **N** **A** **C** **K**	Whole-Wheat Carrot Cake Watermelon Chunks	Hummus & Pita Triangles Tomato Slices	Lemon Squares Baby Carrots	Whole-Wheat Banana Bread Celery Sticks	Apple-Oat Cake Cucumber Rounds

Note: Water is available at every meal and snack. Whole-grain bread or crackers are available at every lunch. Children are involved in preparation and in serving themselves whenever possible.

Source: Contributed by Robert Caspary, Chef at George Brown College, School of Early Childhood.

6 Healthy Active Living

CONTENTS

HEALTHY ACTIVE LIVING   321

Physical Literacy   322

Concerns about Childhood Obesity   322

Urban Sprawl and the Built Environment:
Impact on Active Transportation   325

Biology and Beyond   327

Concerns about Physical Activity Levels
of Children   331

SUPPORTING PHYSICAL ACTIVITY   332

Benefits of Physical Activity   333

Supporting Physical Activity in Early
Childhood Learning and Care
Programs   334

Physical Activity Guidelines   334

Motor Skill Development   337

Active Infants and Toddlers   339

Active Preschoolers and School-Agers   342

Outdoor Play   346

HEALTHY ACTIVE LIVING

What does the term "**healthy active living**" refer to? Generally, that term brings healthy eating and physical activity to mind. There are many other aspects to a healthy lifestyle, but when the term "healthy living" is combined with the word "active," the majority of the literature denotes those two components. However, additional healthy lifestyle components, such as sleep, relaxation, oral hygiene, and stress management, are discussed in Unit 9: Supporting Children's Development (see page 531).

In this unit, we explore the reasons behind the panic about healthy active living in Canada, particularly how this relates to children. Are the concerns hype

To define physical literacy and its importance for children. (LO 1)

To identify at least two major causes of the global obesity epidemic. (LO 1, 2)

To define epigenetics and its possible connections to obesity. (LO 1, 4)

(continued)

To list and describe concerns about childhood obesity in Canada. (LO 1, 2)

To compare what is currently known about optimal physical activity, sedentary behaviour, and sleep for children from infancy through school age. (LO 4)

or reality? What are the implications for early learning and educators? Are we able to contribute to healthy active living that will be sustained for the long term in children's lives? And if so, how?

Physical Literacy

As defined by Physical and Health Education (PHE) Canada, "individuals who are physically literate move with competence and confidence in a wide variety of physical activities in multiple environments that benefit the healthy development of the whole person (PHE Canada 2010)" (PHE Canada, 2018a, p. 1).*

© iStockphoto.com/Imgorthand

Why is **physical literacy** important? During the early years, children who are developing a range of skills with ongoing experience in physical activity are, in essence, also building their physical literacy. Their experience not only contributes to their growth, development, and well-being, but it also prepares them for an active life. The confidence and motivation that emerge as children develop and practise fundamental movement skills are their building blocks to physical literacy. On the other hand, without developing physical literacy, children and youth may choose an inactive lifestyle, which does not contribute to their healthy development.

Concerns about Childhood Obesity

Over the past 40 years, there has been an alarming trend in the prevalence of children and adults who are overweight or obese. The World Health Organization (WHO) reports that "worldwide obesity has almost tripled since 1975" (World Health Organization [WHO], 2018, p. 1). According to WHO, "41 million children under the age of 5 were overweight or obese in 2016. Over 340 million children and adolescents aged 5–19 were overweight or obese in 2016" (WHO, 2018, p. 1).

Obesity is a complex condition, with serious physical, mental, and social implications, affecting all ages and socioeconomic groups. Although this epidemic began with developed countries, it is now growing quickly in developing countries. *For example, "In Africa, the number of overweight children under 5 has increased*

*Source: Reprinted by permission of PHE Canada.

by nearly 50 per cent since 2000. Nearly half of the children under 5 who were overweight or obese in 2016 lived in Asia" (WHO, 2018, p. 2).

"The factors associated with overweight and obesity are complex, and include health behaviours, such as eating habits and daily physical activity, and broader social, environmental and biological determinants that influence these health behaviours" (Roberts et al., 2012, p. 6). We know that several factors are significant with regard to individual tendencies to gain weight, but, ultimately, energy balance is largely determined by calories in and energy expenditure out. Worldwide transitions in nutrition patterns and a reduction in physical activity are having an overwhelming impact. The increasing use of automated transportation to distribute food globally has resulted in less reliance on local foods. For many, this has meant that diets that were rich in vegetables, fruit, and complex carbohydrates have been replaced with foods high in saturated fats, sugar, and salt, often highly processed, with a long shelf life. Insufficient sleep and rest, as well as excessive screen time, are also factors that have been emerging as concerns for childhood obesity as well as overall health of children (and adults).

Courtesy of George Brown College/Richmond Adelaide Child Care Centre

In Canada, many Indigenous communities have had to abandon or restrict their traditional primary sources of food due to changes in hunting, fishing, and harvesting practices that have been out of their control. These dietary changes have contributed to high rates of obesity and type 2 diabetes. These changes have also had devastating effects on "community solidarity, social organization and culture that were strengthened by the necessity of food gathering" (Williamson & Roberts, 2004, p. 195). New immigrants to Canada also face changes from what they know from their country of origin. Unfamiliar foods and cooking practices, differences in opportunities for the physical activity they were used to, and time constraints that may lead to consumption of much more fast foods are just three examples of ways that obesity may result.

WHO is concerned about the major risks of early death, quality of life, and health care costs to society that come with the chronic diseases common in obese children and adults, including type 2 diabetes, asthma, cardiovascular disease, hypertension, stroke, and certain forms of cancer. *For example, "Until recently, this type of diabetes was seen only in adults but it is now also occurring increasingly frequently in children"* (WHO, 2017a, p. 2).

Is this of concern in Canada? "Over the past 30 years, the prevalence of overweight and obesity among children in Canada increased from 15% to 26%, when data from the 1978/79 Canada Health Survey and the 2007–2009 Canada Health Measures Survey are compared" (Alberta Health Services, 2010, p. 22). Not all heavy children have weight problems as adults. However, as children get older, their risk of remaining overweight does increase, especially if they have a parent who is overweight.

Body mass index (BMI) has commonly been used to estimate body fat. The BMI calculates the weight (kilograms) divided by the height (metres squared), which is a rough guide rather than an ideal measure. The following are two examples of the BMI's limitations:

- BMI does not take into account an individual who is quite muscular.

  Although not typical during childhood, a child who has a larger muscle mass may have a high BMI and be classified as overweight using BMI as the measure.

- Children's body fat percentages change as they grow.

  As a result, their BMI will often vary based on gender and age. Most health care professionals currently share a percentile with the parents (e.g., the child is in the 60th percentile of weight and height for his gender and age).

To date, there is no perfect determinant of overweight or obesity. "The prevalence of overweight and obesity among children and adolescents aged 5–19 has risen dramatically from just 4% in 1975 to just over 18% in 2016. The rise has occurred similarly among both boys and girls: in 2016 18% of girls and 19% of boys were overweight. While just under 1% of children and adolescents aged 5–19 were obese in 1975, more [than] 124 million children and adolescents (6% of girls and 8% of boys) were obese in 2016" (WHO, 2018, p. 2). This in itself is of concern. In addition, with the overweight/obesity rate increases since 1975 beginning in the 5-year-old and older age ranges, we must also ask ourselves what this means in the preschool years. In the preschool years, children are developing the lifestyle habits that pave the way for long-term health benefits or detriments. The preschooler who is introduced to a range of healthy foods, is offered a minimum of low-nutritive foods, and has a lot of opportunity for active play that includes adult role modelling is less likely to join the ranks of individuals with obesity later in childhood.

FACTORS AFFECTING CHILDHOOD OBESITY

EATING HABITS

- regularly consume food and drinks high in sugar and fat, including fast food, chips, candy, baked goods, and sugar-laden beverages
- eat to help cope with stress and/or personal issues
- lack access to affordable healthy foods
- come from a low-income and/or very busy family who lacks the resources or time to prioritize healthy eating and active living

- are not physically active on a daily basis
- play a lot of video games, which are activities that do not burn energy
- watch hours of TV that includes constant marketing of non-nutritive, unhealthy foods and beverages to children and families

GENETICS/HEREDITY

- originate from a family with overweight members in which genetics is the main factor in their obesity
- family habits—i.e., healthy eating and physical activity are not part of the family's lifestyle
- have a genetic disease or hormone disorder (e.g., Prader-Willi syndrome or Bardet-Biedl syndrome)

Source: Adapted from *What Is Childhood Obesity?* Childhood Obesity Foundation 2015, April, pp. 2–3. Retrieved March 2018 from http://childhoodobesityfoundation.ca/what-is-childhood-obesity/

Urban Sprawl and the Built Environment: Impact on Active Transportation

In many larger communities across this country, the ever-increasing expansion of the city's boundaries into the surrounding undeveloped or farm land continues. Typically, the residents in these areas are dependent on their cars or perhaps public transportation to move beyond their neighbourhood for work, school, and social activities. Said another way, **urban sprawl** has many of us in Canada walking or biking less due to poor layouts and distance to stores and other community destinations.

In recent years, there has been a lot of interest in the health impacts of what is known as the "**built environment**," which is closely tied to the "physical environment" social determinant of health. "The term 'built environment' encompasses all of the physical structures and elements of the human made environments in which we live, work, travel and play" (Williams, 2013, p. 1). The built environment takes into account the neighbourhoods that we live in and how accessibility affects healthy living in terms of physical activity, access to nutritious food, social connections, stress, and mental health.

Raine et al. (2012, p. S7) acknowledge that changes to the built environment are a huge and very expensive undertaking, involving many levels and layers of jurisdictions. They recommend small, more localized changes, which can include advocacy to adjust local bylaws and input from all stakeholders, taking into account specifics to best reflect local resident needs, such as parental concerns about child safety and the need for parks and other green spaces. Active Healthy Kids Canada (2013a, p. 56) recommends that municipalities establish a baseline for existing sidewalks, trails, and bike paths so that monitoring can be carried out every few years to see the extent of improvement within communities.

Countries or communities that either lack the luxury of motorized vehicles or have planned the infrastructure to be community friendly for pedestrians and cyclists offer a vital ingredient for good health to their citizens: the importance of moving outdoors to get from place to place. Walking to and from school is one way children can engage in physical activity, yet today the majority of kids are driven to school. According to ParticipACTION, "24% of Canadian parents say their kids, aged 5 to 17, typically walk or wheel to and from school, while 62% say their kids are typically driven" (ParticipACTION, 2016b, p. 21). "**Active transportation**" is "any form of human-powered transportation—walking, cycling, using a non-motorized wheelchair, in-line skating or skateboarding. There are many ways to engage in active transportation, whether it is walking to the bus stop, or cycling to school/work" (Government of Canada, 2017, p. 1).* In addition, people in some areas in Canada may be able to engage in skiing, snowshoeing, or other forms of active transportation.

The Importance of Active Transportation

"Walkability is common sense. Factors that make people want to walk include a great walking experience, safety, accessibility, connections, comfort, walkable destinations, and encouragement" (Canada WALKS, n.d., p. 1). More and more municipal officials are listening to the voices of a significant base of public support for making their communities more walkable to ensure the health and well-being benefits for all of us.

The built environment requires attention at all levels. Active transportation, which relates to the built environment, is the focus of the *2013 Active Healthy Kids Canada Report Card on Physical Activity for Children and Youth* (see Concerns about Physical Activity Levels of Children, page 331).

---

*Source: © All rights reserved. *What Is Active Transportation?* Public Health Agency of Canada, 2017. Adapted and reproduced with permission from the Minister of Health, 2018.

HIGHLIGHTS FROM ACTIVE HEALTHY KIDS CANADA'S REPORT

WHY IS ACTIVE TRANSPORTATION SO IMPORTANT?

- Active transportation can easily be integrated into everyday life with little or even no cost, and its benefits are significant. With only 5% of 5- to 17–year-olds meeting the Canadian Physical Activity Guidelines, active transportation presents a major opportunity for improving health among Canadian children and youth.

- Active transportation may also improve fitness and heart health, increase academic achievement, provide social opportunities, reduce stress, and improve air quality and reduce the risk of lung disease.

- If children walked for all trips of less than 1 kilometre rather than being driven, they would accumulate approximately 15 to 20 minutes of walking per trip and have the potential to make a substantial contribution to the 60 minutes of daily physical activity kids need for overall health.

(continued)

- We need to embrace our children's enthusiasm for active transportation. Research suggests that, given the choice, most children would prefer to walk or cycle to school rather than take a bus or be driven by their parents.

© iStockphoto.com/Imgorthand

WHY ARE KIDS NOT TRAVELLING ACTIVELY?

- Barriers, such as distance between home and the end destination, as well as safety concerns, have led to a decrease in active transportation among Canadian children and youth.
- Although a large proportion of Canadian adults (66%) agree that their neighbourhood is safe for their children to walk in, today's children are less likely to walk or bike to neighbourhood destinations without adult supervision.
- Road and neighbourhood safety (e.g., "stranger danger") concerns are other important barriers to active transportation. In fact, increased car trips lead to more car traffic in school zones, and this traffic generally comes from parents whose children live within a reasonable walking distance.

WHAT STEPS CAN WE TAKE TO IMPROVE ACTIVE TRANSPORTATION?

- Small changes can have a big impact, and by increasing active transportation, we can increase the overall physical activity level of Canadian children and youth. Collective action—from parents, policymakers, and schools—is necessary to create opportunities for kids to get out of the car and to their destination actively.
- Parents need to model good physical activity behaviour for their children and encourage healthy habits from an early age. To address time constraints and safety barriers, parents and families can share responsibility for child supervision while actively travelling to and from destinations.
- Schools and school administrators can facilitate active transportation by making bike racks available in highly visible areas of the school yard and by implementing safe walk-to-school travel plans.

Active transportation needs to be considered when new subdivisions and schools are being built. Municipal and provincial/territorial government strategies should ensure urban planning that supports safe communities for biking and walking (Active Healthy Kids Canada, 2013b, pp. 1–3).

Source: Active Healthy Kids Canada, 2013. *Physical Activity Report Card*, http://dvqdas9jty7g6 .cloudfront.net/reportcard2013/AHKC-Summary-2013.pdf. Reprinted with permission.

Biology and Beyond

Obesity should not be the only marker of focus for child health. Healthy active living strategies that are targeted only at children who are overweight are wrought with traps and possible negative consequences for all children. A child in a normal weight range can also be unhealthy when he or she is significantly inactive, has poor eating habits, or both. We must take care to avoid assumptions or judgments about the health of children who are not lean at any age. Remember that we come in all shapes and sizes. Our genetics, biology, ethnic origin, environment, lifestyle, and other factors, some of which we have little or no control over, come into play in the formation of body size. Lifestyle factors do not fully account for this wide discrepancy, and it must be acknowledged that factors contributing to obesity are more complex than a prescription of healthy eating and physical activity. One of the considerations as an underlying cause of obesity is increased levels of the hormone cortisol.

There is ongoing research that links stress in early life to obesity in middle childhood and later life. Stressors such as poverty, food insecurity, inferior relationships with primary caregivers, or adverse childhood experiences (e.g., maltreatment) can have a detrimental influence on the child's healthy development and well-being. "Exposure to chronic and acute early life stressors can disrupt the biological stress regulation system, change the structure of regions of the brain responsible for emotion regulation and other important tasks, and promote obesogenic eating behavior and dietary patterns, as well as lifestyle factors (e.g., poor sleep, low physical activity) that may increase obesity risk" (Miller et al., 2017, p. 1). "Ways to support obesity prevention in childhood are essential, rather than waiting until late childhood or adulthood when interventions to deal with obesity are usually unsuccessful for a range of reasons, including established eating patterns" (Miller et al., 2017, p. 1). On the flip side, children in the healthy weight range are not necessarily fit or eating a diet that is optimal for health.

The rapidly expanding science of **epigenetics** may have a key to one of the complex factors involved in the quick rise of obesity over the past 30 years. In the 21st century, you will most commonly find epigenetics defined as "the study of heritable changes in genome function that occur without a change in DNA sequence" (Epigenome NoE, 2013, p. 1). The literal meaning of "epi" is "on top of or in addition to." The potential for environmental factors to switch genes on or off should motivate us to follow healthy living guidelines. The traditional view of genetics cannot fully explain the very rapid changes in human gene activity that are evident with exposure to environmental toxins. Genetics requires changes to DNA, which takes many generations. It is now evident that genes can be turned on and off without changing their DNA sequence. Nonhereditary factors can cause the individual's genes to express themselves differently.

Epigenetics research is looking at possible connections to many chronic diseases, including studies on the connection between obesity and chemicals that are endocrine disruptors, which disrupt the regulatory system that controls our weight (see Environmental Contaminants, page 444).

CBC's *The Nature of Things* documentary "Programmed to Be Fat?" (Dreamfilm Productions, 2017) describes alarming research into some of the chemicals that may be programming us to be overweight or obese. (See Resource Materials.) Bisphenol A is one of those chemicals that have been studied in lab mice, and reproductive problems and obesity in these mice have raised concern. Chemicals such as bisphenol A, used extensively in plastics (see page 456), including the lining of cans, and perfluorinated compounds, used in some nonstick and stain-resistant materials, may be interfering with the way our metabolism works, impacting weight gain.

NELSONstudy

To access Resource Materials, visit NelsonStudy.

Evidence is growing that early life, especially fetal, exposure to these chemicals plays a role in fat metabolism, which may affect weight gain later in life. (See Resource Materials.) "Endocrine disruptors are all around us—in plastic, in cans, in the water we drink, in the food we eat. They're not supposed to enter our bodies, but they do. If they're proven to cause weight gain, the implications for human health are profound" (Dreamfilm Productions, 2017).

NELSONstudy

To access Resource
Materials, visit NelsonStudy.

Concerns about the potential role that chemical toxins have as one of the multifactored causes of obesity will be unfolding in the coming years. An important precaution that we all should take from this emerging research is to avoid, whenever possible, chemicals over which we have control, with particular care taken during pregnancy. Let's hope that healthy public policy will include the precautionary principle (see Precautionary Approach, page 402) to reduce our exposure to chemical toxins rather than waiting for further human evidence. Nonetheless, it is very likely that positive lifestyle habits support physical, mental, and emotional health, as well as reduce obesity and risk factors. As a society, one of our most important tasks to this end is to reduce barriers to a healthy lifestyle—for all.

Courtesy of Sister Celeste—Fort Norman

Currently, there is worldwide interest, including Canada's push for a zero-plastics-waste charter, to reduce plastics in our environment. In addition to stopping poisoning marine life in the oceans and lakes, the charter would also reduce the chemical toxins in plastics that affect human health. Canadians certainly use more than their share of plastics (e.g., plastic bottles and bags). For example, an estimate suggests nearly three billion plastic bags are used annually in Canada (Weber, 2018, pp. 1–2).

As stated in Unit 1, Indigenous peoples face disparities in housing, education, employment, and food security, as well as in the availability of nutritious and affordable food. On reserves, particularly those in remote areas that are accessible only by plane, and in Northern communities, the costs of vegetables, fruit, and milk make them beyond reach. In 2010, the rates of food insecurity were "27% of Inuit, 22% of First Nations people and 15% of Métis compared with 7% of non-Indigenous people" (Statistics Canada, 2015, p. 1). Addressing these disparities is a priority to eliminate barriers to a healthy active lifestyle, making healthy choices easier rather than almost impossible.

WHO's (2017b, p. 21) *Report of the Commission on Ending Childhood Obesity* reaches the following conclusion:

Childhood obesity undermines the physical, social and psychological well-being of children and is a known risk factor for adult obesity and noncommunicable diseases. There is an urgent need to act now to improve the health of this and the next generation of children. Overweight and obesity cannot be solved through individual action alone. Comprehensive responses are needed to create healthy environments that can support individuals in making healthy choices grounded on knowledge and skills related to health and nutrition. These responses require government commitment and leadership, long-term investment and engagement of the whole of society to protect the rights of children to good health and well-being. Progress can be made if all actors remain committed to working together towards a collective goal of ending childhood obesity.

PROMOTING HEALTHY WEIGHT

Supportive environments and communities are fundamental in shaping people's choices, by making the choice of healthier foods and regular physical activity the easiest choice (the choice that is the most accessible, available and affordable), and therefore preventing overweight and obesity.

At the individual level, people can:

- limit energy intake from total fats and sugars;
- increase consumption of fruit and vegetables, as well as legumes, whole grains and nuts; and
- engage in regular physical activity (60 minutes a day for children and 150 minutes spread through the week for adults).

Individual responsibility can only have its full effect where people have access to a healthy lifestyle. Therefore, at the societal level it is important to support individuals in following the recommendations above, through sustained implementation of evidence based and population based policies that make regular physical activity and healthier dietary choices available, affordable and easily accessible to everyone, particularly to the poorest individuals. An example of such a policy is a tax on sugar sweetened beverages.

The food industry can play a significant role in promoting healthy diets by:

- reducing the fat, sugar and salt content of processed foods;
- ensuring that healthy and nutritious choices are available and affordable to all consumers;
- restricting marketing of foods high in sugars, salt and fats, especially those foods aimed at children and teenagers; and
- ensuring the availability of healthy food choices and supporting regular physical activity practice in the workplace.

Source: *Obesity and Overweight: Fact Sheet*, World Health Organization, 2018, February, p. 4. Retrieved February 2018 from http://www.who.int/mediacentre/factsheets/fs311/en/

The good news is that educators can make a positive contribution by integrating healthy opportunities daily in the lives of all the children and their families. They will have opportunities to

- promote and support healthy habits from an early age; and
- participate in advocating for change in local, regional, national, and global agencies.

Concerns about Physical Activity Levels of Children

How active are preschoolers? This is a difficult question to answer, one that Timmons et al. (2008) investigated by analyzing available studies. From this investigation, researchers found that vigorous intensity of physical activity by preschoolers occurs in short spurts, approximately two minutes per hour, and moderate intensity for about five minutes per hour. Clearly, young children prefer intermittent activity, but most studies also noted large individual differences. Some children are extremely active, whereas others have low interest in vigorous physical activity (Timmons et al., 2008, p. S125). A more recent review (Timmons et al., 2012, p. 7) suggests that an increase in physical activity of preschoolers is related to better body measures (fat, bone, and skeletal), enhanced development of motor skills, and better cardiometabolic health. In addition, there is a positive association with psychosocial health and cognitive development. The conclusion included the following statements: "More studies, especially with infants and toddlers, are needed to address these gaps. No risks of increased physical activity were found. This work can be used as evidence to inform public health guidelines."

The Canadian Society for Exercise Physiology (CSEP) has promoted evidence-based practice through the development of standards, policies, guidelines, and research related to exercise physiology and health and fitness since 1967. The first guidelines for preschoolers from 0 to 4 years for physical activity and sedentary behaviour were released in 2011 and expanded upon in 2016 by ParticipACTION and endorsed by CSEP, the Public Health Agency of Canada (PHAC), and several other national organizations.

ParticipACTION's 2016 report is the most comprehensive assessment of child and youth physical activity in Canada. The report includes guidelines for 24-hour movement for children and youth (see Appendix 6.1, page 379; and Appendix 6.2, page 380).

As discussed earlier, evidence is accumulating that increasing physical activity in the early years contributes to better physical and psychosocial health status (Timmons et al., 2012, p. 7), but it has been difficult to determine how much overall and of each type (**endurance**, **flexibility**, and **strength**) is optimal. There are many variables that make this hard to measure.

Boldemann et al. (2006, p. 301) found that children's physical activity was related to the quality of the preschool play environment, with an outdoor green environment being optimal. Overall, the authors' interpretation of the results was that physical activity is a multidimensional behaviour that depends on social and environmental factors in addition to time spent outside and prompts to be active.

Canada has made some progress, but we have far to go in turning around an appalling record that relates to concerns about the health of children now and

Photo by Roberto Machado Noa/LightRocket via Getty Images

into adulthood. One positive aspect is that awareness of the issue is on the upswing, translating into beginning support for change by parents, educators, communities, and legislators. However, change can be slow. *For example, parents may underestimate the weight and overestimate the physical activity of their own children. The point of reference has changed in recent years, due partly to the normalcy of larger children* (Butler, 2008).

Reaching a broad preschool audience is also not a simple task. Universal accessibility to children age five or six and up in the public school system is not a reality for the four and under age group. Also, developmental milestones vary widely in age, with some two-year-olds ready to jump and hop and others just beginning to toddle without often losing their balance. This reality can make it difficult to get specific messages to parents and educators, although the general message is that daily opportunities for movement exploration with adult supervision and role modelling are essential for optimal healthy development. Active Healthy Kids Canada (2013a, p. 22) notes that "physical activity in childcare settings is related to the availability of indoor play spaces and the presence of both fixed outdoor and portable play equipment; it is also related to staff engagement in active play with preschoolers." Your province or territory and city, town, or community are likely finding ways to support preschool physical activity. Find out about these campaigns or programs and how young children and families can benefit from each. It's worth keeping a list to share with colleagues and families.

According to the *2015 ParticipACTION Report Card on Physical Activity for Children and Youth* (ParticipACTION, 2015, p. 37), further research is needed on physical activity and sedentary behaviours in early childhood learning and care (ECLC) settings. Although the quantity of physical activity participation in ECLC settings is familiar, very little is known about the quality of those activities.

Canadian 24-Hour Movement Guidelines for the Early Years (ParticipACTION, n.d.-b) (i.e., zero to four years old) recommend at least 180 minutes, or three hours, of physical activity at any intensity per day (light, moderate, vigorous). Five-year-olds should be boosting their moderate- to vigorous-intensity physical activity to at least 60 minutes daily (see Appendix 6.2, page 380). A Canadian study confirmed that 73% of three- to four-year-olds are meeting physical activity guidelines of 180 minutes of activity, but only 30% of five-year-olds reach at least 60 minutes of moderate- to vigorous-intensity activity per day (Garriguet et al., 2016, p. 1).

SUPPORTING PHYSICAL ACTIVITY

Every child, taking into account development, individual differences, and physical challenges, can move in ways that fit his or her needs and interests. We know this to be true, but do we walk the talk in providing and promoting these opportunities? There are no hard data to answer this question, but it is doubtful that this question would be answered with a resounding "yes."

OBJECTIVES

To list the three requirements of effective adult role modelling for children's physical activity. (LO 3, 4)

To describe the range of benefits to children from physical activity. (LO 1, 3, 4)

To identify physical activity guidelines embedded in a play-based program. (LO 2, 3, 4)

To list and define types of motor skills. (LO 4)

To discuss educator considerations in promoting physical activity for each age group. (LO 2, 3, 4, 6)

To discuss curriculum guidelines for each age group. (LO 3, 4)

To discuss the reasons for and the elements of an outdoor play environment that supports physical activity. (LO 3, 4)

To list and discuss benefits to greening the outdoor environment. (LO 1, 3)

It is hoped that you can confidently answer yes to these questions as you engage with children in your placements and in your career. In order to become an effective and valued physical activity role model for children, will you be able to

- identify and manage the barriers that you and children may be subjected to, both initially and during ongoing involvement in physical activity?
- understand the developmental and health risks associated with inactive lifestyles at any age?
- understand the need for, and significance of, outdoor programming for children's development, well-being, and ensuing lifestyle choices?

When you are able to answer yes to all three of these questions, you are ready to jump in and develop a culture of physical activity, ensuring that you encourage and create many opportunities for child-directed and some adult-directed physical activity in your curriculum. Support, encourage, and be a positive role model as part of your responsibility as a competent educator. You also benefit!

It is essential to recognize the benefits of physical activity for all children in your program, regardless of body type, size, or physical agility. Sadly, with the current focus on childhood obesity, the inactivity levels of lean children can go unnoticed. Observation of each child's movement during the day may surprise educators who assume that lean children make active choices. Children with special needs must have equal consideration and individualized planning by educators to ensure that they also have ongoing opportunities to move.

Benefits of Physical Activity

Physical activity enables children and adults to release tension, have fun, learn social skills, and build self-esteem as they develop skills. A body that is physically fit works better. Physical activity should be part of everyday life for everyone. It is common knowledge that exercise builds a stronger heart and contributes to increased energy and better eating and sleeping habits. Better posture and balance; stronger bones, muscles, and joints; social interactions; and skill development are other benefits. On the other hand, children's physical inactivity increases their risk of "chronic

diseases like type 2 diabetes, high blood pressure, high cholesterol, and other cardiovascular illnesses" (Government of Canada, 2016, p. 1).

In addition to the physical benefits of moving, there are physiological and psychosocial benefits, many of which are listed in this unit. The Canadian Paediatric Society (CPS) (2015, pp. 10–11) reminds us about additional reasons for ensuring that ongoing opportunities for active play are integrated into the young child's day:

> Active children learn to run, jump and kick while playing. As they develop, basic skills help to support a positive body image and facilitate recreational and sports activities later in life. Inactive children who don't develop these skills may lack confidence or feel awkward during physical activities as they get older. These feelings can contribute to a sedentary lifestyle as children mature and increase the risk of early obesity. Children with more opportunities to be physically active tend to make positive, healthy choices in other areas of life as they mature. Studies show they eat more nutritious foods and are less likely to smoke, use drugs or abuse alcohol. Physical activity is also associated with better mental health because it helps children express intense emotions in a constructive way. Exercise and having fun alleviate stress.*

Supporting Physical Activity in Early Childhood Learning and Care Programs

ECLC programs that place high value on the importance of physical activity will develop policies and practices that include adequate daily time for active movement throughout the seasons. Educators should plan a program that integrates physical activity in ways that invite children's involvement. Most children want to be active, especially when offered a range of possibilities. To encourage involvement, options need to be of equivalent status.

> The choice of outdoor play or a computer game may not hold equal appeal for many children. The high status of computers or other screen time gives that choice an unfair advantage. This can be compared to snack choices: for most children, being offered apple slices or a brownie will result in the brownie choice being made much more often, not supporting healthy eating choices. A healthier choice is apple slices or a banana. The child who is reluctant to join active games or activities may need more encouragement. However, children should never be singled out or embarrassed into physical activity. Instead, educators can use their observation skills to identify clues to explain the reluctance and then find ways to encourage that child's involvement.

Physical Activity Guidelines

By evaluating the variety of opportunities for physical activity embedded in a play-based program, educators can determine to what degree the children are able to be active for short time periods throughout the day, as well as the components of

---

*Source: Reprinted with permission from the Canadian Paediatric Society.

these activities. The following are implementation considerations for educators providing a high-quality physical activity program.

Development

- Ensure that children's development is the basis for planning the curriculum. Refer to developmental milestones for all areas of development, with a focus on, but not limited to, large motor development. In addition to other physical skills, such as small motor, balance, and coordination, cognitive, emotional, and social developmental behaviour and skills are occurring during physical activity.
- Each child has support and encouragement to build skills and energy level.
- At all ages, children learn to move and move to learn.

Infant: Problem solving—how to reach her favourite toy that is on the far side of the table.
Toddler: Problem solving—at the top of a snow bank, his boots are sinking into the soft snow.
Preschooler: Problem solving—how can you jump and land quietly, how small can you make your body, or how wide can you make your body? Predicting—how many giant steps will it take to get to the other side of the playground?
School-ager: Social problem solving—what is a rule of the game that would prevent players from bumping into each other?

- Although children follow the same developmental pattern, they will do so at widely varying times.
- It is important to follow a child's pace and not to make comparisons with others. It is also important to remember that activities that stimulate one child may not interest another. This is true at any age.
- Downplay competition.
- Focus instead on individual mastery and cooperating together with group activities.

Educator/Curriculum

- Model a physically active lifestyle that contributes to the children's interest in activity. When educators participate with children and observe them in active play, they use their observations to design the environment and to facilitate curriculum so that children can challenge themselves in play.
- Appreciate the educators' role in promoting both physical activity and physical education by supporting children's development of basic skills to ready their participation in a wide variety of physical activities.
- Ensure that the indoor and outdoor curriculum planning and implementation for physical activity are an integral part of the program.
- Emphasize fun, socialization, and active living all year round.
- Ensure that most physical activity opportunities are child directed and open ended.
- Incorporate music into activities when possible.

- Fit the tempo of the activity-promoting rhythm and cultural diversity. Ideally, music also reflects the families' cultures and interests.
- Provide children with the opportunity to make choices and actively explore their environment, while educators facilitate and prepare a stimulating environment and challenging activities.
- Movement exploration, guided discovery, and creative problem solving are the most common teaching strategies.
- Include a wide variety of physical activity challenges, which promote the development of children's endurance, flexibility, and strength.
- Promote appropriate opportunities for all children.
- Respect individual skills and abilities, energy, and interest level and encourage and celebrate each child's attempts and successes.
- Use directional instructions often so children practise spatial and body awareness.

Can you walk backward from the playground door to the fence? Or scurry like a mouse to the front wall and back?

- Encourage the development of pro-social skills.

Children go through the obstacle course one by one, learning to respect that their turn follows the child who is in front of them.

- Use clear, simple, and minimal restrictions and directions to promote maximum child-directed involvement in the activity, encouraging children to challenge themselves.
- Recognize the importance of children valuing physical activity as a lifelong habit, but be careful not to plan activities designed to enhance their fitness levels (e.g., running laps).
- Use a family-centred approach in your physical activity curriculum, as in all aspects of the program.

Perhaps a school-ager can teach his peers a skipping or ball game that he learned from his country of origin.

- Observe the children's skills and interests and support opportunities for physical activity through one-to-one support.

Safety/Environment

- Ensure that the environment reflects the developmental skill set of the children in the program and their problem-solving abilities.
- Maintain safety in all aspects of the physical activity program (i.e., equipment is well maintained, clutter hazards are removed, children's level of involvement fits the environment, adults actively supervise).

- Provide various types of equipment in quantities that do not overwhelm children with choices or result in children being left out or fighting over the few pieces of equipment.
- Include active indoor alternatives into the plan when the weather doesn't permit outdoor play.

Family/Community

- Invite parents, older siblings, and extended family members and encourage them to provide input and be involved whenever possible (e.g., share active games from their childhood).
- Provide music and activities that reflect a range in musical styles (e.g., jazz, rhythm and blues, folk, classical, reggae) and ethnocultural diversity, including family preferences whenever possible.
- Consider children's opportunity to move when planning for walks or field trips in the community.

Motor Skill Development

Children's development is integrated, involving more than one developmental domain at a time: physical, cognitive, social, and emotional areas of development occur simultaneously.

The patterning motion involved as an infant is learning to crawl is as much cognitive development as physical. Movement tends to invite sensory exploration and social interaction from infancy onward. However, if we "isolate" motor development, we find that it follows two fundamental principles:

- It proceeds from head to foot.
- It proceeds from the centre of the body outward.

This is evident as the infant must first get control over holding up his head and then sit up before learning to crawl. The small **motor skills** and dexterity develop later than the large motor skills.

Although we acknowledge that motor development is a continuous process of building, refining, and combining skills and abilities, there are four general phases:

- reflexive movement phase (beginning in utero)
- rudimentary (simple) movement phase (ending around two years old)
- fundamental movement phase (from approximately two to seven years old) (basic movement patterns include **locomotor skills**, stability and balance skills, and manipulative skills)
- specialized or sports-related movement phase (seven years old to adolescence)

Growing ability in cognitive and other areas of development (social, emotional, and language) interacts with motor and sensory skills to contribute to more mature levels of performance as the child becomes interested in sport or dance (Gallahue & Donnelly, 2007, pp. 62–63).

Locomotor skills involve moving the body from one place to another, such as walking, running, jumping, galloping, hopping, skipping, sliding, leaping, and climbing. **Nonlocomotor skills** involve moving the body in one place, such as bending, stretching, twisting, turning, swinging, rolling, stopping/landing, dodging, and balancing. **Manipulative skills** tend to involve objects such as balls and include throwing, catching, kicking, trapping, striking, volleying, dribbling, bouncing, rolling (object), and punting. Remember that children are also developing other motor skills, such as body and spatial awareness, and abilities such as balance and eye–hand and eye–foot coordination, which are essential aspects of the locomotor, nonlocomotor, and manipulative skills. Opportunities to practise a range of these (and other) motor skills help a child develop the skills and confidence to master more complex skills, opening up avenues for a lifelong active lifestyle. Refer to Table 6.1 for some activities at each age spectrum to support large motor development and practice.

TABLE 6.1 Some Activities for Large Motor Development

Ages	Skills
Up to 2 Years Old	kicking, rolling over, crawling, sitting independently, pulling to standing, cruising, down and up, standing alone, toddling, scooting, squatting, running, climbing, begin sitting on and moving on riding toys (often going backward first), rolling a large soft ball
2- and 3-Year-Olds	walking forward and backward, running, climbing, crawling through and around, jumping, running and jumping, hopping, galloping, balancing/rotating (e.g., walk along a low balance beam with or without help), bending, stretching, rolling and tossing balls or beanbags (often with both hands), kicking balls, hitting balls with a large object, sitting with balance on a swing (swing with gentle pushing from adult), sitting on and skillfully moving a riding toy with two feet
4- and 5-Year-Olds	walking, running, jumping, hopping, skipping, balancing/rotating/pivoting, climbing large play structures to their own comfort level, bending, stretching, tumbling, rolling/throwing or kicking balls with more accuracy due to developing eye–hand and eye–foot coordination, catching balls, batting/dribbling balls, hitting a ball with a large bat, developing spatial awareness, concept of teamwork developing but not yet most game skills, building stamina for longer duration of vigorous activity

(continued)

TABLE 6.1   Some Activities for Large Motor Development (*continued*)

Ages	Skills
6- and 7-Year-Olds	running/jumping, leaping, rotating/balancing/pivoting, skipping, tumbling, throwing/passing/catching balls, kicking balls, dribbling/shooting to hoop. Fine motor skills require the use of smaller muscles and involve more precise movements, such as using the fingers to draw. Also consider active transportation as much as possible (see The Importance of Active Transportation, page 326).
8- and 9-Year-Olds	running/jumping, skipping, leaping, rotating/tumbling, balancing/pivoting, throwing/catching balls, batting balls, dribbling balls, dribbling/shooting to hoop, building endurance and strength, as well as sports and dance skills, as fundamental motor skills are developed (keeping in mind individual differences as always). Also consider active transportation as much as possible (see The Importance of Active Transportation, page 326).

Active Infants and Toddlers

Infants' need for physical activity changes dramatically in the first year—from holding the head up, sitting, and rolling over, to pulling themselves up, to creeping, crawling, standing, and walking. Educators are continually responding to these needs by providing an environment that is developmentally appropriate, challenging, and safe. Refer to Appendix 6.1 (page 379) for additional suggestions.

Follow the child's lead while she shows interest in

- reaching for her favourite toy over and over as you continue to place it just barely out of reach,
- repeatedly crawling in and out of a box, and
- pulling herself up to standing using a sturdy table and holding on while moving around it.

The integration of cognitive and physical skills in this exploration, as well as the development of strength and confidence in her abilities, forms a foundation for continued motivation to move and explore. Adequate floor time is essential for this process.

Educators set up the environment to enhance each child's physical development. Taking cues from the child, educators engage in one-to-one interaction when the child is alert and interested. This provides an opportunity to focus on the child's needs and interests (e.g., action songs such as *Row, Row, Row Your Boat* to practise rocking or surrounding the baby with soft pillows to topple on as he attempts to sit up independently).

When implementing physical activity with a young infant on a one-to-one basis,

- begin an activity only when the infant is alert and willing. When a child is hungry, tired, or unhappy, it is not an appropriate time to initiate the activity.
- be totally committed to the infant by avoiding distractions and try to reduce distractions for the child.
- adapt the timing of the activity to the tempo of the room and of the day.
- follow the infant's lead in your interactions.
- try an activity with the infant in a relaxed and reassuring way on a soft covered mat or carpet.

  When the child responds by laughing or other signs of enjoyment, continue and possibly repeat the activity several times. However, if not, stop and try the activity again some other time.

- begin with relaxation exercises to establish trust and to set the tone. Then introduce some stretching and bending exercises to increase flexibility and range of motion. Follow with more vigorous activity to support strength, endurance, flexibility, and coordination.

  The process should be enjoyable for the infant and adult.

  Repeat the activities for several days, progressing only as quickly as the infant appears to want to. Follow the child's cues.

- use favourite toys whenever possible.

  It can be part of the activity or help the infant to relax (familiarity/comfort), or it can help draw attention to a movement (e.g., favourite toy is peeking out of the tunnel, which may motivate the infant to creep or crawl toward it).

Remember *not* to

Courtesy of George Brown College/Richmond Adelaide Child Care Centre

- force the infant or the infant's body in any way to tire the child.
- compare the infant's development or accomplishment with that of another child. Each infant is unique and progresses at a unique pace.

Children usually spend time sitting in a car seat or stroller when travelling to and from the centre. Most infants and toddlers go for daily walks sitting in strollers or wagons, which provides them with fresh air and stimulation and sometimes rest. *This is why they need plenty of opportunity to move around freely, out of strollers and wagons, with a minimum of restrictions.*

Toddlers are at a stage of motor development when they often need to run more than walk. They need an adequate open space, small climbing equipment, and slides. Ramps and steps need to be the right size to encourage toddlers' exploration, not to frustrate them or make them prone to falls. Creative movement can be enhanced when the toddlers are in smaller groups.

Provide opportunities to dance to music or move like an animal. Minimize the expectation for sit-down time and maximize opportunities to move in short spurts. Passive activities such as reading a book and singing quiet songs are more appropriate with one or two toddlers, who join and leave the activity as they wish. Of course, toddlers should always be permitted to come and go with group activities, unless supervision and safety are an issue (e.g., walking to the park).

A motor development explosion occurs because once children learn to walk, they quickly develop a vast repertoire of other motor skills, involving body and spatial awareness, locomotor and nonlocomotor skills, and manipulative skills.

Courtesy of George Brown College/Ryerson Early Child Care Centre

When planning and implementing curriculum for more mobile infants and toddlers, keep the following recommendations in mind:

- Physical activity opportunities and curriculum should be embedded into play whenever possible, not seen as a structured time of day. When educators have an active living way of life, they tend to optimize the natural opportunities for physical activity, recognizing and using possibilities. For example, marching or tiptoeing down the hall when coming inside or going outside, singing and moving to an active song when there is a short wait, and "shaking our sillies out" after sitting reading a book are all easy ways to contribute to short but numerous opportunities to move our bodies during the day.

- An environment and adult involvement that promote freedom of movement are essential for children to be able to assess their own motor capabilities and practise accordingly.

- When the children's environment is modified to prevent injuries as much as possible, it is obviously safer and less restrictive.

  As well, the educators are better able to ensure optimal supervision of busy, walking infants and toddlers.

Courtesy of Barb Pimento, taken at the Downtown Montessori (Coatsworth) Childcare Centre

Ensuring that the environment indoors and outdoors doesn't become too cluttered during the day with scattered toys also reduces frustration and makes it easier to practise emerging and acquired motor skills.

- Incorporate the quantitative concepts that toddlers are busy discovering: some, more, big, and spatial relationships such as up, down, inside, outside, behind, and over and under.
- As toddlers acquire more language and begin to develop the ability to pretend, the educator is able to plan for simple games such as Ring Around the Rosey and motor activities with suggested imagery (e.g., "Let's pretend we are fish swimming in the water").

Remember

- to focus on the familiar for the child, ideally integrating ideas that come from the family (e.g., foods, pets, clothing, songs, stories)
- the importance of simplicity when stating instructions

Active Preschoolers and School-Agers

Based on the best available evidence from the range of studies on physical activity (PA) for preschool children, Timmons et al. (2008, p. 8) made the following recommendations for preschoolers' physical activity:

- Allow for the natural traits of their activities, which generally are impulsive and recurrent.
- Focus on activities for overall motor skills with the musculoskeletal system that involve and amuse the children.
- Have adult role models who are animated and show enjoyment of the activities to add to the preschoolers' experiences.
- Have access to playgrounds and outdoor equipment.

These recommendations hold clear messages for educators and parents who value preschoolers' active play: engage with children in physical activities that are spontaneous and enjoyable, fit their motor skills and interests, and are outdoors whenever possible. Young children tend to have bursts of energy, so several short periods of vigorous play throughout the day are best.

An ECLC program should include these **fitness components** into the activities: endurance, flexibility, and strength.

Felix Mizioznikov/Shutterstock.com

FITNESS COMPONENTS
FOR PRESCHOOLERS

- Endurance activities strengthen the heart and lungs.

  Running (e.g., games of tag or red light, green light), jumping in an obstacle course or in an active game, dancing to a quick tempo, and swimming (when your program has access to regular swimming lessons)

- Strength-focused activities build strong muscles and bones, supporting the child's body weight.

  Climbing stairs or swinging across the playground ladder or monkey bars. Many of these activities, including running, develop both endurance and strength.

- Flexibility refers to the ability of various joints to move their full range of motion. Flexibility is enhanced in activities that encourage children to bend, stretch, and reach, such as moving with scarves, simple yoga poses, and playing bowling games with different-sized balls and pins.

  It is important to stretch before and after vigorous activity to support flexible joints.

Courtesy of George Brown College Child Care Centre on Charles Street

As children develop their skills and fitness levels into school age, they will branch out to other endurance activities, such as biking, more active transportation (walking or biking to school), tobogganing, and sports such as soccer, hockey, ringette, lacrosse, or basketball in addition to swimming.

School-agers may build their flexibility and strength through hiking, martial arts, and yoga. These examples point to the importance of a range of activities to build all fitness components for lifelong wellness. In the preschool age group, organized sports tend to be too complex with regard to many aspects of child development in addition to motor skills—cognitively, socially, and emotionally. As children show interest in and are ready for more organized games and sports, educators and parents can encourage those interests. Adults must also take care not to overschedule children or to place a lot of pressure on sport performance, which can take the enjoyment out of the activities and add a lot of stress to children around competing. This can undermine the benefits of physical activity, reduce much-needed family time, and place financial burdens on families

Courtesy of Courtney Thorne

for sports that bring with them added expenses such as equipment or additional fees. However, remember the health benefits for moderate and vigorous activity in this age group for 60 minutes daily. Refer to the CSEP guidelines for this age group (see Appendix 6.2, page 380).

Curriculum Guidelines for Preschoolers and School-Agers

- Although child-directed active play is predominant, adult-guided activities can also be part of the curriculum for preschoolers and school-agers, particularly when active play is not being observed (see Appendix 6.2, page 380).

Ask preschoolers to crawl with a beanbag balancing on one body part or move across the room with one body part leading the way. Children use their imagination, physical skills, interests, and problem-solving skills to rise to the challenge—resulting in all sorts of possibilities.

- Provide instructions that have built-in flexibility so that children can start from their own skill set and point of reference.

Even an instruction that may sound more directive, such as "hop like a frog," provides children with their own unique way of doing so.

  - Adult-guided activities for preschoolers and school-agers can include activities and games that help children learn when to stop and listen to the person leading the activity.
  - When introducing new activities or games, educators do so with patience. Preschoolers and school-agers need time to practise and master new skills.
  - Some children naturally have activity levels that require vigorous activity such as running and jumping as soon as they have the opportunity. Other children are attracted to moderate activity, such as marching and playing hide and seek (see Greening the Outdoor Environment, page 349). When these latter children are warmed up, they may be ready to try more vigorous activity. The hope is that they will, eventually, do some form of cardiovascular activity.

- Plan **cooperative games** for preschoolers and school-agers in which cooperation is incorporated into the rules and goals of the game while keeping competition to a minimum. Cooperative games do not eliminate children, thereby maintaining sustained physical activity for all children in the game. Children can also then join in and leave at any time.

Even traditional elimination games such as Hot Potato or Simon Says can be changed to avoid elimination, such as having two groups, with the child switching groups as he or she is left holding the hot potato or doing the action when Simon didn't "say."

- Educators observe the children's skills and interests and support opportunities for physical activity through one-to-one support.

Eight-year-old Roberto, whose peers are more physically skilled and better coordinated than he is, is embarrassed to play ball games with the group. Roberto always strikes out, highlighting his lack of batting skills, and his peers are impatient because he runs more slowly than they do. You can find a range of issues in this example:

- his lack of confidence
- his reluctance to join group games and sports
- his lack of interest in physical activity, which increases neither his skill nor his fitness level
- his peers' intolerance and focus on competition

The issue of competition is a difficult one to counterbalance when we consider the school-ager's developmental level and interest in rules and the constant messages about winning that bombard us in our society. Focusing on skill competence is developmentally important. Most children of this age have been playing cooperative games since their early preschool days. Educators can do their best to adapt competitive games to be more cooperative (i.e., by moving the emphasis away from winning and losing and toward participation, playing together, and having fun). Educators recognize in Roberto his need for long-term physical fitness and to be part of a social group. First, he is willing to practise ball skills with a trusted educator. As he progresses, one of his peers becomes interested in playing ball with him. Eventually, the group plays the ball game cooperatively (any game can be adjusted with minimal changes) part of the time so that all children can be involved.

dotshock/Shutterstock.com

Educators' sensitivity, creativity, and determination to support children's physical involvement encourage children like Roberto to build the interest, skill, and confidence they need to join in. This example is not meant to provide a recipe for success because, obviously, every child is unique and every group has its own social dynamics. However, educators can be confident that the effort they put into children's physical involvement is worth the long-term benefits.

The number of hours that most school-agers sit in class each day emphasizes the importance of providing physically active school-age programs. Some jurisdictions have mandated daily physical activity, but the short duration may not meet the needs for children from 5 to 11 years old, according to CSEP's guidelines (see Appendix 6.2, page 380). The guidelines recommend that children spend at least 60 minutes a day at moderate to vigorous physical activity.

Some school-agers desire sedentary after-school activities, including reading, playing cards or other games with peers, or doing homework. Perhaps those children can be encouraged by educators to move in 5- or 10-minute bouts to start, even between homework subjects, for example. With the support of the educators, the children can come up with movement ideas they would enjoy. There are also school-age children who are interested in more active options. Often school-agers plan their own active games or activities when encouraged by supportive adults. Problem-solving rules of the game, such as how to take turns, support school-agers' social problem-solving skills. This age group is ready for these additional challenges.

Felix Mizioznikov/Shutterstock.com

Outdoor Play

The increase in sedentary indoor activities has in part been due to the decrease in opportunities for outdoor physical activity. Depending on life circumstances, children of all ages may have few opportunities to be physically active outdoors. Two main deterrents are involved: the dependence on motorized vehicles discussed earlier in Urban Sprawl and the Built Environment: Impact on Active Transportation (see page 325) and the lack of outdoor play spaces deemed safe for children's play.

In most communities, especially in urban areas, parents are concerned about their children's safety outdoors when they are not actively supervised. Media coverage of rare incidents of kidnappings or perhaps less rare violent acts makes for hypervigilance on the part of parents, educators, and the general public. Children may live in urban dwellings (e.g., high-rise buildings) where there is no backyard or a perceived safe area in which to run and play. Parents may feel that they have neither the time nor the place available to take their children for regular physical activity. In addition, parents' lives may be so busy that preparing dinner, doing laundry, or finishing work from the office seems easier and less stressful if their child is safely indoors, watching TV, reading, or doing other passive activities. These issues are beyond the scope of the educator, but awareness of this reality for children and families reminds us of the importance of building physically active outdoor opportunities into the child's day and of promoting ideas and initiatives that will have a positive effect on families' ability to be physically active with their children. It stands to reason that the more engaged children are outdoors in their younger years, the more likely it is that they will build their repertoire of interests and enjoyment outdoors year-round, in later childhood, youth, and adulthood.

Courtesy of Sister Celeste—Fort Norman

Included in Unit 7 is a range of considerations in ensuring that the outdoor play space of an ECLC setting is as safe as possible. However, not only is a risk-free environment impossible, it is also unlikely to offer the essential challenges for children at every stage of development to motivate their skill practice and mastery in all areas of development. The design and arrangement of the outdoor play environment can either limit or enable physical activity for all children.

Manufactured equipment, such as climbers, fire poles, slides, and teeter-totters, entice many, but not all, children to be active. Beyond the stationary equipment in the playground, which offers limited opportunity for movement and skill practice, children can be active on common movable equipment (e.g., asking a preschooler on a tricycle to ride in a zigzag pattern or setting up an obstacle course for a child to ride through). It is ideal, if possible, for school-age children to have opportunities for self-directed play outdoors in all settings—at home, at school, in child care, in the community, and in exploring the natural environment. Infants and toddlers need outdoor spaces that have safe areas for crawling and offer exploration of natural elements. *For example, a grass cover rather than a synthetic surface has so much more to offer in sensory stimulation and motor skills. Crawling on an uneven grass surface, with small mounds to crawl or walk up and down, develops the child's balance and spatial exploration to a much greater extent than the smooth, flat synthetic surface.*

Courtesy of George Brown College Child Care Centre on Charles Street

Pardee et al. (2005, p. 13) suggest the following for infants and toddlers:

- a nonmetal slide with a gentle slope, with a low climbing ramp that has a few steps with a handrail
- sturdy ledges or low railings for infants to pull themselves to standing
- short tunnels and peek-a-boo places
- seating at various levels
- rocking toys that children can sit on inside
- bucket swings at a safe distance from other play
- pushing or riding wheeled toys
- safe water and sand play with simple props*

In addition to sand and water play for a range of manipulative and imaginative play, preschoolers and school-agers need space in which to play and practise their locomotor skills. Although programs must meet the requirements for the amount of space in the early childhood provincial/territorial regulations, remember that those are minimum requirements. Optimizing opportunities for children to move and explore outdoors often means creative thinking and planning on the part of program educators and directors to use the space as efficiently as possible.

The outdoor curriculum should include materials and activities that are available indoors (e.g., easel painting, sand and water play, creative art). However, educators need to ensure that sedentary activities aren't so enticing to

*Source: *CICK Resource Guide—Volume 4: Creating Playgrounds for Early Childhood Facilities*. Published by Local Initiatives Support Corporation, 2005. Reprinted with permission.

children, especially those who are less likely to choose active options, that they are drawn to these options to the exclusion of moderate or vigorous physical activity. The outdoor imaginative play of preschoolers and school-agers often involves moving moderately or vigorously, which is, of course, positive for all developmental areas. Pretending they are in medieval times with dragons and knights, modern superheroes, firefighters, or fairies, or whatever other play themes they have, tends to involve running, jumping, flying, crouching down, and so on.

Children need a variety of play equipment, materials, and activities to develop the three components of physical fitness we have described (endurance, flexibility, and strength). It is quite possible to have a high-quality outdoor physical activity program without large, expensive equipment. Car tires, wide balance beams, scarves, ribbons, hoops, beanbags, balls, pylons, and other movable small equipment can be utilized for many spontaneous and adult-guided activities.

Courtesy of George Brown College/Ryerson Early Child Care Centre

Table 6.2 outlines the benefits of physical activity for all areas of a child's development.

TABLE 6.2 Benefits of Outdoor Play

Physical	• Increases energy and improves stamina
	• Encourages muscle growth and helps develop strong bones
	• Makes the heart and lungs stronger
	• Increases flexibility
	• Improves coordination

(continued)

TABLE 6.2 Benefits of Outdoor Play (*continued*)

Physical (***continued***)	• Helps improve sleeping habits • Helps improve eating habits • Helps maintain a healthy weight

Cognitive	• Helps increase concentration, memory, creativity, and problem-solving skills/abilities and enhances learning
	• Ratey (2008, p. 53) puts forward a compelling argument that exercise sparks new brain-cell growth. Aerobic exercise physically transforms our brains for peak performance. Exercise improves learning on three levels:
	    – It improves alertness, attention, and motivation.
	    – It prepares and encourages nerve cells to bind to one another.
	    – It then spurs the development of new nerve cells from stem cells in the hippocampus (part of the frontal temporal lobe, which plays a role in long-term memory and spatial navigation).

Emotional	• Helps us feel good about ourselves • Presents opportunities to practise self-discipline • Develops positive lifelong attitudes toward physical activity • Reduces anxiety and depression and improves one's ability to deal with stress
Social	• Provides opportunities to socialize and make friendships • Provides opportunities to cooperate with others and develop social problem-solving skills
Cultural	• Encourages healthy family engagement • Provides opportunities to develop motor/sports skills and life skills • Provides opportunities to learn games and songs from various cultural backgrounds

Source: *Have a Ball! A Toolkit for Physical Activity and the Early Years*. Published by Best Start Resource Center, © 2005. Reprinted with permission.

In addition to your outdoor play space, there may be regular opportunities to visit appropriate nearby facilities with the children, such as schools, recreation agencies with gyms, pools, skating rinks, and neighbourhood parks, when a facility isn't in use by others. Of course, these options must be evaluated for developmental appropriateness and safety before use.

Greening the Outdoor Environment

Greening the outdoor environment can offer more options to children of varying needs and abilities and provides green space that may be generally inaccessible to many children. Exploring nature is a joy that should be a right in childhood.

NELSONstudy

To access Resource
Materials, visit NelsonStudy.

Greening the space brings in trees, shrubs, rocks, and logs to define a variety of places in which to run, climb, hide, and socialize. Natural movable materials such as sand, sticks, branches, leaves, and stones offer many opportunities for imaginative play and physical activity such as raking leaves or shovelling sand. For a comprehensive guide to the almost endless benefits, elements, and adult role of supporting children's enjoyment and learning of nature and the outdoors, refer to L. Wilson's *Outdoor Playscapes: Breaking New Ground* (2014). (See Resource Materials.) Refer to Figure 6.1 for an example of a "green" outdoor playground design for preschoolers.

A study for Evergreen Canada found that green school grounds can play a significant role in promoting physical activity, especially moderate and light levels of activity, by increasing the range of enjoyable, non-competitive, open-ended forms of play. When asked to compare their school ground before and after greening, 71% of respondents (parents, teachers, principals) from 59 elementary schools in five provinces indicated that greening has resulted in more moderate and/or light physical activity:

> Through greening, school grounds diversify the play repertoire, creating opportunities for children of all ages, interests and abilities to jump, climb, dig, lift and generally get moving in ways that nurture all aspects of their health and development. These positive findings emerged consistently across the schools participating in the survey, despite the differences in size, student population and geographic location. (Bell & Dyment, n.d., p. 6)

This study found that children want outdoor spaces that are the following (Bell, 2007):

- places they can call their own (i.e., territoriality)
- well-defined places that include trees, rocks, walls, and nets
- natural elements
- places to hide, slide, climb, and jump
- places that can be shaped (by body and mind)
- challenging
- places to socialize*

NELSONstudy

To access Resource
Materials, visit NelsonStudy.

These criteria can promote moderate activity, which also has health benefits and may appeal to children who are not drawn to vigorous activity. Evergreen has published *Small Wonders: Designing Vibrant Natural Landscapes for Early Childhood* (2004) to promote green spaces in ECLC program settings. (See Resource Materials.)

---

*Source: From A. C. Bell (2007, October 3). *The Contribution of Green School Ground Design to Moderate Activity Levels.* Toronto: Evergreen. http://www.cuhi.utoronto.ca/seminars/supportingdocs/Oct0307_ABell.pdf. Reprinted with permission from Evergreen.

FIGURE 6.1   An Outdoor Design

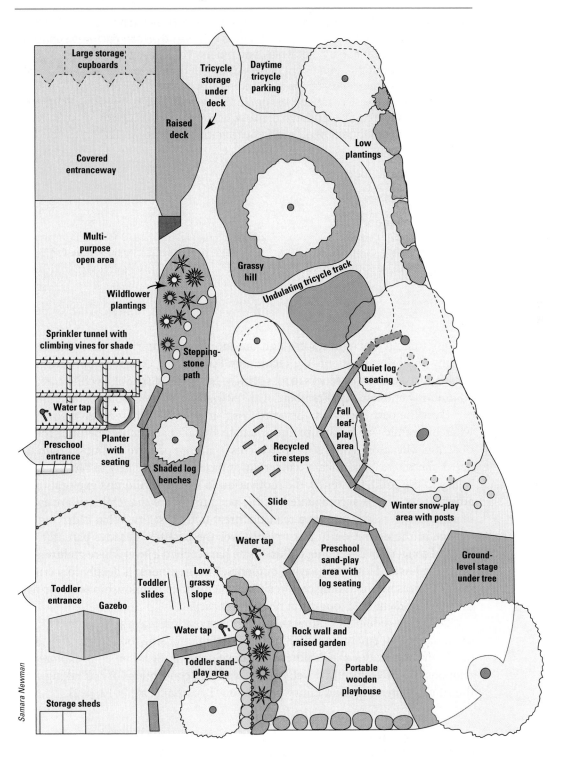

Large storage cupboards

Tricycle storage under deck

Daytime tricycle parking

Raised deck

Covered entranceway

Low plantings

Multi-purpose open area

Grassy hill

Undulating tricycle track

Wildflower plantings

Sprinkler tunnel with climbing vines for shade

Stepping-stone path

Quiet log seating

Water tap

Planter with seating

Fall leaf-play area

Preschool entrance

Shaded log benches

Recycled tire steps

Winter snow-play area with posts

Slide

Water tap

Ground-level stage under tree

Toddler entrance

Gazebo

Toddler slides

Low grassy slope

Preschool sand-play area with log seating

Water tap

Rock wall and raised garden

Toddler sand-play area

Portable wooden playhouse

Storage sheds

Samara Newman

Source: Illustration of the yard at Ryerson University Early Childhood Learning Centre by Samara Newman, based on an original Evergreen design by Adam Bienenstock and Heidi Campbell.

CRITICAL THINKING

In a suburban community, the green space is minimal, including none within the ECLC setting's playground. The playground is composed of manufactured surfaces throughout and stationary metal play equipment. The parents and educators are concerned about the time spent in cars or transit getting to the centre and that their children have little access to green space, both at the centre and in their home surroundings. What can be done to make this wish a reality? For each action, identify benefits, possible challenges or barriers, and possible solutions. Include one component of a green environment that you would like to add for each age group:

- infants and toddlers

- preschoolers

- school-agers

How does each component support moderate or vigorous physical activity? (See Evergreen in Resource Materials.)

NELSONstudy

To access Resource Materials, visit NelsonStudy.

Risky Play

NELSONstudy

To access Resource Materials, visit NelsonStudy.

"Access to active play in nature and outdoors—with its risks—is essential for healthy child development. We recommend increasing children's opportunities for self-directed play outdoors in all settings—at home, at school, in child care, the community and nature" (Tremblay et al., 2015, p. 1).* (See Resource Materials.)

Over the past few years, the word "risk" in play has emerged as "a situation whereby a child can recognize and evaluate a challenge and decide on a course of action" (Brussoni et al., 2012, p. 8). This is a more positive definition than the dated one where "risk" means dangerous or hazardous and likely to cause serious injury to the child. Currently, the motivation to support children's exploration in adventurous play is accompanied by the need to ensure that children are aware of actual dangers that present a realistic threat to their safety. What is driving the change in the definition of risky play? Over the past few decades parental and societal concern over keeping children safe has reached a level where children are spending less and less time playing outdoors. This new norm is deeply concerning for many reasons, including children's well-being, their relationship with the natural environment, and long-term physical literacy.

Of course, educators know that injury prevention plays a key role for children's safety, but emerging research suggests that imposing too many restrictions on children's outdoor play hinders their development. Brussoni et al. explore the relationship between child development, play, and conceptions of risk taking with the aim of informing child injury prevention (Brussoni et al., 2012, p. 2).

---

*Source: Tremblay MS, Gray C, Babcock S, Barnes J, Bradstreet CC, Carr D, Chabot G, Choquette L, Chorney D, Collyer C, Herrington S, Janson K, Janssen I, Larouche R, Pickett W, Power M, Sandseter EBH, Simon B, Brussoni M. "Position Statement on Active Outdoor Play". *International Journal of Environmental Research and Public Health.* 2015, 12(6): 6475–6505.

Manageable risk is part of building confidence in oneself. Every child is unique. One child's idea of a risk may be considered too easy by another child. Some children view a challenge as a task to be mastered, while others avoid a challenge or doubt that they can overcome it. It is an educator's role to support each child's developmental needs and skills, while keeping children as safe as necessary while they take and manage risks.

What Does Risky Play Mean for Educators?

Educators have primary responsibilities for the safety of children in their care. As stated in Unit 7: Safety Promotion, the challenge for educators is to provide an environment that is not only developmentally challenging but also safe so that children can be physically active and gain new skills in all areas of development (e.g., cognitive problem solving, social play with peers, emotional feelings of competence). Educators and parents recognize that bumps, scrapes, and bruises are a normal part of growing up. Children may be injured when using play equipment. However, the likelihood of broken bones or head and internal injuries is minimized when

- the equipment is developmentally appropriate,
- protective surfaces are adequately maintained,
- children use the equipment properly, and
- educators actively supervise children's activities.

By modelling safe but not overly anxious behaviour, adults help children develop an awareness of safety.

You may ask yourself, how can an educator minimize injuries while at the same time provide opportunities for risky play? There are opportunities for children to problem solve and make decisions in child-directed play every day. In addition to stationary playground equipment, for example, educators can

- provide a range of outdoor loose parts so that children can create their own quality play experiences, including discovery, invention, and physical, creative, constructive, and dramatic play. Some examples of loose parts include boxes, buckets, baskets, cloth, and dramatic play props.
- provide recycled items such as cardboard boxes, building materials, old pots and pans, and milk crates.
- offer natural materials for children to learn more about nature and the physical world: bark, seeds, stones, leaves, tree stumps, twigs, and sea shells.
- provide heavier, larger materials for children three and older.

  Children use their whole body, exercise their muscles, and get a sense of their physical capabilities when using large wooden blocks, wheeled toys, and other sturdy, heavy materials.
- offer a wide range of age-appropriate tools and equipment.

  Often by about three years old, they can manage two or more actions using these items.

- follow the children's lead outdoors and encourage them to take the lead (e.g., the child decides on choice of active play).
  - There are some children who are somewhat comfortable with risky play and are able to assess what they can handle.
  - Others, who are seemingly fearless and impulsive, may require close monitoring and need reminders of awareness and safer behaviour to reduce the likelihood of harm (e.g., "Notice how slippery the ground is today.").
  - For children who are somewhat hesitant to try new moves (e.g., climbing up or jumping down from a height that scares them), the educator can support the child with "one step at a time" challenges. Gradual is best as the child feels secure and in control and is building confidence to go higher.
- offer children challenges that they need to decide how to handle (e.g., "You feel your feet gripped in the mud. How will you get them out?").

Educators follow the regulations for playgrounds built for particular age groups in licensed ECLC programs. There is more flexibility in regulations with school-agers, as they are developing their own games with rules. Educators ensure that hazards are eliminated and children are adequately supervised, without limiting their exploration.

High-quality programs recognize the need for children to explore, role play, problem solve, and take risks within their developmental level and temperament. Emphasis on risky or adventurous play has many benefits for children and needs to be incorporated into ECLC programs. Risky play can comply with the parameters of the legislative requirements and opportunities for child-directed play. Educators must keep in mind that when children are with their family, there can be more flexibility to encourage risky play.

Supporting Physical Activity Nationally and Regionally

As we know, societal change contributes to health promotion for all. One example of federal government support to increase public awareness for parents was the reinstatement of funding to **ParticipACTION**, with an identified focus on children and youth. The original ParticipACTION was established in 1971, and for almost 30 years (until its closure in early 2001), it forged numerous successful campaigns to encourage active living for all Canadians. ParticipACTION was known in Canada and beyond for its effective utilization of media with clear, practical messages for everyone to be active. The inclusive nature of the messaging depicted young and old, ethnocultural diversity, large and thin, individuals and families, and persons with disabilities making physical activity part of their life. In late 2006, ParticipACTION received renewed commitment from the federal government's Sport Canada and PHAC and was revitalized in February 2007. A benefit of ParticipACTION's current focus on parent awareness is the likelihood that today's parents grew up with ParticipACTION and are familiar with its messages. In 2015, ParticipACTION began publishing the *Report Card on Physical Activity for Children and Youth* (Active Kids Canada had published it annually for 10 years before 2005–2014).

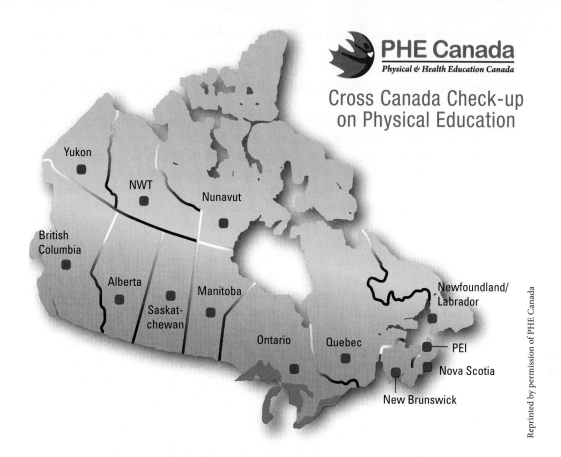

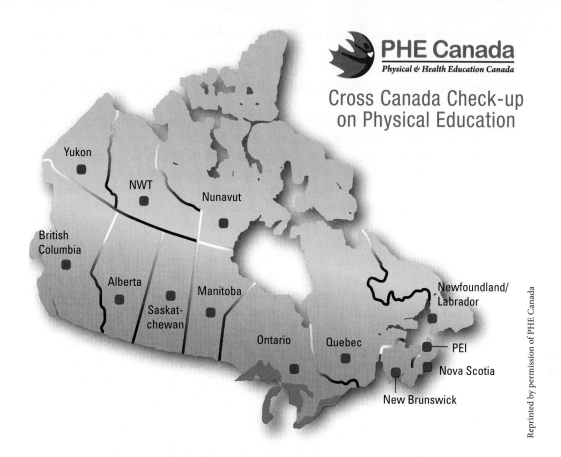

PHE Canada
Physical & Health Education Canada

Cross Canada Check-up
on Physical Education

Yukon

NWT

Nunavut

British
Columbia

Alberta

Saskat-
chewan

Manitoba

Ontario

Quebec

Newfoundland/
Labrador

PEI

Nova Scotia

New Brunswick

Reprinted by permission of PHE Canada

Most provincial, territorial, municipal, and regional governments recognize the substantial concerns regarding the negative consequences from child inactivity. Requirements and recommendations from levels of government have emerged for time devoted to physical activity during the day at school or in the ECLC program and curriculum. Where does your province or territory stand on this issue?

A much broader approach to physical activity as proposed by the Wellesley Institute addresses childhood obesity by tackling social determinants of health. The institute suggests four areas to address childhood obesity: reduce childhood obesity through poverty reduction, focus on early development, address neighbourhood factors, and enhance coordination with a health promotion and whole-of-government focus (Barnes, 2012). "Childhood obesity does not occur because of a single factor—there is a complex chain of factors that lead to it. Therefore, policy interventions are required at various stages along the chain to address its underlying causes. Living conditions and the options and opportunities that are available to people have significant impacts on obesity. Thus high levels of childhood obesity are an important indicator of underlying social and economic challenges" (Barnes, 2012, p. 6).

SUPPORTING HEALTHY EATING HABITS

"For preschoolers, nutrition risk runs the spectrum from under- to over-nutrition and occurs to those in poverty as well as those living in relative affluence. Systematic screening systems that identify these characteristics or risk factors before school

OBJECTIVES

To identify the primary benefits of the NutriSTEP™ preschool nutrition screening tool. (LO 2, 3, 5)

To identify reasons why there may be concerns about children's under- or overeating and appropriate responses. (LO 1, 2, 5)

To explain the concerns about children's consumption of carbonated drinks (pop) and ways to promote healthier beverages. (LO 3)

entry may be an efficient means of identifying children who require services and preventive interventions" (Simpson et al., 2007, p. 2). NutriSTEP™, 10 years in the making, with the involvement of almost 2000 preschoolers and their parents and more than 50 multisectorial partners, is now being used in much of Canada to improve preschool nutrition.

NutriSTEP™, a community-based, parent-administered nutrition screening tool, includes 17 items, with most items focused on the aspects of nutrition risk for preschoolers: physical growth, food and fluid intake, physical activity, sedentary behaviour, and factors affecting food intake for the age group (food security, feeding environment). Responses range in score from 0 (no risk) to 4 (risk), and responses are summed to provide an index whereby a higher score indicates increased nutrition risk. The tool, developed by two faculty members at the University of Guelph and a dietitian from the Sudbury and District Health Unit, has been gaining much recognition across Canada and beyond (Simpson et al., 2007, p. 3) and is partnered with Dietitians of Canada. *For example, it has the backing of the Ontario government and is being piloted in several areas across Canada as part of immunization programs and preschool screening fairs.*

The tool is self-administered by parents or caregivers and takes five minutes to complete, and it is now available online. The authors of NutriSTEP™ have designed and evaluated models for its ethical implementation. It can be used in doctors' offices, public health clinics, child care centres, and schools to identify children who should be further assessed and treated by a dietitian before they have problems.

One of the NutriSTEP™ items was designed to determine parental control over feeding. Of the almost 300 parents who completed the questionnaire in the initial study, 37% reported that they often do not let their children decide how much to eat.

Also of great concern was the high proportion (33%) of preschool children whose sedentary activities, such as TV viewing, exceeded three hours a day. Excess sedentary activity, particularly in the form of TV viewing, presents the potential for nutritional risk, especially in young children (Veugelers & Fitzgerald, 2005). The prevalence of nutritional problems such as overweight and obesity in the three- to five-year-old age group is 21% in Canada (Shields, 2006). Unfortunately, the more recent statistics from the 2009 to 2011 Canadian Health Measures Survey do not include children under five years.

One factor in the nutrition–obesity story may be the practice of exclusive breastfeeding in the first six months of life. A systematic review of nine studies with over 69,000 participants concluded that breastfeeding has a small but consistent protective effect against childhood obesity (Arenz et al., 2004). This can be added to the many benefits of breastfeeding over formula feeding, as a reminder to educators to support and promote breastfeeding whenever and wherever appropriate.

As stated earlier, WHO (2018) has cited worldwide transitions in nutrition patterns as one of the primary causes of the obesity epidemic. These relatively new patterns include such issues as increased food availability and variety through automated transportation, fast-food consumption, increased portion sizes, reduced frequency of family meals, increased consumption of pop and sports drinks, and restricted eating, resulting in meal skipping. This last example speaks to the flip side of the obesity focus, the concern about an increase in healthy-weight children obsessing about weight, and parents projecting fears about fat onto their children. This is not an exhaustive list, but it speaks to the complex nature of food and eating patterns in the obesity epidemic. It is entirely possible for children to be taking in more calories than they need, especially when consuming a large volume of high-calorie, low-nutritive drinks, while being undernourished where essential nutrients are concerned.

Concern about Amounts of Food Eaten

All children and adults fluctuate in the amount of food they eat, for any number of reasons: growth spurts, illness, fatigue, hot weather, time of day, or food preferences. Educators first determine whether the child's eating pattern is one that their program can easily accommodate or whether it is a legitimate reason for concern. To determine this, educators examine two issues:

- their own personal perceptions and preconceived definitions of how much a child of that age should eat and at what times of the day
- the child's body build—in other words, whether she or he is growing within the normal range of growth and development

Let's look at three reasons why children may be temporarily eating a lot of food. When the child is growing within the normal range, there isn't cause for alarm, for the following reasons:

1. Perhaps the child is going through a growth spurt.

   During a growth spurt, the child's body requires extra nutrients and calories (or energy) for a limited time (a few weeks or a month or two). Interestingly, growth spurts often occur in the spring and may also follow a period of illness (e.g., in a child with asthma who had a difficult time during the winter). Understanding growth and development and getting to know children assist educators in expecting growth spurts.

2. Perhaps the child enjoys eating more at a particular time of day.

   One child, like a lot of adults, is a slow starter in the morning and isn't ready to eat much of a breakfast before leaving home. By mid-morning, she is ready to eat more than one serving of the snack. Another child is too busy playing to leave the activity to eat a morning snack, but by lunch time, he is ravenous. It is best that we avoid looking at food intake on a meal-by-meal basis and instead look at overall intake in a 24-hour period (Health Canada, 2011). ECLC programs that have incorporated some flexibility into the nutrition program can accommodate children's body rhythms. At the same time, we recognize that eating regularly during the day helps children maintain their energy level.

3. Perhaps the child does not have access to a lot of food at home.

   The family's budget does not stretch far enough to buy a consistent amount of food throughout the month. As a result, the child comes to the program hungry many days, or even every day. Programs need to have enough food available to provide extras and second helpings for hungry children. Educators' concern for the child and family does not end on Friday afternoon but extends to weekends and their access to enough nutritious food. Some programs work with food banks to supplement the food supply for families who live with food insecurity.

Therefore, daily observation of children and communication with parents are important in meeting children's nutritional needs and in determining their eating habits at home. *For example, a parent tells you that the child eats a large breakfast at home, which explains why he usually does not eat a mid-morning snack or a full lunch. Although, because of their energy levels, most children are more interested in food in the morning or at lunch, every child's body rhythm and metabolism are unique.*

ECLC programs with children who have recently arrived in Canada should ensure that the menus reflect the types of food eaten at home. The nutrition program should include some foods that are familiar to every child in the program. You can achieve this by asking parents for their favourite recipes. This is also one way that children learn about one another's ethnoculture. When you offer children familiar foods, they feel secure and relaxed and enjoy eating. New children are often shy and reserved around snack and mealtimes and need educators' extra support. *For example, a three-year-old boy, who is new to the program and Canada, won't eat at all during the day. The parents and educators are concerned about his well-being. The mother explains to the educator that her son does not like to eat around people he doesn't know. They decide together that she will bring food from home and an educator with whom he is comfortable will sit with him at lunch separated from the rest of the group by a partition. They find that he is more relaxed and enjoys the one-to-one interaction and the familiar food. After a week of this arrangement, the educator and the boy move into the room with the rest of the group but sit at a separate table away from the rest of the children. The child observes the other children, who are more familiar to him now. They begin offering him food that is prepared at the program, which he begins to try. After this week of transition, the child feels much more relaxed, and by the third week, he joins his peers. He is soon eating only the program's food.*

Concern about Body Weight

We all have to be conscious of our society's notion of "ideal" body image and the role that we may play in perpetuating these stereotypes. Nevertheless, some children and adults are either below or above the average range of body mass by age, gender, and height. Physical or emotional concerns may be associated with being **overweight** or **underweight**.

According to Dietitians of Canada and the Canadian Paediatric Society (2010, p. 4), the way children grow says a lot about their health. Growing too quickly or slowly may indicate a health problem. This is one of the main reasons why their report, *Promoting Optimal Monitoring of Child Growth in Canada*, strongly recommends that monitoring growth over time, from infancy through adolescence, should be a routine part of health care for all Canadian children. WHO's growth standards for preschool children (birth to 5 years) and children and adolescents (5 to 19 years) have been adapted for Canada and approved and prescribed by Dietitians of Canada, CPS, the College of Family Physicians of

Canada, and Community Health Nurses of Canada as the gold standard in growth charts to be utilized by all (Dietitians of Canada and CPS, 2010, p. 1).

Indicators of atypical patterns of growth give physicians, dietitians, or other relevant health professionals the opportunity to investigate the cause(s) and follow up appropriately. If there is a connection with eating or other health habits, the health professional can communicate with families how nutrition, physical activity, sleep patterns, genetics, and illness can affect growth. With regular contact or connection with support programs, health care professionals can be a catalyst for improved health habits to regulate concerns about children's growth (Dietitians of Canada and CPS, 2010).

For children who eat large amounts of food, the best time to determine whether an imbalance exists between food energy and the body's demand for energy is when the child is gaining so much weight as to become overweight. If, however, the child is losing weight and is not growing in height, there may be concern about being underweight.

Educators' daily observations of children's eating patterns may assist in identifying the contributing factors. Because children grow at different rates at different times, it is not always easy to tell if a child is overweight. If parents think their child is overweight, encourage them to talk to their health care provider, who will measure the child using WHO growth charts adapted for Canada and let them know if he or she is in a healthy range. Children's growth patterns differ, and other factors may be involved, so it is best to get a health professional's assessment.

Educators' daily observations of children's eating patterns assist in identifying the contributing factors.

A Child Who Is Overeating May	A Child Who Is Undereating May
eat more than the recommended daily servings of any of the four food groups, but in particular the milk products and meat and alternatives.	eat less than the recommended daily servings of any of the four food groups, but in particular the milk products and meat and alternatives, which results in an insufficient fat intake.
choose foods that are high in fat, sugar, or both (i.e., foods outside the four groups) over nutritious foods.	choose not to eat enough food for fear of being overweight.
not participate in physical activity.	have a level of physical activity high enough that more food energy is used than is obtained by eating.
eat because of emotions (e.g., boredom).	not be active, but being more active will increase the child's appetite.
	not eat because of emotions (e.g., stress or sadness).

When educators determine that there is reason to be concerned, the next step is to meet with the child's parents. Obviously, consistency between home and the program is beneficial. Some parents may not share the educators' concern for the child; others may need nutrition education and information to enable them to support their child. Parents should be encouraged to consult with the child's health care provider, and perhaps the child and the parents would benefit from consulting with a dietitian. To ensure that the physician's or dietitian's recommendations are carried out consistently between home and the program, daily communication between parents and educators is essential.

EDUCATORS AND PARENTS CAN ADDRESS THE FOLLOWING REASONS WHY CHILDREN MIGHT BE	
Overeating	Undereating
poor eating habits (e.g., consistently choosing high-fat foods)	poor eating habits (e.g., drinking too much milk or juice, leaving no room for food)
insufficient physical activity for the amount of food eaten	fatigue
watching TV while eating (not being mindful of food ingested)	limited variety of foods they will eat
eating for the wrong reasons, such as emotional reasons	stress at home, the ECLC program, or school that may contribute to poor eating habits
adults in their lives who model overeating	adults in their lives who model excessive dieting or negative stereotypes about larger body types
stress at home, the ECLC program, or school that may contribute to poor eating patterns	security felt only with family and the foods served at home
a physiological or psychological reason for weight gain (a physician would need to diagnose such a medical or emotional condition)	a physiological or psychological reason for the weight loss (a physician would need to diagnose such a medical or emotional condition—for example, anorexia)

There are strategies that parents (or other significant adults, including educators) may try in order to influence a child's eating habits, yet most are not helpful. Restricting food, pressure to eat, a promise of a reward, and exercising control over their eating can have negative effects on the child's accepting a food or overeating. On the other hand, positive role modelling instead of coercion can provide an opportunity for parents to model good eating habits for their child. *The most important point to remember in approaching overeating and children is that dieting is not an option.* Dieting (restricting food) produces a vicious circle of unhealthy eating patterns. It is generally counterproductive when adults begin this dieting cycle, but it's even worse when children begin to diet (Scaglioni et al., 2011, p. 1).

Considering children's great needs for growth, dieting robs them of their potential by

- not providing their body with the daily nutrient requirements;
- contributing to a lowered basal metabolic rate, and when the body is not getting the energy it needs, it slows to function on fewer calories than it needs; and
- making them feel deprived and singled out if the other children are not subject to dietary restrictions.

Depending on the circumstances, some programs that provide lunch may decide to limit the number of helpings to one or two (for example) from the meat and alternatives and/or milk and alternatives food groups. If they do so, it is important that children who are still hungry have access to further helpings from the vegetables and fruit and grain products food groups. When this limit applies to all the children, it is acceptable. However, care must be taken to ensure that individual children are not singled out by limiting their servings while other children are given extra helpings. Exceptions to this, of course, relate to allergies, food sensitivity, and religious or cultural dietary requirements. Having raw vegetable and dip appetizers may benefit all children by ensuring that when hungry, they are taking in at least one or two servings of vegetables, contributing to the recommended five servings a day.

Self-esteem is of great importance to children and adults, and dieting does not contribute to self-esteem, especially when more than 95% of individuals who diet and lose weight eventually regain the weight. In a word, dieting is inappropriate! Rather than consider weight loss, it is more effective to focus on decreasing the child's rate of weight gain. We help children develop a positive and balanced outlook toward healthy eating and physical activity through increased awareness of foods and nutrition, by focusing on enjoyable daily physical activity, and by modelling healthy behaviour, such as being active in the playground and eating well.

Reduce the Consumption of Carbonated Beverages and Low-Nutritive Foods

Beverages

The regular consumption of **carbonated drinks**, often called soft drinks or pop, is counterproductive to the nutrient needs of growing children. In addition to numerous health concerns in the early years, habitual consumption can have lifelong harmful effects (Jacobson, 2005). This reality underscores the importance of preventing children's daily intake of carbonated and other low-nutritive drinks at an early age; it is much more difficult to change unhealthy habits than to form healthy ones. This message is really the essence of healthy active living.

Do you know how much sugar is in the standard can of pop or the larger-sized containers? Pop is the number one source of added sugar in the diet of many children and adults, and it is just empty calories. If you drank one can of nondiet pop a day for a year, you would consume almost 15 kg of added sugar. All of that would be empty calories, which in children replace the essential nutrients that they need for growth and development.

One reason these beverages are so popular is that people like their taste. However, the power of advertising, universal availability, low price, and use of a mildly addictive ingredient (caffeine) have contributed to making pop a routine snack and part of meals instead of the occasional treat it was considered decades ago. Also, many of today's parents grew up drinking

Jose A. Bernat Bacete/Moment/Getty Images

pop and may see it as normal to drink pop throughout the day. Currently, there are a myriad of other beverages in addition to pop, such as sports drinks, energy drinks, and drinks touting a small percentage of real fruit juice. For a few select athletes or in specific circumstances, these products are warranted. For the vast majority of adults and children, they can be a negative factor to optimal health.

Pop is a leading contributor to poor oral health. High acidity (phosphoric acid) causes tooth decay (even from sugar-free drinks), and drinks with sugar (high-fructose corn syrup) make the impact even more severe. The acid in regular or diet pop starts to dissolve tooth enamel in only 20 minutes. For this and other reasons (e.g., concerns about metabolic syndrome), diet pop is not a better alternative unless necessary, such as for individuals with diabetes (Jacobson, 2005, pp. 14–15).

Much of the pop is high in caffeine, with a can of pop typically containing 40 to 45 mg of caffeine, leading to mild addictions over time. This often results in increased caffeine-containing beverage habits in the teen years, with further reduced milk and water intake. In other words, heavy consumption of pop and other nutrient-poor beverages pushes numerous minerals, vitamins, and dietary

fibre out of the diet (Jacobson, 2005, p. 18). In the example of reduced milk intake, calcium needs are very high in childhood and adolescence, building bone density before adulthood, when bone mass begins to deteriorate. Excessive intake of carbonated beverages can impact bone health. Children and youth often replace calcium-rich beverages such as milk with pop, affecting bone mass and increasing the risk of future osteoporosis. A Saskatchewan study of bone mass in adolescents (Whiting et al., 2004) found that replacing milk with pop appears to be detrimental to bone gain in girls but not boys. The gender difference may be due to the fact that girls are consuming less than their requirement for calcium, whereas boys are above their threshold, even with the pop intake. Specific dietary and nutrient recommendations for adolescents are needed to ensure optimal bone growth and consolidation during this important life stage to prevent bone fractures and early osteoporosis. Replacing milk with pop also means that children may be losing out on much-needed vitamins A and D and riboflavin (Jacobson, 2005, p. iv).

You may wonder why this issue is discussed in this textbook when it is very unlikely that your placement or future workplace will be serving pop to the children. However, there are a number of possible ways this issue may be relevant to your work:

- when an ECLC setting does not provide food, and the children bring their lunches from home, which can include pop and other popular low-nutritive drinks that are packaged in convenient juice box containers
- nutrition policies that must include food brought into the setting for celebrations and fundraising, as well as beverages purchased when the ECLC setting provides meals and/or snacks
- your role modelling of beverage choices
- material posted on the bulletin boards and other venues for sharing information with families
- advocacy

In recent years, school boards and municipal and provincial governments in Canada have begun to put policies and recommendations in place to reduce or eliminate the availability of carbonated drinks and junk foods in elementary and some high schools. Some facts on the Ontario Ministry of Education website (2004) include the following:

- Serving sizes of pop have increased by 300% since the 1950s.
- Approximately 27% of boys and 23% of girls in Grades 6 to 8 consume candy and chocolate bars daily.
- Milk consumption is almost 30% lower in schools that also sell pop.
- By the time children reach the "tween" years (9 to 12), many have lifestyle habits that could put them in the fast lane for developing cardiovascular disease as early as their 30s.

Low-Nutritive Foods

"In October 2005, New Brunswick became the first province to impose a junk food ban inside its schools" (MacDonald, 2017, p. 1). The Ontario Ministry of Education banned the sale of pop, sports drinks, energy drinks, and candy and chocolate in all Ontario schools as of 2011. In total, junk food has been banned from schools in six provinces. A study found that the ban is showing a positive impact on student health. Over a five-year period, students in schools with a ban were about two pounds lighter than those without a ban (MacDonald, 2017, p. 1). It is a start in the right direction!

Dietitians of Canada has supported many jurisdictions in their transitions toward healthier policies and practices in schools across Canada. Several ministries of education have made province-wide changes to policies, and other provinces and territories have made recommendations and guidelines for improved policy and practice in nutrition.

"Moving forward" is part of the title for the second edition of Manitoba's *Moving Forward with School Nutrition Guidelines* (2014). This new version is meant to support schools as they *improve* school nutrition environments in Manitoba.

- School food environment guidelines are annually reviewed with staff and student and/or parent committees. The healthy school nutrition policies and guidelines make decisions about breakfast, lunch, and snack programs; cafeterias; canteens; vending sporting events; and special lunch days.
- The foundation is that healthy food and beverage choices need to be available to all the children at school for each of the programs and events listed above. An example of a checklist for beverages is
  - "Water is available daily.
  - Skim, 1% or 2% white milk and/or plain fortified soy beverage is offered daily with breakfast and lunch programs.
  - Chocolate milk OR flavoured, fortified soy beverage OR 100% vegetable/ fruit juice is offered no more than once every two weeks." (Government of Manitoba, 2014, p. 8)

(continued)

Healthy nutrition policies for ECLC program settings are discussed in Unit 5. These policies need to be the cornerstone for moving forward in developing best practices for children's healthy eating and drinking. Healthy drinks for children focus on milk products (whether cow based or soy), tap water, and the occasional 100% fruit juice. There is no place in a child's diet for routine consumption of pop or nutrition-void noncarbonated drinks, which, unfortunately, are so readily available in grocery stores, convenience stores, restaurants, and fast-food eateries. It is hoped that if consumers stop purchasing these beverages, their production and availability will be curtailed, benefiting us all.

CRITICAL THINKING

The children are used to drinking a lot of fruit juice both at home and in the ECLC program. As the director of a centre with preschoolers and school-agers who bring in their own foods and beverages from home, you are concerned about the high-sugar, low-nutritive beverages most children bring in, including fruit drinks, sports drinks, and pop. You want to promote more drinking of milk and water, as well as children eating more fruit rather than having fruit drinks, which have added sugar and colours and miss out on important food components such as fibre. What are some specific ways that you can support this vision with the children, parents, and staff? Consider challenges you may face with each of your suggestions and how you will meet each challenge.

OBJECTIVES

To describe the range of concerns regarding children's excessive screen time. (LO 2, 3)

To identify the link between screen time and sleep. (LO 3)

To identify the link between screen time and eating. (LO 3)

To discuss the educator's role and list strategies with regard to screen time for children. (LO 3)

IMPACT OF SCREEN TIME ON HEALTHY ACTIVE LIVING

The majority of published materials related to children's sedentary time make reference to the significant negative impact of **screen time**. CPS (2017, p. 1) defines screen time as "time spent with any screen, including smart phones, tablets, television, video games, computers or wearable technology. 'Digital media' refers to content transmitted over the Internet or computer networks on all devices, unless particular ones are specified."* Screen time is usually a sedentary activity, meaning you are being physically inactive while most often sitting down in front of a screen. Increasing children's physically active time and decreasing screen viewing from a young age may be advantageous ways to reduce the early onset of inactivity and obesity (Tucker et al., 2006).

*Source: Reprinted with permission from the Canadian Paediatric Society.

The power of modern technology—including television, movies, and computers—attracts and maintains children's attention because of the human brain's preference for visually presented information (Kneas & Perry, n.d.). However, the passive nature of most of these technologies, which often require sitting for hours, does not present children with the quality and quantity of developmentally focused experiences they need. Most of the technologies prevent children from hours of other experiences that they do need for optimal development. This is less true about interactive technologies such as a computer game that requires the child's input for problem solving, independent thinking skills, and potentially some perceptual motor experiences. Even with their input, the time factor is again a major consideration.

In recent years the boom in digital technology has been extra user friendly for young children with touch screens requiring very little, if any, adult help. Young children can control devices such as smart phones and tablets. This ease of use makes it challenging to convince parents and educators that children under two should not have any screen time and preschoolers only a limited amount. It is tempting to entertain young children with a device during the commutes to and from ECLC programs (Barr & Linebarger, 2017, p. 3).

Computers may offer some developmental benefits, such as

- hand–eye coordination and fine motor skills;
- problem-solving, strategy and planning, decision-making, and logic skills; and
- the ability to set and achieve goals.

However, they do not provide enough developmental variety to warrant long periods of the child's time. Nurturing human interactions are vital to healthy development, and this fact needs to be considered in the use of any technology, as well as the timing and time spent (Kneas & Perry, n.d.). Plourde (2006) reported a study of 700 children (aged 10 to 15 years) that followed their TV viewing habits for four years. The children who watched more than five hours a day of TV were five times as likely to be overweight as those watching less than two hours a day. Having a TV in the bedroom is a strong predictor of being overweight, even among preschool-age children (Dennisson et al., 2002). Extended time at a TV can affect postural development and at a computer can contribute to wrist or carpal damage. Both of these can put a child at risk for early musculoskeletal problems.

One of the concerns about screen time is the almost inevitable increase in the duration of time children spend sitting at a screen as they get older. If a two-year-old is watching two or more hours of TV, you can probably predict that the daily screen time will increase substantially as the child starts to use the computer and play video games. A major marketing theme behind interactive video gaming is that children are moving, so it's an ideal way to pair physical activity with technology. Despite this claim, these

products do not replace daily physical activity. Further studies on these products are necessary to examine how they relate to physical activity. Of course, some movement during screen time is better than none, but there is a possibility that children will spend more of their time indoors in front of a screen rather than have access to the many additional benefits of playing outdoors, reconnecting with nature, or being part of a team sport.

As children get older, they are sitting at their computer, socially connecting with their peers through messaging networks. In addition to the concern about the duration of daily time spent on this activity, it has been shown that, rather than connecting children and youth, these networks, in fact, contribute to isolation and can play a role in depression. Active Healthy Kids Canada (2008, pp. 10–11) reports that increased time spent on chatting, emailing, and surfing the Internet not only reduces physical activity levels but also is a significant risk factor for anxiety, depression, a low sense of belonging, and low self-esteem. And, of course, the dangers of potential access to violent and pornographic material on both TV and the Internet, as well as the luring of children and youth by pedophiles or other dangerous online predators, add another dimension of complexity (see Unit 8: Preventing Child Maltreatment, page 469).

Courtesy of George Brown College/Scotia Plaza Child Care Centre

CPS's position statements *Healthy Active Living: Physical Activity Guidelines for Children and Adolescents* (2012) and *Screen Time and Young Children: Promoting Health and Development in a Digital World* (2017) acknowledge the beneficial effects of media on children, particularly children's programs that have messages about positive values such as accepting diversity and cooperating with others. Visual tools in high-quality preschool programs support prereading and numeracy skills, and other developmentally appropriate programs bring children to destinations such as museums, zoos, and geographic locations around the world that may give them a taste of a world beyond their own. TV and computers are an essential component of the new literacy, and the role of parents and educators in supporting children to become fluent in this literacy cannot be understated. From an early age, and at developmentally appropriate levels, parents need to help children manoeuvre their way through the media.

This requires active involvement on the part of adults in their screen time. Parents and educators who are not computer or Internet savvy are often amazed at how quickly some children go beyond their own computer skills. They need to continue to find ways to stay involved and connected to what the child or youth has access to. Simply activating the parental controls on computers and TVs does not replace watching TV with children and discussing it with them or finding out about the computer programs or video games they are playing (see the MediaSmarts website in Resource Materials).

CPS's position statements (2012, p. 2; 2017, p. 5) include concerns about Canadian children having excessive screen time and its connection to being over-weight or obese:

NELSONstudy

To access Resource Materials, visit NelsonStudy.

- Being sedentary in childhood worsens as they get older.
- Sedentary behaviours are associated with reduced physical activity, increased BMI, and obesity.
- Children who watched just an hour of screen time a day were 50% more likely to be overweight than those who watched less.
- Children are exposed to commercials for unhealthy foods and ones encouraging snacking, which increases their overall food intake.
- Children who have a TV in their bedroom are also at high risk.
- Sedentary youth, especially those watching hours of TV each day, may become less attentive, have poor school performance, form a poor self-image, and/or develop conditions such as high blood pressure.*

Here is a selection from CPS's (2012, pp. 3–4; 2017, p. 6) recommendations on screen time:

- Children's cognitive and psychosocial development is negatively impacted by too much screen time.
- Children under two years old should not have any screen time activities.
- Two- to five-year-old children's screen time should be limited to less than one hour a day (see Appendix 6.2, page 380).
- CPS supports Canada's activity guidelines for children five and older, which limits screen time to less than two hours a day, including their smart phones (see Appendix 6.2, page 380).
- Encourage children whose screen time exceeds two hours a day to progressively reduce that time and replace it with a variety of enjoyable and safe active activities that support their natural development.*

The Role of Educators Regarding Screen Time

ECLC programs need to bring awareness of this issue to their policies and practices to promote the optimal health and development of children. In day-to-day routines, computers and TVs should play a *minor* role in the curriculum, particularly

*Source: Reprinted with permission from the Canadian Paediatric Society.

for children under five years of age. Children under two should not be exposed to TV or computers in the program. Keep in mind that screen time in the program is not a babysitter. The more children utilize their minds and bodies to use the media, the more they learn.

If and when a program has screen time, educators need to do the following:

- Be conscientious about the media chosen for young children.

  Is it age appropriate? How will you use it with their learning in mind? The content should be designed to engage the children and promote learning.

- Participate and make screen use interactive.

  Talk about what children are seeing and encourage them to use their minds and bodies as much as possible to maximize learning.

- Set limits on screen time to be sure that children have plenty of time to explore the real world with friends.

- When computer use is one of the activity options in the playroom, set time limits. Of course, adults should be involved when possible.

- Observe which children consistently choose computer time and encourage more physically active activity at other times during the day. When a child continues to choose sedentary activities when opportunities for moving are available, educators should try to involve the child in adult-guided movement activities whenever possible (see Table 6.1, page 338).

- Avoid programming movies and TV watching into the weekly schedule. *For example, when there is a movie every Friday afternoon, the message educators are sending to parents is that sitting in front of a screen for an extended time must be good practice if the educators highlight it every week in their program. Couple this with the reality that many children, after having sat for an extended period, will then be in a car, bus, or stroller for the ride home, followed by more inactivity while the supper is being prepared. It is not unusual for children to watch movies on the way home.*

- When your ECLC program includes a movie or TV program that you feel is particularly appropriate and relevant to the children's current interests, avoid having the room in darkness as this gives the impression that it is the only option for children. Instead,

  - set the movie or TV program up in an area where children who are interested can watch, whereas others can come in and out as they desire.

  - other quiet activities should be available nearby that would not disrupt the movie watchers.

  - when it is a full-length movie, let children know at the beginning that you will be stopping it once or twice so they can stretch their bodies and move around. You could plan adult-guided stretching and other movements that fit into the theme of the movie (e.g., move like the animals in the movie).

- Find ways to support families in their endeavours to balance their busy lives with their children's reasonable use of TV, computers, and video games:

  - Refer parents to the Canadian 24-hour movement guidelines (see Appendix 6.1, page 379; and Appendix 6.2, page 380).

- A bulletin board or pamphlet sent home regarding the effects of media on children, including the ECLC setting's policy and practices, may be another good way to bring attention to this issue.

- After awareness is established, provide an opportunity for discussion (in whatever format the program prefers) to hear parents' views. *For example, some parents may believe that a heavy dose of computers and TV gives their children a head start on computer literacy. If they are aware that physical activity contributes to brain development and learning, perhaps parents will recognize that children will learn the computer skills they need at a developmentally appropriate time (see Benefits of Physical Activity, page 333). Other parents would like their children to spend less time in front of a TV or computer but have not found other ways to get dinner made or their office work done without its use. Although outdoor activities are ideal, they may not suit their immediate situation. A group discussion or concrete suggestions from educators may help to resolve the issue, such as the following:*

  - *While making dinner, parents could put on music that the toddler or preschooler can move to and have a box in the kitchen with scarves, hats, spoons, or other objects to make music or play with.*

  - *Families can create a simple game with recycled paper crumpled into a ball with a wastepaper basket target or "skate" with a piece of recycled paper under each shoe.*

  - *Masking tape on the floor or carpet might encourage the child to pretend to walk on a circus tightrope or balance beam.*

  - *Easy physical activity suggestions to send home to parents at different times of the year increase the likelihood that they'll try them out.*

  - *Screen time is not taboo for children over two years old, and perhaps in encouraging parents to keep the one- to two-hour maximum recommendation daily in mind, they can come up with the most appropriate times of the day. Some children really do need downtime as soon as they get home, and if an hour or less of quality children's programming is available, this may be the best time of day to turn on the TV. The important component is balance rather than unlimited and unsupervised screen time.*

  - *Seasonal ideas encourage families to do things together outdoors. Perhaps an active game with a catchy song that the children enjoy in your program is a good one to send home in a newsletter.*

CRITICAL THINKING

What are the positives and negatives of screen time in an ECLC program? Write a policy on and practices for the use of TV and computers in your preschool program with three- to five-year-olds. Who would you involve in this process and how?

ACTIVE HEALTHY KIDS CANADA'S POSITION ON ACTIVE VIDEO GAMES

As the lure of technology rises and physical activity levels of kids fall, active video games—also called exergames—are often presented as a possible solution to getting kids to move more. Are they a good strategy to get kids closer to the 60 minutes of MVPA [moderate to vigorous physical activity] they need every day as recommended by the Canadian Physical Activity Guidelines for Children and Youth? In 2012, Active Healthy Kids Canada set out to answer these questions by convening an international panel of researchers to take a comprehensive look at all of the evidence on the subject. The result is their official position on active video games.

POSITION

- Active Healthy Kids Canada does not recommend active video games as a strategy to help kids be more physically active.
- Playing active video games does not lead to increased overall daily physical activity levels.
- Active video games may get heart rates up, but they are not significantly helping kids get to the 60 minutes of MVPA required each day.
- Kids find active video games appealing, but the appeal wears off over time and many do not stick with these games.
- Active video games do not offer the fresh air, vitamin D, connection with nature and quality of social interactions that come with outdoor active play.

RECOMMENDATIONS

- Active video games are a good way to break up sedentary time (e.g., sitting on the couch), but not as good as playing real active games or sports.
- While parents can certainly play active video games with their kids and let them enjoy playing these games with their friends, they should understand that the games are not a replacement for real physical activity.
- If money is spent on active video games as a means of exercise, it might be better spent on skipping ropes, balls, ice skates or other sporting equipment.
- In kids with developmental delays, movement challenges or injuries, active video games can be used to help teach motor skills, improve movement and rehabilitate.

Source: Active Healthy Kids Canada (2013). *Active Healthy Kids Canada: Report Card on Physical Activity for Children and Youth—Are We Driving Our Kids to Unhealthy Habits?* p. 23. Retrieved February 2018 from http://dvqdas9jty7g6.cloudfront.net/reportcard2013/AHKC-Summary-2013.pdf

Media Marketing to Children

The media has an impact on young children's perception of what is healthy food and what is not, as well as on their view of the effective play level of toys advertised on TV. The more media children watch, the more mixed messages they take in. Children between two and five years old are particularly vulnerable to these messages, as research indicates that they can't tell the difference between a TV show and the commercials. It is only around age eight that children start to realize that advertisements are not always true and are not part of the TV show (MediaSmarts, n.d.).

In 1980, the province of Quebec passed legislation, the first of its kind, that banned advertisements of fast foods and toys targeted at children under 13 years old, in both print and electronic media. To date, no other province or territory has followed suit, even though the approach has been advocated by many. Outside of Canada it has caught on in countries such as Sweden, Norway, the United Kingdom, and Greece.

It is important for parents to select the types of TV programs, computer games, and other digital media to which their children are exposed. It is also in parents' and children's best interest to ask and answer questions, clarify, and make sure that their children are getting positive, health-promoting messages.

The biggest concern about toy ads, according to the Canadian Toy Testing Council, is exaggeration. Children usually think that a toy can do a lot more than it can because of the way advertisers trick them with bells and whistles. Food ads on TV shows mostly promote fast foods, sweetened cereals, candy, and soft drinks. There are very few ads directed at healthy foods (MediaSmarts, n.d.).

How Sleep Relates to Healthy Active Living

Last, but certainly not least, is the issue of sleep, which has emerged several times in this unit and will be discussed again in Unit 9, related to naps and rest during the day in the program (see Rhythm of the Program, page 556).

Sleep hygiene, as defined by the National Sleep Foundation, is "a variety of different practices and habits that are necessary to have good nighttime sleep quality and full daytime alertness" (n.d., p. 1). Consistent routines for bedtimes and wake-up times, including naps for children up to five years old, contribute to the child's well-being. While every child is slightly different in terms of how much sleep she or he needs, most children require at least 10 hours of uninterrupted sleep in order to be fully rested in a 24-hour period (see Sleep Requirements, page 557).

Connection between Sleep and Screen Time

One may assume that the more screen time a child has, the more likely the child is to be tired and fall asleep. On the contrary, plenty of research demonstrates that the more TV children watch, or video games they play, the more likely they are to have trouble falling asleep or to have an irregular sleep schedule. The brain has an internal clock that tells us when we need to sleep. When it becomes dark outside in the evening, this clock is triggered to make melatonin. Melatonin is a brain chemical that makes us feel sleepy. It is good practice for families to expect everyone, children, youth, and adults, to turn off all electronics (TV, video games, computers, or any screens that emit light) about one hour before bed. The light from screens stops the brain from making melatonin (the hormone that promotes sleep) and can contribute to poor sleep hygiene (Children's Hospital of Eastern Ontario [CHEO], n.d., p. 3). There is also a connection between sleep and physical activity:

- Poor sleep tends to result in low physical activity.
- Outdoor play during the day improves sleeping habits.

IT'S TIME FOR A WAKE-UP CALL

Canadian kids are inactive and they may be losing sleep over it.

If you think kids can get a little physical activity and then play video games into the wee hours, yet remain healthy, you're in for a rude awakening. Emerging research, which spurred Canada to develop the world's first **24-Hour Movement Guidelines**, shows that physical activity, sedentary behaviour – and sleep – are closely interrelated.

Kids who are tired out from running around sleep better, and those who have slept well have more energy to run around.[27] And society is starting to pay attention to the fact that the reverse is also true and troubling: kids aren't moving enough to be tired, and they may also be too tired to move. A groundswell of interest in the connection between these behaviours is highlighting the fact that sleep deprivation is a problem in Canadian kids:

- **Only 9% of Canadian kids** aged 5 to 17 get the 60 minutes of heart-pumping activity they need each day.[2012-13 CHMS]

- **Only 24% of 5- to 17-year-olds** meet the **Canadian Sedentary Behaviour Guidelines** recommendation of no more than 2 hours of recreational screen time per day.[2012-13 CHMS]

- **In recent decades,** children's sleep duration has decreased by about 30 to 60 minutes.[14,15]

- **Every hour kids spend** in sedentary activities delays their bedtime by 3 minutes.[16] And the average 5- to 17-year-old Canadian spends 8.5 hours being sedentary each day at least some of the time.[2012-13 CHMS]

- **33% of Canadian children** aged 5 to 13, and 45% of youth aged 14 to 17, have trouble falling asleep or staying asleep at least some of the time.[2012-13 CHMS]

- **36% of 14- to 17-year-olds** find it difficult to stay awake during the day at least sometimes.[2012-13 CHMS]

- **31% of school-aged kids** and 26% of adolescents in Canada are sleep-deprived.[17]

Even kids who are meeting the minimum requirements for sleep duration are not necessarily getting good sleep. Increased screen time and packed schedules mean that kids are getting poor or inconsistent sleep – for instance, staying up late to do homework during the week, or watching TV in their bedrooms until midnight and then playing catch-up on the weekends.

- **43% of 16- to 17-year-old** Canadians are not getting enough sleep on weekdays.[17]

The perils of a sleep-deprived generation are not limited to kids being tired and cranky; they show their fatigue in different ways.[18] Some effects of sleep deprivation in kids are obvious and some are not so obvious:

- **Too little sleep** can cause hyperactivity, impulsiveness and a short attention span.[19,20]

- **Children with reduced sleep** are more likely to struggle with verbal creativity and problem solving, and generally score lower on IQ tests.[20,21]

- **A short sleep duration** produces adverse hormonal changes like those associated with increased risks of obesity, diabetes and hypertension.[20]

Source: ParticipACTION. *Are Canadian Kids Too Tired to Move? The 2016 ParticipACTION Report Card on Physical Activity for Children and Youth.* Toronto: ParticipACTION; 2016. Reprinted by permission.

- Not enough uninterrupted sleep can also result in low energy, which can cause less physical activity during the day.

In summary, as children grow, consider that poor-quality or too much screen time may be linked to

- irregular or shorter sleep time,
- loss of social skills,
- less time for physically active play, and
- childhood obesity.

It is an important role of educators to keep these concerns in mind as curriculum is planned and implemented.

REVISITING THE HEALTH PROMOTION ACTION PLAN

Recall the Health Promotion Action Plan introduced in Unit 1. The following two examples illustrate this plan in practice in terms of promoting healthy active lifestyles.

Example 1

Supporting children in Canada on the right track to healthy active living involves several recommendations for parents and educators. There are responsibilities at all levels of the health promotion plan to move this critical agenda ahead. Certainly, community action and societal change are instrumental in making healthy options an easier choice for children and families.

Individual Problem Solving and Self-Reliance

Let's begin with a summary of recommendations for young children that we can promote as individuals and collective self-help to promote children's healthy active lifestyles.

Physical Activity Spend at least an hour a day being physically active. This can be in short bouts, especially with preschoolers. At least some of that time should be outdoors (year-round) whenever possible. Six- to nine-year-olds should be moderately active for one hour and vigorously active for half an hour daily.

Eating Habits Eat at least five fruit and vegetables a day (four for children two to three years old). Avoid pop as much as possible. Instead, drink or eat at least two dairy foods a day, as well as water throughout the day when thirsty, and limit fruit juice to no more than one serving daily (have the fruit instead!). Try to keep fast-food and restaurant meals to "once in a while" instead of regularly. Be aware of portion sizes as fast-food outlets and restaurants serve much larger portions than recommended. Avoid low-nutritive snack foods (e.g., chips, candy, most processed cookies and cakes) whenever possible. Many of these contain saturated fats. Read the Nutrition Facts table on packaged foods and help children become aware of these in developmentally appropriate ways. Support children's healthy eating habits by respecting their decision when they state they are hungry or full at meals and snack times. Pressuring children about their eating does not contribute to long-term physical or mental health.

Screen Time Curtail screen time, which includes TV, computers, and video games. Age-related suggestions include the following:

- no screen time for children under two
- an hour or less of screen time (most days) for children 2 to 5 years
- less than 2 hours for children 6 to 10 years
- avoiding eating in front of the TV

Children may not notice they are full when watching TV. Keep in mind that food advertisements do not normally promote healthy foods.

Community Action

Community action, supporting each other through policy, sharing ideas, and consistent healthy active living messages and practices for children, makes it more likely that children will develop healthy habits. Community is a network of support systems. Building healthy communities lowers costs to government through reducing the need for health and social services. To this end, making physical activity and healthy eating easier options in our communities is a worthwhile endeavour that requires input from community members and decision makers.

- Educators and the preschoolers' parents share physical activity ideas that are easy to incorporate, ways to introduce fruit and vegetables or healthy food experiences that the children enjoy, and any new information about changes in legislation that support health (e.g., regarding trans fats, label reading, marketing to children via TV).

- Ensure that all of the program's fundraisers walk the talk. A weekend hike, bowl-a-thon, or other enjoyable activity could be turned into a fundraiser by having sponsors donate to your cause.

- Selling fruit, herbs, or other healthy fare rather than chocolate bars is another possible fundraiser that gives a consistent message. This is not to take away from the reality that the occasional sweet treat is a normal part of life but to make a concerted effort to promote healthy options as positive role models.

- Another impetus for collective self-help in supporting healthy active living is the "walking school bus." This idea involves creating a support system whereby families who live near each other can arrange to have one or two adults walk the children to and from the ECLC setting if it is within walking distance. Of course, infants and toddlers would be in strollers, and preschoolers would only be able to walk a short distance, but they are developing this important habit.

When concerned groups in a community approach municipal governments to support change, a new direction in policy and practices is possible. For example:

- The City of Vancouver's (2009) EcoDensity program was launched in 2007, which supports the greening of Vancouver's communities in multidimensional ways. EcoDensity involves finding ways to help people locate near work and, if that's not possible, putting housing near public transit. The urban landscape is changing thanks to the impetus of concerned citizens and policymakers. Active transportation is one of the important aspects of this initiative.

- Vancouver is creating density in the city to generate more opportunities for walking and cycling. Widened sidewalks, street trees, places to sit, and awnings on city buildings are making walking more attractive than driving. Also, the fastest-growing mode of transportation in Vancouver is bicycling, thanks to continued exploration to make the city bicycle friendly. People who live in suburbs where urban sprawl has created car-dependent communities can work together to effect change. Urban planners are instrumental in creating or changing communities to be more conducive to safe and enjoyable walking and bicycling. Where it is possible to walk to their child care centre, school, work, stores, parks, and restaurants, the need to drive is significantly decreased. This has benefits for individual and environmental health.

- An aspect of an ecodensity strategy that supports healthy eating is the opportunity to buy fresh produce from local farmers' markets, such as the 100-Mile Diet, an idea that started in Vancouver, British Columbia, in 2005 and has set off a worldwide movement. The premise is to eat only foods that have been grown within 100 miles from home. The notion of buying locally is a strategy to reduce the use of motorized transportation in food production, as well as to have fresher produce in season for community members. These are just a few of the changes that can have a positive effect on healthy active living for families in communities.

- Parents are concerned about advertising targeted to children and have noted that products deliberately marketed to children are low-nutritive, high-fat, and high-sugar foods and beverages and games and toys that increase sedentary activity. The directors and staff in the early childhood community can
  - plan a "Buy Nothing Day" or "Logo-Free Day" (see the MediaSmarts website) and
  - contact local media outlets and ask them to cover the day's event to promote awareness of this issue

This example illustrates community action to reduce commercialization in the centre and the community.

Societal Change

Is societal change possible to improve healthy active living? Public policy has certainly made an impact on creating smoke-free environments; beyond public places, some jurisdictions are even passing laws to protect children's rights to a smoke-free environment by prohibiting smoking in cars when children are passengers. Recycling is another example of societal change; in this endeavour, children led the way. As with these and the many other examples of societal change, public policy is required across a range of sectors to adequately address the problems of inactivity and poor eating habits. Legislation at the federal and provincial and territorial levels is needed to ensure that changes at the local level are supported and maintained. *For example, the relatively recent push by a number of provincial governments to ban junk foods (with a focus on trans fats and low-nutritive drinks) in schools and require daily physical activity is a clear message that the provinces recognize the need to support children's health.*

A more comprehensive approach is the Integrated Pan-Canadian Healthy Living Strategy (PHAC, 2005), which was approved by the federal, provincial, and territorial ministers of health in 2005. The strategy provides a national framework calling for a coordinated effort of parents, families, professionals, governments, nongovernmental organizations, and the private sector to address the overweight/obesity crisis. "The Healthy Living Strategy is grounded in a population health approach, which strives to address some of the root causes that lead to poor health outcomes. This approach focuses on the living and working environments that affect people's health, the conditions that enable and support people in making healthy choices, and the services that promote and maintain health" (Government of Canada, 2010, p. 1). (See Resource Materials.)

NELSONstudy

To access Resource Materials, visit NelsonStudy.

Example 2

The children and their families who attend a community centre after-school program are frustrated because safety issues in their playground meant that their equipment was removed. To top it off, the municipally funded recreation programs, such as tai chi, basketball, and swimming, which the educators took the children to each week instituted user fees as a cost-cutting strategy. At the same time, the municipal medical officer of health was dismayed to learn from a recent Health Canada survey that the citizens in her city were found to be the least physically active in the province. This prompted her to declare physical activity a priority public health issue for the city, with a strategic plan to improve population fitness levels.

The children, parents, and staff talked about their frustration at the mixed messages and barriers in their way but decided to make their own call to action. Following two group discussions in which the school-agers participated actively and competently, their action plan was outlined as follows.

Individual Problem Solving and Self-Reliance

The children identified after-school computer use as one of their most powerful distractions from active play and agreed as a group on a system to limit each child's weekly computer use to no more than two hours.

Educators evaluated how they are incorporating the three types of physical activity (i.e., endurance, flexibility, and strength) into the daily program. Weaker areas of programming (e.g., flexibility) are now receiving attention (e.g., a grandparent is running tai chi classes for interested children and adults). Educators ensure, with the children's input, that every program includes play, creative expression, and skills.

Community Action

Over the next six months, the children are helping each other add an additional 10 minutes to their daily physical activity, one month at a time, to incorporate daily active time as part of a healthy lifestyle. They are helping each other by

- suggesting games and encouraging peers to join them;
- helping educators keep large bags of small equipment appealing for the children, sorting out unused or broken equipment on a regular basis, and suggesting new and low-cost equipment; and
- encouraging peers to reduce their allotted computer time further or deciding as a group to reduce it in increments.

Educators have approached the local high-school physical education department with an idea that is a mutually beneficial activity. High-school students under the direction of their teacher are teaching the school-agers team skills in basketball, soccer, and other sports. Students use this experience as co-op placement hours or volunteer hours while developing employability and life skills.

A subcommittee of educators, parents, and children was formed to represent the community centre's interests at community meetings that were held to discuss needs and suggestions. The three goals in the strategic plan are

- child and youth development,
- lifelong health and wellness for all, and
- environmental stewardship.

The subcommittee put together a successful grant proposal for funding to build a "green learning ground," including an adventure playground, under the direction of a university urban planning committee with an environmentally sound focus. Although safety is a cornerstone of the project, meaningful ways to involve children and families are incorporated. The green learning ground integrates a range of options for children's play and youth sports interests and includes a vegetable garden to be maintained by the school-agers and educators. This responsibility offers children moderate physical activity, with a flexibility and strength focus.

Societal Change

The school-agers, parents, and educators are involved in a campaign to write letters to their city counsellors, highlighting the following important directions that the policymakers and funders need to take (Toronto Parks and Recreation Department, 2004):

- Restore (or continue) public availability of swimming pools, ice arenas, soccer fields, baseball diamonds, cricket fields, tennis courts, etc.
- Develop standards for providing no-charge recreation programs.
- Reduce barriers to participation by addressing support needs, including transportation, child care, program supplies, and equipment.
- Strive to make all parks and recreation facilities barrier free.
- Increase the number of youth leadership development programs.
- Target high-needs communities when setting geographic priorities for program and service development.
- Create community capacity by working with community organizations to deliver a wide range of programs reflecting the diverse nature of each community.
- Move beyond indoor facilities to increase the range and number of recreational opportunities in parks and natural areas.
- Help maintain continuous enjoyment of activity throughout life.

CONCLUSION

Healthy active living is important to the health of all Canadians. As educators, we have daily opportunities to support a lifestyle for young children that will help pave the way to lifelong healthy habits, including physical literacy. We can do this in many ways:

- Ensure that the program provides ongoing opportunities for activity and healthy eating through policies that are put into practice.
- Be positive role models in this regard.
- Communicate with and support each parent's endeavours in creating and maintaining the family's healthy active living.
- Become involved in community action and societal change that affect the healthy active living goals of all children and families in communities and in Canada.

"We have changed our environment more quickly than we know how to change ourselves" (Lippmann, 1914, p. 20).

ASSESS YOUR LEARNING

Define terms or describe concepts used in this unit:

- active transportation
- body mass index (BMI)
- built environment
- *Canada's Physical Activity Guide for Children*
- carbonated drinks

- cooperative games
- endurance
- epigenetics
- fitness components
- flexibility
- greening the outdoor environment
- healthy active living
- locomotor skills
- manipulative skills
- motor skills
- nonlocomotor skills
- NutriSTEP™
- overweight
- ParticipACTION
- physical literacy
- reasons for overeating
- reasons for undereating
- screen time
- sleep hygiene
- strength
- underweight
- urban sprawl

Evaluate your options in each situation:

1. A few preschoolers have recently moved to Canada from countries that are much warmer year-round. They are having a difficult time adjusting to winter. The parents have asked you to let them stay inside with another group of children rather than take them outside to play.

2. You are chairing an ECLC centre fundraising committee and are planning a family walkathon event to raise the funds needed for greening your outdoor environment. A company that produces carbonated drinks has offered to provide free refreshments for everyone attending the walkathon.

3. The parents of an active, healthy eight-year-old tell you that they are concerned about their son's weight and insist that he be given only one serving of each food at mealtimes and only fruit or vegetables as snacks. No other children in the room have this restriction.

4. You are an educator in a program for four- and five-year-olds. Your colleague has access to all the newest digital media. Your early childhood learning and care program does not have a policy regarding screen time, and your room partner brings in new media weekly that she puts on for children to watch "to calm them down" or whenever it's a rainy day. The children often ask to watch the same program over and over again.

5. One of the school-agers in your after-school program uses a wheelchair. On the playground, she watches as the other children play active games freely, and you notice that she often practises taking shots at the basketball hoop when no other children are using it. When the ball falls to the ground, however, she rarely retrieves it unless an adult is nearby to throw it back to her.

APPENDIX 6.1

Canadian 24-Hour Movement Guidelines for the Early Years (0–4 Years): An Integration of Physical Activity, Sedentary Behaviour, and Sleep

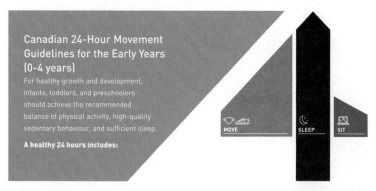

Canadian 24-Hour Movement Guidelines for the Early Years (0-4 years)

For healthy growth and development, infants, toddlers, and preschoolers should achieve the recommended balance of physical activity, high-quality sedentary behaviour, and sufficient sleep.

A healthy 24 hours includes:

MOVE   SLEEP   SIT

MOVE	SLEEP	SIT
INFANTS (LESS THAN 1 YEAR)		
Being physically active several times in a variety of ways, particularly through interactive floor-based play—more is better. For those not yet mobile, this includes at least 30 minutes of tummy time spread throughout the day while awake.	14 to 17 hours (for those aged 0-3 months) or 12 to 16 hours (for those aged 4-11 months) of good-quality sleep, including naps.	Not being restrained for more than 1 hour at a time (e.g., in a stroller or high chair). Screen time is not recommended. When sedentary, engaging in pursuits such as reading and storytelling with a caregiver is encouraged.
TODDLERS (1–2 YEARS)		
At least 180 minutes spent in a variety of physical activities at any intensity, including energetic play, spread throughout the day—more is better.	11 to 14 hours of good-quality sleep, including naps, with consistent bedtimes and wake-up times.	Not being restrained for more than 1 hour at a time (e.g., in a stroller or high chair) or sitting for extended periods. For those younger than 2 years, sedentary screen time is not recommended. For those aged 2 years, sedentary screen time should be no more than 1 hour—less is better. When sedentary, engaging in pursuits such as reading and storytelling with a caregiver is encouraged.
PRESCHOOLERS (3–4 YEARS)		
At least 180 minutes spent in a variety of physical activities spread throughout the day, of which at least 60 minutes is energetic play—more is better.	10 to 13 hours of good-quality sleep, which may include a nap, with consistent bedtimes and wake-up times.	Not being restrained for more than 1 hour at a time (e.g., in a stroller or car seat) or sitting for extended periods. Sedentary screen time should be no more than 1 hour—less is better. When sedentary, engaging in pursuits such as reading and storytelling with a caregiver is encouraged.

Replacing time restrained or sedentary screen time with additional energetic play, and trading indoor for outdoor time, while preserving sufficient sleep, can provide greater health benefits.

Source: *Canadian 24-Hour Movement Guidelines® for the Early Years (ages 0–4 years).* © 2017. Reproduced with permission from the Canadian Society for Exercise Physiology, cssepguidelines.ca

APPENDIX 6.2

Canadian 24-Hour Movement Guidelines for Children and Youth: An Integration of Physical Activity, Sedentary Behaviour, and Sleep

GUIDELINES

For optimal health benefits, children and youth (aged 5–17 years) should achieve high levels of physical activity, low levels of sedentary behaviour, and sufficient sleep each day.

A healthy 24 hours includes:

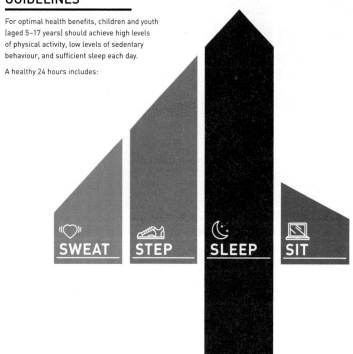

SWEAT **STEP** **SLEEP** **SIT**

SWEAT

MODERATE TO VIGOROUS PHYSICAL ACTIVITY

An accumulation of at least 60 minutes per day of moderate to vigorous physical activity involving a variety of aerobic activities. Vigorous physical activities, and muscle and bone strengthening activities should each be incorporated at least 3 days per week;

STEP

LIGHT PHYSICAL ACTIVITY

Several hours of a variety of structured and unstructured light physical activities;

SLEEP

SLEEP

Uninterrupted 9 to 11 hours of sleep per night for those aged 5–13 years and 8 to 10 hours per night for those aged 14–17 years, with consistent bed and wake-up times;

SIT

SEDENTARY BEHAVIOUR

No more than 2 hours per day of recreational screen time;

Limited sitting for extended periods.

Preserving sufficient sleep, trading indoor time for outdoor time, and replacing sedentary behaviours and light physical activity with additional moderate to vigorous physical activity can provide greater health benefits.

Source: *Canadian 24-Hour Movement Guidelines® for Children and Youth (ages 5–17 years)*. © 2016. Reproduced with permission from the Canadian Society for Exercise Physiology, csepguidelines.ca

Courtesy of Barb Pimento

Safety Promotion

7

CONTENTS

An integral part of growing up is trying new things to become competent. Whether it is learning to walk, ride a bike, cut with a knife, or draw with a crayon, acquiring a new skill is a learning process. As such, it may take a child a number of attempts before he or she masters the skill. Do you remember learning to ride a bike? You probably fell off more than once! Minor scrapes, bumps, and bruises are a normal part of childhood, and exploring challenges is an essential part of development.

It is a tremendous responsibility to ensure children's safety in early childhood learning and care (ECLC) programs, but it is not an insurmountable one. We don't want to design a risk-free environment. The goal of safety promotion in programs is to find a workable balance between a safe and a challenging program. Children who are not physically challenged are understimulated. This understimulation can have the following consequences:

- The children stop seeking challenges, which affects their development and self-esteem.
- They turn to their peers for stimulation, or they turn against them, which, either way, often results in antisocial and hurtful behaviour.
- They direct their natural desire for trial-and-error learning to times and places in which the risks may be much greater (e.g., toddlers climbing up on bookshelves or from chairs onto counters rather than using developmentally appropriate climbing equipment or natural opportunities such as inclines [little hills] in green spaces under adult supervision).
- They spend progressively more time at "safe" activities, such as sitting in front of a screen; this time is far from safe as it contributes to a host of chronic conditions and, in essence, is not physically, emotionally, or socially beneficial after all (see Concerns about Physical Activity Levels of Children, page 331).

High-quality ECLC programs offer children the physical and human resources to experience challenges safely and learn from them. Educators pay attention to the **four components of safety promotion**: training, physical environment, supervision of children, and safety rules. Before discussing how to promote safety, we'll look at childhood injuries from the perspective of the **five W's**: the **who, what, why, where,** and **when of safety**.

Courtesy of George Brown College/Richmond Adelaide Child Care Centre

THE FIVE Ws OF SAFETY

An important role for educators is to design and implement **injury prevention strategies** in ECLC programs. To develop policies and strategies that are relevant, practical, and effective, educators first understand the nature of childhood injuries and factors that increase risk. Educators also draw on their knowledge of children's development and how that affects the types of injuries experienced at different ages.

Safety is an important consideration in everyone's life. An average day for an adult includes several activities with an element of risk: showering, shaving, eating peanut butter on toast for breakfast, navigating the ice-covered front steps of the house, crossing the street, and driving or biking to work. Children face potential risks in their daily lives too. Some children's injuries are the same as adults'. Others

To describe the nature of childhood injuries and factors that increase risk. (LO 1, 4)

To list and describe injury prevention strategies for each of the main injury categories. (LO 4, 5, 6)

are directly related to children's growth and development and becoming competent at small and large motor skills. Learning to crawl, walk, climb, ride a bike, or use scissors involves risks, and children sometimes fall or cut themselves while developing these skills. We can't prevent injuries by stopping children's growth or development any more than our parents could prevent ours. However, it is also true that many injuries are preventable; the word "accident" implies bad luck or fate, so in this unit, as in current safety publications, the word "accident" is not used.

Who and What

Every year, children of all ages are hospitalized because of unintentional injuries. One can suppose that many more children, although injured, are not hospitalized. The Public Health Agency of Canada (PHAC) (2013) reported the following findings between 2009 and 2010:

Unintentional Injuries	Age Groups		
	< 1	1–9	10–14
Falls	649	4262	2082
Motor Vehicle Traffic Crashes	30	340	394
Struck by/Against	46	590	942
Poisonings	78	719	159
Fire/Hot Objects/Hot Substances	59	341	62
Other Unintentional Injuries	481	2810	2008

Source: © All rights reserved. *Injury in Review: 2012 Edition—Spotlight on Road and Transport Safety.* Public Health Agency of Canada, 2012. Adapted and reproduced with permission from the Minister of Health, 2018.

Injuries are the leading cause of death for Canadian children. In fact, this is true for Canadians under the age of 44 (Public Health Agency of Canada [PHAC], 2012, p. 7). By age group, here are the leading causes of injury-related deaths in 2007 for Canadians up to 25 (PHAC, 2012, p. 16):

- infants: suffocation
- ages 1 to 24: motor vehicle collision

Every year, children in Canada are injured or killed from a wide variety of causes; most are unintentional, other than suicide, which is becoming one of the leading causes of injury-based death in North America. A Population-Based Cross-sectional Study in Ontario between 2008 and 2012 included all children and youth from birth to 24 years of age who lived in Ontario with an Ontario health card. This large study found a 44% lower risk of unintentional injury among immigrant children and youth compared with non-immigrant families. The highest risk of injury among non-immigrants was with adolescents, and among immigrants, it was with infants and young children (Saunders et al., 2017, p. E93).

Let's take a brief look at the injury-related causes of death for children based on age and gender, as reported by PHAC (2012, p. 19):

Ages	Leading Cause	Second Cause
< 1 Year Old	Suffocation	Homicide, closely followed by drowning
1- to 9-Year-Olds	Motor vehicle traffic crashes	Other unintentional injuries, closely followed by fire and flame
10- to 14-Year-Olds	Motor vehicle traffic crashes, closely followed by suicides	Other unintentional injuries

Source: © All rights reserved. *Injury in Review: 2012 Edition—Spotlight on Road and Transport Safety.* Public Health Agency of Canada, 2012. Adapted and reproduced with permission from the Minister of Health, 2018.

The causes of death or injury included in this unit are motor vehicle collisions, drowning, burns, threats to breathing (i.e., choking, suffocating, entrapment, and strangling), poisoning, and falls. From the educators' perspective, some of these injuries are more relevant to their day-to-day work than others.

In programs, threats to breathing and falls are, of course, much more likely than motor vehicle collisions. Educators must be aware of choking during snacks and meals. They must be prepared for falls all the time. And even though educators will not be thinking of motor vehicle mishaps during the day, they can help children learn traffic rules when they are riding tricycles (e.g., by encouraging children to stay on the right side of the path and putting up a stop sign at path intersections) or when they are out for walks.

Increasing our awareness of the major causes of childhood unintentional injuries and death can have a significant and positive impact on safety promotion at home and in licensed ECLC settings.

Tables 7.1 to 7.6 provide

- an overview of one of the six types of childhood unintentional injuries,
- age groupings that identify which risks are highest, and
- prevention strategies to implement in ECLC settings.

The placement of the checkmark in the age columns is done where the risk is the highest. Obviously, older school-agers can fall down stairs or get entangled on play structures, but the likelihood is that the risks apply to some ages of children more than others.

Motor Vehicle Collisions

Did you also know?

- Motor vehicle collision is the leading cause of injury-related death for Canadians under 24 years old (PHAC, 2012, p. 7).

- Children are injured riding in school buses and when they are near them.
- Between 1990 and 2009, the Canadian Hospitals Injury Reporting and Prevention Program (CHIRPP) identified the top ways that children were injured on or by school buses (PHAC, 2012, p. 8).

TABLE 7.1 Motor Vehicle Collisions

What

Traffic-related injury, including injuries to passengers in vehicles, pedestrians, and cyclists, is a significant safety issue for all children. Many pedestrian and cyclist injuries have resulted from individuals not obeying traffic rules (e.g., jaywalking or crossing against a traffic light). Traffic-calming strategies reduce the speed of vehicles and lessen the impact. Community pedestrian safety is an ongoing goal, with many agencies at all government levels working for improvements.

Programs that transport children on buses must supervise the children directly. In addition to injuries that occur while in the bus, injuries happen when the child disappears from sight in front of the bus and the bus pulls away. Some children are hit by another vehicle passing the bus as they cross the road.

Risks	Age Groups			
	< 3	3–5	6–8	9–12
not in proper child-restraint seats (1)	✓	✓		
lack or improper use of seat belts (2)		✓	✓	✓
running or playing on the street (3)	✓	✓		

The following suggestions appear in the order in which the risk factors are listed in each category:

1. & 2.   When programs provide transportation for children, appropriate child restraints or seat belts must be used. Consult with the local fire department when unsure of how car seats should be installed or if they have been installed properly. If educators are aware of parents not using proper restraints for their children, be advocates for children (e.g., encourage or assist parents in obtaining and using the restraints). Make sure safety education with preschool and school-age children includes the buckle-up message.

3.   Actively supervise children. Ensure that gates and fences around the playground are maintained. Reinforce the message that very young children are never to run onto the street or cross it without holding an adult's hand. Help preschoolers and school-agers learn traffic safety and laws.

Note: The placement of the checkmark in the age columns is done where the risk is the highest.

These are points to keep in mind when ECLC programs use school buses for outings:

- The most common cause of injury is when the school bus is involved in collision with another vehicle.
- Children are injured when the bus moves suddenly, they are involved in horseplay, and they are getting on and off the bus.
- Almost 20% of the injuries related to school buses are closed head injuries.
- Of pedestrians under 18 years old who were struck and killed by a school bus, 77% of those were between the ages of 5 and 9.

Although the use of seat belts and child restraints is mandated by law across Canada, and although there is evidence that they reduce the rates of death and injuries in motor vehicle collisions, they are still not used 100% of the time. Unrestrained occupants are 3 times more likely to be injured and 16 more times likely to die than those restrained in vehicles (PHAC, 2012, p. 28). Children are at twice the risk for injury when inappropriately restrained than children who are correctly restrained (PHAC, 2012, p. 28). This is the reason why fire departments promote their service to inspect child restraints for families. Refer to Chapter 6 of *Well Beings* (Canadian Paediatric Society [CPS], 2015) for detailed information on optimal restraints for all ages.

Courtesy of Barb Pimento

Bicycle Injuries and Deaths

Bicycle injuries and deaths are higher for children and younger adults than all other ages. In 2005 (Helmets.org, 2018, p. 13),

- 44% of all the bicycle injuries occurred for the 5- to 20-year-olds,
- 23.4% of all the bicycle deaths occurred for the 0- to 20-year-olds, and
- 54% of all bicycle injuries treated in emergency departments were children under 15.

TABLE 7.2   Bicycle-Related Injuries

What

How can educators reduce the number of cycling injuries in programs and help children learn lifelong safety habits? Educators are encouraged to consider including the following practices in their policy:

- Have children wear bike helmets on riding toys and tricycles so that they see them as a natural part of riding.

- Ensure that riding paths are designed so that children can't crash into objects.

- Ensure that children are actively supervised.

- In school-age programs, staff should develop a policy for bikes, in-line skates, and skateboards that stipulates that children travelling to their programs wear helmets and other safety equipment recommended for each activity. Parents may not support your position, but while the children are under your supervision, you can either have them wear the safety equipment or prohibit the activity. When helmets become required by law in your province or territory, you can enforce the law.

Currently, it is unlikely that you will find many programs with toddlers and preschoolers wearing helmets on riding toys and tricycles. Some families find the cost of new or used safety equipment prohibitive. Perhaps programs could canvass families or the neighbourhood for equipment no longer in use. This equipment could be swapped or given to individual families. In the area of bike safety, national organizations provide support and education. (See Resource Materials.)

NELSONstudy

To access Resource Materials, visit NelsonStudy.

Educators who travel to work on bikes are encouraged to wear a properly fitted helmet, not only for their own safety but also to model safe behaviour to children. Legislation making bike helmets mandatory for children under 16 years old is in place in several provinces and under consideration in other provinces and territories.

(continued)

TABLE 7.2 Bicycle-Related Injuries (*continued*)

Risks	Age Groups			
	< 3	3–5	6–8	9–12
riding bicycles on the street			✓	✓

Help children learn bicycle safety rules and ensure that children wear CSA-approved and properly fitted bicycle helmets. Model safe bike riding.

Note: The placement of the checkmark in the age columns is done where the risk is the highest.

Courtesy of George Brown College/Casa Loma Child Care Centre

The majority of deaths of child cyclists are from being struck by a motor vehicle. Injuries are common from falls off the bike. Children most frequently receive injuries to the head and neck (e.g., cuts, scrapes, dental damage, concussions, fractures), as well as cuts, bruises, abrasions, dislocations, sprains, and fractures of the legs and arms. Helmets reduce the risk of injuring one's brain by up to 88%, of injuring one's head by up to 85%, and of injuring one's face by up to 65% (Dennis et al., 2013, p. 7). A head injury can traumatically change a child's life forever. The skull can be fractured or broken by the impact of a speed as low as 7 to 10 kilometres an hour.

Drowning

The rate of children under 10 drowning is declining. That is good news. But adults continue to underestimate the risk that shallow water presents to children. Drowning in less than one metre accounts for 40% of children drowning, and 90% of those children were unsupervised (Canadian Red Cross, 2013, p. 1).

Barbara Taeger Photography/Flickr Open/Getty Images

Threats to Breathing

"Choking, suffocation and strangulation are important causes of unintentional injuries in children and rank as leading causes of unintentional injury deaths in infants and toddlers. Choking and suffocation are responsible for almost 40% of unintentional injuries in infants under the age of one in Canada. For every choking-related death, there are an estimated 110 children treated in hospital emergency departments" (CPS, 2016, p. 1).*

*Source: Canadian Paediatric Society. (2016, April 4). *Preventing Choking and Suffocation in Children.* Position statement (p. 1). Retrieved January 2018 from http://www.cps.ca/en/documents/position/preventing-choking-suffocation-children

TABLE 7.3   Drowning

What

Young children can drown in as little as 5 cm (2 in.) of water, which means that educators must supervise young children around all water and help them develop a respect for it. Remember that even in winter, outdoor drowning is possible if a child falls through thin or melting ice on a body of water. Another possible hazard is an open door that leads from the playroom to the washroom. Educators should remember that children under three years (and some older children) need adult supervision in the washroom to assist with hygiene and ensure safety around toilets, in particular to prevent drowning.

Risks	Age Groups			
	< 3	3–5	6–8	9–12
wading pools and swimming pools (1)	✓	✓	✓	✓
puddles, pails, or large containers of water (2)	✓			
creeks, rivers, lakes, oceans (3)	✓	✓	✓	✓

The following suggestions appear in the order in which the risk factors are listed in each category:

1. Never leave children unsupervised in the pool, regardless of their age. Empty portable wading pools immediately after use and store them upside down. Teach children water safety.

2. Actively supervise infants, toddlers, and preschoolers in the washroom. Check the playground for stagnant puddles of water. Keep diaper pails out of children's reach. Never keep pails or basins filled with water or cleaning solutions near children.

3. Help children learn to respect water, not to play near creeks and rivers, and not to go on ice in the spring. Canals, rivers, and lakes used for ice skating must be safe to use. Boats used to transport children must have an appropriately sized approved flotation device for each child and adult.

Note: The placement of the checkmark in the age columns is done where the risk is the highest.

TABLE 7.4   Threats to Breathing

What

Choking results from inhaling or ingesting food or objects that obstruct the person's airway. Suffocation or strangulation occurs when external forces (such as a pillow over the face or a dangling scarf wound tightly around the neck) prevent air from entering the lungs. Entrapment occurs when a person's body part is caught within or under something that prevents the person from being able to take breaths (e.g., the head is caught in an opening of substandard playground equipment). If a person is deprived of oxygen for four minutes, brain damage can occur.

Educators must focus on

- food, unsafe eating behaviour, and toys that can cause choking. Coins and small magnets pose additional serious risks when ingested (see Risks, page 390).

(continued)

TABLE 7.4 Threats to Breathing *(continued)*

What *(continued)*

Latex balloons (often used in celebrations) should be banned from programs as they are a major choking risk and latex is a potential severe allergen for some children and adults. They have been banned from all children's hospitals in Canada. The use of Mylar balloons is safer; however, once deflated, Mylar balloons must be discarded safely, just like plastic bags.

- clothing that can cause strangulation

Strangulation can result when clothing becomes caught on slides and climbers, and the child's head or clothing gets trapped in play equipment.

- furniture and equipment that can entrap a child

Entrapment can result when a child attempts to climb up a shelving unit that is not securely attached to the wall and the child's weight pulls the unit and its contents onto the child, or a child's head becomes trapped in the opening in a play structure.

Risks	Age Groups			
	< 3	3–5	6–8	9–12
suffocate on pillows, mattresses, and adult waterbeds (1)	✓			
strangle in dangling blind and drapery cords, pull toys, soother strings (2, 10)	✓			
choke on small toys (< 4 cm or 1.5 in. in diameter), toy parts that can be pulled off (e.g., buttons, clothing) (3, 10)	✓			
choke and/or suffer internal damages from swallowing coins, coin-shaped batteries, small magnets (e.g., coins lodged in esophagus; after swallowing two or more small magnets, they can attract to each other, causing intestinal blockages or tearing, requiring surgery) (10, 11)	✓	✓	✓	✓
choke on latex balloons, suffocate from plastic bags (e.g., dry-cleaning bags) (4)	✓	✓		
choke on foods (5)	✓	✓	✓	✓
suffocate when loose scarves and hoods get caught on playground equipment (e.g., slides) (6, 7)	✓	✓	✓	✓
choke when eating too quickly or talking, laughing, or running while eating or eating large pieces of food (8)		✓	✓	✓
become entrapped under furniture or in play structures (9)	✓	✓		

The following suggestions appear in the order in which the risk factors are listed in each category:

1. Sleeping environments for infants should be free of soft bedding that could suffocate a child, such as comforters, pillows, crib bumper pads, and stuffed animals. Remove plastic wrapping from crib mattresses. Never use garbage bags as mattress covers. Do not hang mobiles over the cribs. Keep plastic bags out of children's reach.

(continued)

TABLE 7.4 Threats to Breathing *(continued)*

Risks *(continued)*

2. Strings on soothers and pull toys must not be longer than 20 cm (8 in.). Blind or curtain cords and chains have caused strangulation deaths of children. Design modifications have eliminated some, but not all, types of blind cord hazards. Other types of blinds still present a significant risk (e.g., roll-up blinds). Adults must ensure that blind cords and loose or dangling cords are cut short and anchored.

3. Avoid giving children under four years objects smaller than 4 cm (1.5 in.). If the object can fit into a toilet paper tube, it is a choking hazard for this age group. Check their toys for small parts that can be easily removed.

4. Ban the use of latex balloons in programs because they are a choking hazard and possible serious allergen. Safely discard deflated foil balloons because they can suffocate young children.

5. Know which foods can cause choking in children (see Reducing the Risk of Choking, page 301).

6. Encourage parents to use neck warmers inside coats in place of winter scarves. If scarves are worn, tie and tuck scarves into coats. Ensure that hoods are fastened snugly. Clothing manufacturers are redesigning hoods that fasten with Velcro rather than drawstrings. Have a policy prohibiting drawstrings on clothes. Do not permit children to wear dramatic play clothes on play equipment.

7. Prohibit the attachment of ropes, strings, cords, skipping ropes, etc., to play structures. Use only climbing ropes that are designed and manufactured for play structures. Ensure that children remove bicycle or tricycle helmets before using playground equipment. Note: Older children are at risk for strangulation if props such as ropes around the neck (pretending to be a dog) are used for dramatic play, whether indoors or outdoors.

8. Encourage children to eat slowly and chew properly. Model safe eating habits.

9. Ensure that all shelving and storage units are securely fastened to the walls or flooring. In family home child care, pay particular attention to bedroom furniture such as high/tallboy dressers where children can climb to the top by pulling the drawers out, making the dresser unstable. Inspect the indoor and outdoor play structures for a possible opening where a child's head or neck can become entrapped. Ensure that such equipment meets Canadian Standards Association (CSA) standards.

10. Regularly visit Health Canada's Consumer Product Safety website to remain up-to-date on product recalls related to toys and child-related products. Many directors in ECLC agencies have registered to receive weekly updates of recalled products (e.g., toys, art materials). The alerts can identify possible changes in regulations concerning magnets (you can also enter "toy" and "magnet" as search terms). The Recalls and Safety Alerts website is a comprehensive list of recalls, advisories, and safety alerts, updated daily. This database includes recalls from Health Canada, the Canadian Food Inspection Agency, and Transport Canada.

11. Avoid use of coins and batteries shaped like coins in an ECLC environment with children under three. If coins are used in the program curriculum for three- to five-year-olds, ensure active supervision. CPS recommends that magnetic toys be kept out of environments where children under six years of age are playing. As a precaution, ensure that adult novelty magnet sets (e.g., desk toy of small building magnets) are not permitted in the workplace and that toys brought in by children from their homes are carefully checked for magnets. Small, powerful magnets can also be accidentally swallowed by older children: sometimes they are used as fake tongue or cheek piercings or attached to dental braces. Magnets pose a unique hazard. The individual magnet may be small enough to pass through the digestive tract, but if a child swallows more than one, or a magnet and another metal object, they can attach to each other across intestinal walls, causing obstructions, perforations, or holes that require surgery. In rare cases, they may cause death.

Note: The placement of the checkmark in the age columns is done where the risk is the highest.

TABLE 7.5 Falls

What

Falls are by far the most common cause of injury in ECLC environments—not surprisingly, because they can happen anywhere at any time! These falls can happen both indoors and outdoors. Like adults, children trip on stairs, mats, loose carpets, toys, and other objects and slip in spills of water or sand. Although most falls result in minor injuries such as cuts, scrapes, or sprains, others can be serious or even life threatening, causing broken bones, head injuries, or internal or external bleeding. A fall down the stairs in a baby walker (banned in Canada since 2004) or other mobile device (e.g., play car) is twice as likely to cause a serious head injury. Playground falls are common and can be serious, especially if the child falls onto an inadequate protective surface.

Risks	Age Groups			
	< 3	3–5	6–8	9–12
off furniture, change tables, counters (1)	✓	✓		
out of high chairs, cribs, strollers (1, 7)	✓			
out of windows (2)	✓	✓		
down stairs (3)	✓	✓		
riding toys, tricycles, bicycles, and in-line skates (4)	✓	✓	✓	✓
playground equipment (5)	✓	✓	✓	✓
slip or trip on water, ice, sand, toys, carpeting, extension cords (6)	✓	✓	✓	✓

The following suggestions appear in the order in which the risk factors are listed in each category:

1. Always keep one hand on the child during diaper changes. Never put children on counters or tables even when they are in a baby chair or seat. Until children are able to climb on and off chairs, sofas, etc., never leave them there unattended.

2. Keep furniture away from the windows. Windows should be secured with screens or stops or grills to prevent opening them more than 10 cm (4 in.).

3. Secure safety gates on all stairwells (top and bottom) so that infants and toddlers cannot access stairs without an adult. Safety gates must be screwed securely into the wall (do not use pressure-type gates). Install handrails at children's height. Make sure there is good lighting. Keep stairs clear of toys, shoes, clothing, etc. Model safe behaviour on the stairs. Actively supervise young children using stairs.

4. Actively supervise children. Establish developmentally appropriate rules for riding toys. Create safe riding paths. Begin using bike helmets for children on riding toys and tricycles. Encourage parents to enroll school-age children in bicycle safety courses. Establish a program policy covering school-age children riding bicycles and using in-line skates while in the ECLC program, including parental permission and the use of recommended safety equipment.

(continued)

TABLE 7.5 Falls *(continued)*

5. Actively supervise children. Help children learn the appropriate use of and safety rules for play equipment. Check and maintain play equipment and protective surfaces regularly. Ensure that natural surfaces are topped up seasonally and as needed. Document the regular maintenance checks. Ensure that children are wearing safe footwear for running and climbing.

6. Immediately wipe up spills of water (e.g., water table). Keep sidewalks and stairs clear of ice and snow. Sweep up sand on the floor under the sand table. Keep toys off walkways in the rooms. Do not use scatter rugs. Do not run extension cords across floors where people walk or under carpeting (fire hazard).

7. Never place infant seats, bouncy chairs, and car seats on elevated surfaces.

Note: The placement of the checkmark in the age columns is done where the risk is the highest.

Poisonings

TABLE 7.6 Poisonings

What

"Poison proofing" is the term commonly used to describe the process of identifying and keeping potentially hazardous products out of children's reach. However, it's important to recognize that poison proofing is an ongoing process, not a one-time thing (e.g., in an ECLC setting, you have products locked away, but family members put purses and diaper bags on the floor that may contain products that children can get into). It's logical that poisonings happen much more often in children's homes. ECLC settings usually don't have many hazardous products (pesticides, paints, gasoline, medications, nail polish and remover, ashtrays and cigarettes, alcohol, etc.), and the ones they have are locked out of the children's reach (as part of the poison proofing at the program). Almost any substance taken in sufficient quantities can be a poison.

Poisoning can occur when someone

- eats or drinks a hazardous product,

- touches or spills a product on the skin and the chemical is absorbed through the skin, or

- breathes in fumes of liquids.

Courtesy of George Brown College/Casa Loma Child Care Centre

(continued)

TABLE 7.6 Poisonings (continued)

Risks	Age Groups			
	< 3	3–5	6–8	9–12
consumes potentially hazardous substances such as cleaning products; alcohol; medications (e.g., vitamins); certain flowers, plants, and berries; perfume, nail polish, and remover (1)	✓	✓		
eats cigarettes and butts (2)	✓			
takes dare to seek approval from peers, drinks or eats unknown fluid or substance that is hazardous (e.g., unknown berry on bush) (3)			✓	✓

The following suggestions appear in the order in which the risk factors are listed in each category:

1. Regularly identify and remove potentially hazardous products in the interior space and playground (e.g., during daily playground checks). Keep all medications locked and out of reach of children. Keep first-aid kits out of reach. Staff and parents must keep purses, knapsacks, and diaper bags off the floor and out of children's reach. Post the poison control centre's phone number by every phone. Teach children not to eat plants or berries without checking with an adult first.

2. Enforce the no-smoking policy in programs. Educators who smoke outside must not leave cigarette butts on the ground where young children can pick them up. Ashtrays must be carefully emptied and kept out of reach.

3. & 4. Provide education opportunities on drug and alcohol abuse for school-age children and parents (e.g., invite a guest speaker).

Note: The placement of the checkmark in the age columns is done where the risk is the highest.

Burns

TABLE 7.7 Burns

What

There are four types of burns: contact burns, scalds, electrical burns, and chemical burns. In ECLC settings, children's burns usually result from scalding by hot tap water, soups, or beverages (including burn injuries to the mouth from microwaved bottles) and contact burns from hot metal, such as slides. Young children cannot understand the dangers of hot liquids and other burn hazards and have slower reaction times than older children.

Risks	Age Groups			
	< 3	3–5	6–8	9–12
scalds from hot tap water, beverages, soups (1)	✓	✓	✓	✓
burns from stoves and ovens, heat radiators, fireplaces, wood stoves (2)	✓	✓	✓	✓
sticking objects in electrical outlets, chewing on electrical cords (3)	✓			

(continued)

TABLE 7.7 Burns *(continued)*

Risks	Age Groups			
	< 3	3–5	6–8	9–12
metal buckles and vinyl-covered car seats exposed to the sun (4)	✓	✓		
metal slides exposed to the sun (5)	✓	✓	✓	
playing with matches or lighters (6)	✓	✓	✓	✓
using the stove or electrical appliances while cooking (7)			✓	✓

The following suggestions appear in the order in which the risk factors are listed in each category:

1. Younger children must be supervised around water at all times. Ensure that the temperature of the hot water from faucets does not exceed 43°C (110°F). Hot beverages or fluids are not permitted in the play area, nor may staff drink them while holding children. Preschool and school-age children, if applicable, must learn the safety rules around heating food in microwave ovens and have adult supervision.

2. Kitchens must be inaccessible to unsupervised children. Children must be supervised during all cooking activities. All sources of heat (e.g., radiators, hot-water pipes, registers) accessible to children must not exceed 43°C (110°F). Install physical barriers around fireplaces, wood stoves, furnaces, and hot-water heaters if children have access to them.

3. Cover all unused electrical outlets with plastic outlet covers. Electrical cords should be out of children's reach.

4. Cover car seats, child restraints, and strollers with a blanket or towel to shade them from the sun. Older children and educators should be in the habit of checking vinyl seats and belt buckles before getting in the vehicle.

5. Place metal slides in shaded areas or plant trees or erect a structure that provides shade. Use metal slides in the morning before it gets too hot. If possible, pour cold water to cool the metal; there may be days when the slide is closed.

6. Matches and lighters must never be within children's reach. Keep purses, diaper bags, knapsacks, etc., off the floor and out of reach. Children can learn the fire message "Stop, drop, and roll."

7. See Cooking with Children, page 578.

Note: The placement of the checkmark in the age columns is done where the risk is the highest.

Why

Individual differences in temperament may explain why one child is more of a risk taker, less fearful, more adventurous, or more inquisitive than another. Risk takers are more likely to be in situations that put them at risk for injury. Gender differences play a role in injuries because boys are often involved in more physically challenging activities. Gender differences in this respect are not yet fully understood. Possible factors include risk perception, peer influence on risk taking, and parental responses to children engaging in risky behaviour. Regardless of individual, gender, or family response differences, educators must evaluate the safety of the equipment being used and maintain levels of supervision appropriate for the activity and the age of the children. However, educators' supervision cannot focus only on the adventurous children, or boys in general, because all children are susceptible to injuries.

Children learn through exploration, and with maturation, they reach developmental milestones. Understanding children's growth and development is essential in anticipating injuries and thus preventing or reducing their severity. The physical and cognitive developmental immaturity of young children increases their risk of injury compared with that of older children and adults. Here are some of the reasons why:

- Children go through such rapid growth spurts that sometimes their sensory perception doesn't keep up (e.g., a child gets taller, but she senses that she is shorter, misjudges her height with the monkey bar, and bangs her head).
- Children have yet to learn how to control impulses. They are unaware of the potential harm to themselves when they do whatever comes to mind (e.g., running into the street to retrieve a ball, leaning over into a pail of water, following peers to the highest level of the climber where they aren't physically able to handle the challenge to climb back down).
- Children learn through trial and error. When children's environments are not developmentally appropriate and challenging, their experiments involve activities that can be dangerous (e.g., a toddler trying to walk up the chute of a slide because no climber is available).
- Children under three years of age are usually not aware of others' safety and may contribute to the harm of others.

Let's consider the risk of drowning as a hazard based on a child's growth and development. Most children under age five are attracted to the sensory opportunities of water but lack a sense of potential danger. This puts them at risk for drowning if not carefully supervised. Also, their heads are relatively much larger and heavier than the head of an older child or adult, making them more vulnerable to fall in head first, quickly filling their small lungs with water. You have likely heard that young children can drown in very shallow water (as little as 5 cm/2 in.).

Vikulin/Shutterstock.com

Starting with infants and toddlers, we'll examine aspects of children's growth and development as they relate to safety.

Infants

Infants are learning to roll over from front to back, which puts them at risk for falling from heights (e.g., change tables, counters, furniture) or suffocating if placed on a soft or buoyant surface. They may roll onto their tummy but then, unable to roll back, smother themselves when their face is buried in a pillow or adult water bed.

Infants and Toddlers

Infants and toddlers are developing stronger grasps, and those who can stand, crawl, or walk are at risk for

- falling down stairs,
- pulling on an appliance cord hanging down the front of a counter,
- grabbing a cup of hot coffee or tea from a table,
- becoming tangled in drapery cords and strangling, or
- pulling off small parts from a toy and choking.

They have not yet developed an awareness of potential harm. Toddlers will run in front of a moving swing. At this age, most children love playing in water and are not yet able to discern the difference between supervised water play and playing in the toilet water alone. They also have a tendency to put everything in their mouth (sensorimotor learning), which puts them at risk for poisoning and choking. Children at this age are active explorers and thus are prone to bumps, bruises, and scrapes from losing their balance and attempting new tasks and are often like little whirlwinds because their quest for learning about their world leaves little time for caution.

Preschoolers

Preschoolers are adept at running, climbing, and pedalling a tricycle by the time they are four. They are becoming more competent and confident on playground equipment and are looking for new and advanced challenges (e.g., climbing even higher up the climber, jumping off the swing while it is still moving). Children this age are in the preoperational stage of cognitive development. As a result, they are unable to judge the speed of a car, the height of the climber's fire pole, or the danger of deep water or matches. They are also unable to distinguish clearly between reality and fantasy. Many children watch television, especially cartoons, which focus on invincible superheroes. These shows may lead some preschoolers to believe that they, too, can leap from high places or fly. Preschoolers want and need to have increasing levels of independence, but with this comes risk (e.g., a child can't learn to cut with a knife without using one, so he or she may cut herself even when using a dull one).

School-Agers

School-agers are developing competencies in many areas and need to be given more independence and responsibility. Issues concerning children's personal safety arise both at home and in the school-age program. In school-age programs, there are fewer educators per child (a higher staff–child ratio), resulting in less direct supervision. Children are required to use their own decision-making skills and judgments in various situations, such as leaving the playground to go into the school to use the bathroom. In licensed child care, a buddy system may be used for the bathroom, for riding a bike and in-line skating to school, and by parents when children are using a neighbourhood playground in the evening without a parent. Before delegating new responsibilities to a child, adults must consider the child's age, level of maturity, track record, and reliability, as well as the inherent safety risks within the school, program, or neighbourhood.

Jessica took off her bike helmet after rounding the corner and didn't make full stops at stop signs. She is not permitted to bicycle to school until she demonstrates that she can follow safe cycling practices consistently.

School-agers may be paying more attention to interacting with their peers than to what they are actually doing (e.g., a child who is busy talking to friends on the ground may not notice that he or she has moved to the edge of the climber), so physical injuries often result. On the other hand, children can get so involved in an activity that they are oblivious to everything around them (e.g., during a game of tag, a child determined not to be tagged runs into someone else while running away).

Aside from injuries attributable to these growth and development factors, children are injured from both the use of developmentally inappropriate or poorly maintained equipment and the lack of adequate supervision or rules.

Where

Houses and apartments are designed for adults. Most children spend more time at home than they do in ECLC programs, so it is not surprising that children are more often injured at home and outside their homes, for example, in motor vehicle traffic collisions.

Compared with other environments, ECLC settings are less dangerous places for children. Yet these facts do not mean that we can be complacent about safety in ECLC programs because injuries happen there too. Children can slip in spills from a water table, pinch their fingers in a door, and run into each other. The playground is the site of the highest number of injuries at centres, mostly due to falls onto inadequate protective surfaces under and around playground equipment. Injuries have decreased over recent years due in part to strict adherence in some provinces and territories to **Canadian Standards Association (CSA)** requirements. School-age children in particular are at risk for falling on stairs because of frequent use in many school buildings and the likelihood of going up and down unsafely (e.g., taking two stairs at a time, jumping down, not using the handrail).

When

Injuries can happen at any time. But there are particular situations or conditions in which the likelihood of injury increases. *For example, "Playground injuries occur most often in summer (43%), followed by fall (27%), spring (24%), and winter (6%)"* (CPS, 2014, p. 1). Childhood injuries in programs often happen

- when children are tired or hungry;
- when children new to the program are not fully aware of the environment or don't know how to use play equipment safely;
- when educators relax their level of supervision (e.g., while talking among themselves in the playground), overestimate a child's abilities, or do not anticipate potential consequences of an activity or a child's behaviour;
- when educator–child ratios are not adequate for the activity, whether it is cooking with children or going for a walk;
- when the daily routine is disrupted (e.g., a familiar educator is absent and the care routine and level of supervision are affected);
- when a new piece of play equipment arrives and the children become too excited and preoccupied to follow safety rules; or
- when field trips introduce children to unfamiliar situations and unexpected hazards.

HOW CAN WE PROMOTE CHILDREN'S SAFETY?

The challenge for educators is to provide an environment that is not only developmentally challenging but also as safe as possible so that children can be physically active and gain new skills in all areas of development (e.g., cognitive problem solving, social working with peers, emotional feelings of competence). Educators and parents recognize that bumps, scrapes, and bruises are a normal part of growing up. Children are inevitably injured when using play equipment. However, the likelihood of broken bones and head or internal injuries is minimized if the equipment is developmentally appropriate, the protective surfaces are adequately maintained, the children use the equipment properly, and the educators actively supervise their activities. By modelling safe but not overly anxious behaviour, adults help children develop an awareness of safety. The adage "Do as I say, not as I do" does not apply to safety, or to anything else for that matter. Children will adopt adults' behaviour, whether it is appropriate or not.

E.G.Pors/Shutterstock.com

OBJECTIVES

To identify the role of public policy in safety promotion. (LO 3)

To describe the importance of education and training, including emergency training, in safety promotion. (LO 2)

To identify strategies in an ongoing evaluation of the indoor and outdoor environment as primary in safety promotion. (LO 6)

To view active supervision as an essential component of injury prevention and to identify the various factors that affect the level of supervision. (LO 2, 4)

To clarify the limited role that safety rules play in injury prevention and describe the essential considerations in developing and adapting rules for each age group. (LO 4, 6)

It is much more likely that children will learn safe pedestrian behaviour when they see adults using crosswalks (pushing the crosswalk's flashing light and pointing), waiting for walk signs, stopping to look both ways before crossing the street, and not walking between parked cars. The opposite can also be true. Adults who do not focus on their surroundings to walk safely (e.g., talking or texting on their cellphone) are taking unnecessary risks. If children see adults breaking safety rules that they have been told to follow, they will not see how these rules apply to their own safety.

Educators' observation skills are continually tested in terms of identifying the following elements to ensure children's safety:

- changes in children's physical and cognitive abilities
- the need for changes in the play area's design or layout
- hazardous equipment and playing surfaces
- inappropriate use of equipment
- tired or hungry children
- questionable use of safety rules or levels of supervision for specific activities

We use scenarios throughout this section to illustrate how educators can anticipate and prevent serious childhood injuries. Educators' understanding of children's development is essential in injury prevention.

You would not permit a toddler to use the school-ager's slide any more than you would permit a 10-year-old to drive. Although the toddler might manage to climb the steps and sit down before sliding, he or she could fall at any time. Moreover, the slide itself is designed for children much larger than a toddler and has spaces between the steps and at the top that toddlers could fall through. Similarly, although the 10-year-old could reach the gas pedal and drive a car in a straight line, that child is not yet capable of handling potential road hazards. In both of these examples, the children are neither physically nor cognitively ready to accomplish these tasks.

Role of Public Policy in Promoting Safety

Overall, between 1979 and 2007, the rates of mortality from the leading injury causes declined, as did hospitalization rates from the leading injury causes between 1994/95 and 2008/09 (PHAC, 2012, pp. 7–8). The primary reason for this positive direction is successful public policy changes with regulatory functions (monitoring) that make children's environments safer. Safer environments, such as municipalities and businesses installing speed bumps, provincial and territorial governments passing legislation on car seats and booster seats, and some provincial and territorial governments having legislation for bike helmets, and the establishment of national standards and guidelines on children's play spaces and equipment (Canadian Standards Association [CSA], 2016) are all examples of strategies that promote safety and reduce injuries for all children. An example of federal legislation that is effecting positive change with safety information for all

Canadians is the *Canada Consumer Product Safety Act* (CCPSA), which came into force on June 20, 2011, and is administered by Health Canada (2014).

The CCPSA adopts modern tools and techniques to strengthen protection and bring Canada's consumer product safety system in line with our key trading partners. The CCPSA reflects years of extensive consultations with a broad range of stakeholders, including industry, consumer groups, children's organizations, standards development organizations, other levels of government, and the general public. This law applies to a wide variety of consumer products, including children's toys, household products, and sporting goods, but excludes products such as motor vehicles and their integral parts, food, drugs (including natural health products), and animals as these are regulated by other Canadian laws.

Health Canada helps protect the Canadian public from potential health hazards by posting advisories, warnings, and recalls from industry concerning consumer products.

The Recalls and Safety Alerts website provides easy access to a comprehensive list of recalls, advisories, and safety alerts. (See Resource Materials.) This site includes recalls from Health Canada, the Canadian Food Inspection Agency, and Transport Canada.

NELSONstudy

To access Resource Materials, visit NelsonStudy.

Although injuries and deaths have decreased, even one preventable death of a child and many thousands of preventable serious injuries continue to be unacceptable. As stated earlier, injuries are the leading cause of death for children in Canada. Our track record on childhood injuries and injury-related deaths and hospitalizations needs improvement. One child dies every nine hours. The vast majority of these injuries are preventable. Parachute is working on bringing attention to injury prevention, especially considering that unintentional death is the number one cause of death for Canadians aged 1 to 44 (Parachute, 2014, p. 13).

Parachute is a national charitable organization. It united the former organizations of Safe Communities Canada, Safe Kids Canada, SMARTRISK, and ThinkFirst Canada into one strong leader in injury prevention. Here are just a few highlights from *The Cost of Injury in Canada: The Clock Is Ticking* report on preventable injuries (Parachute, 2015, p. 1):

- Almost a quarter of a million Canadians were hospitalized as a result of an injury.
- Emergency rooms were busy treating 3.5 million patients with injuries.
- Injuries resulted in 60,000 Canadians being disabled, either partially or permanently.
- Treating injuries has cost the health care system $15.9 billion.
- Every hour in Canada, more than 400 people suffer a *preventable* injury.

In addition to safety-specific targeted policy and legislation in Canada, we need to address the social determinants of health. Risk factors for unintentional injury and death, including exposures to **environmental contaminants**, are strongly influenced by poverty, inadequate housing, and other social determinants.

At the centre of prevention is what is known as the precautionary approach, also referred to as the precautionary principle. The Canadian government began to adopt this approach in 2000, and its application is continuing to emerge in science-based regulatory programs. The impetus for this approach is to strengthen risk management practices across the federal public service.

Precautionary Approach

The absence of full scientific certainty (often called "burden of proof") is not a reason to postpone decisions that may result in serious or irreversible harm. In other words, "better safe than sorry" is an easier way of putting it! This is known as the **precautionary approach** or precautionary principle within science-based risk management. Although scientific, evidence-based research is essential in all matters of public health and safety, there are times when absolute proof of harm or death would likely mean unnecessary injury, disease, or death. Precautionary measures should also be reconsidered in future, based on possible scientific advancements, technology, and society's expectations of protection (Government of Canada, 2001, p. 6).

At its best, the precautionary principle is essential to understanding the commitment that democratic governance has under the rule of law regarding environmental issues. The precautionary principle must only be applied when

- the suspected risk is severe,
- the relationship between cause and effect is likely, and
- precautionary measures are tolerable.

If the three conditions are not met, the precautionary principle will likely be overused (Weir et al., 2010, p. 397). Here's an example: Health Canada needs to go further in addressing the bisphenol (BPA) concerns outlined in *Focus on Bisphenol A: Statement of Health and Environmental Organizations on Endocrine Disrupting Chemicals*. "New data from the Government of Canada reveal that 91 percent of Canadians have detectable levels of BPA in their urine, with levels highest among children" (Canadian Partnership for Children's Health and Environment [CPCHE], 2010a, p. 2).

In no way is the previous discussion on policy and legislative changes meant to undervalue the essential practices in day-to-day prevention strategies. Educators have an important responsibility in following policies and practices to ensure optimal safety for children in their care. Tables 7.1 to 7.7 (on pages 386–394) and the next section in this unit outline how this is done.

Implementing Prevention Strategies

The following four components are interconnected, and one or more can either cause or prevent injuries:

- training
- physical environment
- supervision of children
- safety rules

The climber is developmentally appropriate, but the protective surface is not maintained. The children understand the safety rules for using the climber, and an educator is assigned to supervise the children. Kamal loses his balance on the ladder and falls to the ground. He suffers a mild concussion because the protective surface was not up to standard.

Training

Once you complete your early childhood education (ECE) training, you will be equipped with entry-level skills and knowledge. No one should expect you to be ready or willing to accept a supervisor's role. However, you will be able to take an active role in safety promotion because you will know the fundamental principles of child development and how to integrate them with your observation skills. Your knowledge and abilities in injury prevention will be enhanced as you improve your observation skills through work experience. Promoting safety in early childhood learning and care programs involves positive attitudes, knowledge, and behaviour. Committing to seeking up-to-date information about safety, putting this information into practice, and modelling safe behaviour yourself is your responsibility. Training opportunities may be on the job or through courses, conferences, and possibly ongoing committee work or networking.

One possible consequence of injuries is the need for educators to administer first aid to children. Although regulations vary across Canada, all early childhood regulations stipulate that a specified number of educators in a program must have current first-aid and cardiopulmonary resuscitation (CPR) certificates. First-aid techniques cannot be learned solely from a book. Try putting on a sling properly from looking at a picture! It's not as simple as it may appear. Educators must know how to manage choking in children and adults and how to apply first aid. Ideally, ECE training programs ensure that their students take a standard first-aid course applicable to children and receive a certificate from a first-aid training program recognized by their early childhood licensing agency. Every student is strongly encouraged or required to obtain certification in CPR, including infant/child CPR. Certification in first aid and CPR not only demonstrates your professional commitment to safety but also is an important and relevant skill on a resumé. A second consequence of injuries is that educators must document all injuries that occur while children are under their care, even when first aid was not administered (see Injury Reports, page 460).

Serious Occurrences

Training can also arise from analyzing serious occurrence reports. Every province and territory child care licensing agency defines what is reportable as a serious occurrence and outlines the procedure and forms to be completed. The category of **serious occurrences** covers more than the obvious injuries that happen to children and adults, or even death, and includes other incidents, such as

- a child being missing, even for a short period of time;
- a disaster on the premises, such as a fire;
- a threat of disaster, such as a bomb scare;
- any allegations of abuse or mistreatment of a child against staff, ECE students, volunteers, or other adults; and
- any serious complaint made by or about a child, a parent, or staff.

Serious occurrence reporting is an ongoing process with annual summary and analysis reports. These reports provide the opportunity for the child care office to review and reflect on possible patterns of occurrences. Patterns of serious occurrences suggest a need for changes, such as training, support, or internal policy amendments, as well as steps to address any of these needs. Upon reviewing the report, ministry personnel may also identify other issues or additional action. For optimal safety promotion, it is essential that educators recognize the importance of reporting serious occurrences consistently and view the annual review process as a training opportunity to continue learning about high-quality ECLC environments. Reflecting and acting on program changes mean that everyone benefits. The provincial or territorial child care office goes beyond requiring accountability. It also plays a critical role in advising and training to improve the quality of ECLC programs.

Physical Environment

Children's safety is one of the main priorities when designing and furnishing the physical setting. When prioritizing steps in promoting children's safety, the physical environment tops the list (ahead of supervision and safety rules). Regardless of the level of adult supervision or children's own awareness, children are at undue risk when the environment itself is inherently dangerous. Safety features should include the safe placement of electrical outlets and heating radiators and vents or electric baseboard heaters, safety glass in doors and the windows that separate rooms, doors that won't crush fingers, handrails on stairs for children, and hot-water temperatures that won't scald. These and other safety features, such as smoke alarms and carbon monoxide detectors, are the concern of the child care licensing agency, director, and board of directors.

Indoor Environments

Infants and toddlers are rapidly changing and learning new skills. Educators draw on their knowledge of growth and development and their observation skills to identify changes in each child and in the social relations among the children as a group. In response, educators may have to adjust the overall layout of the play area and frequently remove or add new and more challenging play material and equipment to meet individual children's next stage of development. Toddler programs that are sterile environments devoid of large motor challenges can result in children withdrawing, becoming aggressive (e.g., biting), or physically challenging themselves in inappropriate ways.

CRITICAL THINKING

Ten-month-old Jared is learning to climb. He is particularly fond of climbing on the box that covers the heat radiator in the playroom. On one attempt, he falls backward onto his bottom and bangs his head on the floor. How could you have prevented this injury?

Organizing the indoor space provides opportunities for educators to prevent injuries for all age groups:

- In planning the room arrangement, consider the traffic areas so that paths lead children between activity centres rather than through them, without creating congestion.
- Provide areas with enough space for children to explore material and so that other children don't have to walk through that area.

- Establish boundaries by using shelves or dividers and carpeting to your advantage, to break up open spaces that children would run in.
- When considering where to place the table and chairs in the playroom, allow enough space for the chairs to be pulled out while the children stand and sit during an activity and for a clear walkway behind the chair. (The walkway will reduce the likelihood of children tripping on chair legs.) This rule also applies to easels.
- Provide storage units and organize the space so that children can return materials and supplies. Add pictorial labels to shelves, boxes, and so on to guide children in putting toys and material away during cleanup.
- Secure all shelving so that it cannot be tipped over. Limit the height so that educators can view the room.
- Ensure that the block area is away from the traffic area.
- Choose round or curved tables rather than straight-edged tables.
- For the water and sand tables:
  - Place them on tiled floor for easy cleanup (because children and staff can slip in spilled water and sand).
  - Keep cleanup tools handy at children's level (e.g., dustpan, broom, mop).
  - Sand on the floor should either be discarded or put into the outdoor sandbox.

Furniture

Furniture should meet the needs of both the children and the adults. Tables, chairs, cots, activity centres, bookshelves, and so on, must be durable and of a size that suits the children who use them. However, ECLC settings are also workplaces, so they must also meet the physical needs of the adults who work in them. Adult chairs should be available in the eating area and comfortable chairs or sofas in the play area for educators to read books, cuddle children, and feed infants. But don't forget that the adult-sized furniture must also be child-safe.

- A 15-month-old boy is crawling around a rocking chair at the same time that an educator is giving an infant her bottle. The boy's fingers become caught under a runner.
- A preschooler uses the levered handle for a recliner's footrest, and her hand gets caught in the metal mechanism when she closes it.

From the standpoint of safety, much of the furniture manufactured for infants must meet the safety criteria established by Health Canada's Consumer Product Safety division. The division's website and online publications assist educators and parents in purchasing used furniture that meets safety standards. With the cribs, highchairs, strollers, and possibly playpens in place in programs, what practices are needed to ensure children's safety on a daily basis? (See Table 7.8, page 406.)

Did you know that it has been more than 10 years since the sale, import, and advertisement of baby walkers has been banned in Canada? These walkers are dangerous equipment, and Canada's ban is the first in the world. It is a criminal offence to sell new or used baby walkers or give them away. Baby walkers can be

Courtesy of George Brown College/Casa Loma Child Care Centre

purchased in the United States. As such, Canadians living closer to the American border are provided with easy access to these walkers. Walkers gave young infants a vehicle that could propel them at speeds that they are unable to handle, resulting in thousands of head injuries, broken bones, and some deaths from tipping over or down a set of stairs. The height gave infants access to reach items such as cords and objects from low tables, which led to burns, poisonings, and other injuries.

In addition to the safety hazards, walkers put infants in an upright position, although many of them may not be able to sit unsupported. Infants' physical development evolves through a series of stages, each of which prepares them for the next. Walkers not only confined children but also prevented them from moving naturally and using their developing skills and abilities. The lesson learned from the deaths and injuries over the years from baby walkers is that new ideas and designs in furniture and play equipment must be evaluated for safety on an ongoing basis.

Indoor Play Equipment

Programs provide children with play materials, equipment, and toys manufactured for children. Play materials can also be inexpensive objects found around the house—empty containers, wooden spoons, measuring cups, blankets, scarves and hats, used clothes, pillows, cardboard boxes, pieces of wood, sand, and water. Toys and materials must be developmentally appropriate to ensure the safety of the particular age group using them. For children under three years old, toys or toy pieces must be too large to fit into a toilet roll tube to be deemed safe. Toys for school-age children, for example, often have small pieces and removable parts, such as doll clothes and accessories or limbs, which can be pulled off and might choke younger children. Paints, glues, and coloured paper must be nontoxic to protect children who put them in their mouth. Battery-operated toys should be avoided for young children: batteries are toxic (see Environmental Contaminants, page 444) and may wind up in the mouth or, worse, swallowed, in addition to the likelihood that there is little play value in battery-operated toys. Health Canada provides specific updated warnings and advisories on its website. (See Resource Materials.)

NELSONstudy

To access Resource Materials, visit NelsonStudy.

TABLE 7.8   Using Infant and Toddler Equipment Safely

Equipment	Safety Practices
Cribs	• The railing must be up and secure after putting the child in to sleep. *For increased safety, most cribs are now built with railings that do not move up and down.* • Bumper pads and large stuffed toys should not be in the crib once the child can stand up inside so that neither can be used by the child to climb over the side. • Never provide an infant under 12 months with a pillow because of the risk that an infant who has rolled face down will be unable to roll over and avoid suffocation. • To prevent strangling, blind and drapery cords must be secured away from cribs. Strings attached to mobiles and crib gyms must not be within children's reach (lying or standing).

(continued)

TABLE 7.8   Using Infant and Toddler Equipment Safely (*continued*)

Equipment	Safety Practices
Highchairs	<ul><li>Never leave children unsupervised.</li><li>Always use the safety belts, but don't assume that children can't wiggle out of or unfasten them.</li><li>Ensure that the child's fingers, hands, and head can't be trapped when putting on or taking off the tray.</li><li>Help children learn that they must always sit down in the chair and that standing is not permitted.</li><li>Don't place chairs near doorways, stoves, fridges, or walls where children could tip the chair over by pushing against it with their feet.</li><li>When chairs are not in use, keep them out of reach of children to prevent toddlers from trying to climb on them.</li></ul>
Strollers*	<ul><li>Never leave children unsupervised.</li><li>Check all the brakes.</li><li>Use brakes when children are getting in and out or when parked with children inside.</li><li>Always use the safety belts, but don't assume that children can't wiggle out of or unfasten the belt.</li><li>Help children learn that they must always sit down.</li></ul>
Playpens**	<ul><li>Ensure that the sides are up and secure.</li><li>Avoid large stuffed toys and boxes, etc., that children can use as steps to climb over the side.</li><li>To prevent strangling, blind and drapery cords must be secured away from playpens; mobiles and crib gyms with strings must not be within children's reach (lying or standing).</li><li>Keep playpens out of direct sunlight as hot vinyl might burn the child's skin.</li><li>Check the vinyl mattress or railings for tears that children could bite off and choke on.</li><li>Do not use for children who either are tall enough or weigh enough to crawl over or tip over the playpen.</li></ul>

*The Government of Canada (2012, p. 1) provides a number of recommendations for stroller and carriage safety:

Choosing a safe stroller or carriage

- Pick a sturdy model and follow the manufacturer's guidelines for child height and weight.

- Whether a carriage or stroller is new or used, only choose one that comes with a label and instructions.

- Choose only a stroller that comes with a safety belt or lap harness that is solidly attached to the frame.

- Ensure the brakes and locking mechanisms on folding models are in working order.

- Make sure the wheels are securely attached.

Using a stroller or carriage safely

- Always supervise your child when he or she is in the stroller or carriage (and each child if a stroller built for more than 1 child).

- Always use the safety harness and lap belts, and make sure your child is seated properly.

- Use the brakes when stopped or when helping your child into and out of the stroller or carriage.

(*continued*)

TABLE 7.8 Using Infant and Toddler Equipment Safely *(continued)*

- Never use a stroller on an escalator.

- Make sure your child's hands and feet are out of the way when making adjustments to the stroller/carriage (e.g., watch that hands and fingers are clear before reversing the handle).

- Regularly check for signs of damage and that the wheels are securely attached.

- Do not use pillows or blankets as padding; they can cause suffocation.

- Always follow the manufacturer's instructions for putting additional items or accessories in or on the stroller (e.g., don't overload the handles with knapsacks, and bags, that can cause the stroller to tip).

**When not sleeping, infants and toddlers must have the freedom to explore, play, and socialize in environments that are safe and secure. The routine use of playpens is discouraged for children of any age. Some programs use them for young infants outside or as a temporary safe place before returning children to the play area after diapering.

Toys

Each day, educators inspect toys for the following:

- broken parts or pieces; when found, they are repaired or put safely in the garbage;
- torn seams on stuffed toys and dolls that could permit stuffing to come out;
- chipped paint, rusting metal, etc.;
- sharp or splintered edges;
- exposed hinges or pinch points between moving parts;
- frayed rope;
- small parts or objects;
- small puzzle pieces;
- puzzle pieces that have small pegs;
- soft toys and dolls with small attachments like eyes and buttons;
- brittle plastic toys or parts; and
- unsecure battery compartments;

As an addendum to Threats to Breathing (see page 388), the Government of Canada warns that "small objects present choking, ingestion and inhalation hazards to young children. Any toy likely to be used by a child under three years old should be large—with no small, detachable parts when used in a reasonable, foreseeable way" (2014b, p. 1).*

In addition, the Government of Canada warns of the dangers of two products:

- "Small, powerful magnets, which are considered a danger to human health or safety. Their sale is prohibited in Canada. Children can swallow these magnets and be seriously injured. These injuries can lead to emergency surgery, lifelong health problems and even death" (Government of Canada, 2015b, p. 1).*

- "Many batteries are small enough to be swallowed by children. This can cause serious internal injuries and even death. Batteries can also overheat, leak, burst, and even explode and catch fire, causing serious injuries if they are not properly:
  - installed
  - used
  - stored
  - disposed

Seek *immediate* emergency medical attention if you suspect your child has swallowed a button battery. These small batteries can get stuck in your child's esophagus and burn through it, the wind pipe and the main artery. Serious or fatal injuries can happen in a matter of hours. Report any battery-related injuries directly to the manufacturer"(Government of Canada, 2017a, p. 1).**

A choking tester tool is widely available in stores for testing small toys, toy parts, and other objects. If an item such as a die fits in the cylinder, it is a choking hazard for children three years old and younger. If an item such as a domino piece does not, it is not likely to be choking risk for this same age group. These are the dimensions of the tester. A quick Internet search will show you a variety of images of these testers.

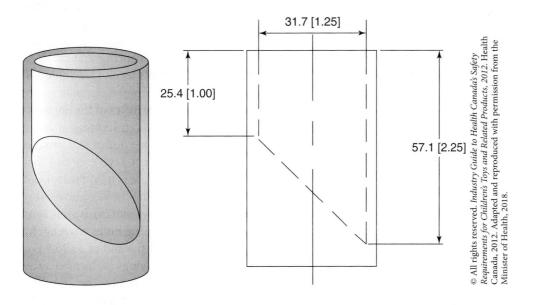

Outdoor Play Equipment

The outdoor environment in the ECLC program is filled with joy and learning, especially when it is designed to meet the needs and interests of the children and when educators give the outdoor curriculum the ongoing attention it deserves. The play-based nature of the outdoor environment provides an opportunity to enhance all areas of the child's development, such as motor skill development (see Unit 6, page 337), problem solving, language, social development, creative expression, and, of course, self-confidence. Outdoor play can enhance physical agility and fitness, reduce stress through games, provide contact with nature, fuel the imagination, and bestow freedom of movement—the list is almost endless. Many resources are available to support educators' awareness and planning of the outdoor curriculum, which is essential to a high-quality ECLC program (see Resource Materials).

NELSONstudy

To access Resource Materials, visit NelsonStudy.

Most serious injuries in ECLC programs occur on the playground. Twenty-nine thousand children or more under 15 years of age are treated for playground injuries at hospital emergency departments annually in Canada (CPS, 2014, p. 1). CSA standards are intended to promote and encourage the provision and use of play spaces that are well designed, well maintained, innovative, and challenging, and, in so doing, contribute to the development of healthy children (CSA, 2016, p. 11). If operators do so, the contribution to children's health is substantial. At present, the challenge with stringent standards is achieving optimal safety, but not to the extreme, which can eliminate the integrity of developmentally appropriate risk. Wherever possible, the standards indicate modifications to the development of play spaces and equipment to make them accessible to children with a range of special needs.

CSA suggests a broad scope of environments and equipment for play activities, dividing the age groups into preschool (18 months to 5 years old) and school age (5 to 12 years old), recognizing 5 as a transitional age for physical growth and development and acknowledging the fact that as children get older, their abilities, interests, and needs change. Educators are responsible for ensuring that children safely use equipment designed for appropriate age and ability levels (see Table 7.8, page 406; and Table 7.9, page 411).

In the vast majority of playground injuries, two characteristics of the environment have a major influence on the severity: the quality of the cushioning material and the height from which the child falls. The ground space under and around each piece of equipment, called the **encroachment area**, must have a surface that cushions a child's fall as much as possible. Encroachment areas help protect not only the children using the equipment but also those walking by. Whenever possible, the areas should be clearly marked off to create pathways that can be followed by children and staff. This should prevent anyone from getting hit by a swing, by a child jumping off the climber, or by someone coming off the end of a slide. For example, CSA (2016, p. 53) Clause 15.6.1.1 requires that swings be located away from other play structures and areas where children move freely. The standard (2014, Clause 15.6) modified previous swing requirements and includes a swing seat impact test for every new swing apparatus to ensure that newer products being developed are tested rigorously before approval.

TABLE 7.9 Suggested Facilities and Equipment for Play Activities

F.3.1 PRESCHOOL AND KINDERGARTEN CHILDREN (TODDLERS)

Suggested facilities and equipment for preschool and kindergarten children are shown in the following table:

Activity	Suggested facilities and equipment*
Physical play	• a hard-surface route, preferably a large or circular one for wheeled toys • facilities and space for large-muscle activities such as climbing equipment or swings • soft open space for running or ball games; the space for physical play should approximate 40% of the space in a playground
Social play (playing in small groups)	• playhouse and other structures to encourage imaginative play • landscaped enclosure • table and benches or chairs
Manipulative cognitive play (to create or manipulate)	• sandbox • natural areas, pots and pans, outdoor blocks, boards, outdoor drawing boards, and water play such as spray pads
Quiet retreat play (to rest, imagine, or watch)	• enclosures, landscaped or fenced • table with seating • perch or hideaway

*Facilities should be used only under supervision.

F.3.2 SCHOOL-AGED CHILDREN

Suggested facilities and equipment for school-aged children are shown in the following table:

Activity	Suggested facilities and equipment
Physical play • Games with balls or aerial objects (such as Frisbee, ball hockey, or kite flying)	• open and level expanse of grass or hard surface, uninterrupted by trees or electric wires • enclosure—fence or berm • seating at periphery
• Ground-related games using the whole body (such as tag or roller skating)	• open, level, hard-surface area or grassy area, not necessarily flat • enclosure—fence or berm • seating at periphery
• Strategy games requiring smaller spaces (such as marbles, hopscotch, or tether ball)	• protected small areas, 1 to 3 m^2 (39.37 to 118, 11 in^2) • smaller hard-surface or grass areas
• Activities that challenge dexterity and muscular control	• climbing structures, balance bars, or swings • table with seating • perch or hideaway
• Specific skills (such as skateboarding)	• See Clause F.3.4
Manipulative cognitive play	• loose materials, such as blocks, boards, ropes, sand, water sprays, natural areas (some of these activities require supervision; see Annex A of CAN/CSA-Z614-4)
Social play	• tables and seating, table games such as chess, sheltered space, natural area

(continued)

TABLE 7.9 Suggested Facilities and Equipment for Play Activities *(continued)*

F.3.3 SAND PLAY AREAS

F.3.3.1 Size

The sand area should be large enough to encompass the activities of several groups of children without interference. The total sand play area should be in proportion to the size of the overall play area. Where there are likely to be large numbers of children of varying ages, the total area for sand play may be divided into several smaller sand play areas. A 2 × 2 m (78.74 × 78.74 in) sand area can be a comfortable cognitive sand play area for a group of up to ten children. A minimum total sand play area of 6 × 7 m (236.22 × 275.59 in) is desirable in public parks and other public play areas. (This total should not include impact sand in the equipment area.) Sand play is a popular play experience for children of all ages, and the play area design should maximize the total amount of space for sand play.

F.3.3.2 Types of sand

The sand for creative play should pack together for moulding. Thoroughly washed brick sand or an equivalent such as seaside sand should be used. Blow sand should not be used.

The sand should be free of organic material, dirt, clay, silt, iron, asbestos, and other contaminants.

F.3.3.3 Depth of sand for play

The sand depth should allow for major excavations by the child without disturbing the foundations and drainage. A minimum sand depth of 200 mm (7.87 in) is recommended. The preferred depth of sand is 450 mm (17.72 in), see Figure F3 of CAN/CSA-Z614-4.

F.3.3.4 Location

The sand play area should be exposed to the purifying effects of sun and rain, but some natural shade and shelter (from wind and sun) should be provided.

F.3.3.5 Drainage

The sand play area, regardless of soil conditions, should be designed to drain well. Means of drainage should be prevented from clogging. For day or poorly draining soils, drainage tiles to an outlet are recommended.

F.3.3.6 Protection

The design, the location, and the maintenance schedule should discourage pets from soiling the sand. Sandbox covers, where used, should be designed to be safely secured both in the open and closed positions.

F.3.3.7 Design recommendations

The design recommendations for a sand play area are as follows:
(a) The sand play area should be located so that children are discouraged from using it for active play. It should not be located in the physical play zone.
(b) Where it is undesirable to have sand tracked onto other nearby surfaces, a paved strip or a strip of pea gravel can be provided. A sand grate at a building entry also reduces the problem of tracking sand.
(c) The sand container should provide flat ledges or tables for children to use. If the container edge is provided as a ledge, it should be a minimum of 85 mm (3.34 in). A curb at the periphery of the ledge to prevent sand from falling over the edge is desirable (see Figure F.3 of CAN/CSA-Z614-4).
(d) The sand play area may have access to water for moistening the sand.
(e) A seating area for adults should be located near the sand play area.

(continued)

TABLE 7.9   Suggested Facilities and Equipment for Play Activities (*continued*)

F.3.3.7 Design recommendations (*continued*)

(f) Young children show a preference to locate their play in corners and edges of sand play areas. A design that maximizes edges and corners is preferable.

(g) Where possible, natural elements (e.g., trees, boulders) should be included in the sand play area.

F.3.4 SKATEBOARD HILLS

Skateboard hills, when provided, should be designed with the awareness that they will also be used by unauthorized users such as cyclists and roller skaters. A skateboard facility should have a detailed plan to minimize collisions between users. Appropriate fencing or other barriers should be provided at the top of the slope (see Figure F.4 of CAN/CSA-Z614-4).

Source: Section F.3.1, **CAN/CSA-Z614-14—Children's playspaces and equipment**. © 2014 Canadian Standards Association.

Pressure-treated wood is infused with a mixture of copper, chromium, and arsenic salts (CCA) to protect the wood from insects, mould, sun, and water. More than a decade after pressure-treated wood began to be phased out of playground structures, it can still be found in some community playgrounds. These chemicals potentially have an impact upon the health of children. You must be aware if a playground in the vicinity of your workplace has pressure-treated wood in order to avoid its use for the children in your care.

The layout of the equipment is a key factor in the design of a safe playground, requiring an obstacle-free protective surfacing zone depending on the type of play equipment. CSA (2016, p. 14) defines a play space as "an area containing playground equipment, play structure(s), protective surfacing, etc., that is intended for the use of children between the ages of 18 months and 12 years." In addition, play spaces for children under five years of age are to be "completely surrounded by a fence at least a 1.2 m (47.24 inches) with a lockable entrance gate" (CSA, 2016, p. 15).

A child can receive a fatal head injury from falling just 30 cm (12 in.) onto protective surfacing or concrete. CSA standards specify the types of materials that can be used for each piece of equipment and how deep these materials must be. Sand, pea gravel, or wood bark chips are used. Some programs use synthetic (manufactured) materials as the cushion material in playgrounds. This material, made from recycled tires, comes in sheets of various thicknesses and allows for water drainage. The best-suited material depends on the specific piece of equipment, the age of the children using it, weather conditions, availability, and cost (e.g., sand that is constantly soaked by rain loses some of its impact-absorbing quality, so pea gravel that allows water drainage may be a better choice). Various materials are used as **protective surfaces**, which are used to cushion a fall, under and around playground equipment, with any defined fall height (see the CSA website). The material most suitable may also depend

Mat Hayward/Shutterstock.com

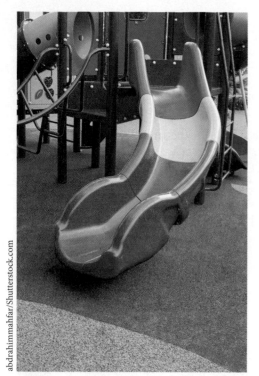

abdrahimmahfar/Shutterstock.com

on the focus of the play space. *For example, if a program has a vision to develop an outdoor space that is as natural an environment as possible, sand or wood chips are obviously more compatible with this vision.*

Cushioning materials are critical safety features. "Research shows that fall height and impact (i.e., the surface a child falls on) influence the nature and extent of injuries. One study found that falling from higher than 1.5 metres (4 ft 11 in.) quadrupled the risk of injury. Falls from higher heights cause even more serious injuries. Impact-absorbing materials, such as sand or pea gravel, provide better protection than a grassy surface, with one study finding that risk of injury is reduced by 1.7 times when playgrounds are surfaced with sand rather than grass" (CPS, 2014, p. 2).* Challenging, enjoyable playgrounds offer a wide range of experiences; they do not place the emphasis on the limited challenges that the height of the equipment offers to children.

Over time, equipment shows the effects of daily use and weathering. Walking and running pack down some protective surfaces, such as sand. Whatever material is used must be maintained to ensure that it is fulfilling its purpose. For these reasons, educators are responsible for regularly checking the surfaces and maintaining the equipment. Programs that use public or school playgrounds cannot assume that the equipment is inspected regularly. Educators should check the equipment and promptly report problems and concerns. The next time you walk by a school or public playground, stop and examine the condition of the protective surfacing under the climbing equipment. You may have legitimate cause for concern for children's safety!

Imgorthand/E+/Getty Images

Depending on the problems with equipment, educators decide whether children can use a particular piece of equipment. Ultimately, staff are responsible for the children's safety. Staff are accountable if they knowingly permit children to use defective equipment or if it is shown that an apparent defect was not identified. In addition, educators take children off-site to other playgrounds and need to be able to assess the safety of that environment. Placing children at risk in an inherently unsafe environment, regardless of the level of supervision, is not ethically acceptable and can affect liability.

Ultimately, even if equipment and surfaces fulfill all safety requirements, ongoing, focused supervision of children is essential for safe play.

---

*Source: Reprinted with permission from the Canadian Paediatric Society.

CRITICAL THINKING

One winter day, eight-year-old Joanna is playing on the climber in the school playground. The protective surface under the climber is covered with ice. Her hands slip from the rungs, and she falls to the ground. She is admitted to the hospital's emergency department with a broken arm. Her friend Michael had to run to tell an educator that Joanna was lying on the ground. What risks should have been identified? How could Joanna's injury, and other injuries, have been prevented?

Conducting Safety Checks

Educators' observations obviously play a significant role in preventing injuries throughout the day. Children, activities, issues, concerns, and other distractions will prevent any educator from identifying every potential safety risk in the environment. For this reason, regular safety checks are an essential component of injury prevention. Each day, the first educator who arrives in the morning, preferably before the children arrive, will walk through the interior of the space and playground, looking for items that must be attended to immediately. This could include replacing a burned-out light bulb in the stairwell, putting the plastic outlet covers in unused electrical outlets, or removing cat feces from the outdoor sandbox. An obvious suggestion to prevent animal feces in the outdoor sandbox is to have a cover that is placed on top of the sandbox at end of day. As well, cupboards may have been left unlocked or hazardous products left out on a counter or floor when the space was cleaned the night before.

Before children go out to the playground each morning, educators need to conduct a quick check, looking for garbage, sharp objects (e.g., broken glass, discarded needles), discarded condoms, animal feces, protruding nails, puddles of water, ice on the protective surfaces, or wood chips that have been scattered by the wind or through use. Many ECLC settings, depending on municipal regulations, must complete written checklists daily, often in both the morning and the afternoon. Ask to see and perhaps assist one of the educators in completing the checklist at your practicum placement. Like our homes, ECLC settings experience considerable wear and tear. Ideally, directors design standard checklists that are relevant to their particular building and playground. Weekly, monthly, and yearly **safety checklists** can be used to identify hazardous items, faulty equipment, and general maintenance requirements. These are available from a variety of sources, including CPS's *Well Beings* (2015) and your municipal and provincial or territorial licensing agencies.

Documenting these checks and subsequent actions is part of an overall risk management program that also reduces the risk of legal liability. There are three levels of potential hazards on the playground. Any hazard needs to be dealt with to promote a safe environment:

- A condition that could cause a major injury or fatality needs to be corrected immediately (e.g., an entanglement point on a slide).
- A condition likely to cause serious injury with temporary disability needs to be corrected as soon as possible, before the next scheduled inspection (e.g., sand needs topping up under a climber).
- A condition likely to cause minor injury or that doesn't meet CSA standards may require long-term planning or budgeting but must be attended to in a timely fashion.

Reference must be made to CSA's publication whenever a playground evaluation, a new playground, or changes or additions (i.e., retrofitting) are under consideration to make the most informed decisions and reduce the risk of legal liability in the event of an injury.

Supervision of Children

Child care regulations have established minimum educator–child ratios and maximum group sizes for the different age groups. Do you know your province or territory standards? Refer to your early childhood regulations to complete the following information:

Educator–Child Ratio	Group Size
infants:	___ : ___
toddlers:	___ : ___
preschoolers:	___ : ___
school-agers:	___ : ___

Adequate staffing is essential in the supervision of children. Children are naturally curious and often do not understand the potential dangers or consequences of their actions. Combine this fact with the excitement felt by children who are having fun or trying something new, and the potential for children to forget safety rules or use equipment unconventionally is much higher. While supervising children, educators should always assume that children can do more today than they could do yesterday. The comment "I didn't think Tony could roll over yet, so I thought it was safe to leave him on the diaper change table for a few seconds!" indicates the educator's inability to apply developmental theory to early childhood practice. This comment points out that the educator did not follow a very basic safety practice with infants and toddlers. In some ECE training programs, this student's behaviour would be grounds for expulsion. Making assumptions about children's abilities can lead to injuries. Therefore, educators must actively supervise children.

Afternoon naps usually begin after lunch, when children are naturally tired and have full tummies. This is the time when educators take their own lunch breaks. With some staff off for lunch, fewer educators are working, unless additional adults come in to cover during these times. Here is the challenge: How do the remaining educators adequately supervise all the children? Both those children who are napping and those who are playing require supervision. For preschoolers, the nap and play areas are usually in the same room, which facilitates supervision. However, for infants and toddlers, the nap room is usually separate from the play area. As well, infants and toddlers typically sleep at different times during the day and for extended periods. Educators regularly go into the nap room to check on, resettle, or bring out the children who have awakened. Baby monitors are an inexpensive but valuable piece of equipment for educators to use in addition to regular supervision. What program could support having an educator in the nap room most of the day? (As an aside, position young infants on their backs or sides to sleep. Research has indicated a link between sleeping on the tummy and sudden infant death syndrome, or SIDS. Once children can reposition themselves while sleeping, this practice is not applicable.)

During Indoor Play

Equipment, toys, supplies, furniture, storage, and physical space should be developmentally appropriate for the children using them, so that much of the educators' supervision is focused on facilitating play and guiding children's social behaviour. From the standpoint of injury prevention, the level of supervision depends on the inherent risks of the activity, the ages of the children, and the applicable rules.

- Infants and toddlers must never be left alone during water play. Older preschool children do not necessarily need an educator to be directly at the water table at all times.
- Preschoolers and school-agers involved in woodworking must be supervised directly.
- A small group of school-agers are playing a board game in the hall. Although they are out of view, you know where they are; they are still within earshot.

Courtesy of George Brown College/Scotia Plaza Child Care Centre

During Outdoor Play

Outdoor play presents educators with unique supervisory challenges because of the greater risk of injury from increased physical activity and a less structured environment. Outdoor play needs to be scheduled when all educators are working rather than when some are away at lunch or on a break. Outdoor play time is not a time when staff can be distracted by talking together. *Active supervision involves focusing your attention on the children, listening, and staying close.* The outdoors, including regulated rooftop spaces, provide children with a much less confined place in which to play. The equipment is physically challenging, and some pieces, such as the climber, have inherent dangers because they enable children to climb high off the ground. And although abductions are not typical occurrences, children must be protected from people who pose a potential threat, including parents without custody and strangers.

Ideally, the layout of the area provides and encourages smaller groups of children to gather throughout the playground (e.g., sandbox, garden plot, water table, painting easels, places in the shade, swings, slides, climber) rather than congregate in one or two areas. Educators should spread out throughout the playground and move among the play spaces for which they are primarily responsible. Equipment, especially the climber, should have one educator who is directly responsible for supervision. Another person could supervise children on the swings and slide.

Courtesy of Barb Pimento, taken at the Downtown Montessori (Coatsworth) Childcare Centre

Tubular slides present special safety concerns because the tube blocks educators' view of children sliding down. Furthermore, a child's clothing, hood, or scarf could become caught and cause strangulation. Although a national voluntary standard requests that Canadian manufacturers not make clothing with drawstrings, it is not always honoured as these items remain available. This is why programs should have a policy that bans drawstrings on hoods and that requires scarves, if worn, to be tucked into the coat. A neck warmer provides a safe alternative to a scarf. As well, educators must be vigilant in ensuring that skipping ropes, cords, ropes, and so on, have not been tied to play structures and, when found, are taken down immediately. A program policy should spell out that only ropes designed for climbing should be attached to such structures. In addition, if a child is wearing a helmet while riding a toy, ensure that it is removed before the child plays on the equipment. The helmet's straps pose a risk of strangulation.

Outdoor play is a time for preschool and school-age children to choose the activities they will take part in. Although these older children do not always need educators to take as active a role in their activities, educators should not be any less involved in supervising what the children are doing. Joining in children's activities on their level often means the adult is jumping in a leaf pile, playing tag, or being a partner in ball play. Following the child's lead doesn't mean that the adult cannot suggest new ideas to extend play, and then the children decide whether or not to accept your suggestion. Remember, being active outdoors is good role modelling as well as good for the educator's well-being! (See Supporting Physical Activity in Early Childhood Learning and Care Programs, page 334.)

For infants and toddlers, educators cannot let their guard down for a second. Infants who haven't yet learned to creep or crawl can sit on a blanket with toys and books. But once they can travel, there is no end to what they can do. Of course, it is wonderful that they have opportunities to explore their world physically and cognitively. However, this reality also means that educators must be vigilant in supervising their outdoor play. Take a close look at what young children can find in the grass and soil.

> Although a stone could cause choking, the potential risks should not exclude these children from outdoor play. Even very young children can begin to learn what they can and cannot safely put in their mouth, with educators' guidance. Of course, the educators will be carefully checking the environment first to reduce the likelihood of hazards!

Beyond the regular level of supervision, more vigilant supervision is required at certain times, such as when a new piece of equipment is added to the playground. At first, this piece of equipment will be more popular, and children will need extra supervision until the novelty wears off. Children need time to become familiar with any necessary safety rules; children age four and older can be involved in developing them. Field trips are also times when additional supervision is required. Directors generally arrange for volunteers, often parents, to provide extra adults to improve the adult–child ratio (see Walks and Field Trips, page 436).

CRITICAL THINKING

On a field trip to the zoo, a group of 24 preschoolers and 3 educators takes time out to use the small playground. While there, 2 children crash into each other and another child is hit by someone on the swing. What can you learn from this scenario? What would you do differently next time to prevent injuries?

Prevention of Missing Children

Educators must know the whereabouts of all children at all times. Preventing children from wandering away from the group on a field trip or out of the playground is far easier than trying to locate a child after he or she has gone missing—and easier than suffering the emotional consequences experienced by the child, other children, educators, and, of course, the parents.

Implement the following measures to ensure children's personal safety:

- Maintain a daily attendance record that provides educators with a head count and tells them quickly who is absent or who has already gone home with his or her parent.
- Secure all exits from the building and ensure that young children cannot open them.
- Control entry into the building with a security system, which in some regions may involve simply locking the outside doors.
- Lock the playground gate when children are outside and have one educator responsible for conducting regular head counts.

- Establish the steps to follow if a child goes missing from the program, the playground, or a field trip. Design a search plan for the building, playground, and surrounding neighbourhood. Staff may find it useful to contact an agency that deals with missing children, or the local police department, to assist them in developing a plan that meets their needs (see Planning Successful Field Trips: Preschoolers and School-Agers, page 438).

Safety Rules: A Learning Process

Most of us don't consciously think about the fact that our daily lives are governed by rules. Yet we don't plug in the electric radio near the bathtub. We follow traffic laws while driving and understand the consequences if we are stopped by the police. And we read the instructions before connecting a propane tank to the barbecue—or at least we should!

Society must have rules so that people can coexist. We cannot get a driver's licence until we are 16 years old or older. Society has determined that by that age, we are physically and cognitively ready to operate a vehicle, understand and follow traffic laws, and accept the serious responsibility of driving.

Adults guide children with rules necessary for their own safety and the safety of others and for respecting shared property. The ultimate goal is to learn to behave responsibly and to develop self-control during childhood. To promote this development, we try to provide children with an ECLC program that respects their need for autonomy and independence, their need to have some control over their world. The process of learning takes time. Children gradually gain more independence and responsibility based on their level of cognitive, physical, emotional, and social development. Children start to learn to follow rules with a simple rule for an activity, and, gradually, they work toward an understanding of rules that are more complex. This process enables older children to learn problem-solving and decision-making skills based on their own safety and their respect for others and property. At this point, they rely on the attitudes, knowledge, and skills that they have developed and less on adult guidance and supervision. Rules learned in childhood pave the way for lifelong patterns of behaviour.

An educator guides a toddler, wearing a helmet, to pedal her riding toy along the path. As a preschooler, Allison learns to put on a bike helmet, not to ride double on tricycles, and to slow down on the curves of the path. As a school-age child, she attends a bicycle safety course and rides to and from school. By the time she is a teenager and young adult, Allison is capable of making her own decisions about riding bikes and can transfer this knowledge and these skills to driving a vehicle.

Whose Need for Control?

Most of us, children included, want to enjoy the feeling of independence and a sense of control over our lives. Consequently, young children often say, "You're not the boss of me!" in response to an adult's power over them. Children react this way for one of two reasons. First, they naturally want to be in complete control, so the rules imposed by adults are considered to be an infringement on their freedom and desire for independence. Nurturing educators recognize this but also know that a secure environment for children includes consistent expectations. Second, the children may be legitimately reacting to adults who are inappropriately using their own need for power to control children. When educators are in a power struggle with children, they must always ask themselves whether a particular rule is really in the children's best interest or is simply a way to control them. Educators who have overwhelmed children with rules for absolutely everything have set themselves up for countless power struggles with children. In the long term, this practice increases the potential for making children feel incompetent and lacking in the confidence to make independent decisions.

There are always situations that require educators to act immediately, regardless of the child's response, because the child or others are in danger. Following the incident, the educator can then talk with the child about what has happened and help him or her understand the reasons behind the safety rule.

- A toddler stands up to run down the slide.
- Two children are fist-fighting.
- A school-age child jumps from the top landing of the stairwell.

Often educators observe a child breaking a safety rule but putting no one in danger. To prevent a power struggle with the child, the educator takes a moment to reflect on the intent of the rule rather than react immediately:

- Should the rule be adapted or eliminated because the child's skills and abilities have increased?
- Has the rule any foundation? If not, it should be eliminated.

Educators should meet regularly to evaluate the safety rules. This enables them to validate their assumptions about the rule by considering the children's changing skills and abilities, the activities and inherent risks, the condition and maintenance of equipment, and the children's responses to the rules. This can also be an opportunity to evaluate other rules and to revise or eliminate unnecessary ones. Whenever possible, children should be included in developing and evaluating rules for specific activities. These are opportunities for children to begin learning to look at the bigger picture of safety, developing observation skills, identifying risks and anticipating possible outcomes, understanding the rationale behind the rule, and so on. A potential danger to children can be our own attempt to protect them. If they can't understand the rationale for rules, or if the rules are unbending, we could be setting up children for injuries. They will be denied opportunities to build their decision-making skills, develop their confidence in their ability to think for themselves, and consider the reasons for their being asked or pressured to do something by others.

Guidelines for Safety Rules

Whenever you are in the process of developing safety rules, remind yourself that rules play a role in injury prevention, but they should not be the primary preventive strategy. Rules alone cannot ensure children's safety. Educators will consider the following elements in developing rules:

- the age of the children
- whether the activity is developmentally appropriate

- the potential risks in the activity or play equipment and possible outcomes
- the design of the physical environment
- the level of supervision and modelling
- previous injuries related to this activity

Obviously, if an activity is not developmentally appropriate, it should be either adapted or cancelled. A long list of rules does not ensure injury prevention. In many instances, rules are unnecessary or can be reduced in number when the proper prevention strategies have been implemented.

- Before permitting children to use the climber in a neighbourhood playground for the first time, educators check that the climber is developmentally appropriate and well maintained. They will be sure that enough staff are available to supervise the climber and the remainder of the playground before developing rules for the preschool children.
- A three-year-old can say, "Stop, look, and listen before you cross the street." However, even though the child does that when you're there, you cannot assume that he or she is able to cross the street safely alone.

No one list of safety rules fits every ECLC program's requirements. Rules depend on the philosophy of the program and the age of the children, as well as the particular group of children, types of equipment, design of the physical indoor and outdoor space, and so on. Rules are ever-changing, requiring an ongoing awareness for appropriateness and utility. It is better not to have a rule than to have one that has lost its value. Similarly, it is better to have fewer rather than more rules.

You are invited to participate in an activity, but before you begin, you are presented with this list of rules:

- Don't run.
- Don't eat during the activity.
- Stay away from the red area.
- Keep your hands to yourself.
- Keep your voice down.
- Don't climb on the furniture.
- Put everything away when you're done.

Now close your eyes and recite all the rules you have just read. Then repeat them tomorrow morning without reading the list. Unless you have a photographic memory, you probably will not remember more than one or two rules either now or tomorrow. Then how can we expect children to remember and follow a list of rules for each piece of play equipment and activity? How many of these rules are stated in positive terms?

It is often easy to come up with many rules for using equipment or other activities. When a piece of equipment or activity has more rules attached than are essential, they may reduce everyone's enjoyment, may cause children to become frustrated, and may, in fact, be either unsafe or developmentally inappropriate. Educators who continually restate the same rule many times a day probably should reevaluate either the rule or the activity. Limit the number of rules by prioritizing what is most important for the children's safety. To ensure that safety rules are appropriate and effective, think about the following criteria:

- Consider children's development. (A rule that expects toddlers to share is frustrating for everyone, yet older preschoolers can be expected to share. Instead, positively reinforcing toddlers when they do share helps promote sharing.)
- State rules in positive terms. They should focus on what children can do rather than what they can't do.
- State rules in clear and simple language, especially those for younger children.
- Make sure rules are realistic, with enough freedom to encourage creative play but enough restrictiveness to prevent unsafe behaviour.
- Enforce rules consistently using gentle reminders and positive acknowledgment when children follow them. Threats, yelling, sarcasm, or any other tactics that can scare, intimidate, or embarrass children should never be used—this is emotional abuse. Children who have difficulty following important safety rules, even after being reminded, should be removed from that particular activity with an explanation of why removal is a logical consequence.

The educator says, "Sand can get in children's eyes when you throw it. You need to find something else to do right now." However, give the child the opportunity to return to the activity later, which demonstrates your confidence in the child's ability to follow the rule.

- Rules are modelled by educators. Modelling helps children understand the importance and necessity of rules.
- Rules are developed, whenever possible, with the involvement of preschoolers and school-agers. (When a new toy is available, you can ask children what could happen if...? and what would then be important guidelines or rules for using it.)
- Rules provide teachable moments to point out sensible safety guidelines.

When a child or adult trips over a toy, it is an ideal time to mention why the rule about putting toys away before moving to the next activity is important. Yet care must be taken not to lecture or nag children constantly, or else they are likely to tune us out!

- Rules are reviewed with children before they begin an activity that they haven't done for several months (e.g., woodworking, using the riding toys outside now that the snow has melted).

RULES AND BALL PLAY

Let's use ball play to demonstrate some possible rules for children in different age groups and how the type and number of rules would evolve.

INFANTS AND TODDLERS

Ball play involves exploring, throwing, or rolling balls with little accuracy across a room, in a playground, or to an educator. Infants' and toddlers' eye–hand coordination is still developing, they are just becoming aware of cause and effect, and they are not yet ready to share. Therefore, a rule for ball play is usually unnecessary for this age group. Instead, educators should provide children with plenty of soft, light, mid-sized balls to prevent problems. Constant active supervision and guidance are required.

PRESCHOOLERS

Between the ages of two and five, children improve their accuracy in throwing balls. They may play simple games with peers, such as pitch and catch, Hot Potato, or soccer. It is a good idea to continue using softer rubber or inflated balls and light ones. Appropriate rules for this age group would be the following:

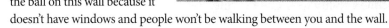

Courtesy of George Brown College/Casa Loma Child Care Centre

- Throw the ball to someone, not at someone.
- Put away the balls when you are finished so no one trips over them.
- Keep balls in the large area when playing inside.
- When outside, you can bounce the ball on this wall because it doesn't have windows and people won't be walking between you and the wall.
- When a ball goes over the fence, an adult will get it.

Obviously, only one or two of these rules would be needed at any one time!

SCHOOL-AGERS

These children develop more complex ball skills, play cooperative and competitive games and sports, and often break up into teams. They may be quite accurate and powerful in throwing balls and using bats. Except for the general guidelines about not harming self, others, or property, rules depend on the particular ball game. While they are learning a ball game such as soccer, dodge ball, street hockey, baseball, or volleyball, educators can help them develop and understand the safety rules of the game. In baseball, for example:

- Play in an area away from other children.
- Wear a helmet when at bat.
- Put the bat down after swinging. Don't throw it.

In dodge ball (if permitted in the program), for example:

- Use a light, soft rubber ball.
- Aim below the waist.

WHAT'S THE REST OF THE STORY?

OBJECTIVES

To describe safety issues related to seasonal changes. (LO 4, 6)

To discuss the principles and practices in planning and conducting field trips. (LO 6)

To list the reasons why children are more vulnerable to environmental contaminants than adults. (LO 4, 6)

To identify environmental concerns known to affect children's health. (LO 1, 3, 4, 6)

To be aware of situations in which child protection is a concern. (LO 2, 6)

The remainder of this unit is devoted to other safety-related issues that educators should consider. Some of these pertain to safety on a daily basis, such as protecting children from the seasonal elements and going for walks; others are of a more general nature, such as injury reports and responding to emergencies.

Being Outdoors Safely: Summer and Winter

Can you imagine living in a place where the weather is always the same? Maybe you can if you're reading this unit in the middle of winter with a wind chill of −34°C (−29°F)! Canada's changing seasons provide us with wonderful opportunities to participate in a variety of activities and sports, but the hot and cold weather pose certain safety considerations.

A written policy includes all routine practices regarding both summer and winter outdoor safety. The policy is communicated to families and staff at the beginning of spring and late fall, is posted in the centre, and is reinforced in newsletters or other communication vehicles to ensure that everyone is aware of the practices and their rationale. The policy includes practices around

- sun safety, smog alerts, mosquito and other insect control measures, summer excursions, and any other specific issues relevant to the specific program; and

- outdoor play, wind-chill reports, and appropriate winter clothing for the age groups in your care.

Summer

Sadly, the suntan remains popular—a symbol associated with health, active living, and attractiveness. Cases of melanoma, the deadliest form of skin cancer, are on the rise. In 2017, it is estimated that

- 7,200 Canadians will be diagnosed with melanoma.

- 1,250 Canadians will die from melanoma.

- 4,000 men will be diagnosed with melanoma and 790 will die from it.

- 3,300 women will be diagnosed with melanoma and 450 will die from it. (Canadian Cancer Society, 2018, p. 1)*

After a long winter, the allure of the sun can be overwhelming, especially when one feels the warmth on the face and skin. In the past few years, however, there has been a concerted effort to educate the public about the dangers of sun exposure. Pamphlets, magazine articles, and television commercials outline the relationship between ultraviolet radiation and skin cancer (e.g., melanoma), eye damage, and premature aging of the skin.

Children are more sensitive to UV exposure than adults because the outer layer of their skin is thinner and, on average, they spend more time outdoors than adults, especially in the summer. Infants should be shaded from the sun at all

---

*Source: Canadian Cancer Society, *Melanoma Skin Cancer Statistics*. Retrieved April 2018 from http:// www.cancer.ca/en/cancer-information/cancer-type/skin-melanoma/statistics/?region=qc Reprinted by permission of the Canadian Cancer Society.

times. Their skin protection system is not fully developed, and for most of their first year, they cannot move out of the sun on their own. And they can't tell you when they are getting too hot or thirsty. Even children born to parents with dark skin need full protection. The skin can suffer a lot of damage in childhood as the younger the child, the more skin they have, relative to the body mass of an adult. This damage is a risk for later skin cancer.

UV Index and the Humidex

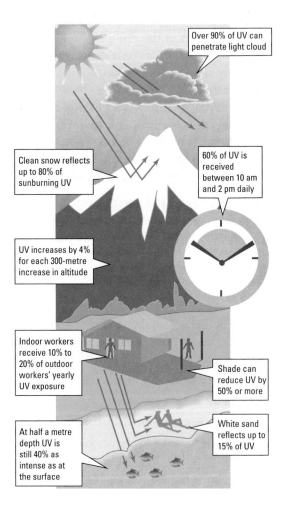

Source: Reproduced, with the permission of the publisher, from World Health Organization, "Ultraviolet Radiation and Health," *Ultraviolet Radiation and the INTERSUN Programme,* http://www.who.int/uv/uv_and_health/en/.

The more UV rays we are exposed to, the faster our skin is damaged. Cloudy days don't necessarily protect us from UV rays. Fluffy and thin clouds don't block UV rays, and UV rays that are reflected off bright surfaces (e.g., sand, concrete, water, snow) increase our exposure. In Canada, people living at higher elevations (e.g., in the mountains) get more UV rays because the air is cleaner and thinner. And UV exposure increases the closer you are to the equator, so there will be more

UV exposure in southern Ontario than in the Arctic. UV rays are strongest in the summer, but during other seasons too, educators need to be aware of UV rays (e.g., a sunny winter day in the Rockies). In the summer, the weather reports usually provide the **UV index** for the day. UV is measured on a scale of 11, with 11 indicating the shortest sunburn time, typically on a sunny summer day. Table 7.10 (Government of Canada, 2017b, pp. 1–2) puts the UV index into practical and relevant terms so that educators can prevent skin damage to children and themselves.

TABLE 7.10 What Does the UV Index Mean to Me?

UV Index	Description	Sun Protection Actions
0–2	Low	• Minimal sun protection required for normal activity. • Wear sunglasses on bright days. If outside for more than one hour, cover up and use sunscreen. • Reflection off snow can nearly double UV strength, so wear sunglasses and apply sunscreen on your face.
3–5	Moderate	• Take precaution by covering up, and wearing a hat, sunglasses, and sunscreen, especially if you will be outside for 30 minutes or more. • Look for shade near midday when the sun is strongest.
6–7	High	• Protection required—UV damages the skin and can cause sunburn. • Reduce time in the sun between 11 a.m. and 3 p.m. and take full precaution by seeking shade, covering up exposed skin, wearing a hat and sunglasses, and applying sunscreen.
8–10	Very high	• Extra precaution required—unprotected skin will be damaged and can burn quickly. • Avoid the sun between 11 a.m. and 3 p.m. and seek shade, cover up, wear a hat, sunglasses, and sunscreen.
11+	Extreme	• Values of 11 or more are very rare in Canada. However, the UV index can reach 14 or higher in the tropics and southern U.S. • Take full precaution. Unprotected skin will be damaged and can burn in minutes. Avoid the sun between 11 a.m. and 3 p.m., cover up, wear a hat, sunglasses, and sunscreen. • Don't forget that white sand and other bright surfaces reflect UV and increase UV exposure.

Source: © Her Majesty the Queen in Right of Canada, as represented by the Minister of the Environment, 2018.

Depending on where you live, you may be used to hearing weather reports on the radio or television include not only the day's temperature but also the UV index and the humidex (e.g., "It's 32°C today, but the relative humidity makes it feel like 42°C"). The more moisture there is in the air, the less sweat evaporates off skin, which is why people feel hot and sticky when it's very humid outside. Basically, the humidex value is calculated using the temperature and the relative humidity. How does the humidex tell us what it's like outside (Government of Canada, 2016b, p. 1)? See the table on page 428.

Humidex	Degree of Comfort
20–29	comfortable
30–39	some discomfort
40–45	great discomfort; avoid exertion
above 45	dangerous; heat stroke possible

Source: © Her Majesty the Queen in Right of Canada, as represented by the Minister of the Environment, 2018.

Educators use their discretion when the humidex reading is high to ensure that children playing outside do not become dehydrated or sick. Perhaps outdoor activities could be limited in duration and restricted to quieter play in the shade, or perhaps water play could be made available.

What Is SPF?

> All sunscreens have a sun protection factor (SPF) on their labels. The SPF tells you the length of time that your sunscreen-protected skin can be exposed to UVB rays before it starts to get red, compared to the length of time it takes on your unprotected skin. In other words, it tells you how much longer you can be exposed to the sun before getting a sunburn. (Government of Canada, 2017d, p. 2)*

How quickly our skin burns without protection in the summer varies among individuals. As a rule, the length of time multiplied by the **sun protection factor (SPF)** number gives you a general idea of how long you can stay in the sun using that sunscreen. For example, it takes you about 20 minutes for your unprotected skin to burn in the summer sun. Applying a sunscreen with SPF 30 provides you with approximately 600 minutes of protection, although sweat and water reduce its protection time. "Sunscreens are not meant to increase the amount of time you spend in the sun. They are meant to increase your protection when you have to be outside" (Government of Canada, 2017d, p. 2).* Choose lotions that

- are broad spectrum, acting against UVA and UVB rays;
- have an SPF of at least 30;
- are water resistant, when playing in water; and
- are recommended for children.

You generally don't need to go higher than SPF 30 as you don't gain much more protection but are exposed to more chemicals.

For children, look for products that are fragrance free. Look for ones that are approved by the Canadian Dermatology Association (CDA) and contain reflecting physical blockers such as titanium dioxide (CPCHE, 2010b, p. 1).

Apply sunscreen before you go outside and "reapply 20 minutes after going outside, and at least every 2 hours after that" (Government of Canada, 2017d, p. 1).*

---

*Source: © All rights reserved. *Sunscreens*. Health Canada, modified 2017. Adapted and reproduced with permission from the Minister of Health, 2018.

Use the amount recommended on the product's directions. When children are very active and sweating, lotion should be applied more often to give 100% UV protection. Children using wading pools or sprinklers either need to wear a waterproof sunscreen or have regular sunscreen reapplied when they get out of the water. Don't forget that sunscreen should be applied in the early spring and also late into the fall. Remember to apply lotion above where shorts and sleeves stop because they ride up the legs and arms while the children are playing and to the top of the children's feet when they are wearing sandals. As added sun protection, children can wear T-shirts over their bathing suits to protect their shoulders, back, and chest. Remember to have the children change into dry T-shirts once they are finished playing in the water as the wetness reduces the fabric's sun protection. If parents do not wish their child to use sunscreen (perhaps due to allergies), alternative arrangements for sun protection must be made. *For example, the child will need to wear a wide-brim hat; a lightweight, loose-fitting, long-sleeved shirt; full-length pants; and socks whenever outdoors.*

Programs may prefer to use communal bottles of lotion because it is much faster to do one child after another than to use 20 different bottles of lotions and try to keep them all straight. As well, all the bottles must be kept out of reach of children. In these programs, staff check with parents to ensure that they approve of the type that is used. Some children may have a skin reaction to a particular brand of sunscreen. Educators do not have to wash their hands after each application. Not only is that time consuming, but also the risk of spreading infection through sunscreen is negligible even when someone has a cut or scrape because these should be covered with either clothing or a bandage. The only time that hand washing may be warranted is when a child has an allergy to the sunscreen brand used by the program; then the educator needs to wash off the program's lotion before applying this child's own. Older preschoolers should be learning to apply their own lotion. These children need supervision to ensure that they don't get lotion in their mouth or eyes and that they adequately cover all exposed skin. By the time they are school age, most children should be responsible for this task.

Additional Sun Protection

How do educators protect themselves and children while outside during the summer? They can begin by limiting or avoiding outdoor play and walks between 11 a.m. and 3 p.m. (Peak hours may vary by an hour one way or the other.) However, if children are to get outside even twice a day, a compromise needs to be reached: shade must be available, fluids must be offered, and sunscreen, hats, sunglasses, and clothing must be used.

Everyone should wear hats, preferably with a wide (7.5 cm or 3 in.) brim that shades the face, ears, and neck. Some children don't like wearing hats but may be more likely to wear baseball caps, which are very popular. Don't forget to put sunscreen on their ears and the back of their neck. Child-sized shatterproof sunglasses with 100% UV protection are now available at low prices; parents should be encouraged to provide their child with a pair. Although many toddlers and young preschool children may not keep them on, this at least introduces them to the idea.

344512847l/Shutterstock.com

Ideally, children wear long-sleeved shirts and long pants, although this seems impractical when it is very hot or humid. Whatever clothing is worn, it should be loose fitting and cool to help reduce sweating.

Ensure that shade provided by trees, table umbrellas, awnings, or other structures is accessible to children to play in. Children should be encouraged to come into shade every half hour while outside. Wading pools should be placed in the shade. Sunscreen is not a replacement for shade.

Physical activity in hot weather puts children at risk for becoming dehydrated because the body loses water through sweating. Offer water to children before they go outside and encourage them to drink water several times while outside and again after they are back inside. Pay particular attention to children who are using the play equipment and running around as they will be losing more water through sweat. Children can be dehydrated and not complain of thirst.

© iStockphoto.com/Marilyn Nieves

Remember how germs are spread and do not use a communal drink bottle or shared cups. If you don't have access to running water outside, bring out a jug and enough cups for everyone.

Keep in mind that infants

- should get plenty of fluids even if they are just lying on a blanket in the shade. Young children can become dehydrated very quickly because they have more surface area (skin) in relation to their body mass than adults do. Signs of dehydration and treatment are discussed in the section on diarrhea (see page 185).

- should wear T-shirts over their bathing suits when they are in the wading pool.

- should not, when under the age of six months, have sunscreen applied because they may put lotion-covered hands or feet in their mouth. Also, the lotion may irritate their skin.

- should, whenever possible, be dressed in loose-fitting clothes that have long sleeves and pants (or long-sleeved cotton jumpers) and should wear hats.

Certain medications can cause skin reactions such as rashes, swelling, blisters, or redness that looks like an exaggerated sunburn. Photosensitivity reactions are relatively common. Symptoms can appear immediately once the skin is exposed to sun or several hours after exposure has ceased. Interestingly, symptoms may develop only on skin that wasn't covered by clothing or may appear anywhere on the body. Symptoms can last for several days, even after the prescription is completed. Some of the commonly prescribed medications that can cause photosensitivity are some antibiotics, antihistamine creams, oral contraceptives (the pill), and sunscreen containing PABA. Some of the medications prescribed for the management of diabetes, cystic fibrosis, and mental health disorders can cause photosensitivity reactions (see Administering Medication, page 195).

Do you ever hear adults say to children, "Just do what I say because I'm the parent" or "I don't have to do that because I'm the adult"? Take a moment to think about the behaviour that educators model if they sunbathe, compliment one another on their tans, or refuse to wear hats and sunglasses or to apply sunscreen at work. The adult who tells children that they must do things because he or she told them so is, in fact, controlling children and certainly not being a positive role model.

Insects and Repellent

To avoid attracting insects, wasps, and bees, avoid serving sweet food and beverages outside and keep garbage containers far from the play area. Exercise caution when a child has an allergy to bees or wasps, and be sure that his or her adrenaline kit is outside with the educators and the child. Remember that if the insects are prevalent and are biting, the best option may be to keep the children inside or to arrange to use a community centre or school gym to get physical exercise, even if it's only for a few days.

Repellents are used to repel mosquitoes, ticks, fleas, and biting flies. Repellents are poisonous and must be kept out of reach of children. The West Nile virus is becoming more of a concern across Canada (Government of Canada, 2016c). But we also need to put this virus into perspective as the risk of infection is low for most Canadians, especially those under 50 years old, and the risk of serious health effects from the virus is even lower (Government of Canada, 2015c, p. 1). Eliminating places for mosquitoes to breed is a first step. In ECLC programs, the staff are likely already doing that for the safety of children:

- Empty all water-holding containers (e.g., wading pools, pots, pails, birdbaths) at the end of each day.
- Ensure that all areas of standing water, such as puddles or under drainpipes, dry up at least every other day; if not, do so manually.
- Monitor the length of the grass (if applicable) in play areas and the buildup of debris, and inform the director of the need for immediate action when a situation warrants.
- Encourage families to provide light-coloured, tightly woven clothing for their children and long pants, long-sleeved shirts, and socks for their children to use during early morning and late afternoon and for walks where there is a lot of foliage.

- Ensure that the window screens fit properly.
- Mosquitoes are most active at dawn and dusk, which are times that are outside the hours of operation for most programs. Even so, at those times of day, it is very unlikely that staff and children would be outside.
- Pay attention to the provincial/territorial and regional reports during the summer.

Do not apply DEET on children under six months old. Use clothing or mosquito netting over strollers and carriages or avoid going outside if the insects are particularly bad. A drop of white vinegar or oil of citronella behind the ears, knees, and wrists may help keep insects away.

For children between 6 months and 2 years old, repellent with DEET should *not* be applied more than once a day and only at a concentration of 10% or less. For children between 2 and 12 years old, a product with 10% or less is recommended, and it shouldn't be applied more than three times in a day. For anyone older than 12, a concentration of no more than 30% DEET should be used (Government of Canada, 2016a, p. 2).

Remember the following points if you use repellents:

- Select products intended for children and ones that have Health Canada's PCP number (CPCHE, 2010b, p. 1).
- Choose lotions rather than sprays.
- Look for a product that is not combined with a sunscreen.
- Apply sparingly and only on exposed skin, not under clothes or diapers.
- To prevent children getting the repellent in their mouth, do not apply it on their face, hands, and fingers.
- Never permit young children to put repellent on themselves or others. Older preschoolers may apply it with supervision, and most school-agers should have learned how to apply it safely.
- Once children are back inside, wash off the repellent.
- Obtain the parents' written permission before using repellent.

Winter

Winter conjures up pictures of chattering teeth, knee-high snowdrifts, and icy roads. Yet winter also has beautiful blue skies, clean crisp air, and snow that sparkles like diamonds. Snow is a wonderful play medium for winter activities and sports. Children can have great fun in playgrounds, even though in most regions of Canada, it will be very cold. Getting outside in the winter provides all of us with much-needed physical activity, fresh air, and sunlight, which is the best source of vitamin D.

Dressing appropriately for the weather goes a long way toward making winter activities enjoyable and safe. Scarves and hoods can become caught on play equipment, resulting in strangulation. Families should be encouraged to provide neck warmers rather than scarves for children. If scarves are used, ensure that they are tied, with the ends tucked into the coat or parka, and that hoods are tied snugly around faces. Some clothing manufacturers are now making cordless hoods that fasten with Velcro rather than cords.

Most of our body's heat is lost through our head. Wearing appropriate winter hats, toques, hoods, and so on, is equally important for adults and children in protecting us from chill and our ears from **frostbite**. Exposed skin freezes in just a few minutes when it is cold enough outside. Noses, cheeks, ears, fingers, and toes are most prone to frostbite. Watch the children to ensure that their hats, hoods, and scarves do not slide out of place and that someone hasn't got a boot full of snow.

Watch for children who take off their mitts when using play equipment. Toddler snowsuits often come with mitts (without thumbs) that snap onto the cuffs. Toddlers quickly become frustrated with mitts and pull them off because they can't do anything with their hands. Parents should be encouraged to provide toddlers with non-slippery mittens with thumbs. Unless the mitts or gloves are leather, they get wet quickly during play. Wet mitts not only chill children's hands but also increase the likelihood of frostbite. Programs may have mitt-drying racks, or parents can be asked to send two or three pairs of mitts each day so that children have a dry pair to wear during the afternoon.

As discussed in the section on summer safety, educators have a professional responsibility to dress appropriately for the weather conditions when supervising outdoor play. If it is cold enough for children to be wearing hats, mitts, winter boots, and zipped-up coats, educators should wear the same. This is not only to model the behaviour for the children but also to protect themselves from chill and frostbite.

Children may complain that they are cold or wet. Obviously, if they are wet, they must go indoors and change into something dry before going back outdoors. However, some children will tell you that they are cold from the moment they step out the door. Often they need to be encouraged to start moving around so that they warm up. Educators can help them by moving around themselves and inviting children to join them. Yet after being outside for some time, some children will be cold and should go inside to warm up. Keep in mind that children have less muscle mass than adults and therefore don't generate as much body heat, which is a natural response to being out in the cold.

Allen Donikowski/Flickr/Getty Images

We often begin our winter mornings by listening to the day's temperature and **wind-chill factor**. "Anyone who has ever waited at a bus stop or taken a walk on a blustery winter day knows that you feel colder when the wind blows. This cooling sensation that is caused by the combined effect of temperature and wind, is what is known as wind chill" (Government of Canada, 2017f, p. 1). Canada's wind-chill index is reported using temperature-like units, but because it is not the actual air temperature, it is given without the degree sign. The index represents the degree of chill your skin senses. "For example, if the wind chill is –20 while the outside temperature is only –10°C, it means that your face will feel as cold as if it was a calm day (no wind) with a temperature of –20°C" (Government of Canada, 2017f, p. 1).

CPS suggests the following:

- Children should remain indoors when the temperature or wind-chill factor brings the temperature below –27°C (–16°F) or lower. At this temperature, exposed skin begins to freeze!
- Children should have reduced time outdoors when the temperature falls to –15°C (5°F), with or without wind chill.
- "Know and follow provincial/territorial child care regulations for your jurisdiction if they differ from these recommendations" (CPS, 2015, p. 81).*

Some child care regulations stipulate an outdoor temperature below which it is deemed too cold for children to play outdoors. Obviously, in some regions of Canada, people are accustomed to long, cold winters and have appropriate winter clothing to minimize the amount of exposed skin. In other regions, where cold weather occurs less frequently, children may have to remain indoors for several consecutive days. Table 7.11 (Government of Canada, 2017f, pp. 5–6) identifies possible health hazards and what to do to prevent them for a range of wind-chill temperatures. Centre staff may want to explore options within the community that would provide space for children to be physically active every day. You will read that scarves are included in the table's "What to Do" column, but for children, scarves present a safety issue when playing outdoors (see Activities in the Winter, page 436).

*Source: Reprinted with permission from the Canadian Paediatric Society.

TABLE 7.11   Wind-Chill Hazards and What to Do

Wind Chill	Risk of Frostbite	Health Concern	What to Do
0 to –9	**Low Risk**	• Slight increase in discomfort.	• Dress warmly. • Stay dry.
–10 to –27	**Moderate Risk**	• Uncomfortable. • Risk of hypothermia and frostbite if outside for long periods without adequate protection.	• Dress in layers of warm clothing, with an outer layer that is wind resistant. • Wear a hat, mittens or insulated gloves, a scarf and insulated, waterproof footwear. • Stay dry. • Keep active.
–28 to –39	**High Risk:** exposed skin can freeze in 10 to 30 minutes	• Risk of frostnip or frostbite: Check face and extremities for numbness or whiteness. • Risk of hypothermia if outside for long periods without adequate clothing or shelter from the wind and cold.	• Dress in layers of warm clothing, with an outer layer that is wind resistant. • Cover exposed skin. • Wear a hat, mittens or insulated gloves, a scarf, neck tube or face mask and insulated, waterproof footwear. • Stay dry. • Keep active.

(continued)

TABLE 7.11   Wind-Chill Hazards and What to Do (*continued*)

Wind Chill	Risk of Frostbite	Health Concern	What to Do
−40 to −47	**Very High Risk:** exposed skin can freeze in 5 to 10 minutes	• Very high risk of frostbite: Check face and extremities for numbness or whiteness. • Very high risk of hypothermia if outside for long periods without adequate clothing or shelter from wind and cold.	• Dress in layers of warm clothing, with an outer layer that is wind resistant. • Cover all exposed skin. • Wear a hat, mittens or insulated gloves, a scarf, neck tube or face mask and insulated, waterproof footwear. • Stay dry. • Keep active.
−48 to −54	**Severe Risk:** exposed skin can freeze in 2 to 5 minutes	• Severe risk of frostbite: Check face and extremities frequently for numbness or whiteness. • Serious risk of hypothermia if outside for long period without adequate clothing or shelter from wind and cold.	• Be careful. Dress very warmly in layers of clothing, with an outer layer that is wind resistant. • **Cover all exposed skin**. • Wear a hat, mittens or insulated gloves, a scarf, neck tube or face mask and insulated, waterproof footwear. • **Be ready to cut short or cancel outdoor activities**. • Stay dry. • Keep active.
−55 and colder	**Extreme Risk:** exposed skin can freeze in less than 2 minutes	• **DANGER!** Outdoor conditions are **hazardous**.	• **Stay indoors**.

Source: © Her Majesty the Queen in Right of Canada, as represented by the Minister of the Environment, 2018.

Catching falling snowflakes on our tongue is a lot of fun. Blankets of fresh white snow are inviting to eat. Yet children should be discouraged from eating fallen snow (on the ground, fences, benches, etc.) or licking icicles, which can be contaminated with dirt or pollution or animal or bird feces or urine. On mild days, it's hard for any of us to resist picking up snow and making snowballs. Children naturally want to throw balls, and snowballs are no exception. However, people can easily be injured by snowballs that are thrown too hard or that contain stones or ice. Perhaps you can reach a compromise on snowballs. Designate a wall (without windows) or a tree that snowballs can be thrown at, although you will still have to supervise to ensure that children do not throw balls at one another. Children can also be encouraged to build walls, animals, people, and so on, with snow.

carol.anne/Shutterstock.com

It would be hard to find an adult who grew up in Canada who didn't try to stick his or her wet tongue on cold metal, contrary to parental warnings. So you won't be surprised if some children freeze their tongue to metal objects and perhaps suffer a painful injury. Frostbite occurs when the skin and underlying tissue get frozen. Frostbite may not always be painful, but the skin or patch of skin (e.g., nose, cheeks) looks white and in advanced cases may be blistered. Your first-aid course should cover how you will respond to children in either of these situations.

Activities in the Winter

Winter sports such as skating, tobogganing, and skiing all have the potential to cause injuries. To reduce the risk of injury, educators must ask themselves five safety questions when they are planning winter sports:

1. Is this activity developmentally appropriate for the children?
2. Is the location designed for children to use (e.g., the height of the tobogganing hill), and are there potential hazards—trees, walking paths, ditches, or a road—at the bottom of the hill?
3. What are the potential dangers? How can they be reduced or eliminated?
4. What safety equipment must children wear? Is there enough equipment for each child?
5. Can we recruit enough staff or volunteers for supervision?

> Toboggans and sleds are dangerous if improperly used and can cause head, pelvic, and back injuries.

If planning such an activity, please keep the following safety considerations in mind:

- Avoid sliding near roads, driveways, trees, poles, rocks, and water.
- Make sure children wear protective helmets.
- Stay seated and don't overload toboggans or sleds.
- Remove all scarves and drawstrings.
- Climb the hill to the side, away from others sliding down.
- Be extra careful on icy hills as children will go faster than they expect.

We can get sunburned in the winter too, because snow and ice reflect the sun's rays. Sunscreen and lip balm with SPF should be used when children are outdoors for several hours. The lotion also helps protect the skin from windburn.

Walks and Field Trips

Children need to expand their world in many ways and directions, and walks and field trips provide opportunities for learning and enjoyment. Yet unfamiliar surroundings increase the opportunity for injuries, especially for children. Whether educators are taking a small group for a walk to the public park or a group of six- and seven-year-olds to the planetarium by public transit, advanced planning ensures that the outing is safe as well as developmentally and educationally relevant.

Programs have developed written policies and procedures regarding walks and field trips. Walks are often a regular part of an ECLC program, as when infants and toddlers go out in strollers or wagons every day. Educators at programs without a playground need to walk children to neighbourhood playgrounds daily. In both cases, staff obtain written parental permission for walks at the time of enrollment. Parents then know that their children are frequently being taken off the premises and can discuss any concerns that they may have with the staff.

Stroller Walks with Infants and Toddlers

Stroller walks and regular outside time are the best way to meet the needs of infants. Field trips at this age are not developmentally appropriate as they take the children away from their comfort and routines for long periods of time. Daily walks in the community around the ECLC setting, where infants are talked to, responded to, and exposed to interesting sights, smells, and sounds, are developmentally appropriate and very exciting for them. There is no need for transportation in addition to "active transport" (i.e., walking) with young children in strollers or wagons. Getting to know shopkeepers and other people in their neighbourhood will help them build trust in significant adults and community (e.g., shopkeepers waving from the windows of their store). Take different routes for interest and variety; ensure that the director or other designate knows which route will be taken. Ensure that you have covered the safety considerations that are relevant to infants and toddlers (see Safety Considerations for Walks and Field Trips, page 442).

Although infants (or toddlers) may fall asleep during the walk, avoid that as a goal: view the walk as a wonderful opportunity for them to begin to enjoy the many wonders of the outdoors (see Environmental Contaminants, page 444). Take opportunities for children to be taken out of the stroller to explore when safely possible. Toddlers, who are developing autonomy and like to practise their new skills, may enjoy a trip involving a short walk or wagon ride. On these short walking trips, one adult to every two children is a safe ratio. Of course, toddlers need opportunities to be physically active without a lot of restriction. They need outdoor time in a fenced playground to fulfill that criterion. Toddlers who are approaching preschool age may be ready for a short field trip, again ensuring that it is planned and implemented with safety and age-appropriate considerations. They may enjoy a half-day trip where they will still be able to eat and sleep in familiar surroundings.

Before putting children in strollers, for each trip, ensure that the brakes, wheels, and handles are in good working order. Check very carefully that the five-point harness system and lap belt are solidly attached to the seat or frame and that the child is securely buckled to prevent falls out of the stroller, which can cause serious injuries, including head trauma.

"Active Transportation" with Preschoolers and School-Agers

When motorized transportation is unnecessary, short excursions and field trips are less complicated in planning and implementing, although safety precautions are always essential. On any walk with preschoolers and school-agers:

- Ensure that the supervisor (or designate) and staff at the centre have written information with the field trip destination address (and phone number, if applicable).

- Establish the route to be taken each way and leave a copy of the instructions for staff at the centre. Keep in mind, programs in rural areas may need more specific information to identify their location.
- Ensure that you have covered the safety considerations that are relevant to walks and field trips with preschoolers and school-agers (see Safety Considerations for Walks and Field Trips, page 442).

This process makes it much easier to know your whereabouts, and to contact you if needed (e.g., unexpected bad weather has resulted in a delay coming back from the field trip while the children and adults find shelter; a parent needs to pick child up earlier than expected).

Planning Successful Field Trips: Preschoolers and School-Agers

The key to safe field trips is careful planning. All aspects of your field trip planning are clearly outlined in the program's field trip policy, including permission forms that families need to sign. It is important to reiterate the educators' responsibility for children's safety at all times. Remember that you need to consider all aspects of the field trip, including

- preparing the children and adults,
- transporting the group to and from the destination,
- assessing the actual activity and physical environment, and
- evaluating the trip on returning.

An itemized list is useful in planning, but educators also have to brainstorm to anticipate other issues that may come up and determine how they can prevent confusion or injuries. Organizing the routine walk to the local playground is quite different from bussing a group to a conservation area. Posting a checklist for walks saves time and ensures that educators take everything they need. But even a routine walk may present a surprise that requires educators to make a decision and ensure the group's safety. You have probably planned an event down to the last detail, and then something unexpected happens. That invariably happens on field trips too. Educators need to think on their feet and apply their safety knowledge and skills to make responsible decisions.

- Finding that half a block of sidewalk has been ripped up, educators and toddlers have to walk along the road past the construction to get to the playground. This is not ideal, but the staff carry it out as safely as possible. Responsible educators will talk about what happened with the children on returning to the program and next time choose a new route, if possible, until the construction is completed.
- Two of the parents who had volunteered to accompany your group to the children's theatre presentation announce at the last minute that they are unable to attend. What do you do: cancel the trip, phone around for other volunteers, or…?

Educators have some basic but important questions to ask themselves when they plan field trips:

- Is the trip developmentally appropriate for the age group? Taking young preschoolers to a traditional museum where there are no interactive opportunities will not hold their interest, but a fire station where they experience a fire truck up close is likely more in tune with their interests.
- Is the trip educationally appropriate? Taking a preschool group to the mall because the adults want to shop is irresponsible. Trips that do not relate to the interests and learning needs of the children are also more likely to be unsafe because bored children of any age tend to look for other stimulation, such as pushing one another or wandering away from the group.
- Do the educators believe that the children are able to understand and follow the trip's guidelines?

Taking a newly formed group of preschoolers on a field trip that requires several rules may be asking for problems. Instead, start with short walks and excursions, helping children develop an awareness of safety rules, and progress from there.

- With regard to pedestrian safety, it is important to remember that children are at higher risk than adults for several reasons. Their small size and more restricted peripheral vision mean that they may not notice approaching cars. Until older school age, they don't have the ability to determine a car's speed and distance, may be impulsive, and are curious (CPS, 2015, p. 125).

When you're out walking, remind children of these simple **road rules** and model them yourself at all times:

- Look left-right-left for traffic at every intersection. Preschoolers can be taught to look ALL WAYS.
- Cross only when the street is clear of traffic and the signal says it's time to go.
- Keep looking for cars as you're crossing the street.
- Do not walk between parked cars.

Constant supervision in and around motor vehicles and roadways and meticulous use of appropriate child restraints are the best protections you can provide while transporting children in your care. Being a good model yourself and sharing information with parents will also help to instill a lifetime's worth of safe behaviours. (CPS, 2015, p. 125)*

*Source: Reprinted with permission from the Canadian Paediatric Society.

- Is there a consistent way to quickly identify the members of their group while out in a public place where there may be other groups of children (e.g., T-shirts, smocks, or ball caps all in the same colour, or a visible tag with the program logo and phone number)? School-age children don't want to be embarrassed; involve them in the decision of identifiable clothing. Why is it important not to have the child's name on a tag on his or her clothing?

- Ensure that one educator does regular head counts before leaving the program, several times during the trip, before leaving again, and on arrival back at the program. Educators are encouraged to have a recent colour photograph of each child as well as his or her age, height, weight, and eye colour. If a child is missing, a photo and description will be useful (see Prevention of Missing Children, page 419).

- Are there enough adults to ensure safety? Make sure to have more than the legislated minimum number of adults—that is, improve on the adult–child ratio, especially on trips with younger children or children with specific needs. Some programs find it difficult, if not impossible, to recruit volunteers or family members to join them on trips. Staff may take smaller groups of children at a time, over a few days (on visits to the fire station on Tuesday, Wednesday, and Thursday, for example). These programs may have included this model in their field trip policy.

- Is there quick access to a phone? Bringing a cellphone is the best solution; if this is not possible, ensure that a phone is nearby in case it is needed.

In addition to the safety considerations (see pages 442–443) for walks with preschoolers and school-agers, further considerations for field trips include the following (not an exhaustive list):

Preparation Before the Field Trip

- Obtain reliable information about the destination, including washroom and drinking water availability; accessibility for all children and adults, including wheelchairs and strollers; and shade if outdoors. If possible, have a staff member visit the destination to ensure correct information. Find out about costs, hours of operation, etc.

- Inform staff at the destination of your estimated time of arrival and find out where and how they will greet your group upon arrival.

- Notify parents *at least* 24 hours in advance, with trip details including when you are leaving and returning to the ECLC setting.

- Although parents may have signed an all-inclusive permission form for walks and field trips at admission, many programs have an additional form signed for specific off-site field trips.

- Establish your route and leave a copy of directions with the director and parents.

- Prepare children for the trip, including what to expect and rules for safety and appropriate conduct (also review on the day of the trip). Remember the "rule about rules": if there are too many of them, you need to reevaluate whether this trip is appropriate.

- Ensure that at least one educator going on the trip has first-aid training. Know the location of the nearest hospital and how to get there.
- Prepare for food safety if applicable (e.g., ice packs for transporting).

Preparation for the Day of the Field Trip

- Follow the list of safety considerations (see page 442) for taking preschool and school-age children for walks.
- Each adult is given a list of children for whom she or he is responsible during the trip and additional instructions as appropriate.
- Ensure that all necessary items are packed.
- When reviewing safety rules with children, include what to do if they get lost or separated from their group:
  - Choose a central, recognizable meeting spot, which is pointed out to the group upon your arrival at the destination.
  - Have a consistent message for the children about what to do if they get lost.

After the Trip

It is always important to evaluate a field trip, as soon as possible, upon your return. When possible, get children's feedback. Some questions for the evaluation include the following:

- Did any issues arise with reference to the transportation/route back and forth?
- Did any issues arise with staffing and volunteers with regard to supervision, group size, or best practices?
- Were there any health or safety issues with the location and facilities?
- Although you planned the trip with age-appropriateness in mind, was it suitable for the children's interests and developmental levels?
- Learning and enjoyment: how did the trip rate?
- Would you consider attending this site again? Why or why not?
- If you would go back, are there any suggestions for groups attending this site in the future?

A planned field trip that involves motorized transportation, such as cars, school buses, or public transportation (e.g., buses, subway), has additional risk and safety considerations with young children. CPS's *Well Beings* (2015) has a complete chapter dedicated to transportation safety, providing very specific guidelines for transporting children in ECLC programs. The information is prefaced with this proviso:

> Every child care facility should have a transportation policy that specifies when child care practitioners may transport children, the rules to follow when transporting them, the responsibilities of staff members who are driving or accompanying children, and emergency procedures. Share this policy with parents at the time of enrolment and with all staff. (CPS, 2015, p. 111)*

---

*Source: Reprinted with permission from the Canadian Paediatric Society.

Decision making about trips and outings will depend on many factors and, by focusing on the children's interests, there may be valuable learning opportunities close to the centre without the expense and effort of elaborate field trips. The realities of safety and liability issues and stretched budgets may also mean that ECLC settings view program enhancement as an alternative to field trips. *For example, bringing in one or two visitors to the centre to provide a unique experience rather than the cost and transporting issues to take all children off-site may be the most effective way to achieve the goals and objectives for the group.* Field trips can offer wonderful opportunities for children's learning and enjoyment. Comparing the advantages and challenges of field trips and program enhancements may come down to a case-by-case basis.

Safety Considerations for Walks and Field Trips

Safety considerations for walks and field trips will depend on many factors, such as the location of the ECLC setting (urban, rural) and the age and needs of children. Specific details will be outlined in the program's policies. This list is not exhaustive and is based on infants and toddlers going for walks in strollers and the preschoolers and school-agers going for walks and on field trips.

Age Groups	Safety Considerations
Infants Toddlers Preschoolers School-agers	• A first-aid kit and emergency information for all children and staff in the group is taken on each outing, including medication that may be needed for specific children with chronic conditions (e.g., EpiPen (epinephrine) Auto-Injector, asthma inhaler).
	• A charged cellphone is taken by staff.
	• Maintain child–staff ratios at all times.
	• Do "head counts" regularly during the outing and match with names. This is applicable to toddlers if they get out of the strollers in a green space.
	• Children are dressed appropriately for the weather (e.g., hats and sunscreen in summer).
	• Obey traffic signs and signals at all times.
Preschoolers School-agers	• Children wear identification (of the program, not the child's name) on all outings.
	• Assign one adult to the front of the group and one to the back. Other adults should be close to children who require assistance.
	• Use the buddy system for children four years old and up. Buddy checks should be done throughout the trip in addition to regular attendance checks.

(continued)

Age Groups	Safety Considerations

- Consider packing a snack for longer walks.
- Accompany children to public washrooms when away from the ECLC setting.
- Take along a knapsack for additional items such as a snack or water for longer walks and a camera to take pictures on the trip.

Walking While Holding on to a Rope?

Many programs use a walking rope for children to hold when walking as a group outside the program's property. Staff believe that by holding on to a knot or handle attached to a rope, the young children are safer. Educators assume that they are able to keep track of the children because they are in an orderly line and that children will not dash off. The use of ropes is a debatable issue among educators. The authors do not, however, support the use of ropes, for a number of reasons:

- The use of ropes implies that the educators don't believe that the children are competent enough to follow the rules for walks. Toddlers who aren't ready to follow the rules should be in strollers or wagons that they can get out of to walk around in a park or playground.
- When one child trips, all the children holding on may also fall, which is potentially more hazardous than not having a rope.
- Educators who rely on the rope as a security measure may not notice when one child lets go.

Ulrich Baumgarten/Getty Images

- Holding on to a rope is not a natural way to walk and thus doesn't provide young children with a realistic experience. It also may encourage them to depend on educators rather than to develop a natural awareness of their surroundings and safety.

- Some people in the community already view early childhood as an institutional setting. Seeing children walking along the street holding on to a rope may reinforce that negative view of early childhood.

Environmental Contaminants

We have discussed concerns about UV rays, humidity, and wind chill, but there are many other environmental factors that environmentalists and researchers are bringing to our attention. Since the 1940s, hundreds of thousands of new chemicals have been introduced into our world in the name of progress and a better standard of living.

The impact of this chemical onslaught on the environment, wildlife, and humans is alarming and still unfolding. Many toxic substances are classified as neurotoxins, hormone disruptors, carcinogens, and respiratory irritants. Some chemicals fit into more than one of these categories. Cell and reproductive changes are becoming more evident as affected generations develop and reproduce. Largely unknown, however, is the impact of synergy: the effect of chemical combinations to which we are exposed. We are not typically exposed to only one toxin at a time! There is still much we need to learn about multiple interactions.

We all breathe the same air and drink the same water, so these chemicals know no boundaries, and that makes pinpointing their effects even more complex. The effects of climate change (global warming), much of which is the result of dependence on carbon fuels, are resulting in a scramble for solutions. Canadians are all aware of the obvious: we wouldn't be here without the three basic elements: air, water, and land. Shouldn't our right to a healthy environment be a core value, as much as our human rights, which we take for granted? *For example, many Canadians assume that safe drinking water is available in all regions of Canada.*

IMPACT OF THE WATER CRISIS

For several consecutive years there have been more than 100 First Nations communities across Canada living under drinking water advisories, which have lasted for at least one year or much longer. If you have always had access to safe drinking water, it is hard to imagine what many people in First Nations communities have to deal with on a daily basis. Neskantaga First Nation, Ontario, and Shoal Lake 40 First Nation, across the Manitoba and Ontario border, have been living with a boil water advisory for about 20 years each. Imagine how hopeless it feels for an entire generation who do not have safe tap water, and how concerned they are for the next generation—their children.

"Contaminants in drinking water on First Nation reserves visited by Human Rights Watch included coliform, *Escherichia coli* (*E. coli*), cancer-causing Trihalomethanes,

(continued)

and uranium" (Klasing, 2016, p. 3). The ongoing water advisories result in frustration, leading to many individuals and families drinking non-boiled tainted water, risking exposure to contaminants. In addition, using the non-boiled water to bathe, wash dishes, or wash clothes can result in disease such a range of skin problems, severe gastrointestinal disorders, and a heightened risk of cancer (Klasing, 2016, p. 4).

In 2017, the Government of Canada created the new Indigenous Services Canada (ISC) department, which is working collaboratively with First Nations partners to empower and enable Indigenous peoples to independently provide services and address the socioeconomic conditions in their communities. Upgrades, repairs, and improvements to the water treatment plants with financial support from ISC are expected to end long-term drinking water advisories by March 2021 (Government of Canada, 2017c).

The water crisis has a destructive impact on many lives, social conditions, cultural rights, and international rights for access to safe water. It is with great hope that it will all come to an end on or before March 2021.

Awareness and action by government, groups, and individuals are the keys to moving away from a destructive path. As environmental science continues to evolve, new information seems to surface daily, making it challenging but important for educators to keep updated on legislative and regulatory changes in environmental safety issues that affect children. The Canadian Environmental Protection Act (CEPA) regulates toxic substances with strict timelines in order to protect the environment and human health (Government of Canada, 2017e, p. 1). We still know far less than we should about the impact of these environmental factors on children and youth, making biological indicators of environmental substances important to research. A longitudinal cohort study in Canada to research the effects of chemicals, such as lead and mercury, on the well-being of children is needed. Over the last few years there has been an upsurge of allergies, and asthma rates. "The environment is believed to be a substantive factor which, following further research, should lead to appropriate clinical and environmental changes that will positively impact the health of Canadian children and youth" (Leitch, 2007, p. 90).

An emerging piece of the puzzle in research on the effects of environmental toxins is the relatively new science of "epigenetics," which is defined and discussed in Unit 6 (see Concerns about Childhood Obesity, page 322). Epigenetic scientists believe that the environmental conditions of parents, grandparents, and even great-grandparents can, in a way, flip "on/off switches" on the genes. The traditional view of genetics cannot fully explain the very rapid changes in human gene activity that are evident with exposure to environmental toxins. Genetics requires changes to DNA, which takes many generations. It is now evident that genes can be turned on and off without changing their DNA sequence. The study of environmental exposures and subsequent epigenetic changes, including both natural (e.g., climate change) and human-made (e.g., toxic chemical) conditions, is growing (Marsit, 2015, p.76).

The discussion below focuses on why children are more vulnerable to environmental contaminants, environmental concerns known to affect children's health, and possible actions using

- the health promotion action plan (see Revisiting the Health Promotion Action Plan, page 464) and
- *Advancing Environmental Health in Child Care Settings: A Checklist for Child Care Practitioners and Public Health Inspectors* (CPCHE, 2010a).

NELSONstudy
To access Resource
Materials, visit NelsonStudy.

For further information and to stay current on environmental safety issues, consult the comprehensive list of resources (see Resource Materials). At the forefront, CPCHE is an affiliation of groups with overlapping missions to improve children's environmental health in Canada. Working across traditional boundaries, their website includes downloadable resources with a comprehensive guide entitled *Playing It Safe*. (See Resource Materials.)

Children's Exposure and Vulnerability to Environmental Toxins

Although a wide range of opinion exists among professionals regarding the impact of environmental factors on health and safety, there is no doubt that fetuses and young children are more exposed and vulnerable than adults to environmental contaminants, both immediately (acute reactions) and in the long term (chronic effects). Children's environmental exposures and vulnerabilities are unique. Even before conception, parental exposure can affect a child's lifelong health. For example, sperm, which is produced continuously in adult males, may be damaged by occupational or environmental exposure.

IMPACT OF TOXIC POLLUTANTS ON SURROUNDING COMMUNITIES

A striking study in a First Nations community near Sarnia, Ontario (Mackenzie et al., 2005), highlights how the proximity of this community to a group of large petrochemical, polymer, and chemical industrial plants has potentially changed the ratio of male-to-female births quite dramatically. The proportion of male live births of the Aamjiwnaang First Nation had been declining continuously from the early 1990s to 2003 (the research period), with the most pronounced decrease observed during the most recent five years studied.

More recently, in Aamjiwnaang it has become brutally evident that the toxic pollutants have continued to be at levels far above Ontario government standards.

Benzene is one of the chemicals of most concern being emitted from spills and leaks from petroleum refineries in the area. Three petrochemical facilities in the Sarnia area had benzene levels 3 to 10 times that of the current standard in 2016, as indicated in a Ministry of the Environment report that year (Cribb, 2017).

(continued)

The World Health Organization (WHO) has identified exposure to benzene as a major public health concern. "Human exposure to benzene has been associated with a range of acute and long-term adverse health effects and diseases, including cancer and aplastic anaemia.… Benzene is highly volatile, and exposure occurs mostly through inhalation" (World Health Organization, 2010, p. 1).

What does this mean for the health of residents in Aamjiwnaang and in the surrounding Sarnia area? A substantial phone and online survey of over 500 residents in 2010–2011 indicated that approximately 80% of the respondents believed that the pollution was causing health issues for them and their children. Cancer and respiratory problems were of greatest concern. Essentially, there is no such thing as a safe level of benzene (Cribb, 2017).

A lot of finger pointing among the petrochemical industries in the area and municipal (Sarnia-Lambton) and provincial (Ministry of the Environment) governments has been ineffective in improving the situation. The actions necessary to control and monitor benzene and other dangerous pollutants should have been resolved and corrected long ago. Residents of Aamjiwnaang and the nearby area have continued to be poisoned due to lack of focus on this huge problem. The short- and long-term health of children and adults in this Indigenous nation is in jeopardy!

The term "**windows of vulnerability**" refers to periods of fetal development or other sensitive stages of childhood when "safe" doses for adults are not necessarily safe for children. *For example, there may be lifelong effects on lung function from early exposures to air pollution, permanent brain damage to preschool children exposed to lead, or reproductive abnormalities of children in utero whose parents worked with organochlorine pesticides.*

Several reasons contribute to the increased exposure and vulnerability of children when it comes to environmental toxins (CPCHE, 2005, pp. 20–24):

- Proportionality

  The surface area in a child's lungs is larger in proportion to the rest of the child's body, and, proportionally, a child breathes in more air than an adult. In addition, a child's brain is proportionally larger and therefore receives more blood flow per unit weight compared with an adult. Children eat more food and drink more liquids in proportion to their body weight than do adults. Therefore, their potential exposure to toxins such as lead, pesticides, and nitrates is greater.

- Behaviour

  Young children explore their environment by spending more time close to the ground (e.g., crawling) and often put their hands or toys in their mouth and swallow nonedible items. These actions expose them to toxins in dust, soil, and carpets, as well as to pesticide vapours floating close to the ground. This also can increase the different pathways or routes of exposure: inhaling, skin contact, and ingesting.

- Physiology

  Physiology refers to how living organisms function. The physiological differences between children and adults place children at higher risk. Children's tissues and body systems (e.g., nervous, respiratory, reproductive, digestive, and immune) are not fully developed and are thus more susceptible to damage. Their growth is regulated by hormones, and many environmental toxins are possible "hormone disruptors." Young children's rate of breathing is normally faster, slowing down as they get older. Therefore, young children inhale toxins more quickly than older children and adults, and the rate of intake speeds up as they are more active, especially outdoors. Children absorb nutrients in the gastrointestinal tract more quickly than do adults, increasing their susceptibility. *For example, children have a greater need for calcium; they absorb more of this mineral when it is present in the gastrointestinal tract, but the body will absorb lead instead of calcium if it is present.* Another physiological difference is that the blood–brain barrier is more permeable in a child, resulting in easier access by toxic contaminants to the brain of a child than to an adult's.

  In infancy, skin is more permeable than in later life, allowing the passage of substances through the skin into the bloodstream. Additionally, a child's airways and lungs develop from the early years through adolescence, during which time exposure to toxic substances can overburden the respiratory system. These exposures can cause temporary symptoms, or can actually affect the physical development of lung tissue, such that the lungs are more susceptible to pollutants later in life. (CPCHE, 2005, p. 24)*

- Metabolism

  Metabolism is the combined package of all the life-sustaining chemical processes occurring in any living organism. Children tend to have a faster metabolism than do adults. They need to take in more oxygen per unit of body weight per minute to support their growth and activity needs, which are driven by their higher metabolic rates. (CPCHE, 2005, p. 24)*

- Life expectancy or latency

  Another aspect of risk for children is what is called a "latent effect." Being exposed at a younger age gives more time for health-related problems to develop. Substances that build up in the body, perhaps in fat cells or bones, may not result in health effects until the child has reached adulthood. This is particularly a concern with exposure to carcinogens, such as radiation.

There are additional risk factors for some children, particularly those living in poverty, with inadequate nutrition, or living in a home with smokers (CPCHE, 2005, pp. 28–29).

---

*Source: Reprinted with permission from the Canadian Partnership for Children's Health and Environment.

Children who live in poverty are disproportionately at risk for exposure to environmental toxins: they are more likely to live in industrial areas and closer to smokestacks, garbage dumps, and highways with exhaust fumes. Their home environments are more likely to be improperly designed and poorly maintained buildings, with poor indoor air quality, old paint (which may result in lead exposure), old plumbing, and parking lots backed onto apartment buildings. Indoor dampness causing mould growth, dust mites, and cockroach and rodent problems can all be factors in respiratory difficulties. Environmental exposure doesn't recognize the social determinants of health as major risk factors, although they are likely primary factors in risk. Poverty is not a "lifestyle choice"! Poor nutrition can be experienced by any children, but, again, children who live in poverty likely have less access to the range of foods needed to reduce intake of environmental contaminants. *For example, a "poor diet can compromise a child's immune system and the ability to detoxify and excrete pesticides. Some pesticides may have larger effects on the immune systems of children who lack iron"* (CPCHE, 2005, p. 28).*

Environmental tobacco smoke (ETS), formerly referred to as second-hand smoke, is associated with respiratory system problems, especially the development and irritation of asthma. It is also common knowledge that ETS contains over 40 known carcinogens. When other risk factors are present, the risks of ETS are multiplied.

Environmental Concerns and Children's Well-Being

The following section covers four environmental issues of concern to children's health and safety: air pollution, lead, pesticides, and chemicals in plastics. These are certainly not the only contaminants of concern. Further information, and keeping current in the area of environmental safety, is an important responsibility of educators and parents.

Air Pollution

Climate changes are contributing to increased air pollution. How? Greenhouse gases in our atmosphere hold in the heat. These trapped gases are increasing with the use of fossil fuels (i.e., oil, coal, natural gas) to create power and heat. This blanket-type effect is gradually increasing the average temperatures in Canada, which can have serious consequences to our health. As billions of tons of greenhouse gases, including toxic pollutants such as ground-level ozone, sulphur dioxides, and nitrogen oxides, are added to the atmosphere every year, smog is produced.

---

*Reprinted with permission from the Canadian Partnership for Children's Health and Environment.

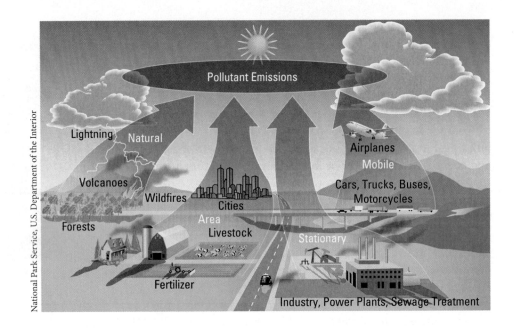

National Park Service, U.S. Department of the Interior

SEVEN THINGS TO KNOW ABOUT CLIMATE CHANGE

Andrea Danti/Shutterstock.com

1. **The world is getting warmer.**

   Earth's temperature goes up from year to year—but over the past century it has gone up a lot.

   (*continued*)

2. **It's because of us.**

   Carbon dioxide warms the planet, and we've increased the amount in the air by nearly half, mostly since the 1960s.

3. **We're sure.**

   More than nine out of 10 climate scientists agree: Our carbon emissions are the main cause of global warming.... A 2013 review of 4014 research papers found that 97 percent (and 98 percent of the authors) said humans cause global warming.

4. **Ice is melting fast.**

   Arctic sea ice is shrinking, and glaciers are retreating worldwide. Seas could rise three feet by the year 2100—or maybe more.

5. **Weather is wreaking havoc.**

   Worldwide, the number of climate related disasters has more than tripled since 1980.

6. **Species are being disrupted.**

   Animals and plants are already vanishing from parts of their range that are now too hot. Extinctions come next.

7. **We can do something about it.**

   Switch from fossil fuels (oil, natural gas, coal), which are considered non-renewable energy sources.

"Renewables, the fastest-growing energy source, are projected to triple by 2040." They include solar, wind, hydro (water) power, geothermal energy, and biomass (wood) energy. "If climate change weren't a serious danger, would 195 countries have signed the Paris Agreement, pledging to try to keep the warming below 2°C (3.6°F)?"

Source: Reprinted by permission of National Geographic Creative.

In 2008, the Canadian Medical Association (CMA) (n.d., p. 2) conducted a national analysis of air pollution impacts on human health to estimate the scale of damages that it could potentially have over the next 20 years in Canada. Their conclusion was that the health and economic damages of air pollution on Canadians' health is significant and will become more so over time. Based on their study, CMA's policies "encourage governments, health professionals and urban planners to work together to ensure that health impact assessments are incorporated into all planning and development initiatives in the public sector" (Canadian Medical Association [CMA], n.d., p. 2).

For the reasons listed earlier, children are severely affected by air pollution. Air pollution, both indoors and out, can affect respiratory health and influence children's behaviour (e.g., irritability may result from mild reactions to air contaminants). Although there is controversy about the overdiagnosis and the causes of asthma, there is substantial evidence that asthmatic and non-asthmatic children have significant adverse health responses to many air contaminants (see Asthma, page 205). The leading concerns in outdoor air pollutants have been ozone, suspended particles, and sulphur compounds.

There are a number of ways to improve indoor air quality and reduce children's exposure to environmental contaminants. One obvious way, which has been successful in public places in Canada, is to ban smoking indoors. Parents and educators who have not yet been able to quit smoking need to recognize the importance of smoke-free environments for children. Some jurisdictions have taken the concern about the effects of ETS on children one step further by banning smoking in cars when children under 19 are present. Nova Scotia became the first province in Canada to do so in 2007, followed by most of the provinces, excluding Québec. Other suggestions for improving indoor air quality concern children's exposure to dust and other potentially harmful substances. Ensure that the facilities' surfaces, furniture, counters, and shelves are easy to clean and that they are cleaned on a regular basis. Use unscented cleaning and laundry products and encourage staff not to wear perfumes or colognes, which some people are allergic to. Limit the amount of carpet used within a program. Avoid its use in high-traffic areas where people are wearing shoes or boots and where food or play materials such as paint and play dough are used. Purchase carpeting that is hypoallergenic and cleans well. Ensure that it is vacuumed daily and steam-cleaned regularly. In programs without infants and toddlers, consider eliminating carpeting altogether. Even in those programs with infants and toddlers, other things could be used on the floor instead of carpets (e.g., mats). Window coverings, especially horizontal blinds, tend to trap dust. When selecting window coverings, consider roller blinds. Select fabrics and designs that can be removed and washed easily.

To help protect children outdoors, enforce a no-idling zone during pickup and drop-off times and prohibit smoking close to the building.

Radon

Indoor air pollutants include substances such as tobacco smoke, carbon monoxide, radon, formaldehyde, mercury, and asbestos. Ironically, the use of these substances was intended to improve quality of life. The presence of some of these substances has resulted in better insulation, decreased ventilation (which has contributed to problems with airtight buildings), increased indoor humidity and higher temperatures, and more furniture and conveniences.

Radon, one of the indoor air pollutants listed above, is a radioactive gas that comes from rock and soil (CPCHE & Canadian Child Care Federation [CCCF], 2017, p. 1). There are urgent concerns about radon, as the gas is invisible, tasteless, and odourless, easily seeping into homes and other buildings. Long-term exposure to high levels of radon is the second leading cause of lung cancer for non-smokers (CPCHE, n.d., p. 1).

Although radon is one of several carcinogens with which we come in contact, it is relatively easy and inexpensive to test and to remedy, ensuring that radon levels are not above Canadian guidelines. How can we prevent our youngest children from coming in contact with dangerous levels of radon? The obvious answer is a clear strategy with the licensed child care sector in Canada to work toward mandatory radon testing. Voluntary approaches, although a start, tend to prove to be inadequate; a range of challenges such as less commitment from busy educators and low response from families do not reach the goal to effect consistent improvement. Specific requirements for radon testing in ECLC facilities in Canada are few, although in the United States it is growing. For example, the states of Illinois, Iowa, New Jersey, and Rhode Island have mandatory radon requirements in ECLC settings (Phipps et al., 2017).

> Indeed, it is our position that a mandatory approach is imperative to ensure child care facilities and other early learning environments are not a source of preventable lung cancer risk for both children and staff. Options to achieve a mandatory approach could include regulations, licensing requirements and (or) ministry-organized and funded radon testing and remediation programs.... It is time, Canada, for comprehensive and mandatory radon safety in child care programs. (Phipps et al., 2017, p. 80)*

CPCHE partnered with CCCF to initiate a health promotion action strategy, following all three levels of health promotion (individual, community, and societal) to reduce, and ideally extinguish, radon seepage into ECLC buildings. Young children in these programs spend a substantial amount of time indoors. Many programs are located on the main floor or in a basement, which are known to have higher radon levels, increasing the exposure to radon (Government of Canada, 2014a). Therefore, radon testing and making any necessary improvements in the building to reduce radon seepage could decrease exposure considerably during childhood, which can have lifelong effects. (For more information on radon testing, see the Take Action on Radon website.) (See Resource Materials.)

CPCHE and CCCF (2017, pp. 1–2) have developed a radon health promotion action plan for early childhood professionals:

NELSONstudy

To access Resource Materials, visit NelsonStudy.

- Individual problem solving and self-reliance

  Test your ECLC facility to protect the children in your care and yourself.

- Community action

  Encourage families to test their homes for radon seepage and share the radon testing results with others.

- Societal change

  Advocate for mandatory testing, helping to protect all children. Policies for radon testing are starting to emerge in Canada.

For a full explanation of what you can do as an educator to reduce and ideally extinguish radon seepage into all settings, including ECLC buildings, visit the Take Action on Radon website. (See Resource Materials.)

There are promising signs that radon as an environmental hazard is gaining awareness as an important issue in Canada. Saskatchewan, Yukon, New Brunswick, and Nova Scotia had all their schools tested once or more in the past 10 years (CAREX Canada, 2017, p. 1).

NELSONstudy

To access Resource Materials, visit NelsonStudy.

---

*Source: "Call for Action on Radon in Child Care Settings," *Environmental Health Review,* 2017, 60(3): p. 80. Retrieved January 2018 from http://pubs.ciphi.ca/doi/pdf/10.5864/d2017-020

Most recently, in British Columbia, the May 2017 Interior Health newsletter to all licensed child care facilities announced that Interior Health is requiring radon testing by all licensees and license applicants. This progressive move, although only applicable to a portion of the province, is relying on authority in existing legislation that requires licensees, via general language, to protect children from harm. These examples demonstrate that action on radon can be achieved. (Phipps et al., 2017, p. 80)*

Lead and Cadmium

Lead exposure has been associated with serious illness and even death. "Recent scientific studies show that negative health effects are occurring at lower levels of exposure to lead than previously thought. Low-level exposure may have subtle effects on the intellectual development and behaviour of infants and children. They are particularly vulnerable to the harmful effects of lead because their growing bodies absorb lead more easily and get rid of it less efficiently than adults" (Health Canada, 2013, p. 1). It is impossible to avoid lead exposure completely, but safety awareness and precautions limit exposure, which is important because no level of lead is considered safe. A great public health success in the 1970s was the elimination of lead from gasolines. Lead-based paint, found in and on the exterior of older buildings (lead was used as a pigment in paints until shortly after World War II), remains a hazard for many children. Information about how to determine if this is a problem and how to safely remove lead-based paint is readily available.

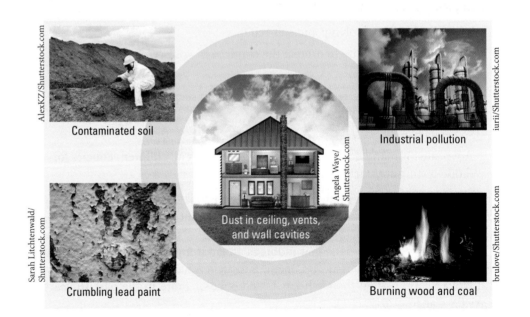

Contaminated soil

Crumbling lead paint

Dust in ceiling, vents, and wall cavities

Industrial pollution

Burning wood and coal

AlexKZ/Shutterstock.com

Sarah Litchtenwald/Shutterstock.com

Angela Waye/Shutterstock.com

iurii/Shutterstock.com

brulove/Shutterstock.com

Exposure to lead in dust and soil is a main concern because preschoolers are likely to ingest dust and soil every day. Houses and apartments and ECLC settings situated near industries that have used lead or situated on busy streets may contain

*Source: "Call for Action on Radon in Child Care Settings," *Environmental Health Review,* 2017, 60(3): p. 80. Retrieved January 2018 from http://pubs.ciphi.ca/doi/pdf/10.5864/d2017-020

high levels of lead because lead can remain in the soil for decades and contaminate vegetables grown in that soil.

Another source of lead contamination is lead-soldered pipes. Municipally treated drinking water is almost lead-free when it leaves the water plant, but it may pick up lead from the plumbing systems of older houses or apartments or from a lead-containing solder common in newer copper systems. In some areas, plumbing codes now limit the content of lead in solder. Lead accumulates when water stands in the pipes, so the first water out of the tap generally contains the most lead and should be flushed for a minute every morning. Even if your facility is new and doesn't have lead pipes and solder, the water travelling through your community's water system will have passed through lead pipes.

Cadmium may be increasingly substituted for lead in making costume jewellery (Government of Canada, 2015a, pp. 1–2). "It is illegal to import, advertise or sell jewellery designed for children under 15 years of age if it contains more than the allowable lead limits set out in Canadian regulations" (Government of Canada, 2015a, p. 1).* "Exposure to lead or cadmium may pose a significant health risk to children who chew, suck or swallow items made with these metals. Current science indicates that ingestion of even very low levels of lead or cadmium may be harmful to children" (Health Canada, 2018, p. 1). Health Canada is further reducing the levels of allowable lead and introducing a strict limit on amount of cadmium in children's jewellery (Health Canada, 2018, p. 1).

How can you tell if a toy contains lead? If a toy seems very heavy compared to its actual size or if it is bright red, orange, or dark metallic grey, it may contain lead. Also be wary of toys made with plastic that is malleable as lead can be used as a stabilizer to allow for plastics to be flexible.

If a family is concerned that their child may have been exposed to lead, suggest that they ask their physician for blood testing. Refer to Toy Safety on the Government of Canada's website for a comprehensive look at specific safety requirements. (See Resource Materials.)

NELSONstudy

To access Resource Materials, visit NelsonStudy.

Pesticides

Pesticide products registered by the federal government to control pests such as insects, rodents, and weeds have been an ongoing concern because of their obvious toxicity. Recently, there have generally been more stringent standards and regulations to prevent acute (immediate) episodes of toxicity, although children may be more liable than adults to experience latent (delayed) effects over the course of their lifetime (CPCHE, 2005, p. 23). Using chemicals to treat our lawns and gardens and to deflea our pets exposes us to long-term hazards. Insect repellents are likely more hazardous than the bug bite itself. A number of health concerns—allergies, hormone disruption, and developmental neurotoxicity, to name a few—have possible associations with pesticides.

In 2000, the Supreme Court of Canada upheld a bylaw passed by the town of Hudson, Québec, that banned the cosmetic use

Warren Goldswain/Shutterstock.com

Public Health England/Science Photo Library

of pesticides within the town's borders. This ban includes both public land, such as parks, and private property. This landmark decision has paved the way for a number of communities in Canada to pursue similar bylaws. Of course, the attempts are challenged by lawn chemical companies, but it seems that the movement to ban pesticide use is gaining momentum. The general public is becoming more aware of natural alternatives to pest control as many municipalities have put bylaws in place banning cosmetic use of pesticides, with subsequent fines. Where does your community stand on this important issue? Has your province or territory banned cosmetic pesticides?

Plastics

In our modern world, we have come to depend on plastics in much of our everyday life. Plastics can be in our clothing, toys, eyeglasses, computers, phones, dishes, utensils, and furniture—the list goes on.

One look around (indoors and outdoors) any ECLC setting and it is obvious that we have come to depend on plastic toys, equipment, and utensils. Historically and currently, most plastics are made from petroleum, a nonrenewable resource, and petroleum-based chemicals. The manufacturing of plastics pollutes air, land, and water and exposes workers to toxic chemicals. In terms of health risks after manu-

Leah-Anne Thompson/Shutterstock.com

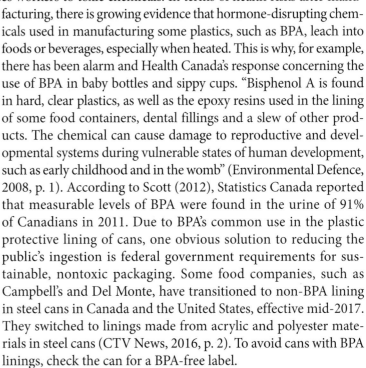

facturing, there is growing evidence that hormone-disrupting chemicals used in manufacturing some plastics, such as BPA, leach into foods or beverages, especially when heated. This is why, for example, there has been alarm and Health Canada's response concerning the use of BPA in baby bottles and sippy cups. "Bisphenol A is found in hard, clear plastics, as well as the epoxy resins used in the lining of some food containers, dental fillings and a slew of other products. The chemical can cause damage to reproductive and developmental systems during vulnerable states of human development, such as early childhood and in the womb" (Environmental Defence, 2008, p. 1). According to Scott (2012), Statistics Canada reported that measurable levels of BPA were found in the urine of 91% of Canadians in 2011. Due to BPA's common use in the plastic protective lining of cans, one obvious solution to reducing the public's ingestion is federal government requirements for sustainable, nontoxic packaging. Some food companies, such as Campbell's and Del Monte, have transitioned to non-BPA lining in steel cans in Canada and the United States, effective mid-2017. They switched to linings made from acrylic and polyester materials in steel cans (CTV News, 2016, p. 2). To avoid cans with BPA linings, check the can for a BPA-free label.

When purchasing food and beverages packaged in plastic, avoid selecting products with a 3, 6, or 7 in the triangular symbol, as illustrated in Figure 7.1.

FIGURE 7.1 Safer Choices for Food and Beverages

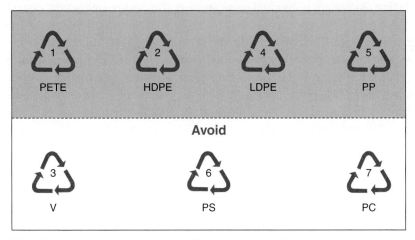

Note: While PC (polycarbonate) plastic #7 should be avoided, some #7 plastics, such as bio-based plastics and co-polyester, are currently considered safe for use.

Source: Institute for Agriculture and Trade Policy (2008). *Smart Plastics Guide Healthier Food Uses of Plastics.* https://foodsecurecanada.org/sites/foodsecurecanada.org/files/smart_plastics_guide.pdf.

Leaching of chemicals used in making plastics increases when the plastic comes in contact with oily or fatty foods, during heating, and from old or scratched plastic. Types of plastics shown to leach toxic chemicals are polycarbonate, polyvinyl chlorides (PVCs), and styrene (Institute for Agriculture and Trade Policy, 2008, p. 2).

PVCs are used to produce plastics for cling wrap, some plastic squeeze bottles, cooking oil and peanut butter jars, and detergent and window cleaner bottles. These plastics last for many years and are difficult to destroy, adding to our overflowing landfills. When they are burned, the fumes are even more toxic, emitting dioxins and other known toxins, which then settle on land and are often ingested by grazing animals. Humans then ingest them in food.

PVCs and the phthalates that are added as a plastic softener captured a lot of national and international media attention in the late 1990s due to efforts to ban their use in mouthing and teething toys and rattles. The most immediate concern with phthalates in PVCs is that they leach out of the plastic fairly easily and are thought to be hormone disruptors (i.e., they interfere with the hormone systems) in children. In 1998, Canada's federal government followed the lead of the European Union and banned the use of phthalates in teething rings and other infant toys. Another concern with plastics is the use of lead, cadmium, and other heavy metals, along with various chemicals, in their manufacturing to make them stronger or more flexible. The consumer may incorrectly assume that any product intended for children would have undergone stringent testing before being put on the market. To ensure children's safety, the precautionary approach (see page 402) has been adopted by Health Canada in the banning of BPA use in the manufacturing of baby bottles. In April 2008, Canada became the first national jurisdiction to designate BPA as a toxin. However, as stated earlier, this is just one of many toxins that need attention. "Canadians deserve a strict law on toxic substances that requires the government to reduce exposure when substances are found to be toxic. We need a truly precautionary policy that puts people first. Although individual consumption choices are important, our control over these everyday exposures is constrained by legislation, political institutions and power relations" (Scott, 2012, p. 1).

As we all know, pollution caused by plastics is an increasing problem worldwide, with a rising movement to reduce plastic waste. Until further government action results in sweeping changes, rethinking the use of some plastic products is worthwhile. Suggested ways to reduce children's exposure to hormone disruptors found in PVCs include the following:

- Never microwave food in plastic containers as the chemicals leach out. Use glass, Pyrex, china, or ceramic dishes. Baby bottles should be warmed in hot water. Silicone nipples and pacifiers or soothers do not contain phthalates.
- Use fabric teethers when possible.
- PVC mini-blinds contain lead that breaks down and becomes a dust on the surface. Wash this away carefully and often.

The following are tips for safer, more sustainable food use of plastics:

- Avoid using plastic containers in the microwave. Chemicals are released from plastics when heated (especially for fatty foods because of more leaching of chemicals into fatty foods).
- Beware of cling wraps, especially for microwave use. Use waxed paper or paper towel instead for covering foods.
- Use alternatives to plastic packaging whenever possible. For example, bring reusable bags or cardboard boxes to the grocery store.
- Avoid water in plastic bottles unless you're travelling to or live in an area where the quality of water is questionable. Bottled water is less regulated and has less certain purity and safety than tap water.
- If you do use plastic water bottles, take precautions. If you use a polycarbonate water bottle, to reduce leaching of BPA, do not use the bottle for warm or hot liquids and discard old or scratched bottles.
- Use alternatives to polycarbonate plastic baby bottles and sippy cups. (Institute for Agriculture and Trade Policy, 2008, pp. 2–3)

Actions to Promote Environmental Health and Safety in Early Childhood Learning and Care Settings

When we consider the vast and still relatively unknown aspects of environmental contamination, we can become overwhelmed and feel powerless to make a difference. However, there are everyday strategies we can incorporate into ECLC programs that reduce exposure to known environmental contaminants. *Advancing Environmental Health in Child Care Settings: A Checklist for Child Care Practitioners and Public Health Inspectors* by CPCHE (2010a) is a useful tool for students and educators to evaluate their facility from the perspective of environmental health and safety. Appendix 7.1 provides educators with guidelines when purchasing products used in the program (see page 467). In addition, our favourite Canadian environmentalist,

David Suzuki, is supporting Canadians in making small changes. Everyday changes found on the David Suzuki Foundation website make a difference and help us feel that we have some control over our future. (See Resource Materials.)

NELSONstudy

To access Resource Materials, visit NelsonStudy.

Is there action we can take to address the concern about lead in our water source? Lead-soldered copper plumbing, although banned in the late 1980s, is still quite widely available in existing plumbing. When water sits overnight (or all weekend!) in contact with these joints, lead can go into the water. This is particularly true if the source water is "soft" or acidic, such as can occur on the Canadian Shield.

Since lead is probably harmful at any exposure level, the precautionary approach has meant that some jurisdictions, Ontario for one, legislate that all ECLC settings flush their water system for at least one minute every morning from a cold water tap on the branch of plumbing where water is used for drinking. The Ontario legislation requires that this process is documented in writing and the records are kept for at least five years.

Never use water from the hot water tank for cooking or drinking as hot water picks up more lead than cold water.

Being Prepared for Emergencies

Educators should have an up-to-date first-aid certificate that equips them with the knowledge and skills

- to help them remain calm,
- to administer basic first aid or at least to ensure that their actions do not make an injury worse while waiting for emergency medical services (make sure you know the number for dialing emergency medical services),
- to use the supplies in a first-aid kit, and
- to know when to call emergency medical services.

Throughout your early childhood education, you will work in programs, and one of your first tasks when starting in a new program will be to familiarize yourself with its emergency policy and procedures and take part in fire and evacuation drills. In response to our changing society, programs are now required to be ready to respond to a wide range of situations beyond fires, such as

- possible violent situations,
- bomb threats,
- lock-down situations (e.g., a school-age program located in a school, a section of the neighbourhood that is locked down), and
- environmental situations such as chemical spills and weather emergencies (e.g., blizzards, tornados).

Be sure you know where the following are located in the building:

- emergency exits and posted evacuation routes (floor plan with exits indicated)
- first-aid kits

- fire extinguishers and fire alarms (read the operating instructions)
- smoke detectors and carbon monoxide detectors
- emergency phone numbers within the community, as well as the children's parents' numbers
- blankets and flashlights

Courtesy of George Brown College/Casa Loma Child Care Centre

Injury Reports

An injury report should be completed whenever a child or educator is injured—even when the injury appears to be minor. Minor cuts can become infected. A head injury may show no immediate observable symptoms, but changes in behaviour can develop hours later. When in doubt, always complete an injury report. Educators should also document the injury in the child's file and make reference to the completed injury report.

The primary purpose of the injury report is to serve as a legal document. Clear and succinct documentation is required to report the injury as objectively as possible. Depending on the child's injury and the outcome, these reports may be reviewed by the early childhood office, police, or lawyers if the question of professional liability or suspected child abuse is raised. A copy of the injury report is usually placed in the child's file.

The report also serves as a tool for staff in developing injury prevention strategies. Educators use the report to evaluate a specific injury or a series of similar injuries in their program. From this information, educators first consider the five Ws of safety:

- who
- why, such as the level of supervision, what the child was doing at the time, and his or her developmental stage
- where, such as on a particular piece of play equipment, its general condition, the protective surface, or on a walk or field trip
- when, such as the time of day and weather conditions
- what happened in chronological order, the type and extent of the injury, and what the injury looks like (size, colour, location on the body)

Educators then consider everything they learned about this incident to determine and implement the necessary changes to prevent similar injuries in the future or at least to reduce the severity. More serious injuries will be reported as serious occurrences (see Serious Occurrences, page 403). The following are a few possible alterations either in practice or to equipment:

- Increase the level of supervision.
- Modify, repair, or remove a piece of play equipment.
- Review the safe use of play equipment with the children.

- Reorganize a particular planned curriculum with children (e.g., reduce the number of steps in a preschool cooking activity and the number of children to supervise them better with cutting and cooking).
- Eliminate a particular planned event with children (e.g., a field trip to horseback ride with preschoolers).

Children's Safety at Pickup Times

Educators are responsible for the safety of children until the children leave the premises with their parents or persons authorized by the parents. Program staff may be faced with a situation in which an unauthorized person arrives to pick up a child, conditions are deemed unsafe for releasing a child to the parent or no one comes to pick up the child at the end of the day, or school-agers are permitted to leave unattended.

School-Age Children

School-agers range in age from 6 to 12, and their abilities, skills, and need for independence vary. Some parents feel that their children are competent and can handle the responsibility of being at home alone, and the children may want it that way. Other families feel they have no option but to leave their children at home on their own after school. In response, many communities have a phone number that children can call if they are lonely, need someone to talk to, or are worried about something. The community in which they live may also play a role in parents' sense of safety and their level of comfort in having children home alone. School-age children who are at home alone are clearly at increased risk for injury, missing meals, and other health and well-being problems.

The law requires that parents provide reasonable provision for the safety of children under age 16. However, this law is vague in terms of what is considered reasonable. School-age programs are then faced with the dilemma of creating a policy on the release of school-agers at the end of the day. Programs' policies depend on their philosophy, their setting (urban versus rural), their location within a city, and the parents using the program. Ultimately, educators and parents all want children to gain increasing levels of independence and responsibility. Most adults realize that developing autonomy through opportunities to manage some risk is beneficial for children.

- Children in pairs move independently of an adult from their classroom to the school-age program within the building or outside to a portable.
- Children go inside the school to use the washroom (e.g., in buddy pairs) and then return to the playground.

Programs work out the specific arrangements for each child with the parents. This agreement is put in writing in the child's file. Before parents permit their children to walk home alone, for instance, school-agers' educators and parents determine the child's readiness and safety factors. As stated above, a program policy or guideline may include a peer buddy system. The following questions should be asked:

- Has the child asked his or her parents to allow walking home alone, and does the child understand what it will be like to be home alone? If this request has not been made by the child, he or she is unlikely to be ready for this responsibility.
- Does the child's teacher feel that the child is developmentally ready? Teachers can provide parents and educators with valuable insights into children's behaviour (e.g., "Every time I step out of the classroom, Sandra is doing something that endangers her safety," or "Danny follows guidelines well and demonstrates initiative").
- What are the potential risks for the child on the way home from the ECLC setting?
- What kind of adult support is available to the child at home (e.g., neighbour, clerk in the corner store, children's telephone help line, telephone access to parents)?

Unauthorized Persons

Parents must feel confident that educators will not permit an **unauthorized person** to take their child from the program. To protect children from abduction, programs require an authorization policy and procedures that ensure that only authorized individuals pick up children. Parents and the program must have a written agreement that lists the people that parents authorize to take their children from the program. (Some parents will authorize one person only.)

If the list is part of a contract with the parent and an employee releases a child to a person not named in the list, the program will be in breach not only of contract but also of their provincial or territorial regulations. If the child is injured, a negligence action (lawsuit) may follow. Staff cannot release a child to anyone who has not been authorized in writing. A parent cannot add a name to the list over the phone. However, due to unexpected work responsibilities or travel problems, parents may find themselves in situations in which they can't get to the program in time to pick up the child. A parent might then call and tell the educator that a friend will come to the program even though this person isn't on the authorized list. These situations are grey areas. Educators have to be practical and exercise common sense. The parent has called the program first and authorized the person for this specific day, and the child knows that person. It would be unlikely that the staff would refuse to release the child to this individual. There may be times when someone arrives who is not on the list and the parent has not called the program. Even if the child is happy to see that person and would be comfortable leaving with him or her, educators are legally responsible not to release the child to this unauthorized person. In this situation, the educators must call the parents. The parent may simply have forgotten to tell the staff that morning. To avoid a similar situation in the future, the parents can add this person's name to the written agreement. The least likely occurrence, but the one of most concern, is that this person is, in fact, attempting to take the child without the parent's permission.

Noncustodial Parents

Many children live in families in which parents are either separated or divorced. Many of these families have workable agreements for child custody and visitation. In cases of joint custody, there usually aren't concerns for the child's safety. However, there are situations in which agreements are not straightforward. From educators' perspectives, parents must provide a copy of the custody order and a photograph of the noncustodial parent. If situations arise when the custodial parent releases the child to the other parent, the custodial parent must provide the staff with written permission. All educators must be apprised of these custody agreements to ensure that a child is not released to a noncustodial parent without authorization. Educators should be cautious if the noncustodial parent arrives on a day other than the one that had been agreed on. Staff can't assume that releasing the child is acceptable to the other parent simply because it's a different day. Parents, not strangers, are responsible for most child abductions.

What do staff do when an unauthorized noncustodial parent insists that the program release the child to him or her? Educators may face a verbal or physical confrontation with this parent. In this situation, staff need to

- calmly ask the parent to move to an area with more privacy (more than one educator should be with the parent) or at least have staff move all children away or outside.
- have someone call the custodial parent so he or she knows what is happening. Depending on their rapport, the custodial parent may be able to talk to the other parent or quickly come to the program.
- call the police if the parent loses control or tries to leave with the child.

Children in Need of Protection: Intoxicated Parents

It may be hard to imagine that parents could actually arrive to pick up their children while intoxicated with alcohol or drugs. Yet it does happen, and educators must know how to handle such situations for the safety of the child and the parent. Educators have a number of concerns:

- releasing the child to a parent whom they consider to be incompetent to care for the child
- the safety of parent and child on the way home
- the safety of others if the intoxicated parent is driving
- the child's safety and well-being once at home, especially if there is no second adult in the home
- the potential liability of the program if staff knowingly allow an intoxicated parent to drive and a motor vehicle mishap occurs

From both an ethical and a legal perspective, educators cannot release a child to someone who could cause the child harm. Each situation is different. Each depends on the age of the child, the staff's relationship with the parent, whether the problem is a recurring one, and so on, and, as such, releasing the child is a subjective decision on the part of staff. The situation could be difficult to handle.

Educators should

- offer the parent coffee and calmly talk about safety concerns for the child and parent (the child should not be present);
- ask the parent whether someone could come and pick him or her up and ensure that the child is cared for when they arrive home, such as
  - the other parent, if he or she is active in the child's daily life, or
  - another authorized adult;
- in extreme cases, call the child protection agency and discuss the situation with them; and
- if the parent is belligerent or confrontational, or wants to or has already taken the child from the program and is driving away, call the police and tell them that a drunk driver is leaving the program with a child. If possible, provide the police with the make, model, and colour of the car, as well as the licence plate number.

When No One Arrives

What happens if half an hour after closing the program, the parents have not yet arrived and cannot be reached by phone? Staff should try contacting the following people:

- the alternative adults listed in the emergency information
- people on the authorized list
- as a last resort, the child protection agency, which will provide staff with guidance in handling the situation

REVISITING THE HEALTH PROMOTION ACTION PLAN

With reference to the health promotion action plan introduced in Unit 1, the following are examples of what we can do to reduce exposure to and production of environmental contaminants.

Individual Problem Solving and Self-Reliance

- Ensure that carbon monoxide monitors and smoke detectors are installed and maintained on a regular basis.
- Test your home for radon.
- Pay attention to air-quality advisories and the air-quality index.
- Limit activities that contribute to air pollution.
- Minimize contact between food and plastics (e.g., use glass containers in microwave ovens).
- Minimize the use of plastic mouthing toys.
- Run the water taps (or water fountain) for a few minutes each morning to reduce the contaminant load, including lead.
- Eat pesticide-free foods (e.g., organic fruits and vegetables) when possible.

- Use nontoxic repellents to control pests (e.g., dab white vinegar behind ears, knees, and wrists; spray a hot pepper and water mix on leaves to deter caterpillars).
- Minimize the ingestion of toxic chemicals through routine hand washing.

Community Action

- Insist on non-smoking environments.
- With other educators and possibly families in your ECLC program, follow the recommendations in the *Advancing Environmental Health in Child Care Settings: A Checklist for Child Care Practitioners and Public Health Inspectors* (CPCHE, 2010a). (See Resource Materials.)
- Test for lead in paint, soil, dust, solder, and drinking water. (See Resource Materials.) Share your findings with others in your neighbourhood or your workplace.
- Demand full disclosure if pesticides are used in public places (school yards, parks, and roadsides).
- Interested citizens can meet with the local supermarket manager to request organic produce or start a "fresh food box" program. A number of communities in Canada have started programs in which affordable locally grown produce (both organic and nonorganic) is made available on a weekly or monthly basis.
- Find out if your community is or is in the process of becoming a pesticide-free zone. If it is not, find out how to advocate for this.
- Establish green teams in the workplace to support policies and practices in environmental improvement.

Societal Change

- Join a national organization that advocates for children's environmental health. Advocacy results in legislated changes that benefit everyone.
- Support the campaign for a cleaner environment and health protection laws in Canada, as well as legislation that helps to reduce poverty.

NELSONstudy

To access Resource Materials, visit NelsonStudy.

CONCLUSION

Since 1980, the rate of hospitalization due to injury has been decreasing. We must remain vigilant and act on behalf of children to decrease the injury rate further in the coming decades. One senseless death of a child is too many. Air bags in cars, for example, are a preventive measure that can be detrimental to young children. The ongoing role of social public policy, legislation, and monitoring to continue Canada's trend to reducing children's injuries is paramount. On a daily basis, families and educators have an integral role in helping children learn lifelong safety behaviour. As children grow and develop, the educators' role moves from one of protecting children to one of enhancing their understanding of safety, identifying potential risks, and preventing injuries. Our communities and society have an important role in safety promotion through research, education, and legislation based on children's needs.

ASSESS YOUR LEARNING

Define terms or describe concepts used in this unit.

- Canadian Standards Association (CSA)
- encroachment area
- environmental contaminants
- five Ws of safety
- four components of safety promotion
- frostbite
- injury prevention strategies
- precautionary approach
- protective surfaces
- road rules
- safety checklists
- serious occurrences
- sun protection factor (SPF)
- unauthorized person
- UV index
- wind-chill factor
- windows of vulnerability

Evaluate your options in each situation.

1. The daily routine usually ends with outdoor play, and parents pick up their children from the playground. Children need active supervision on equipment, but parents also need the opportunity to speak with an educator about their child's day.

2. The new climber on the playground is designed for safe use by preschoolers and school-agers, and the sand underneath is regularly maintained. In addition, there is always adequate staffing to follow regulations. Safety rules for children are developed to foster safety and respect for themselves, property, and peers. Using the criteria discussed in the unit, consider examples of rules that could be appropriate for (a) preschoolers and (b) school-agers.

3. The winter has been extremely cold and windy, yet a number of the school-agers are not wearing their boots and hats because "it's just not the thing to do." Before and after school, the children have a choice between staying in and going out to the playground. These same children choose to stay indoors. Some haven't played outside all month.

4. You are on a long summer walk with the preschoolers before lunch and suddenly you remember that none of you are wearing sunscreen.

5. The carpeting in the play area of the infant room needs a good cleaning, and your director wants to have it professionally cleaned. You and your room partner are aware of the environmental toxins, not only from the chemical cleaners but also from the carpet. The infants crawl around on it daily, with ongoing exposure.

APPENDIX 7.1

Playing It Safe: Buying Products for the Child Care Centre

■■■■■■■■■■■■■■■■

PLAYING IT SAFE:
BUYING PRODUCTS FOR
THE CHILD CARE CENTER

In early learning and child care environments, children receive care and nurturing, learn to socialize with their peers, and develop important skills. They may also, however, come into contact with a variety of potentially harmful chemicals or pollutants.

Children may take in such chemicals by mouthing certain plastic or painted toys, eating foods heated in plastic containers, breathing in fine dust from art and craft materials, or absorbing chemicals through their skin from cleaning products. While chemical exposures from individual products may be small, they can add up and, in combination, potentially contribute to asthma, learning disabilities, cancer and other chronic conditions.

The good news is that many environmental exposures can be prevented. You can play an important part in this prevention by choosing safer products for your child care centre and using potentially hazardous products safely.

Toys

- If buying plastic toys, look for PVC- or phthalate-free toys. Avoid toys with "vinyl" or "PVC" on the label, or those with a strong chemical smell. PVC (polyvinyl chloride) contains potentially harmful phthalates.
- Be aware that most inflatable toys (such as those for water play) are made of PVC.
- If possible, choose unpainted wooden toys, toys with lead-free paint, or machine-washable cloth toys.
- Avoid second-hand, donated or inexpensive toys that may contain lead. Metal objects (such as play jewellery) that feel heavy for their size may also contain lead.
- Visit the Health Canada Consumer Product Safety website and subscribe to the e-mail list (cpsn-subscribe-request@list.hc-sc.gc.ca) to learn of consumer advisories, warnings and product recalls.

Art and Craft Materials

- Choose art and craft materials specifically labelled "intended for use by children" and avoid products that bear hazard symbols. A product labelled "non-toxic" is not an assurance of safety.
- Look for products with the "Approved Product" (AP) seal from the American Arts and Creative Materials Institute (ACMI). This label assures some measure of safety.
- Select liquid, gel and paste art materials rather than powders and sprays, and water-based art and craft materials rather than solvent-based products.

Personal Care Products

- Choose fragrance-free products.
- Do not use antibacterial hand soap. Proper hand washing with plain soap and water removes most germs.
- When soap and water are not available, an unscented, alcohol-based hand sanitizer is an acceptable alternative.
- When buying sunscreen, look for products bearing the Canadian Dermatology Association (CDA) logo with a sun protection factor (SPF) of 30 or higher.
- Favour sunscreens that contain reflecting physical blockers, such as titanium dioxide, and avoid those containing chemical blockers, such as octyl methoxycinnamate or oxybenzone. To play it safe, write to companies to find out if the sunscreens you choose contain nanoparticles— ultra-small particles that may be absorbed through the skin.

Disinfectants

- Use bleach solutions when and where required and in the concentrations recommended by your public health unit.
- If choosing alternatives to bleach for disinfection, ensure products have a drug identification number (DIN) or *Pest Control Products (PCP) Act* number.

Cleaning Products

- For tasks other than disinfection, choose products with the fewest hazard symbols. Plain soap or detergent will suffice in many cases.
- Use fragrance-free and biodegradable laundry soaps. Do not use dryer sheets or scented fabric softeners.
- For routine cleaning tasks, choose reusable cloth wipes instead of disposable chemical wipes.
- Choose the least toxic carpet and oven cleaners.
- Look for products bearing the EcoLogo. These are typically less toxic than conventional ones.
- Do not use deodorizers or air "fresheners" (including plug-ins). Most rely on potentially harmful chemicals to cover up offensive odours.

Pest Control Products

- Use preventive measures—such as regular cleaning, building maintenance and safe food storage—to reduce the risk of infestations.
- For minor pest problems, select chemical-free and non-toxic measures whenever possible.
- If an infestation occurs, use traps rather than poisons. If poison must be used, choose pastes and gels instead of powders and sprays, and follow label instructions carefully. Always ensure that pest control products are inaccessible to children, and work in consultation with your local public health unit.

Choosing to buy safer products is one way you can protect the health of children in your care. The way you use products and the practices you engage in on a daily basis are equally important.

For more information and practical tips on healthier, greener practices in the child care setting, refer to *Advancing Environmental Health in Child Care Settings: A Checklist for Child Care Practitioners and Public Health Inspectors* at www.healthyenvironmentforkids.ca

(continued)

Insect Repellents

- For DEET-containing repellents, select only those specifically intended specifically intended for children. Choose those with the lowest possible DEET concentration, and not higher than ten per cent. Use as directed.
- When choosing alternatives to DEET, select products registered by the Pest Management Regulatory Agency.
- Avoid eucalyptus-based repellents or products containing citronella or lavender oil, as these can be harmful to children.

Furnishings

- Most sleeping mats are covered with vinyl (PVC). Air out new mats for three days before using them indoors, and ensure children do not mouth or chew on them by covering them with a washable fabric.
- When replacing carpets, choose smooth hard flooring (not vinyl) and cover where needed with machine-washable area rugs. Avoid wall-to-wall carpeting.

Food Storage and Serving Ware

- When purchasing food storage containers, opt for glass, lead-free ceramic or stainless steel.
- For dishes and cutlery, consider glass, lead-free ceramic, stainless steel or bamboo as alternatives to plastic.
- If you use plastic, polypropylene (#5) is a better choice. Avoid storing hot food in plastic.

Following these tips is not always simple. Alternative products can be more expensive and they may be hard to find. And simply reading labels won't always tell you everything that is in a product.

When you make the effort to ask for and choose safer products, you are not only protecting the health of the children in your care, you are also helping to push the marketplace so that everyone can access safer, reasonably priced products.

We can all play a part in securing better laws to protect children from toxic chemicals in consumer products, including mandatory product labelling and full disclosure of ingredients.

For CPCHE's position on these and other issues, see *First Steps in Lifelong Health: A Vision and Strategy for Children's Health and Environment in Canada*, at www.healthyenvironmentforkids.ca

Where Can You Get More Information?

Advancing Environmental Health in Child Care Settings (CPCHE) — see box, over

Child Health and the Environment: A Primer (CPCHE)
www.healthyenvironmentforkids.ca/resources/child-health-and-environment-primer

Childproofing for Environmental Health: An Examination of Food Related Exposures (Toronto Public Health)
www.healthyenvironmentforkids.ca/resources/childproofing-food-related-exposures

Online Collection on Toy Safety (CPCHE)
www.healthyenvironmentforkids.ca/collections/toy-safety

Consumer Product Safety Warnings and Advisories (Health Canada)
www.hc-sc.gc.ca/cps-spc/advisories-avis/aw-am/index-eng.php

Safety in the Arts (Canadian Child Care Federation)
www.cccf-fcsge.ca/docs/cccf/RS_21-e.pdf

Well Beings: A Guide to Health in Child Care (Canadian Paediatric Society)
www.caringforkids.cps.ca/wellbeings/index.htm

Online Collection on Pesticides (CPCHE)
www.healthyenvironmentforkids.ca/collections/pesticides

Insect Repellents (Health Canada)
www.hc-sc.gc.ca/hl-vs/iyh-vsv/life-vie/insect-eng.phg

Insect Repellents for Children (Canadian Paediatric Society)
www.caringforkids.cps.ca/keepkidssafe/repellents.htm

Online Collection on Phthalates (CPCHE)
www.healthyenvironmentforkids.ca/collections/phthalates

Online Collection on Bisphenol A (CPCHE)
www.healthyenvironmentforkids.ca/collections/bisphenol

Smart Plastics Guide: Healthier Food Uses of Plastics (Institute for Agriculture and Trade Policy)
www.healthobservatory.org/library.cfm?refid=102202

Guide to Less Toxic Products (Environmental Health Association of Nova Scotia)
www.lesstoxicguide.ca

Source: Canadian Partnership for Children's Health & Environment (2010, March). *Playing It Safe: Buying Products for the Child Care Centre*, www.healthyenvironmentforkids.ca. Used by permission of the Canadian Partnership for Children's Health and Environment (CPCHE).

Preventing Child Maltreatment

8

CONTENTS

The United Nations (UN) Convention on the Rights of the Child, proclaimed in 1989, is the first legally binding international instrument to incorporate the full range of human rights for all children. The Convention spells out the basic human rights that children everywhere are entitled to.

- survival;
- optimal development;
- protection from harmful influences, abuse, and exploitation; and
- full participation in family, cultural, and social life.

(See Appendix 8.1, page 529.)

Although most children in Canada do develop in safe, predictable environments in which their rights are met, this is not the reality for many others. From human rights and health promotion standpoints, all children have the right to the conditions for optimal health, growth, and development. Society has an obligation to ensure that parents have the essential resources to raise their children. In Canada, we still have a long way to go before this becomes a reality for all.

Trained and experienced educators often identify child maltreatment as an area in which they need further education. Although it is impossible to know the true extent of child maltreatment, because much goes unreported, even conservative estimates of the number of reported cases make it likely that educators will come in contact with children who are victims of maltreatment. Participating in continuing education opportunities, combined with work experience and collaboration with professionals and agencies, enhances your understanding and skills in the area of child maltreatment: abuse and neglect. Since educators are frontline professionals and work closely with children and families, they are in a position to identify children whom they suspect are being maltreated and are able to activate primary, secondary, and, in some situations, tertiary prevention. In other words, early childhood learning and care (ECLC) programs can contribute to the prevention of child maltreatment in several ways:

- by ensuring that the environment in the program is rich with responsive, respectful role modelling in relating to both children and adults (primary prevention)
- by early identification of suspected child maltreatment and by reporting suspected maltreatment to a child protection agency (secondary prevention)
- by supporting both children and their families when child maltreatment has been confirmed (secondary or sometimes tertiary prevention if educators are asked to be involved in the treatment process)

As professionals, educators are required by law to report their suspicions of child maltreatment. Suspected child maltreatment reporting requirements are under provincial/territorial jurisdiction; educators must know these requirements.

Educators' relationship with children and their families also creates an ethical responsibility to report. These reports make it possible for child protection agencies to provide protection for children who are at either immediate or future risk and to assist the children and their families in recovery.

Failure to recognize and to help stop child maltreatment can result in serious consequences for children, including long-term emotional and physical problems and, in extreme cases, death. Another devastating consequence is that adults who were maltreated as children may themselves become abusive or be further victimized (e.g., spousal abuse), so the cycle of abuse continues.

Courtesy of George Brown College/Scotia Plaza Child Care Centre

EXPLORING YOUR FEELINGS

As individuals, we need to understand our own feelings about this sensitive and emotional subject. Working with families involves a wide range of philosophies, parenting practices, and lifestyles. Educators' openness to diversity in values and customs contributes to their sensitivity and effectiveness on a personal as well as a professional level.

OBJECTIVES

To identify your feelings about child maltreatment and how you can deal with them. (LO 2)

To identify your level of openness to family diversity. (LO 2)

About Child Maltreatment

Each of us brings different life experiences and spiritual and cultural beliefs to the program. Some people find it incomprehensible that someone could inflict emotional and physical pain on a child, or they may feel anger and hatred for those who maltreat or neglect children. Others are themselves survivors of child maltreatment. Even if you were not maltreated as a child, you probably know someone who was. For survivors, the realm of emotional and physical reactions to child maltreatment may be overwhelming. Attempting to understand child maltreatment from a professional rather than a personal perspective is challenging. Even if we have only read or heard about child maltreatment, we may still have strong feelings.

- You are so angry at the thought of a parent hurting a child that you question your ability to provide further support to the child and family.
- As an adult survivor of child maltreatment, you feel that this is the time for you to seek professional help.

EXPERIENCING INTENSE EMOTIONS

What do we do with all these emotions and responses? You may feel the need to acknowledge and work through your feelings to respond effectively to this complex issue in your work.

Child maltreatment of any kind can generate a range of intense emotional reactions. We all experience some reaction when faced with disturbing behaviour. *For example, when you read or hear a story in the media about sexual abuse, such as sexual exploitation of children by a religious leader, doctor, teacher, or athletics trainer who may have crossed ethical boundaries, how do you feel? Perhaps you feel disbelief that anyone could do such a thing to a child. Perhaps you feel anger at the child for not telling someone when it started.* It is important for anyone caring for children to explore her or his feelings about sexual abuse. Our reactions can affect our understanding of sexual abuse and the way we respond to children who have been victimized.

Those who have concerns about their confused feelings or about approaching issues that may not have been resolved since childhood may find it necessary to talk with a trusted friend or a counsellor. Your college's counsellors and instructors can provide students with names of referrals (e.g., social workers, counsellors, or psychologists) and community services.

About Family Diversity

The region of Canada we live in and, more specifically, the location of the program we work in may determine the diversity of families' structures, living styles, social and economic situations, ethnocultural backgrounds, religions, and so on. It is important to realize that you don't have to adopt someone else's values and beliefs,

FIGURE 8.1   The Diversity Iceberg

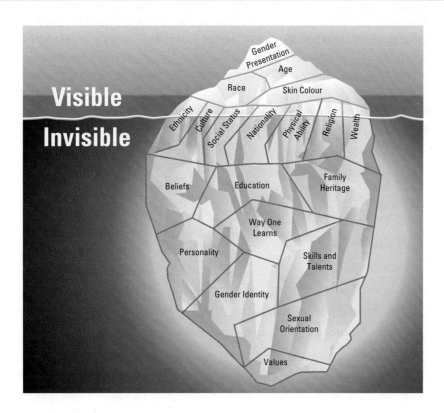

but you do need to develop a level of understanding and respect for others' values and beliefs. Diversity is similar to an iceberg (see Figure 8.1): most of what we know about people is out of sight, below the surface (e.g., value systems, beliefs, thinking style, perspectives, sexual identity).

Many practices are obviously not harmful to children, even if they are different from your experience. Many foods, rituals, and family practices are an important part of cultural or religious heritage and socialization. However, when it is possible that a practice may be harmful, the child protection agency must be consulted.

While helping preschoolers with their bathing suits for the wading pool, you notice that Niran has small burns over his chest and back. When you ask, "I see you have marks on your back. What happened?" the four-year-old replies, "Mommy rubbed my back to make me better." The child is not upset and is generally a content child who is always happy to see his mother at the end of the day.

Coining or "cao gio" (pronounced *gow yaw*) is a common Southeast Asian alternative treatment for minor illnesses such as cold, flu, headache, fever, pain, cough, or low energy. "Cao gio" literally translates to "catch the wind." It is believed that too much "wind" in the blood is the cause of many illnesses. Coining brings the blood to the surface, which releases the "bad wind."

The practice of coining involves rubbing heated oil on the skin, most commonly the chest, back, or shoulders, and then strongly rubbing a coin over the area in a linear fashion until a red mark is seen—a doorway for the wind to get out. This practice is very similar to "gua sha," a Chinese alternative medicine, which often uses rounded stones or other tools (California Childcare Health Program, 2010).

Although minor burns are the most common complication of coining, consulting with a child protection agency should occur.

Learning to work effectively with diverse families requires an open attitude and skills. These skills can be developed from

- the family, in a respectful manner;
- coworkers;
- post-diploma courses and training focused on diversity and equity;
- relevant agencies in the community; and
- literature and audiovisual training materials.

To summarize, you must ask yourself two important questions before you can manage suspicions of child maltreatment in a practical way in ECLC programs:

1. What are some of the feelings I have about child maltreatment—such as fear, anger, frustration, and sadness—and how can I deal with these in a way that enables me to work effectively with families?

2. How open am I to living styles, values, and parenting practices that are different from my own?

OBJECTIVES

To define and describe each category of child maltreatment: physical abuse, emotional abuse, sexual abuse, neglect, and exposing children to family violence. (LO 1)

To develop a heightened awareness of the complex consequences of maltreatment on children. (LO 1, 3)

CHILD MALTREATMENT

The definition of **child maltreatment** has evolved over time and will continue to do so. Thirty-five years ago, child maltreatment was thought to concern mainly children who were severely physically abused. Since then, we have become aware of the high incidence of child sexual abuse, especially when considering the far-reaching consequences of child pornography on the Internet. We are more aware of the consequences for children who have been abused emotionally, including issues such as children exposed to the abuse of their mother or other family member. The various ways that children are neglected has also become much more evident, making neglect the most prevalent type of child maltreatment reported to child protection agencies in Canada. Child maltreatment is always a misuse of power—a person with greater physical, intellectual, or emotional power and authority controls a child in a way that does not contribute to the child's health, growth, and development. Although we use the term "parent" in this unit, it is important to note that the alleged offender could be another family member, such as an aunt or grandfather, or another caregiver in the child's life, such as a babysitter, educator, or coach. In all four categories of substantiated abuse, in the third nationwide study to examine the incidence in Canada, almost all alleged perpetrators (99%) were family members or other persons related to the child (Public Health Agency of Canada [PHAC], 2010, p. 41). In 2014, parents were responsible for a very high percentage of violence against their children (see Figure 8.2).

FIGURE 8.2   Relationship to the Victim in Police-Reported Family Violence, 2014

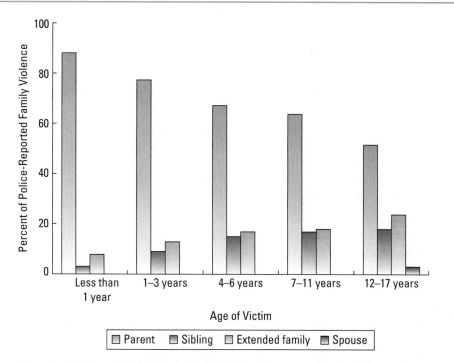

Notes on the date: Parent—includes biological, step, adoptive, and foster parents. Sibling—includes biological, step, half, adoptive, and foster brothers and sisters. Extended family—includes all family members related by blood, marriage, or adoption. Spouse—includes current or former legally married and common-law spouses.

Source: © All rights reserved. *The Chief Public Officer's Report on the State of Public Health in Canada 2016: A Focus on Family Violence in Canada.* Public Health Agency of Canada, 2016. Adapted and reproduced with permission from the Minister of Health, 2018.

Child maltreatment means that the child's rights are not being met, as outlined in the UN Convention on the Rights of the Child. Child maltreatment can occur within the home, in institutions, and even at the community or societal level:

- Parents or other individuals may abuse children.
- Institutional practices may be abusive to children, such as the inappropriate use of physical restraints.
- The physical, emotional, and social consequences can be devastating for the more than one million children in Canada who live in poverty.

In the *Canadian Incidence Study of Reported Child Abuse and Neglect—2008*, over one-third (31,506) of the 85,440 children whose maltreatment was substantiated were under six years of age. Rates of victimization were highest for younger children (17.10 per 1000 children in the population) under one year old compared to

14.57 per 1000 for five-year-olds, but there was no clear pattern by sex (Trocmé, 2012, pp. 1–2). This substantiates that the younger the child, the more vulnerable she or he is to child maltreatment.

Types of Maltreatment

Generally, child maltreatment is categorized into five types: neglect, physical abuse, emotional abuse, sexual abuse, and witnessing family violence. Although this categorization can be useful, it implies distinctions that don't always exist. In reality, the five types of maltreatment do not operate exclusively of one another. In fact, it is common to find that categories of child maltreatment coexist.

- Gemma is being physically abused and is also abused emotionally or at least suffers emotionally as a result of pain inflicted on her.
- A child is being emotionally abused when she or he is exposed to violence in the home. This child may also be the victim of physical abuse through injury intended for that parent, such as being cut by shards of glass from a bottle thrown across the room or suffering a blow while trying to "protect" the non-offending adult.
- An educator who belittles a child's attempts at mastery of a skill and who ignores the child's needs for comfort when needed is being both emotionally abusive and neglectful.

Neglect

Neglect occurs when parents and caregivers fail to meet the child's physical, emotional, and social needs, through inattention or omission.

The *Canadian Incidence Study of Reported Child Abuse and Neglect—2008* (PHAC, 2010) identified neglect (34%) and exposure to intimate-partner violence (34%) as the highest substantiated forms of child maltreatment (see Figure 8.3). The consequences of neglect can be extreme, especially for infants and young children. Inadequate emotional and physical stimulation and malnutrition cause a condition known as "failure to thrive." Infants who suffer from this condition gain little weight, with no medical explanation, and experience delays in development, particularly in language, during the second year of life. The consequences of children's exposure to intimate-partner violence are discussed later in this unit (see Emotional Abuse, page 486).

The *Canadian Incidence Study of Reported Child Abuse and Neglect—2008* (PHAC, 2010, p. 30) outlines eight forms of neglect, with failure to supervise being the most prevalent form reported:

- Failure to supervise or protect leading to physical harm, *for example,*
  The child is left alone on a balcony and falls over.

- Failure to supervise or protect a child from possible sexual abuse, *for example,*
  The parents leave a child with a babysitter even though they suspect the babysitter may be sexually fondling her.

- Physical neglect, *for example,*

  The caregiver failed to care for the child adequately: inadequate nutrition or clothing and unhygienic or dangerous living conditions.

- Medical neglect (including dental), *for example,*

  The caregiver refused to allow medical or dental treatment to alleviate physical harm or suffering.

- Failure to provide psychiatric or psychological treatment, *for example,*

  The caregiver did not provide treatment for a child suffering from severe anxiety, depression, withdrawal, self-destructive or aggressive behaviour, or a condition that could seriously impair his or her development.

- Permits maladaptive or criminal behaviour, *for example,*

  A child has committed a criminal offence with the caregiver's encouragement or because of the caregiver's failure to supervise the child adequately.

- Abandonment or refusal of custody, *for example,*

  The caregiver has died, without making adequate provisions for care and custody, or the caregiver refused to take custody of a child.

- Educational neglect, *for example,*

  A caregiver knowingly allowed a child to miss school regularly, repeatedly kept the child at home (at least five days a month), or failed to enroll the child in school.

FIGURE 8.3 Primary Category of Substantiated Child Maltreatment in Canada, 2008

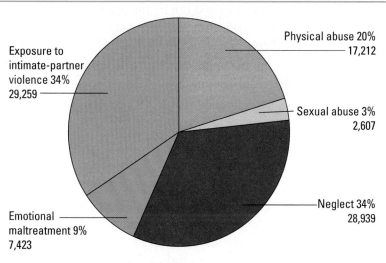

Physical abuse 20%
17,212

Exposure to intimate-partner violence 34%
29,259

Sexual abuse 3%
2,607

Neglect 34%
28,939

Emotional maltreatment 9%
7,423

* Total estimated number of substantiated investigations is 85,440, based on a sample 6,163 substantiated investigations.

Source: © All rights reserved. *Canadian Incidence Study of Reported Child Abuse and Neglect.* Public Health Agency of Canada, 2008. Adapted and reproduced with permission from the Minister of Health, 2018.

Physical Abuse

Children who have suffered injuries that were inflicted by parents, older siblings, extended family members, or others have been physically abused. In some cases, abuse occurs only once, but in most situations, the child is abused over a period of time. The physical abuse usually becomes more severe over time; the abuser often justifies his or her actions in terms of discipline and may not have initially intended to hurt the child. There are as many types of injuries as there are ways and objects with which someone can physically abuse. The *Canadian Incidence Study of Reported Child Abuse and Neglect—2008* identified several forms of physical abuse (Jud & Trocmé, 2013, p. 1):

- Slapped or spanked (54%)
- Shaken, pushed, grabbed, or thrown (30%)
- Hit with objects (21%)
- Punched, kicked, or bitten (8%)
- Other physical abuse, such as choking, poisoning, or stabbing

The percentage of these methods of inflicting physical abuse total more than 100%. Frequently a child will experience a combination of methods that cause the injuries.

The following is a list of the five physical injury categories that can result from **physical abuse**. Certain types of injuries are common to physical abuse.

1. **Bruises.** Figure 8.4 illustrates the common areas of bruising on the body and areas where bruises are questionable (not likely accidental).
2. **Burns.** Burns to a child's skin such as scalding the skin with very hot water or burning the skin using something like a lit cigarette are deliberate, not accidental, injuries.
3. **Fractures.** Bone fractures in a child can be the result of twisting, pulling, or shaking an arm or leg. Also, punching or kicking any part of a child's body can cause a fracture elsewhere.
4. **Head injuries.** Injuries to the brain are the most common causes of death in children. (See Abusive Head Trauma, below.)
5. **Abdominal injuries.** A deliberate fist or kick to the abdomen can injure internal organs.

Abusive Head Trauma

Abusive head trauma (AHT) is a form of nonaccidental head injury with or without impact, occurs when an infant or young child is shaken violently, usually by a parent or caregiver. You may be familiar with the term "shaken baby syndrome." The term "abusive head trauma" is replacing "shaken baby syndrome" because it accurately describes the serious injuries that are inflicted on a child's brain and eyes (Payne, 2015, p. 1). The Canadian Paediatric Society (CPS) (2005), together with other organizations, endorsed the *Joint Statement on Shaken Baby Syndrome* to contribute to public awareness.

The demands of caring for an infant, especially a baby's crying, may trigger a frustrated parent or caregiver to shake the infant. Although it can happen with small children, shaken baby syndrome is so named because infants under the age

FIGURE 8.4   Children's Bruises

Areas of Bruising

Common (over bony prominences)

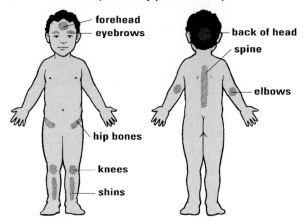

- forehead
- eyebrows
- back of head
- spine
- elbows
- hip bones
- knees
- shins

Questionable (over soft, fleshy areas)

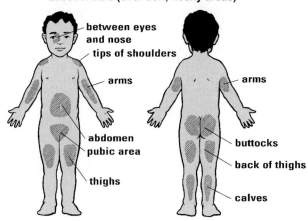

- between eyes and nose
- tips of shoulders
- arms
- arms
- abdomen
- pubic area
- buttocks
- back of thighs
- thighs
- calves

of one are the most common victims. They are particularly susceptible to injury because of their large head, heavy brain, and weak neck muscles, coupled with the fact that the offender is much larger and stronger than the infant.

It is never acceptable to shake or harm a baby or toddler, or anyone for that matter. There are usually no outward signs of trauma even if the shaking occurred against something (it is often something soft, such as a mattress), but the damage to the brain can be very serious (CPS, 2005). The rotational force cuts off blood vessels around the brain and leads to internal bleeding, sometimes resulting in swelling of the brain, which causes further damage. Depending on the severity of the symptoms, a physician may not diagnose a head injury. *For example, a physician may observe a baby who is mildly shaking or trembling and experiencing some vomiting.* This could be explained by the flu. On the other hand, the baby's symptoms could include seizures or loss of consciousness, or the baby could die. Approximately 25% of children who were clinically diagnosed (with an abusive or traumatic head injury) die, and about 80% of those who survive have lifelong neurological damage, such as blindness, cerebral palsy, learning disabilities, and behavioural problems (Barr, 2006).

What can help prevent parents from shaking their baby, or other violent behaviour, causing abusive head trauma? There is evidence indicating that very young babies' crying pattern is the most common trigger for abusive head trauma. "In part, this is because infant crying, especially prolonged unsoothable crying, has been interpreted clinically as something wrong with the infant, the infant's caregiver, or the interactions between them" (Barr, 2012, p. 17294). However, evidence has found that early increase in crying in normal infants is typical and short-lived behavioural development and usually does not reflect anything wrong or abnormal. If parents and caregivers learn this, before or soon after birth, there are positive implications for preventing infant abuse.

NELSONstudy

To access Resource Materials, visit NelsonStudy.

The National Center on Shaken Baby Syndrome is the only worldwide organization that is dedicated solely to the prevention of this form of child maltreatment and encourages the widest distribution of their materials possible to health care facilities and the general public. (See Resource Materials.) According to the Period of PURPLE Crying program, a baby may cry more each week from birth, the most in the second month and then less by the time the baby is three to five months old. (See Resource Materials.) This is a typical pattern for all infants and nothing you try seems to soothe them. This program is based on over 50 years of research on normal infant crying conducted by Dr. R. G. Barr and other scientists worldwide. Such a prevention program helps parents and caregivers understand the pattern of crying in infants, validates the frustration that comes when one can't soothe a crying baby, and suggests how one can cope positively with this developmental phase in infants.

Female Genital Mutilation/Cutting

Female genital mutilation/cutting (FGM/C) is an extreme form of physical abuse that has come to the attention of the general public in Canada since the early 1990s. The severity of the mutilation is classified into the four types described below (World Health Organization [WHO], 2008, p. 24):

1. partial or total removal of the clitoris and/or prepuce (clitoridectomy)
2. partial or total removal of the clitoris and the labia minora, with or without excision of the labia majora (excision)
3. narrowing of the vaginal orifice with creation of a covering seal by cutting and appositioning the labia minora and/or the labia majora, with or without excision of the clitoris (infibulation)
4. all other harmful procedures to the female genitalia for non-medical purposes, for example, pricking, piercing, incising, scraping, and cauterization.*

The short- and long-term health effects of this practice can be physically, emotionally, and socially devastating to the girls and women who are subjected to it, causing excruciating pain and sometimes death. According to UNICEF (2013), more than 200 million girls and women alive today have been subjected to this

---

*Source: Reproduced, with the permission of the publisher, from World Health Organization, "Eliminating Female Genital Mutilation: An Interagency Statement, 2008," http://apps.who.int/iris/bitstream/10665/43839/1/9789241596442_eng.pdf

violence in 30 countries in Africa, the Middle East, and Asia, where the vast majority of FGM/C takes place. Increasing migration, including to Canada, has increased the number of girls and women living outside their country of origin who have undergone FGM/C or who may be at risk for being subjected to the practice (Bennett, 2010, p. 134). Possible indicators that girls may be at risk include the following (Bennett, 2010, p. 138):

- The family comes from a country where FGM/C is common, and the child talks about going for a long holiday to her birth country with a relative.
- The child confides that there will be a special procedure and celebration for her.

FGM/C is usually done when girls are between the ages of 4 and 10 years, without anesthetic and under unsterile conditions. Culture, tradition, and religion are used as justification for this violent abuse, but in reality, no religion dictates this practice. Therefore, using religion as a rationale for violence is insupportable. WHO (2008, p. 8) holds the following position regarding female genital mutilation:

> Seen from a human rights perspective, the practice reflects deep-rooted inequality between the sexes, and constitutes an extreme form of discrimination against women. Female genital mutilation is nearly always carried out on minors and is therefore a violation of the rights of the child. The practice also violates the rights to health, security and physical integrity of the person, the right to be free from torture and cruel, inhuman or degrading treatment, and the right to life when the procedure results in death.*

The UN Convention on the Rights of the Child (see Appendix 8.1, page 529) refers to the evolving capacity of children to make decisions, but due to cultural or religious expectations, a girl's decision to undergo FGM/C is not free of coercion. A common, coordinated approach promoting positive social change at community, national, and international levels could lead to FGM/C being abandoned within a generation (WHO, 2008).

Many girls and women who come to Canada are victims of FGM/C. A range of issues may emerge for these girls and women, and they must be treated with sensitivity. If you have had this procedure, seek out caring and enlightened physicians and other professionals who will be supportive to your physical, emotional, and social well-being. Child protection agencies, particularly those in large Canadian cities, have developed a policy to respond to victims of FGM/C. These policies acknowledge that girls who have already undergone the practice need compassion and support—particularly culturally relevant support. Child protection agencies also aim to protect young girls where there is the risk of this physical abuse. Canada's Criminal Code prohibits citizens and landed immigrants from being removed from the country and subjected to FGM/C. Parents who insist on continuing this practice do so illegally, using untrained persons in unhygienic conditions and putting their daughter at substantial risk.

---

*Source: Reproduced, with the permission of the publisher, from World Health Organization, "Eliminating Female Genital Mutilation: An Interagency Statement, 2008," http://apps.who.int/iris/bitst ream/10665/43839/1/9789241596442_eng.pdf

CANADA'S RESPONSE TO FEMALE GENITAL MUTILATION: IS CANADA FAILING OUR GIRLS?

In 1997, the Parliament of Canada passed an amendment to the *Criminal Code* of Canada expressly prohibiting all forms of female genital mutilation in Canada. Under the code, it is prohibited to aid, abet or counsel such assault and to interfere with genitalia for nonmedical reasons. Moreover, the amendment expressly prohibits the transport of a child outside of Canada for the purpose of obtaining female genital mutilation. Anyone found to have carried out these offences faces up to 14 years in prison and/or a fine.*

However, the authors make the following points:

- Female genital mutilation has been banned in Canada since 1997.
- Other Western countries that have also long banned the practice have recently seen prosecutions, but there have been no prosecutions in Canada.
- A number of countries are taking proactive measures to prevent the practice; Canada should consider adopting preventive measures as well.*

*Source: "Canada's Response to Female Genital Mutilation: Are We Failing Our Girls?" C. Packer, V. Runnels, & R. Labonté. *CMAJ-JAMC*. 2015, April 7, 187(6): E188-E189. Copied under licence from Access Copyright. Further reproduction, distribution or transmission is prohibited except as otherwise permitted by law.

Between WHO's 2008 statement on female genital mutilation and 2013, there have been legislative steps to ban the practice of FGM/C in all countries where it had been permitted. This step has built awareness and increased the movement worldwide to protect girls and encourage their full development. The next important step is to enforce the law, to send out a strong message determined to prevent girls from being cut, and support those who have undergone FGM/C by holding the offenders accountable. There is still much more to be done to eliminate the practice of female genital mutilation/cutting, but it is hoped that broader strategies will have impact (e.g., a strong monitoring and evaluation system to demonstrate progress in the progression of social change and ensure accountability) (UNFPA & UNICEF, 2014, p. 36).

Discipline versus Punishment

The practice of corporal punishment, often a hotly debated issue in parenting, illustrates how difficult it is to define physical abuse. Violence in our society is not only accepted, it is also often revered. Some of the most popular movies of our time depict extreme violence. At the same time, the media bombards us with images of war and political unrest, institutional and family child abuse, date rape, murders of young women, spousal abuse, and elder abuse. In our society, it is common to see violence and, in many situations, accept violence. It is not uncommon to excuse the violence or even blame the victim. We say, "It was the alcohol" or "He had a bad day." We may even ask, "What did she do to provoke the violence?"

Federal and provincial/territorial governments have acknowledged the prevalence of child and intimate-partner abuse and have begun to take a stronger stand against violence in the home. Children are not their parents' property, nor is one spouse (or common-law partner) owned by the other. *For example, it may be hard to believe that only in the last 35 years was the* Criminal Code *amended to state that husbands have no legal right to force their wives to have sex.*

Corporal punishment is the use of physical force to discipline children. It is not against the law in Canada, but it is illegal in over 56 countries, many of which are in Europe. A growing number of countries in Africa have signed their support of the Global Initiative to End All Corporal Punishment of Children. This initiative has a mandate to uphold Article 19 of the UN Convention on the Rights of the Child: *You have the right to be protected from being hurt and mistreated, in body or mind* (see Appendix 8.1, page 529).

The *Criminal Code* of Canada defines assault as the use of physical force on an individual without consent. Assault charges can be laid any time that an adult strikes, shakes, or kicks another adult. However, Section 43 of the *Code* gives adults permission to use physical force on children. Children are the only people in Canada who can be legally "assaulted." Their assailants need not fear legal reprisal unless the force is deemed to be unreasonable. This difference between the way the *Criminal Code* deals with hitting children and hitting adults reflects a lack of societal respect for the child. The *Criminal Code* of Canada defines the degree to which corporal punishment is legal, beyond which it is excessive and is considered child abuse. "Excessive" is sometimes difficult to distinguish from "not excessive," and the difficulty can lead to a vast range of interpretations. Some examples of when punishment crosses the line include leaving marks, shapes, bruises, cuts, or scrapes; when the skin is burned; when bones are broken; and when hair is pulled out in clumps.

Many parents who adhere more closely to authoritarian discipline believe that corporal punishment in the form of slapping, spanking, or even beating is an appropriate form of punishment. These parents may use the familiar refrain "spare the rod and spoil the child" or insist that their own parents spanked them as children and they've turned out fine. Much of raising children has been subtly or overtly concerned with being master over them—controlling children or breaking their spirit. Even when parents or educators have some understanding of child development, they may feel an overriding need to exert authoritarian control over children. In some ECLC programs, we hear phrases such as "Can the teacher control the children?" or "Does she have control over the group?" This is not surprising because many adults have been raised with these principles. No one is implying that children shouldn't learn respect for others, but we must be aware of methods and motivations in guiding children if our goals are to promote self-esteem and model self-control. Children benefit when parents learn to guide their children with positive discipline, instead of viewing corporal punishment as an option.

Corporal punishment often results from an adult's failure at self-control—as a means to relieve anger, stress, and frustration. Who benefits? What are children learning from being slapped, spanked, shaken, beaten, constantly yelled at, or told hurtful things? Anti-spanking advocates believe that children learn the following from corporal punishment:

- it's permissible to hurt and humiliate someone, especially someone smaller than you ("My parents do it to me, so it's acceptable");

- the reason they need to obey rules is to avoid being hit;
- when they get bigger, they will have power over others; and
- violence is an acceptable way of expressing anger and solving problems.

Parents who believe that spanking is acceptable and appropriate may justify their actions in the following ways:

- "We are teaching them right from wrong." In reality, spanking teaches children only what is not acceptable. They will not learn right from wrong without being taught what they should be doing. Spanking may also communicate to children that they are "bad" persons.
- "It is an act of love." This is a confusing message for children, who learn that people who love them also hurt them. It's not surprising, then, that so many women choose husbands and boyfriends who abuse them because traditional gender socialization teaches girls to be submissive and boys to dominate.
- "It's a cultural practice." Hitting children is a widespread practice throughout Canada. Many adults today, regardless of culture or race, were hit as children and believe that it is an acceptable parenting practice.
- "They need to respect adults." Rather than respecting the adults who spank them, they fear them. Eventually, when they are beyond fear, they often lose respect for those adults.
- "I don't want them to become spoiled." Children who are "spoiled" learn disrespectful behaviour from inconsistent parenting, insufficient provision of necessary structure, and neglect of children's needs, not from a lack of spanking.

A review of over 150 studies demonstrated overwhelmingly that corporal punishment is harmful to children, adults, and societies. A Canadian study (Afifi et al., 2017) researched the connection between harsh physical punishment in childhood and intimate-partner violence in adulthood. Their conclusion was that children who are pushed, grabbed, shoved, hit, or slapped or are exposed to domestic violence in their homes have an increased probability of experiencing intimate-partner violence when they are older.

All of the associations with corporal punishment have shown negative outcomes, and no studies have found evidence of any benefits (Global Initiative to End All Corporal Punishment of Children, 2016, p. 35):

> Corporal punishment causes direct physical harm to children and impacts negatively in the short- and long-term on their mental and physical health and education. Far from teaching children how to behave, it impairs moral internalisation, increases antisocial behaviour and damages family relationships. It increases aggression in children and increases the likelihood of perpetrating and experiencing violence as an adult. It is closely linked to other forms of violence in societies, and ending it is essential in combatting other violence, including partner violence. Respect for children's rights to protection, health, development and education requires that all corporal punishment of children be prohibited in law and eliminated in practice.

The debate over spanking becomes relevant when we discuss child maltreatment. Corporal punishment by parents is not, in itself, against the law, but child advocates agree that it is not a positive way to discipline children. Built into the use of corporal punishment is a lack of societal respect for the child. This is evident in the legal ambiguity. Assault charges can be laid whenever an adult strikes, shakes, or kicks another adult. There is no ambiguity here. It is important to realize that children benefit when parents, rather than viewing corporal punishment as an option, learn to guide their children with positive discipline, not punishment.

The many good reasons not to use corporal punishment for the long-term well-being of Canada's children should motivate policymakers, educators, and parents to put much effort into alternatives. In 2004, the Supreme Court of Canada decided to uphold several national and regional groups concerned with children's rights who advocated for a number of years for the repeal of Section 43. These groups continue to advocate for the criminalization of any kind of corporal punishment, including spanking. To date, Section 43 has been successfully used by some parents as a defence for injuring their children. Repealing this law would send a strong message to the community that this method of "child rearing" is no longer condoned. In handing down the 2004 decision, the Supreme Court offered certain parameters for assisting a court in deciding whether the physical force was "reasonable," such as forbidding the use of an object and slaps across the face or blows to the head and forbidding any physical force of children under two years old.

The lack of legislation against corporal punishment has a direct impact on the number of physical abuse cases in Canada. This was evident in a nationally representative study of 8164 perpetrators whereby physical abuse was substantiated (supported with evidence) (Gonzalez et al., 2008). The findings suggest that the perpetrators (mostly parents) did not predict injury to the child; their intent was to discipline their child. In other words, Canada's tolerance of corporal punishment makes the boundaries between punishment and abuse unclear for families. Anger and loss of control can lead to unintentional physical abuse.

CRITICAL THINKING

As of 2018, Canada has not yet joined the countries that have abolished corporal punishment, including spanking. Identify how the parameters discussed above (a) support or (b) do not support a child's rights according to the UN Convention on the Rights of the Child (see Appendix 8.1, page 529) and Global Initiative to End All Corporal Punishment of Children's website. (See Resource Materials.)

NELSONstudy

To access Resource Materials, visit NelsonStudy.

Two essential components of effective parenting skills are responsiveness and discipline. Appropriate discipline is firm but not excessively restrictive and does not involve humiliating or shaming. There are clear limits to and expectations regarding children's actions; children are encouraged to take responsibility for their actions and learn from the consequences of their behaviour. When confrontation becomes necessary, parents should encourage children to find acceptable alternatives to actions that are not acceptable. The parenting style that combines a high level of caring and involvement with high but reasonable expectations is most likely to help children develop the confidence and coping skills needed to maintain competence and the sense of perspective that shapes how they react to stress. The interaction of these factors also contributes to the development of resiliency. Support for parents in developing knowledge and skills with regard to child development can go a long way in focusing on positive ongoing relationships with their children.

Emotional Abuse

Emotional abuse is likely the most widespread type of abuse, yet it is also the most difficult to prove. Children are unlikely to escape emotional harm when they are physically or sexually abused or neglected. Although the physical injuries may heal, the impact of emotional abuse may be long lasting. Although no parent or caregiver is immune from getting angry or frustrated at times, emotional abuse is characterized by the patterns of behaviour listed below.

PATTERNS OF BEHAVIOUR: EMOTIONAL ABUSE

- **Terrorizing or threat of violence:** A climate of fear, placing the child in unpredictable or chaotic circumstances, bullying or frightening a child, threats of violence against the child or child's loved ones or objects.
- **Verbal abuse or belittling:** Nonphysical forms of overtly hostile or rejecting treatment. Shaming or ridiculing the child, or belittling and degrading the child.
- **Isolation/confinement:** Adult cuts the child off from normal social experiences, prevents friendships, or makes the child believe that he or she is alone in the world. Includes locking a child in a room or isolating the child from the normal household routines.
- **Inadequate nurturing or affection:** Through acts of omission, does not provide adequate nurturing or affection. Being detached, uninvolved; failing to express affection, caring, and love; and interacting only when absolutely necessary.
- **Exploiting or corrupting behaviour:** The adult permits or encourages the child to engage in destructive, criminal, antisocial, or deviant behaviour.

Source: © All rights reserved. *Canadian Incidence Study of Reported Child Abuse and Neglect.* Public Health Agency of Canada, 2008. Adapted and reproduced with permission from the Minister of Health, 2018.

PHAC's list includes permitting children to witness violence in emotional maltreatment, which we cover in Family Violence.

Emotional abuse can occur without children being abused in any other way. Parents and caregivers who never use physical discipline may not realize that they are being abusive when they ridicule children, frequently use sarcasm or harsh criticism, or make inappropriate demands. This ongoing rejection is harmful to children's feelings of self-worth. For some parents, particular times create situations that trigger feelings of anger, disapproval, frustration, etc. Perhaps it is at the time of a developmental milestone (e.g., learning to use the toilet) or a time of the day (e.g., bedtime). In some family situations, one child is singled out as the scapegoat—the target at which the parent's anger is inappropriately directed. This may also be an issue in an ECLC program! Awareness of how each child is regarded by educators and other staff is essential.

Family violence can erupt in all families, and does not exist solely in male/female relationships. Family violence is also found in any intimate relationship and in homes where extended families live together. In heterosexual relationships, men are not the only perpetrators of family violence. However, statistically, women are more likely to be victimized by family violence and the perpetrator is most likely to be the male partner. Therefore, the partner being abused is referred to using feminine terms and the abuser using masculine terms.*

Family violence is any form of maltreatment or neglect that children or adults experience from a family member, or from someone with whom they have an intimate relationship. It is an abuse of power by one person to hurt and control someone who trusts and depends on that individual. Intimate-partner violence is defined as violence perpetrated against spouses and dating partners, either in current or former relationships (Government of Canada, 2014, p. 1).

Any youth or adult can be a victim of intimate-partner violence, although women make up the majority of cases. We refer to women as the victims in these discussions; however, this in no way should be interpreted as negating the abuse of men in interpersonal relationships. Also, family violence occurs across all ethnic, cultural, racial, and class backgrounds (Canadian Women's Foundation, 2014).

Exposing children to domestic violence is often categorized as a form of emotional abuse. However, the development of child welfare policies and responses to domestic violence (often called "intimate-partner violence") remains uneven across Canada. In some regions, it is recognized as a separate category of maltreatment. The majority are cases in which the child's mother is being abused by her partner (e.g., the child's father or stepfather, the mother's boyfriend or same-sex partner). However, the child may be witnessing abuse of another or additional family members, such as grandparents.

Here are some facts on family violence in Canada (Government of Canada, 2017, pp. 1–2):

- Of all reported violent crime in 2015, more than one quarter (26%) resulted from family violence.
- Almost 70% of family violence victims were women and girls.
- Experts know that rates of all forms of family violence are underestimated. For example, in 2014, fewer than one in five (19%) who had been abused by their spouse reported abuse to police.
- Among children and youth victims of violence reported to police [in 2015,] 30% were victims of family violence perpetrated by parents, siblings, extended family member or spouse.**

There are many reasons why people don't report family violence. One is because of the stigma associated with it. Young children may not report violence because they may have limited contacts outside the family in whom they can safely confide.

---

*Source: Excerpted with permission from P. Rimer, 2018. *Making a Difference: The Community Responds to Child Abuse*, Eighth Edition (Toronto: Boost Child & Youth Advocacy Centre), p. 99.

**Source: Statistics Canada, 2017. *Family Violence: How Big Is the Problem in Canada?* Retrieved February 2018 from, https://www.canada.ca/en/public-health/services/health-promotion/stop-family-violence/problem-canada.html. Reproduced and distributed on an "as is" basis with the permission of Statistics Canada.

INTIMATE-PARTNER VIOLENCE

Women are more likely to experience severe spousal violence compared to men

Compared to men, women who experience spousal violence are:

- twice as likely to report being sexually assaulted, beaten, choked or threatened with a gun or a knife.
- more likely to report higher rates of injury caused by abuse (40% of female victims compared to 24% of male victims).
- more likely to experience long term Post-Traumatic Stress Disorder (PTSD)-like effects than men.
- more likely to report being put down or called names than men.

Indigenous women are more likely to experience spousal violence

- Nearly 60% of Indigenous women who reported spousal abuse also reported being physically injured as a result of it versus 41% of non-Indigenous women.
- Half of the Indigenous women experiencing violence reported the most severe forms of violence: being sexually assaulted, beaten, choked, or threatened with a gun or a knife.

Young women have the highest rates overall

According to police-reported data in 2015, women aged 15–24 present the highest rates of dating violence.

Same-sex relationships

Women who self-identified as lesbian or bisexual reported significantly higher rates of violence by a partner than heterosexual women (11% vs. 3%). (Government of Canada, 2017, pp. 1–2)

Source: Statistics Canada, 2017. *Family Violence: How Big Is the Problem in Canada?* Retrieved February 2018 from https://www.canada.ca/en/public-health/services/health-promotion/stop-family-violence/problem-canada.html. Reproduced and distributed on an "as is" basis with the permission of Statistics Canada.

WITNESSING VIOLENCE IS A FORM OF EMOTIONAL MALTREATMENT

PHAC includes children witnessing violence within the category of emotional maltreatment; however, the authors have covered a child's exposure to violence in this section:

- **Direct witness to physical violence:** The child is physically present and witnesses the violence between intimate partners.
- **Indirect exposure to physical violence:** Includes situations where the child overhears but does not see the violence between intimate partners or sees some of the immediate consequences of the assault (e.g., injuries to the mother), or the child is told or overhears conversations about the assault.
- **Exposure to emotional violence:** Includes situations in which the child is exposed directly or indirectly to emotional violence between intimate partners. Includes witnessing or overhearing emotional abuse of one partner by the other.

(continued)

- **Exposure to non-partner physical violence:** A child has been exposed to violence occurring between a caregiver and another person who is not the spouse/partner of the caregiver (e.g., between a caregiver and a neighbour, grandparent, aunt, or uncle).

Children exposed to family violence live in an atmosphere of threat and fear, even though they themselves may not be assaulted, and are in physical and psychological danger. They are caught up in a complex dynamic of physical or verbal violence in which they feel powerless. In addition, if they escape violence in the home by leaving with their abused parent, children often live in poverty.

On any given night in Canada:

- 3,491 women and their 2,724 children sleep in shelters to escape abuse.
- 300 women and children are turned away because shelters are already full. (Canadian Women's Foundation, 2014, p. 2)

In addition to seeking safety for themselves, the desire to protect their children from suffering or witnessing abuse is a driving force for women to seek shelter.

Violence often escalates after leaving home, so the fear continues. Because so many incidents of family violence are unreported, the estimate that 1 in 10 women are abused is conservative, and the number of children who witness violence in their home is substantial. Children's neglect and exposure to intimate-partner violence, at 34% each, are the two highest substantiated forms of child maltreatment (PHAC, 2010) (see Figure 8.3, page 477). The consequences of children's exposure to intimate-partner violence, especially of their primary caregiver, often result in the same types of emotional and behavioural problems that children who have been directly abused experience. These may include symptoms of the following (Rimer, 2018):

- attachment disorder
- post-traumatic stress disorder
- lower self-esteem and social competence
- aggressive behaviour
- conduct problems
- anxiety
- depression

Sexual Abuse

Child **sexual abuse** is generally defined as the involvement of children in sexual activity in which the offender uses power over the child. The offender seeks sexual gratification from the child, who may or may not be of the same gender. Sexual abuse includes oral, anal, genital, buttock, and breast contact or the use of the penis, fingers, or objects for vaginal or anal penetration, fondling, and sexual stimulation. Technology-assisted exploitation includes sexual exploitation over the Internet and exposing a child to or involving a child in pornography or sex trafficking.

TYPES OF CHILD SEXUAL ABUSE

PHAC's (2010, p. 65) definition of child sexual molestation or exploitation includes

- oral, vaginal, or anal sexual activity;
- attempted sexual activity;
- sexual touching or fondling;
- exposure;
- voyeurism;
- involvement in prostitution or pornography; and
- verbal sexual harassment.

Exploitation of the child for pornographic purposes and making a child available to others as a child prostitute are additional forms of sexual abuse. Inappropriate solicitation, exhibitionism, and exposure to erotic material for the purpose of sexually arousing a child or to use to stimulate oneself are also forms of sexual abuse. Over 15 years, the massive increase in Internet sexual exploitation has added a terrifying level of sexual abuse.

Research suggests that 13% to 19% of children and youth in the Canadian population have experienced online sexual exploitation. Sexual exploitation of children, mostly girls, has gradually involved younger children and includes crueler images. Cybertip.ca, Canada's tipline to report online sexual exploitation of children, stated in 2012 that 82% of the images reported were of children under 12 years old, and 57% of those are younger than 8 years old. There is also concern that compulsive pornographic Internet usage and online networks of offenders may encourage offenders to abuse children and young people in person (Public Safety Canada, 2015, p. 9).

J. Rimer's (2007) comprehensive literature review highlighted the magnitude of this issue, even when written over 10 years ago. Rimer stated that the accessibility, production, and trade of child sexual abuse images through the various popular forms of Internet-related technology have provided a means by which child pornography can flourish as an industry. The term in the *Criminal Code* of Canada is "child pornography," although "child sexual abuse images" is a term that more specifically reflects abuse of children and youth in these situations.

This industry is worldwide through cyberspace, and its perceived anonymity, instant and adaptable capabilities (such as webcam, digital photography, and pseudomorphing images, to name a few), and ease of electronic transmittal have created a "monster" industry for child sexual abuse. Even old images and films of child abuse from decades ago are scanned or uploaded and digitized, adding to the estimated hundreds of thousands of child sexual abuse images being sent weekly worldwide.

In recent years, the *Criminal Code* of Canada has been amended to create new criminal offences relating to child sexual assault and amending the provisions on child sex tourism. Ongoing Department of Justice Canada legislative proposed amendments before Parliament and Royal Assent aim to protect children from sexual exploitation by criminalizing a number of specific actions, including luring children on the Internet and transmitting, making available, or exporting and intentionally accessing child sexual abuse images on the Internet. New technologies present law enforcement with updated, helpful tools to track and catch offenders. Sadly, networks of offenders also find progressively secure devices to circulate child sexual abuse images over the Internet (Public Safety Canada, 2015, p. 8).

Abuse is never the child's fault. Some offenders use the excuse that the child or adolescent initiated the contact ("She came on to me") or was a willing participant. This assumes incorrectly that the child had the choice to refuse. The offender is in a position of power and must exercise self-control. Children are vulnerable not only because of their physical size but also because they depend emotionally and economically on adults and are easily manipulated due to their limited understanding of adult sexuality. It is more common to observe behavioural indicators of sexual abuse than physical indicators, although it is possible that the genitals have been injured or there is a sexually transmitted infection, including genital discomfort, pain on passing urine, and blood in the diaper or underwear. The more common indicators are unexplained changes in personality, nightmares and sleep disturbances, clinging or extreme seeking of affection or attention, and age-inappropriate sexual behaviour or knowledge (Rimer, 2018, p. 28). Children may also complain about headaches and stomach aches, which are related to the stress of sexual abuse.

The increase in reported cases of online child sexual exploitation is linked to the growth of Internet use and constantly evolving technologies, such as mobile devices. For example, from 2009–10 to 2011–12, Cybertip.ca registered a 214% increase in the number of reports concerning mobile devices (Public Safety Canada, 2015, p. 8).

An unknown percentage of sexual offenders are pedophiles who are sexually excited by children. Pedophilia is a medical diagnosis that requires certain criteria to be present. The victims of pedophiles are more likely to be boys than girls. However, most sexual offenders are heterosexual males who have sexual relationships with adult women as well as the children they sexually abuse.

The vast percentage of child and youth victims know the offender. In 2011, 89% of child and youth victims of sexual assault were victimized by somebody other than a stranger (Department of Justice Canada, 2013, p. 1). Offenders can be found among all ages (including adolescents), ethnocultural communities, and social classes. Most sexual abuse takes place in the context of an ongoing relationship between the abuser and the child. This longer-term relationship provides the offender with the opportunity to manipulate the child's desires and fears to exploit the relationship. Due to the nature of these relationships, the abuse can go on for years. Even in cases in which sexual abuse happened only once, children may experience an enormous degree of emotional turmoil. The sooner children are able to seek professional help the better.

Children often feel confused, especially because, in many cases, the sexual abuse is not painful and may even feel somewhat pleasurable. For some children, this contact may be the only physical affection they receive. When children realize that a trusted adult has betrayed them, children may feel guilt about "causing" the abuse or shame that it felt good sometimes. Children with a strong sense of self-worth and communication skills may be less likely to be sexually abused, but it is clear that the abuse is never the child's fault. It is almost impossible for the child to resist the abuse; offenders put a great deal of thought into how they will manipulate children.

Behavioural and Emotional Indicators of Maltreatment

This section examines some of the **behavioural and emotional indicators** that educators may observe in children who suffer from any type of maltreatment. What are behavioural and emotional indicators? They are signs, symptoms, or clues seen in a child, or in the adult in the child's life, that lead educators to suspect that the child is being maltreated. Unless we actually witness abuse, or a physician diagnoses physical injuries or symptoms consistent with abuse, we must remember that no single behaviour confirms child maltreatment.

Lars, usually a cheerful, sociable seven-year-old, now acts withdrawn. To suspect abuse immediately in his case is making a big leap. We must know more about what is happening in Lars's life and family. Perhaps his whole family is anxious about his mother's loss of her job. Maybe Lars is afraid of being bullied on the school playground.

Maltreatment can lead to serious emotional distress in children and a diminished sense of self-worth. Behavioural indicators differ depending on the child's personality and temperament. The following short list focuses only on general behavioural indicators that may be exhibited in children who are being maltreated in any way. The child may

- seem overcome with sadness, anger, or indifference
- appear not attached to anyone—withdraw from family, friends, and educators
- be afraid or unwilling to go home or run away
- withdraw and show no interest or curiosity in friends recently enjoyed play, activities, and friends
- be suspicious of physical contact (e.g., cringe when touched, including by someone familiar, but may cling to strangers)
- not show confidence in own abilities and be overly compliant with peers and with educators
- express anger directly, in tantrums or acting out physically or verbally; exhibit manipulative, passive-aggressive behaviour all of a sudden; demonstrate unacceptable behaviour to get attention (e.g., hitting a child for no reason, giving a high-five that hurts, or hugging someone too hard)
- exhibit self-damaging behaviour (e.g., unsafe risk-taking behaviour, hitting or cutting self, showing no reaction to pain, describing self as bad and as deserving punishment)
- demonstrate significant developmental delays in language, motor skills, or age-appropriate social connections with peers (Odhayani et al., 2013)

The examples above of behavioural indicators and many others of concern can apply to any of the types of maltreatment. However, because of the individual nature of the different types of abuse, some indicators tend to be more relevant to one type of abuse than another.

- In physical abuse, the child often demonstrates aggressive, acting-out behaviour.
- In emotional abuse, including exposure to family violence, the child sets unreasonably high expectations for self and refuses to try again if he or she doesn't succeed the first time.
- In sexual abuse, the child has an unusual level of sexual knowledge, sexual play, or excessive self-stimulation (masturbation) for his or her age and developmental level.
- In neglect, the child hoards food or continues to ask for helpings at lunch beyond what seems a reasonable amount of food for a child.

Possible Consequences of Maltreatment

Depending on a number of factors, abuse may affect some or every aspect of a child's life; it may have consequences that are psychological, physical, behavioural, academic, sexual, interpersonal, self-perceptual, or spiritual (Department of Justice Canada, 2002, p. 4).

Factors that influence the way in which the child is affected include (Lamont, 2010b, p. 2)

- the age and developmental status of the child when abuse occurred;
- the severity of maltreatment;
- the frequency and duration of maltreatment;
- the relationship between the child and the perpetrator; and
- the type(s) of abuse/neglect.

The topic of possible consequences of maltreatment is such a vast and multidimensional area of study that this textbook is unable to offer the depth required to do it justice. Each child is unique in terms of development, personality, and temperament. It is impossible to make generalizations about all children or about children who are survivors of maltreatment. Effects may appear at the time of the maltreatment or surface only in adolescence or adulthood. No one can predict the outcomes that children will experience as a result of maltreatment. Physical abuse such as abusive head trauma will likely have immediate consequences such as neurological damage, which may include blindness or other lifelong consequences. However, other consequences may emerge later, such as behavioural or mental health issues.

P. Rimer (2018, pp. 114–120) lists a range of feelings that may impact a child who has been maltreated: self-blame, fear, powerless and vulnerable, betrayal, loss, destructiveness to self or others, and hopelessness. Any or all of these feelings can obviously influence the child's emotional and social well-being.

Emotional and social difficulties affect children in the areas of attachment, security, trust, confidence, motivation, social sensitivity, and play behaviour. Frustrated by their limited social skills, their lack of achievement, and difficulties in their home environments, children who have experienced maltreatment are frequently aggressive or withdrawn. During the first few years of a child's brain development, we know that a young child's genetic potential is optimized when her or his world is rich in nurturing relationships and learning opportunities. These are the conditions that strengthen higher-level complex functions, such as self-regulation and problem solving, in the neocortex. However, the child who is exposed to threat and chaos strengthens the lower-level limbic functions, activating the stress hormone cortisol and adaptive responses to help him or her survive. *For example, it is well known that the attachment relationship between an infant and a primary caregiver has a profound impact on the infant's current functioning and future development. Jordan and Sketchley (2009, p. 4) note that research has demonstrated that up to 82% of maltreated infants suffer from serious disturbances of attachment with their caregivers.*

Research suggests that specific types of abuse are more closely related to some adverse outcomes than others—for example, the links between physical abuse and external violent or aggressive behaviour. Gender is often also associated with internalized behaviour, such as self-harm and eating disorders. Experiencing chronic and multiple forms of abuse increases the risk of more damaging and severe consequences for children and into adulthood (Lamont, 2010a).

At the other end of the life spectrum, there is much research into the connections between early adversity, markedly the experience of maltreatment as a child, and disease in adults. For example,

A scientific consensus is emerging that the origins of adult disease are often found among developmental and biological disruptions occurring during the early years of life. These early experiences can affect adult health in 2 ways—either by cumulative damage over time or by the biological embedding of adversities during sensitive developmental periods. In both cases, there can be a lag of many years, even decades, before early adverse experiences are expressed in the form of disease. From both basic research and policy perspectives, confronting the origins of disparities in physical and mental health early in life may produce greater effects than attempting to modify health-related behaviours or improve access to health care in adulthood. (Shonkoff et al., 2009, p. 2252)

There is a lot of research focused in recent years (and will be into the future) on the power of resilience: why one child who experienced one incident of abuse may suffer far more than another who had been abused for a number of years. Resilience is the individual's ability to bounce back from stress and adversity and take on new challenges (Hall & Pearson, 2004, p. 1). Much of the research focus presently is on ways to foster resilience, in all children as well as in children who have met with adversity. This is an area of knowledge and developing skills that, as upcoming professionals in ECLC, you are or will be learning about and practising.

Research supports focusing treatment on socioemotional problems because an increased belief in oneself, trust in others, and positive social skills are springboards to developing other competencies. Perry (2004, p. 4) identifies what he calls "Six Core Strengths for Children," which are strengths that trained educators promote daily in a program of best practices.

TABLE 8.1 Six Core Strengths for Children: A Vaccine against Violence

Attachment:	being able to form and maintain healthy emotional bonds and relationships
Self-regulation:	containing impulses, the ability to notice and control primary urges as well as feelings such as frustration
Affiliation:	being able to join and contribute to a group
Attunement:	being aware of others, recognizing the needs, interests, strengths, and values of others
Tolerance:	understanding and accepting differences in others
Respect:	finding value in differences, appreciating worth in yourself and others

For more information on the Six Core Strengths, visit the "Meet Dr. Bruce Perry" page at http://teacher.scholastic.com/professional/bruceperry.

Source: *Maltreatment and the Developing Child: How Early Childhood Experience Shapes Child and Culture* by Bruce D. Perry (2004), http://www.lfcc.on.ca/mccain/perry.pdf (April 2008). Reprinted with permission from Professor Bruce D. Perry, Child Trauma Academy.

Causes of Child Maltreatment

Child maltreatment is a complex issue that cannot be explained by any one theory. Many factors are involved in causing and perpetuating child abuse and neglect. Society consists of a number of interacting components, including economic, social, educational, cultural, individual, familial, and religious ones. The Department of Justice Canada (2002, p. 4) acknowledges the connection between child abuse and marginalization:

> There is increasing understanding that a child's vulnerability to abuse may be increased by factors such as dislocation, colonization, racism, sexism, homophobia, poverty and social isolation. For example, in the past, many children sent to institutions experienced abuse. Most of these children were from marginalized groups in our society including, among others, children with disabilities, children from racial and ethnic minorities, Aboriginal children and children living in poverty.

It is well known that over several generations, many Indigenous (First Nations, Inuit, and Métis) children and families in Canada have been plagued by numerous affronts, including institutional child maltreatment. Native residential schools across Canada, which operated from 1883 to 1996, resulted in the maltreatment of and a cultural and language void for many Indigenous children, often without recovery for individuals or their communities. There are varied estimates, but in all, more than 150,000 children were removed from their communities and forced to attend the schools with mostly dismal results, including rampant child maltreatment. Justice Murray Sinclair, chair of the Truth and Reconciliation Commission, revealed that the deaths of over 6000 children at residential schools have been documented, but that there are very likely more, due to lost or destroyed documents (Schwartz, 2015, pp. 1–2).

In 2015, the Truth and Reconciliation Commission released 94 calls to action to address the legacy of residential schools and the process of reconciliation. These fall under two main themes—legacy and reconciliation—with specific areas such as child welfare, education, health, language and culture, and justice listed under the former.

Even today, Indigenous children who experience maltreatment at home are placed in foster care at a rate twice that of non-Indigenous children. Statistics Canada's (2011, p. 19) National Household Survey reported that "3.6% of Aboriginal children aged 14 and under (14,225) were foster children, compared with 0.3% of non-Aboriginal children (15,345). Almost half (48.1%) of all children aged 14 and under in foster care were Aboriginal children."

Many Indigenous children are put into foster homes based on neglect, very often due largely to living conditions based on dismal poverty—unsafe housing, no running water, overcrowding, and many other circumstances that require changes from a social systems level.

According to Macdonald and Wilson (2013, p. 13), although 17% of all children in Canada live under the poverty line, 40% of Indigenous children but only 15% of non-Indigenous children do so.

This highlights the added vulnerability that Indigenous children and families face. Many foster homes may be positive environments for children, especially if culturally similar, but the opportunity to build families and communities "from the inside" is more complex when children are removed.

Although there are many stress factors that can affect parents' lives, not all parents under stress abuse or neglect their children. Just because parents are separating, for example, doesn't mean that you should look for signs of maltreatment. If you have developed a relationship with the family, you probably know how they have coped with stress in the past. If a family is experiencing several life events at the same time, the increased stress may be more than they are able to cope with, which can contribute to child maltreatment. Some families are under ongoing stress, such as those living in poverty or those in which one or more members have a chronic debilitating illness. Again, these families do not necessarily abuse their children. Similarly, a family's financial stability does not necessarily mean that a child cannot possibly be suffering maltreatment within the family.

We live in a mobile society, and for a variety of reasons (e.g., employment, education, housing), many adults live far from their parents, siblings, or extended family. New immigrants to Canada may feel disconnected at first without their families and friends, and they may struggle with having cultural differences from those around them in Canada and adjusting to a different climate. Refugees are people who are forced to leave their home countries because of serious human rights abuses. Many refugee individuals and families have a well-founded fear of being maltreated for reasons of race, ethnicity, religion, nationality, and sexual orientation, among others. In Canada, they also may worry about being sent

Courtesy of Barb Pimento

back to their country of origin or of facing persecution in Canada. While many Canadians are supportive of refugees, unfortunately this isn't always the experience for refugees.

Having access to social support networks is one of the determinants of health. "Far too many children grow up without the number and quality of relational opportunities needed to organize fully the neural networks to mediate important socio-emotional characteristics such as empathy" (Perry, 2004, p. 4). As a society, as a community, and as individuals, we can help parents raise children in more positive environments by reducing stressors and helping them cope. Some parents are fortunate enough to have a network of friends or extended family members (e.g., their adult siblings or parents) who provide emotional support or help, sometimes in the form of respite, when needed. Those families who are isolated, with no one to turn to in times of extreme stress, can be at higher risk for abuse or neglect. When the ECLC program is a support system for families, it reduces the sense of isolation. Families are then more likely to seek help when needed.

Courtesy of Sister Celeste—Fort Norman

PREVENTING CHILD MALTREATMENT

Everyone in society has a role to play in preventing child maltreatment. Educators are professional advocates for children, and they can make a significant contribution to prevention. Educators' and ECE students' roles can be divided into three

To describe the function of child protection agencies with regard to child maltreatment. (LO 5)

To define primary prevention and outline the educators' role in the ECLC environment and beyond. (LO 1, 2, 4, 6)

To define secondary prevention and discuss the educators' role in identifying suspected child maltreatment and in documenting and reporting it to a child protection agency. (LO 1, 2, 4, 5, 6)

To define tertiary prevention and discuss the educators' role in working with children, families, and agencies. (LO 1, 2, 4, 5, 6)

To identify individual, community, and societal levels of child maltreatment prevention. (LO 1, 2, 4, 5, 6)

levels of prevention: primary, secondary, and tertiary. We begin this section with a brief introduction to child protection agencies that are involved in prevention.

Child Protection Agencies

Child protection legislation and services are under provincial or territorial jurisdiction, as are health, education, and ECLC. Although the laws themselves are quite similar in all provinces and territories, the application of the laws varies across the country. As a result, the delivery system varies not only across Canada but between regions within a province or a territory. Due to differences, and for the sake of clarity, we use the term "child protection agency" throughout this unit. The primary goal in all jurisdictions remains the same: prevention and community support services. Child protection agencies are required by law to assess all reports of suspected child maltreatment and to take steps to protect children from further abuse or neglect. This discussion touches on the broad responsibilities of the agencies.

The job titles of the personnel working in an agency's office vary. We use "child protection workers" to describe the people who take the calls from directors or educators, teachers, and other members of the public and who are assigned to the child's case. They are usually social workers trained to assess situations in which children are "in need of protection." As it relates to ECLC programs, the child protection worker talks with the staff, family member, or other adult who is reporting and advises how to proceed. The staff may be asked to continue to observe the child and document observations in the child's file. Based on this report, a child protection worker is assigned to the child's case. In the section Secondary Prevention, you will read more about this process. There will occasionally be situations in which the worker believes that the child is at immediate risk, and the worker, perhaps with the police, may apprehend the child. Also keep in mind that you must follow the procedures required by your child protection agency, which may or may not approve of all suggestions offered in this unit.

There is recognition that in Canada today, significant changes to child welfare legislation are required to ensure that children's health and safety are the first priority. Noteworthy is that each of the 10 provinces and 3 territories has its own child welfare laws (an "act"). These agencies make up the Canadian child welfare system.

The agency's priority is to maintain the family unit while preventing further maltreatment to the child. There is recognition that in Canada today, significant changes to child welfare legislation are required to ensure that children's health and safety are the first priority.

With that in mind, the agency's investigation determines what it believes is in the best interests of the child. Criminal charges are laid when the offender is found guilty of abuse according to the *Criminal Code* of Canada, which happens in only a small number of cases.

Primary Prevention

Primary prevention refers to ECLC programs' policies and practices that support relationships with children and families so that child maltreatment doesn't happen. Educators are not immune to maltreating children. For this reason, programs' policies address child maltreatment, child guidance, child-centred programming, nutrition, and health and establish procedures that are consistently implemented by staff. These policies and practices, combined with training, enhance educators' ability to provide and model high-quality care.

The Educator's Role in Primary Prevention

Educators have a unique opportunity to demonstrate that maltreatment can be prevented. Prevention begins within ECLC programs by

- supporting children in developing their core developmental strengths (see Table 8.1, page 495),
- providing a positive role model for parents, and
- supporting parents in their parenting rights and responsibilities.

Creating a Positive Early Childhood Learning and Care Environment

High-quality ECLC environments are caring and nurturing and respect children and their families. Parents see how educators interact with their

child and other children and how they guide behaviour and provide a safe, suitable physical environment for children. Knowing that their child is well cared for in their absence alleviates stress for parents.

In terms of the children, a high-quality ECLC program promotes children's health—and helps prevent child maltreatment. The most obvious example is promoting children's developmental strengths as an essential part of all practices and curricula. Children who are building their skills and confidence may be better protected from maltreatment than those who are not. They may be more aware of their rights and those of others. A high-quality program also helps prevent sexual abuse by integrating children's awareness of their bodies, healthy sexuality, and personal safety (see Sexuality, page 546). Recognizing the strength of the brain's capacity for growth in the early years through positive relationships and environments, the focus needs to be placed on resources to prevent the incidence of child maltreatment, resulting in fewer children and adults who need costly treatment with uncertain outcomes as a result of maltreatment (see Figure 8.5, page 500).

Enrollment interviews are ideal opportunities for directors (or educators) and parents to begin getting to know one another. Over time, educators develop meaningful partnerships with families. Often these result in parents sharing more personal information, such as their views on discipline, their support systems, or their relationship with a spouse or partner. Educators combine this information with observations of parents and children interacting to help them understand the parent–child relationship. Some parents do not feel comfortable sharing personal details about their family. This is perfectly acceptable, and they deserve the same

FIGURE 8.5   The Brain's Capacity to Change

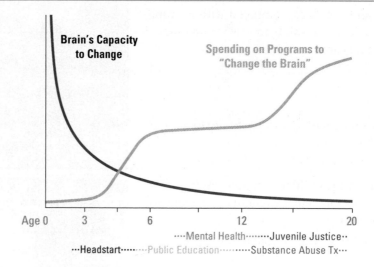

Source: *Maltreatment and the Developing Child: How Early Childhood Experience Shapes Child and Culture* by Bruce D. Perry (2004), http://www.lfcc.on.ca/mccain/perry.pdf (April 2008). Reprinted with permission from Professor Bruce D. Perry, Child Trauma Academy.

respect as other parents. Educators need to be careful not to pry or make judgments based on the family's wish for privacy. They shouldn't assume that parents are trying to hide something. Providing parents with nonjudgmental support is a positive primary strategy.

A parent rushes into the program at the end of each day. She seems to be in a never-ending battle with her three-year-old. He doesn't want to go home and often has a tantrum. This is an upsetting way to begin the evening. As the educator, you have two options. You can either do nothing, which in some ways contributes to the tension—the tired, frustrated, rushed mother may yell at or slap her child—or you can recognize the stress she is under as she tries to leave work on time and travel across town to pick up her son. By acknowledging how difficult this is for her, by talking about how the two of you can work together, you can make the stress more manageable. Perhaps the mother could call the program when she is leaving work or try to arrive at the same time each day so that you can have her son prepared for the transition. As well, spending 10 minutes together in the play area before getting ready to leave or sitting down and relaxing together over a snack before the commute home may be options that the parent and child like.

Educators can contribute to promoting positive discipline strategies for families by

- role modelling positive guidance with children;
- being open to discussion with individual parents about discipline issues and avoiding being judgmental or prescriptive, which undermines a parent's authority;

- providing access to resources on discipline and parenting, such as articles, books, audiovisual materials, support groups, or courses for parents;

- providing opportunities for group discussions, such as parent meetings or workshops (e.g., PHAC's Nobody's Perfect program; see Resource Materials), and ensuring that culturally relevant facilitators are flexible, able to suspend judgment, and trained to recognize suspected child abuse;

- keeping abreast of community resources that may be of assistance to parents, including ethnoculturally relevant resources, if available; and

- becoming involved in organizations that are committed to reducing violence in society and, in particular, advocating for positive environments for children.

NELSONstudy

To access Resource Materials, visit NelsonStudy.

Child Maltreatment Prevention Programs for Children

Caring adults want children to be safe. Prevention programs seem, on the surface, an obvious way to help protect children from harm. Ultimately, it is essential for adults to be clear that it is their responsibility to protect children and that children should never be given the message that they are responsible for protecting themselves. Also, any prevention programs for children must take developmental and cultural appropriateness into consideration to meet the needs of children of different ages and populations. Before deciding to evaluate a specific prevention program for children, consider the following potentially misleading assumptions about such programs:

- The main challenge of primary prevention is that it is a socialization process as well as an educative one—child maltreatment, particularly sexual abuse, occurs in a society that fosters the sexualization of children and the absolute power of adults. We want children to have tools that can help them in a potentially abusive situation, but we don't want them to feel responsible for protecting themselves or to believe that they failed in any way if they were unable to protect themselves from victimization. *For example, children may not believe they can say "no" to a powerful adult, or they may not be able to evaluate a situation for potential danger, including an adult's motives.*

- Prevention programs may be presenting concepts that make sense to adults but are beyond the young child's cognitive capacities. All children relate to prevention strategies on different emotional and cognitive levels and respond in accordance with their developmental stage (see Table 9.1, page 540).

- Young children can acquire skills and concepts, but the issue is whether they can retain the information over time. Interactive and comprehensive programs in which children can role play and practise skills are likely helpful, although children won't necessarily be able to apply the skills in real-life situations. Programs that include relevant information and resource materials for parents and educators likely reinforce the learning and involve the adults in a meaningful way. This potentially reduces the burden of responsibility that children may feel.

- The inclusion of self-defence strategies is controversial. They may help the child develop self-confidence and skills to escape, but their use could potentially place the child in greater danger. The program must stress that the goal of using self-defence is flight, not fight.

- A child's disclosure of abuse already suffered may be the most solid result of these programs. It is important for educators to be both aware of and prepared for this possibility. It is regrettable that disclosure is "secondary prevention" rather than primary prevention, as these programs are intended. However, stopping the abuse as early as possible is positive action.

- Educators must be committed to critically examining the assumptions behind a particular prevention program, as well as the specific content.

WHAT MAKES A CHILD ABUSE PREVENTION PROGRAM SUITABLE FOR CHILDREN?

P. Rimer (2018) provides a helpful list of questions to ask when examining the appropriateness of a prevention program for children in your care:

Staff must be prepared to follow through on disclosures and suspicions of abuse if a prevention program is conducted with children.

1. Are the materials comprehensive, socio-culturally relevant, and include information for staff, parents/caregivers, and children/youth?

2. Is the information in the program accurate and up-to-date?

3. Is the language clear, and appropriate to the ages and developmental levels of the children/youth?

4. Does it empower the children/youth, supporting development of communication and problem-solving skills in a variety of situations (e.g., negotiating, expressing feelings, assertiveness)? Prevention programs should not be limited to sexual abuse and/or touch discrimination.

5. Does the program recognize the value of healthy relationships and include strategies for building them (e.g., activities that promote prosocial behaviours and interpersonal skills, such as cooperation, helping, and giving and getting consent)?

6. Does it reduce the child's sense of isolation, giving children/youth the message that there are people who will help?

7. Are there opportunities for interactive teaching and practice? These have been found to be the most effective in providing children with skills that may be helpful in preventing an occurrence of child abuse. Learning new concepts requires gradual introduction and regular exposure over time in order to maximize retention. Although children repeat words, it does not mean they understand the concept, for example "rights," "a bribe" or "a secret."

8. Does the program include ways to open up thoughtful discussion? Programs should include learning opportunities for parents and caregivers that provide guidance and assistance for them in talking with children/youth. Educational materials do not replace discussion.

9. Is there a clear message that the child is not responsible for their own protection, and information on how to get help?

Source: Excerpted with permission from P. Rimer, 2018. *Making a Difference: The Community Responds to Child Abuse*, Eighth Edition (Toronto: Boost Child & Youth Advocacy Centre), p. 172.

Networking with Community Resources

Every program has access to professionals and printed resources on child abuse. Access to parenting consultants and parenting courses may be limited to larger urban communities. Programs must have the name and phone number of the child protection agency and a clear understanding of the program's role in reporting and documenting suspected child maltreatment. In-service training for staff on child maltreatment is always beneficial. Educators are also in a position to respond to parents' requests for information or consultation with a specific agency related to parenting, health, housing, or finances. Programs should make it a priority to ensure that their staff are aware of ethnoculturally and language-sensitive resources.

Preventing Child Maltreatment by Educators

The primary focus of this unit is the prevention of child maltreatment within families. However, any person of authority, including educators, can violate their power over children. Factors that contribute to maltreatment in families are not unlike those that may lead to abuse within programs. Feelings of frustration or being trapped lead to short tempers and striking out physically or emotionally as a way of regaining a sense of control and power. Although it is unlikely that educators would hit or spank a child, they might be at risk for shaking or restraining, threatening, using sarcasm, or yelling at a child. Work environments that con-

Courtesy of George Brown College/Richmond Adelaide Child Care Centre

tribute to educators' physical, emotional, and social health are vital in providing educators with a true sense of autonomy, job satisfaction, and improved overall well-being. When graduates seek employment, it is important to ensure that prospective employers provide clear job descriptions, personnel policies, a process of staff orientation and performance review, and other ways in which educators' rights and responsibilities are considered. Opportunities for professional development to address areas that require further educator knowledge and skill also reduce frustration and stress while increasing competence and best practices with children and families.

CRITICAL THINKING

After half an hour, Shelly is still unable to comfort a toddler. She is becoming increasingly frustrated and has said, "I just want to leave him in the crib until he stops crying." You can see that she is handling the child less and less gently. How could you manage this situation to reduce Shelly's stress, and the stress experienced by the child, and reduce the risk of physical abuse? What steps might prevent these types of situations in the future?

To prevent the possibility of maltreatment in an ECLC program, try to pair new adults in the room, such as supply staff or students, with familiar staff. Listen to parents about any concerns they have and try to understand them from their perspective. This helps educators know best how to address the issue. Remember that if a parent believes that her or his suspicion is warranted, it is also the right and responsibility of the parent to report the suspicion to the child protection agency.

One of the most important areas of professional development for educators is the working knowledge and problem-solving skills based on your provincial or territorial Early Childhood Educators' Code of Ethics. If one is not yet available, you can refer to the Canadian Child Care Federation's Code of Ethics. The code, which was adopted by the Canadian Child Care Federation and its affiliate organizations Canada-wide, consists of eight principles originally developed by the Early Childhood Educators of BC. The code guides practitioners in protecting the children and families with whom they work by working through ethical dilemmas using the principles put forward. Recognizing that ethical issues arise often, and the value of developing an ethical problem-solving approach to make the best decisions, the Manitoba Child Care Association offers a four-part Code of Ethics workshop series for educators' professional development.

Sexual abuse in programs is rare, yet it is understandably alarming for parents to realize that this, and other forms of maltreatment, can happen when they entrust their child's care to others. This realization has had both positive and negative effects on ECLC programs. On the positive side, parents demand that programs have an open-door policy for parents. Parents may want to be more closely involved in the program to understand what the children are doing all day and to ensure that all policies and procedures are respectful of children.

Educators may be overly cautious about the physical affection they give to children. They may feel inhibited because of the possibility that parents will misconstrue appropriate behaviour as inappropriate. This is particularly the case for male educators, who may feel that they are suspect because of their gender. Although it is not common practice, there are programs in which staff are, unfortunately, discouraged from reciprocating children's hugs or having children sit on educators' laps. Policies and practices must provide checks and balances, combining warm, sensitive caregiving with ways to ensure that educators' behaviour is verifiable. CPS (2015, p. 361) offers some commonsense practices to avoid misunderstandings that could lead to false accusations of abuse:

- Exercise good judgment about the kind of language used with children (e.g., never use any words that could have a sexual connotation).
- Avoid play or care in secluded areas and keep coworkers and parents informed of activities when you are alone with a child.
- Be sensitive to how a child feels about being touched and ask permission if you're not sure.
- Confine touching to a child's head, back, and shoulders when offering comfort, affection, or reassurance.
- Learn to intervene and redirect children appropriately when they are engaged in self-stimulation or sexual play.
- Use correct terminology for all body parts and encourage children in your care to do the same.*

---

*Source: Adapted from Canadian Paediatric Society, *Well Beings: A Guide to Health in Child Care*. (Ottawa: Canadian Paediatric Society, 2015), p. 361. Reprinted with permission from the Canadian Paediatric Society.

Education and training in early childhood education is extremely important in all aspects of working with groups of children. Working with children is hard work, both physically and emotionally, and the difficulty can be compounded by educators' low status and wages. Educators should have the knowledge and confidence to create programs that are caring, interesting, varied, stimulating, and rewarding for both children and themselves. Those with little or no formal early childhood education often lack the knowledge and skills necessary to manage the everyday stresses of the work. Teamwork is a crucial component of working effectively in ECLC programs. Of course, new graduates want to focus their efforts on a high-quality team approach to their work and learn from their more experienced educators. This is ideal when educators are positive role models, but not if a coworker uses harsh disciplinary strategies. In worst-case scenarios, a new graduate or any other educator takes on some of the negative behaviour, such as grabbing, shaking, or restraining children. As trained educators, they should recognize that this behaviour is unacceptable and reportable to the child protection agency. The director must take action with staff who begin to demonstrate inappropriate behaviour before it leads to child maltreatment, or the educator should ask the director for assistance.

Secondary Prevention

Secondary prevention encompasses

- identifying children who may be victims of maltreatment,
- documenting observations and possible indicators, and
- reporting to a child protection agency.

This is a balancing act for educators, whose role in secondary prevention is complex. First, educators are not "child abuse police." Although they must address the situation when a child comes into the program with a bruise or in dirty clothes or yells at a doll in dramatic play, educators don't leap to a conclusion of child maltreatment at first glance. Second, educators make numerous observations about dramatic changes in a child's behaviour, emotional state, or physical appearance. Using these indicators, the educator attempts to find out why the child's behaviour has changed. Third, educators must understand that it is a child protection agency's responsibility to respond to suspicions, decide whether to investigate, and identify the offender. It is not your job to prove that maltreatment has occurred and, if so, who the offender is. However, it is the educator's responsibility to document and phone a child protection agency whenever she or he has questions or suspicions.

Identifying Suspected Child Maltreatment

The identification of suspected child abuse or neglect and the subsequent intervention with children and families are complex and difficult issues. Since educators spend so much time with children, and because of their observation skills, they are often the first people in children's lives to suspect the possibility of maltreatment. They are also in a position to provide support to the family. This can often create a conflict for the educator. Stopping maltreatment now can have long-term positive effects for children and often for their entire family.

Educators who suspect that a child in their care is being maltreated may have the following reactions:

- They may refuse to believe that this parent would do this to the child. This may be especially difficult if they've known the parent for a while and have established a relationship.
- They may be afraid
  - of the parent's anger and, as a result, fear for the child's safety or their own safety;
  - of having falsely suspected the parent; or
  - that the child will be removed from the home or withdrawn from the program.

Ultimately, the child's welfare is your overriding concern. Most families love their children and don't want to continue to hurt them once they understand the negative effects on children. Educators need to ensure that families always feel welcome in the program, regardless of the process or outcome with the child protection agency—otherwise, staff are not fulfilling their role as child advocates. It's important for educators to support positive change within the family and not to expect miracles to happen overnight. Educators are a part of the child's life for only a few years, whereas the family is involved for a lifetime.

Educators know each child's temperament, personality, and family. They observe children achieving developmental milestones and the normal range of behaviour. Educators draw on this experience in making judgments about children's behaviour and observing physical injuries. By asking themselves questions, educators rule out other possible explanations, such as illness, vision or hearing problems, anxiety about specific stressors (e.g., a grandmother's recent death), developmentally appropriate fears, or developmental delays unrelated to abuse. In a scenario in which a child has signs of an injury, it is routine practice for an educator to ask the parent or other family member who accompanies the child to the program questions such as "Sam has a bruise on his knee. Do you know what happened?" The educator uses an interested but nonthreatening tone, asking what happened and how, not why it happened. However, if the cause of the child's injuries, account by the child, or behaviour of the child or adult is unclear, the educator must call a child protection agency to discuss concerns and seek direction. The child protection worker will guide the educator regarding whether or not to approach the parent or other adult and provide further direction about possible formal reporting. Such consultation may lead to a resolution that works in the child's best interests (e.g., feedback to the family, referral for counselling, a change in your program that may help the child during a crisis period).

Identifying Suspected Family Violence

Mandated reporting acknowledges the position that being exposed to family violence is a form of child maltreatment, whether the child actually sees or hears the violence, witnesses the aftermath of the violence (e.g., non-offending parent's injuries or emotional upset, police intervention), or is an unintentional victim of the violence (e.g., the child is hurt while in the mother's arms). Also, due to the power and control tactics that are used by the offender, the child may be used as a pawn in the violence. *For example, the offender may claim that the child's "bad behaviour" is the reason for the assaults against the non-offending parent or may engage the child in the abuse of the other parent.*

When faced with the knowledge or suspicion of any of the following indicators of family violence, a call to a child protection agency is required.

EXAMPLES OF WHEN TO CALL

The following are some examples of indicators that would require a call to a child protection agency when family violence is known or suspected:

- A child who has been physically harmed or almost injured by either partner, deliberately or "accidentally," during or after a violent episode.
- A child who has "accidentally" been hurt when caught in the crossfire of objects thrown during a violent episode, or injured in any way because of the situation (e.g., the child has cut their foot stepping on broken glass).
- A child who has been physically harmed while trying to protect a sibling or other family members.
- A child who believes that they are responsible for precipitating or stopping the abuse.
- A child who has been threatened with physical harm or death, or an abusive partner who threatens to harm a child(ren).
- An abusive partner who has assaulted or thrown objects at someone holding a child.
- A child who is exhibiting [serious] symptoms of emotional distress because of exposure to family violence or is likely to suffer emotional harm (e.g., by being forced to observe or listen to the assault).
- A child expresses fear for their own safety or the safety of other family members.
- The family returns to an abusive partner who is believed to pose a threat to the child(ren).
- Conditions of release, probation or parole, or a restraining order with respect to the abusive partner not having access to the child(ren) have been violated, and no one has reported this to authorities (i.e., a child protection agency or police).
- The primary caregiver requires hospitalization, and there is no suitable alternate arrangement for the safe care and supervision of the child(ren).
- A child who is denied the necessities of life because an abusive partner does not allow the other partner access to financial resources and/or isolates them.
- One or both parents are substance abusers or have mental health issues that impair their capacity to adequately care for their child(ren).
- There is an awareness or suspicion that the alleged abuser is in a situation with access to other children.

Source: Excerpted with permission from P. Rimer, 2018. *Making a Difference: The Community Responds to Child Abuse*, Eighth Edition (Toronto: Boost Child & Youth Advocacy Centre), pp. 110–111.

It is very important to support the non-offending parent when she or he takes steps to disclose family violence. Although you may not feel ready or equipped to handle this type of disclosure, your level of acceptance and support for the victim are most important. ECLC programs can display information that acknowledges family violence and a willingness to help (e.g., a poster from the local or regional women's shelter that includes a phone number).

The parent may decide to call the help line or may decide to talk to an educator or the director, believing that this must be a safe environment in which to talk about it. Remember that her safety and that of her children are paramount, so you must be very sensitive. Although you may believe that she should leave the abusive situation immediately, remember that the woman knows her reality and you don't. Violence often escalates when women leave, or try to, and afterward—sometimes resulting in murder.

Table 8.2 lists suggestions to consider if a non-offending parent approaches you about her situation.

Family violence is a very complex issue, with many other considerations in addition to those highlighted here. Graduates of an early childhood education program require further knowledge and understanding of their role in supporting families in these situations—particularly in supporting children exposed to family violence.

TABLE 8.2   Dos and Don'ts of Disclosures of Family Violence

If a woman divulges family violence, her concerns, fears, worries, and situation must never be minimized or discounted. Her decision to talk to someone usually indicates her desire to consider options to change her situation. The response of the person to whom she discloses has a significant impact on her ability to take positive steps toward ending the abuse; alternatively, an inappropriate or judgmental response may reinforce her guilt, isolation, feelings of powerlessness, and loss of hope. Recognize that emotional abuse has as much of an impact on someone's overall well-being as physical violence.

If family violence is divulged, keep the following in mind when responding to the disclosure.

Control Your Emotions

- If she is calling you on the phone, determine how safe it is for her to talk.

- Try and stay calm and relaxed, no matter what she tells you—she needs to sense that you are able to help.

- Validate her feelings and experiences—never minimize how she has been treated—give her the message that you think the abuse is reason for concern.

- Do not say negative things about her partner—although he has mistreated her, they may still care about one another.

- Do *not* confront the abuser. This could put her or her children at further risk and jeopardize successful safety planning.

- Do not judge her inability to take action today. If your tone is judgmental and she chooses to stay with her partner, she may feel she cannot call back for additional help and support. Do not say things like, "If it were me, I never would have stayed so long."

(continued)

TABLE 8.2 Dos and Don'ts of Disclosures of Family Violence (*continued*)

Provide a Respectful Perspective

- Reinforce that family violence (domestic violence, woman abuse, intimate partner violence) is a crime.

- Emphasize that she is not responsible for her partner's behaviour—she did not cause the abuse, no matter what he claims she said or did—it is not her fault. This may be the first time she is hearing that the way she has been treated is unjust, and that she does not deserve it.

- Acknowledge any steps she has taken toward safety and change, no matter how small, including her disclosure to you.

- Always recognize the impact of cultural values and beliefs on someone's perception of choices.

Present Options

- Strongly encourage her to seek medical treatment if she (or the children) has sustained any injuries.

- Brainstorm with her about her options and any formal or informal avenues where she might get help, but remember *only she can decide what is right for her, taking into consideration what feels safe.*

- Express your concern for her safety and the safety of her children (see Examples of When to Call, page 507). Encourage her to develop a safety plan both for staying and leaving—offer the names and numbers of local specialized services with expertise in safety planning (e.g., the local women's shelter, a crisis line, police and a child protection agency). Ensure she understands and knows how to call 911.

- Inform her that there are services available (including legal options) to protect and help families—abuse does not stop without outside intervention. Ask her if she wants to involve police. (Be sensitive to the fact that immigrant or refugee women who have been abused may have experienced police as cruel and oppressive, and may, therefore be fearful of them.)

- Encourage her to seek legal advice before she takes any steps that could have legal ramifications; this is particularly important if children are involved.

- Do not give advice or try to make decisions for her, even if you feel your advice is sound (e.g., "I think you should …" or, "If it were me, I would …").

- Ask her what she wants to see happen, what are her main concerns now, and how you can help.

- Do not overwhelm her with too much information—she may have to begin with small steps on her way to taking control of the situation (e.g., making a list of who she can call for help).

Source: Excerpted with permission from P. Rimer, 2018. *Making a Difference: The Community Responds to Child Abuse*, Eighth Edition (Toronto: Boost Child & Youth Advocacy Centre).

CRITICAL THINKING

The next-door neighbour notices that the children are playing outdoors without coats on in cold weather *and* does not realize that the mother has sent them outside to prevent them from witnessing her impending assault. This example is not meant to underplay the children's needs for proper clothing but to highlight the mother's assessment of risk and her strategy to protect her children from the greater risk. Consider all players in this scenario: children, the non-offending mother, and the offending partner. Identify each player's issue and decide what the neighbour's next step should be.

Suspecting Child Maltreatment

Educators' suspicions of physical abuse require them to contact the child protection agency.

Whenever a child is hurt, you must ask yourself, "How did this happen?" and "Did adults fail to protect the child?" Just as in programs, injuries that occur at home are understandable: bumps and bruises are a normal part of every child's life. Figure 8.4 (see page 479) illustrates the parts of the body on which educators are most likely to see bruises due to everyday activities, as well as the locations where bruises may be a cause for concern. Even though it is not your role to determine which bruises are suspicious or to interpret their origins, some markings do have identifiable shapes. Use non-leading questions such as "What happened to your arm?" followed by "What happened next?" Leading questions such as "Who did this to you?" or "Why did your mother hurt you like that?" not only put ideas or answers into the child's mouth but may also contaminate a possible investigation.

It is important to stay within your role boundaries and to remember that you could potentially jeopardize the investigation if you seem to ask leading questions. Confirmation of trauma is made by child protection workers, often in consultation with physicians. One of the strongest indicators of suspected physical abuse is a delay in seeking medical treatment for extensive and serious injuries. Although some children are more injury prone, children who repeatedly injure themselves raise serious concerns about the possibility of physical abuse or the level of supervision and guidance at home.

Disclosures of Maltreatment

Educators often establish closer, more personal relationships with some children than with others. These relationships are essential for children if they are going to trust an educator enough to disclose maltreatment. There may be times when you have concerns about a child, although he or she hasn't said anything to you or any other educator. In this situation, the educator with the closest relationship with the child is probably best positioned to talk with the child. Discuss your observations of the child's behaviour. You might say, "I have noticed lately that you are getting angry with your friends and storming off a lot. Is something bothering you?" The child may actually have something to talk about that has nothing to do with abuse or neglect. Opening the door in this way may help the child to feel comfortable enough to talk. Children may not want to talk at first but may approach you at another time when they know that an educator will listen and is concerned about them. However, if a child doesn't disclose abuse to you, but your observations lead you to suspect abuse, you must call a child protection agency. For a number of reasons, a child may not disclose maltreatment or may recant, saying that it didn't really happen after an earlier disclosure.

When children decide to disclose, it is a call for help. When they approach educators, educators must listen to their account and support them. It is difficult for children to disclose abuse for a host of reasons. Here are a few:

- The child has only started to realize that something "not right" is happening to him or her.
- The child has been threatened with physical or emotional consequences if she or he tells.
- The child feels it is his or her fault and will be blamed.
- The child feels vulnerable or powerless and does not think she or he will be believed.

Responding Effectively to Disclosures

If you have seen or heard something that leads you to suspect child abuse, remember to

Control Your Emotions

- Try to be relaxed and casual.
- Do not project your own reactions, disgust, revulsion or moral indignation. Listen and respond in non-judgmental and supportive ways.
- Do not display shock or disapproval of the alleged abuser—do not describe alleged offenders as criminals, pedophiles, predatory strangers, or their relationship as abusive. The alleged abuser in both offline and online situations may be deeply loved, or have a close relationship with the child, youth or family, even though the situation may have been abusive. Although the child/youth/parent or anyone else can have positive feelings toward the offender, *the primary responsibility is to protect the children.*
- If the identity of the suspected abuser is not disclosed, do *not* make assumptions about who it is.
- Do not assume that the abuse was a terrible experience (e.g., a child who has been sexually abused by an attentive and gentle person may perceive the abuse as pleasurable). Many children/youth have been manipulated into thinking that the alleged offender loves or cares about them, and this is not the time to challenge the nature of the relationship. Assuming the abuse was awful only adds to the child/youth's guilt.
- Be aware and accepting of your own feelings.
- If you feel that you cannot control your emotional responses, talk to your immediate supervisor.

Offer Reassurance

Reassure children/youth by letting them know that:

- they were very brave to tell;
- you are glad they are telling you about what happened;
- it is not their fault;
- you are sorry that this has happened to them;

- they are not alone—this happens to other children/youth too; and
- you will do everything you can to help.

Avoid victim-blaming and comments about the incident, including those referring to the alleged offender or the impact of the abuse, such as:

- "How can you say those things about…?"
- "I hope you're not lying about this."
- "You must be mistaken."
- "They are sick and didn't mean it."
- "How could you let them do those things to you?"
- "Who would take such terrible pictures of you?"
- "Why would you send a picture like that?"
- "Why didn't you tell me this before?"

Children/youth are further reassured when:

- you give them your undivided attention;
- you let them know that you want them to tell you the truth—it won't make you mad, shocked or embarrassed;
- their feelings are acknowledged and validated. *If the child/youth asks,* tell them that you believe them. If a disclosure occurs in a group setting say, "That sounds important. Let's talk more about that later," and try to find an unobtrusive way to speak with the child/youth privately, as soon as possible;
- you reinforce to the child/youth that they can come to you at any time to talk;
- a trusted adult stays with the child/youth, unobtrusively if necessary, until a child protection worker arrives; and
- continued, unconditional love and support are given to anyone who has recanted.

Be Aware of the Child's Developmental Level and Use of Language

- Use language appropriate to the developmental capacity of the child.
- Accept a child's terminology or "slang" words to describe an event, particularly as children often do not know the correct terminology for body parts or sexual behaviours. Listen to the language that the child/youth is using, and mirror that in your responses. For example, if a youth is referring to her trafficker as her "boyfriend" do not correct her by saying, "he is not your boyfriend." This is not the time to correct the words the child/youth uses, or their definition or description of what happened. *It is critical for the investigation that they use their own language in giving the account of the abuse.*
- If the child/youth has a disability that affects communicating, let them use the most familiar method of communication (e.g., sign language, assisted communication, gestures, writing, drawing, or a computer). Where necessary, obtain assistance from a trained professional for anyone with a communication barrier.

- Do not interrupt or fill in any silences with your own words, even if the account is incomplete or unclear. For individuals whose second language is English, do not offer English words. If the child/youth/adult speaks a different dialect of English or any other language, do not offer words in the dialect with which you are most familiar.
- Answer any questions as simply and honestly as possible.
- Refrain from using trigger words or adult terminology such as rape, incest, abuse, wife assault or jail, since they may be alarming or may hamper the disclosure or the investigation.

Ask Questions That Are Open-Ended, That Are Not Leading or Suggestive of a Specific Answer

- "Can you tell me more about that?"
- "What happened next?"
- "How did you get that bruise?"

Be sure to:

- ask only those questions necessary to confirm your suspicions, such as, "How did you get that mark on your back?" or "Where did you learn to play that game?";
- ask questions calmly, without interrogating or confronting;
- ask questions in a manner that does *not* suggest to the child/youth/adult what happened or who did it (e.g., "Did you get that bruise because Mommy hit you with a brush?");
- refrain from questioning the child/youth/adult's account (for example, by asking, "Are you sure it was Uncle Ted who took the picture with his cell phone?");
- refrain from asking "Why?" as many children do not understand the motivation and may understand a "why" question to imply blame—a better alternative is "how come?";
- resist trying to change the mind of anyone who has recanted, since coaching or suggesting that something did or did not really happen will hamper the progress of the case; and
- refrain from asking questions or showing "evidence" (e.g., any images or text messages) because you want to prove or disprove abuse.

Respect the Person Who Discloses

- If a child/youth/adult is telling, listen. Be patient—this may be difficult for the person to share with you.
- If a child/youth/adult is quiet, do not interrogate them.
- Do not undress a child (e.g., forcibly removing clothing to view injuries).
- Do not display a child's injuries to others.
- Respect everyone's privacy—this should not become the topic of "gossip."

Tell the Child/Youth What Will Happen Next

- Do not make promises you cannot keep. For example, do not agree to keep the disclosure a "secret." It is important to explain that some secrets must be shared in order to get help or to keep people from being hurt, and that the information will be shared only with people "whose job it is to help kids."

- Do not try to answer questions when you do not have the answers. For example, if a child asks, "Will Daddy have to go to jail now?" you can only reply, "I don't know. Other people decide that."

- Do not promise to stay with the child/youth after the authorities arrive, until you have clarified if you will be permitted to sit in the investigative interview. If it is appropriate, reassure the child/youth that you are there to support them.

- Do not agree if a child/youth/adult asks or begs that you do not tell anyone else. You may want to remain silent out of respect for their wishes, the confidentiality of the relationship, or out of loyalty. Silence places you in collusion with the abuser, and violates the law. It is helpful to understand that:
  - without outside intervention, the abuse will probably continue;
  - other children may be at risk of abuse; and
  - if any attempted intervention fails, and calling a child protection agency is used as a threat, then the child protection agency is seen as punitive and not a resource and supportive service to families in need, as it should be seen.

Follow Through on Legal and Moral Responsibilities

- Know the child protection laws in your jurisdiction.
- Know your agency's policies and reporting procedures.
- Report your suspicions to the designated authorities.
- Record what the child said using the child's own words, as soon as possible.
- Document objectively any observations of the child's behaviour, or the behaviour of any others relevant to the situation.
- Write down the name of anyone the child has indicated as the possible abuser, and any description that the child provides.
- Document any conversation between yourself and the child.
- Consult with a child protection authority before contacting the child's family, or speaking to other family members (e.g., a sibling who is also in the program).
- Do not tell the child to keep any of your discussions with them secret.

Those working with children, youth and families are not to attempt to prove their suspicions of child abuse or family violence, nor are they to "interview" the child/ youth and/or the family for this purpose. Such attempts could contaminate an investigation and jeopardize the process. When you suspect a child/youth is being or has been abused or if a child/youth/adult discloses abuse, it is mandatory to report this information. The investigation will be conducted by trained authorities. *

---

*Source: Excerpted with permission from P. Rimer, 2018. *Making a Difference: The Community Responds to Child Abuse*, Eighth Edition (Toronto: Boost Child & Youth Advocacy Centre), pp. 59–63.

Clarifying with Parents

Even when there are concerns about suspected child maltreatment, ongoing communication with families is of the utmost importance in promoting children's well-being. When approaching parents or other family members, your goal is to clarify a situation, not to suggest that they are the offenders.

Start with your observation and follow with a question:

- "Jacob has a black eye. Do you know how it happened?"
- "Josie has seemed very sad for the past week and hasn't been interested in playing. How has she been at home?"

Additional observations or questions depend on the parents' responses to your initial observation and question.

- You may ask Jacob's mother, "Did he see the doctor? Were there any special instructions to care for him or concerns about his eyesight?"
- Josie's dad has noticed her lack of interest too. You respond by saying, "Do you have any idea why Josie seems so sad?"

Take the parents' lead while being careful not to put them on the defensive. Questions starting with "Why did you …?" or "Why weren't you …?" are inappropriate, and most parents, whether or not abuse is an issue, will feel they are being judged. In most instances, the parents' explanation is sufficient, and your questions and concerns are resolved. The parents usually appreciate your concern, and your positive relationship with them is maintained. Even in cases in which you are no longer concerned, it is important to document your initial concerns and the conversation in the child's file. Jacob may have recurring black eyes or other injuries that may begin to form a pattern that is of concern later on.

There are times when the parents' response reinforces your suspicion of child abuse. If the explanation for the black eye seems unusual, the parent seems nervous in her or his response, and perhaps the child looks fearful, you will likely wonder about the validity of the explanation and call a child protection agency for guidance.

Educators are strongly discouraged from approaching parents for clarification in the following situations:

- Whenever sexual abuse is suspected. There are a number of reasons for this. If the mother's husband or boyfriend is suspected of sexually abusing the child, and he talks with the child's mother before the child protection worker or police do, he may convince her that he could never have done such a thing. After all, who would want to believe that her partner is capable of sexually abusing her own child? It is even more devastating for children if their mother does not believe them.
- When you are concerned that the child may be abused again as a result of your conversation with the parents.
- When you fear the family would disappear, making follow-up difficult. You may base this decision on the family's history of moving frequently.

In fact, child protection agencies prefer that any action beyond clarifying a situation be checked with them first. In other words, contact the child protection agency for direction. The child protection worker may indicate that they or the police will contact the parents. Or the child protection agency may advise the director to call the parents and ask them to come in for a meeting. It is important to follow the direction of the child protection agency.

An educator's role is to objectively and carefully document his or her observations (which aid the child protection agency in their investigation). It is not the educator's role to identify the abuser. Remember that as a professional you are legally and ethically obliged to report your suspicions of child maltreatment. If you are unsure of whether your observations are reportable, consult with your local child protection agency.

Documenting Indicators

Educators may hesitate to document their suspicions in children's files for the following reasons:

- They don't fully understand the importance of documentation in proving a case of child maltreatment.
- They believe that they don't have time to document suspicions.
- They are concerned that their report may be made public.

Documentation is an important part of the administrative responsibilities of educators for a range of health care concerns. Every program's work schedule needs to provide staff with the time to write relevant notations in children's files concerning illness, observations on their development, or suspected child abuse. Due to the serious legal implications of child maltreatment, documenting your observations, concerns, and questions is critical in that it provides a reliable account. Although the child's file and the educators involved may be called to testify in court, this is the exception rather than the rule.

Timely and detailed documentation is important. As an ECE student or recent graduate, it is important that you do your best to document your observations and immediately report the situation to the child protection agency. Remember that the child protection agency will guide you through this process. No one expects your documentation skills to be at the level of an experienced educator. But as you gain experience and further knowledge of the process, your documentation and reporting skills will build. The more complete and comprehensive the information is, the more able the agency is to fulfill its important role in protecting children. Verbal accounts based on your memory are not as reliable as careful documentation written at the time. Child protection agency staff see educators conducting themselves as professionals when they are able to refer to their documentation during this reporting process, which in turn builds credibility in the role of educators as child advocates.

Documentation: What Is Involved?

What makes a document objective, clear, concise, and complete? Every time you document, observe the following guidelines:

- Complete the correct form identified in the child abuse policy of your agency. Note that other incidents not related to suspected child maltreatment are completed on a different form (e.g., Serious Occurrence Form or Injury Report).

- Include the full name of the child, the date and time of recording, and the date and time of your observations.

- Describe clearly whatever you observed—the child's physical injury or behaviour—that is of concern. Note the type of injury (i.e., burn, bruise, cut), shape, size, colour, and number. A form that has a line diagram of a child's body makes it easier for educators to indicate where the mark(s) appeared on the body in addition to the written documentation. "It was 3 inches (6 cm) to the left of the belly button and maybe 2 inches (4 cm) above." In terms of behaviour, document any patterns that contribute to your suspicions (e.g., aggressive behaviour toward others, unexplainable fears) and direct quotations (if possible) of comments the child made (e.g., during dramatic play).

- In chronological order and using direct quotations, if you can remember exactly what was said, write it down. This should make it evident that you did not ask the child leading questions, such as "When did your dad hit you so hard?"

- Document objectively what was actually seen or heard. Do not include how you feel about the incident or ideas about what you think might have happened.

- Include anything that someone else has said; it might be important.

- Complete the documentation as soon as possible after you become aware of the physical or behavioural indicators or after a child's disclosure.

- Sign and date your form in ink.

- Record everything in your own handwriting.

- Use a new form if you have concerns on another day.

Unless otherwise instructed by the child protection agency, the educator will follow the child abuse policy and practices outlined by the early childhood program. Your municipal early childhood office may require notification whenever child maltreatment is suspected. This and other requirements should be outlined in the policy.

Reporting to a Child Protection Agency

Program staff are typically included in the provincial/territorial child protection legislation list of professionals working with children who are legally obliged to report to a local child protection agency when they have reasonable grounds to suspect child abuse. You are expected to become familiar with the child protection legislation in your province or territory and to understand your legal and moral responsibilities. In addition, you must know the child abuse policies and procedures of your agency.

The staff member, student, or volunteer who initially suspects abuse is required by law to call a child protection agency. Ways in which the person reporting can assist in a child abuse investigation are outlined below.

The following information is intended to serve as a checklist for staff who may be part of a child abuse investigation. It is a summary of roles and responsibilities should this situation occur. It is the expectation that supervisory staff will be supportive throughout this process. It is also expected that staff will cooperate with authorities.

1. Be attentive to indirect disclosures and physical and behavioural indicators of abuse.

2. Consult with a child protection worker before speaking with anyone else about the details of your suspicion.

3. When making the report to a child protection agency, provide complete information, including your name and where you can be reached. Ask for the full name of the child protection worker with whom you are speaking. Be sure to obtain information from the child protection worker as to who will be following up on the case, and who you should contact with any questions or further information.

4. Do not inform a parent/caregiver that a suspicion of child abuse or family violence has been reported unless a child protection worker has given you permission to do so.

5. Document in detail the grounds that form your suspicion of child abuse or family violence (e.g., behaviours observed, the child's disclosure and your responses to the child). Document only the facts—do not include how you are feeling about the incident, or personal thoughts about what might have happened.

6. Continue to monitor the child, being attentive to further indicators and/ or potential risks to the child. Report any suspicions or new information to the child protection agency. Complete new documentation for each report/ consultation made.

7. Know your legal and moral responsibilities, and the internal policies and procedures of your agency with respect to abuse.

8. Be aware of your emotional responses to the situation and deal with them, in order to be as effective as possible through the investigative process.

9. In consultation with the child abuse investigators, ask if it would be helpful to the child for you to be present to support the child in any investigative interviews. If you are present in the interview, follow the directions of the investigators as to your level of participation.

10. Respect the confidentiality of the child, the family and any proceedings in which you may be involved. Be aware that child protection workers are also bound by policies of confidentiality regarding details of the case.

*Do not conduct an independent investigation of suspicions of child abuse or family violence. **You must call a local child protection agency**. It is not the role of staff to prove that abuse/violence has occurred. In fact, doing so would contaminate the investigation and have detrimental effects on the prosecution and court proceedings.* *

As you are probably aware, reports can be made anonymously by educators or by anyone else. Educators are professionals, have specialized skills and knowledge, and have a relationship with the child and likely the family. They are able to work

---

*Source: Excerpted with permission from P. Rimer, 2018. *Making a Difference: The Community Responds to Child Abuse*, Eighth Edition (Toronto: Boost Child & Youth Advocacy Centre), p. 89.

effectively with other groups of professionals. If an anonymous report is made, there is loss of the centre as a safe, familiar place that may be the best environment for the investigators to interview the child, if deemed a necessary part of the investigation. The child protection agency staff may incorporate educators into the child's treatment plan, but if they don't know who is calling, this obviously can't be done. For these and other reasons, it is in the best interests of the child to identify names and contact information when reporting.

A common fear of educators is that there is a chance that maltreatment has not occurred or cannot be proved. It is important to keep in mind that it is your legal duty to report suspicion and not your role to investigate or prove maltreatment. You are fulfilling your responsibilities under the law and are not making any accusations. The child protection agency investigates allegations and decides on action to be taken on behalf of the child. Even if maltreatment cannot be proved, someone who reports is not vulnerable to any consequences unless the report was made maliciously or without reasonable grounds. Educators have opportunities to get to know children, to understand what is "normal" for individuals, and to have a positive impact on the child's life. It is rare for educators' reports to be considered malicious.

What Happens during Investigations

The child protection worker decides if the reported concerns require an investigative response based on the conditions set out in the provincial or territorial child protection legislation. If the case doesn't meet at least one of the conditions, the agency does not have legal grounds to intervene. If a decision is made by the child protection agency not to intervene, your report and the information obtained in the investigation are retained. The agency may not always inform the individual who reported of this decision. Every situation is unique, so the response depends on the circumstances.

Child protection workers may not conduct the investigation on their own but may include others on the team. Many communities have put protocols in place that determine how investigations are responded to and conducted and by whom. *For example, a police officer may be involved, as defined by the community protocol or to decide if there are reasonable grounds for a criminal investigation.* Reports of suspected sexual abuse and family violence are usually investigated jointly with the police when the alleged offender is someone in a position of trust or authority, and not for "stranger assaults." For other types of maltreatment, police may be consulted. If there is concern for the child protection worker's safety, a police officer may accompany her or him when going to the child's or alleged offender's home. The agency staff often consult with other social service and health professionals during the investigation. Investigative interviews are analyzed according to specific criteria, findings of medical exams are gathered, and a thorough assessment of the circumstances surrounding the allegations is conducted. Family dynamics and the presence or absence of indicators of abuse are taken into account.

There are three possible outcomes of a child protection investigation (Rimer & Prager, 2016, p. 113):

1. *Unfounded/unsubstantiated/unverified*: The evidence shows that it is unlikely that abuse or neglect has happened, is happening, or is likely to happen.

2. *Suspected/inconclusive*: Substantial evidence does not exist to confirm or exclude the possibility of abuse or neglect; therefore, it is not possible to establish a firm conclusion.

3. *Substantiated/verified*: The evidence shows that it is very likely that abuse or neglect *has* happened, is happening, or is likely to happen.

Remember your legal and ethical responsibilities to contact a child protection agency whenever you have suspicions of child maltreatment. It may be your report that brings to light further evidence that makes the difference to the child and the family (Rimer, 2007).

When we report suspected child maltreatment, children in difficult situations learn that someone significant in their life is telling them that this should not be happening to them. This information can be instrumental for children in the long term. We send important messages to children that they are not to blame for the maltreatment, that it should stop, and that someone cares enough to try to stop it.

Coping with Your Emotions

It is a very emotional experience to respond to a situation of suspected child maltreatment. Most educators experience a range of conflicting emotions, including anger, anxiety, empathy, frustration, concern, sadness, denial, and disbelief. There are often several multifaceted reasons for these emotions. Anxiety, for example, may be based on worry about the child's well-being, about the possibility of the alleged offender's reaction, about not having enough "proof," and about inadequacy in handling the situation. These feelings are normal. It is important, for your own well-being, to acknowledge your feelings and find ways to cope constructively with them. If you are fortunate, you will be working in a supportive environment where you can speak with your coworkers or the director about your feelings after reporting. Perhaps a counsellor would be helpful. You may find that your usual ways to relieve stress (e.g., physical activity, deep breathing, tai chi) are good coping mechanisms too. In any case, you need to find ways to care for yourself and your own health and to ensure that you are in control of your emotions. This is important so that you have an effective response to the entire situation (e.g., the anger must not come through to the child or the frustration to the parent).

Suspected Child Maltreatment by Educators

The line between child maltreatment and excessive discipline may be blurred at times—when observing both parents' and educators' behaviour. Remember that corporal punishment and emotional putdowns are never to be tolerated in ECLC programs. Suspicions that a coworker is maltreating children physically, emotionally, or sexually or is neglecting their needs are stressful, to say the least.

Any allegation must be responded to immediately. Not responding quickly creates the feeling that the program is not prepared to deal with the situation and that there must be something to hide. When clear policies and procedures are in place, the agency can respond effectively.

Document any concerns, questions, or suspicions about educators maltreating children. If you witness physical or sexual abuse, your actions are much more clear-cut. Because emotional abuse can be more subjective than other types of abuse, you must carefully document what was said and by whom, what was going on at the time (e.g., the activity), and the child's behaviour in response to the educator. Commonly, an educator is emotionally abusive to certain children, perhaps only one or two from the group. Often, when talking with this educator about the group, you will find that she or he shows hostility toward those children. Comments such as the child "never listens" or "does things just to annoy me" and "is basically a bad kid" are objective clues that may support your suspicion.

An educator who has suspicions about another educator's behaviour with children needs to call a child protection agency. Any individual who suspects maltreatment, whether an educator, a parent, or someone else, must call the child protection agency for advice. The children's parents or other people involved will be notified according to the child protection agency's recommendations. It must be clear to the individual reporting that there are no sanctions or reprimands for phoning the child protection agency and no pressure from anyone not to do so. As a relatively inexperienced professional, it can feel somewhat overwhelming to have the legal and ethical responsibility to report suspected child maltreatment if this relatively infrequent scenario arises. However, it is likely that your director, another colleague, or the child protection agency staff will support you as you go through the process.

CRITICAL THINKING

Maltreatment by educators may be identified through the child's disclosure or by parents who approach the director with their concerns and perhaps their suspicion of a particular educator. How does the director proceed?

Another difficult situation arises when staff suspect the director of child maltreatment. The educator documents the concerns and follows the protocol set out by the program's policy. Consultation should occur with the child protection agency with respect to who should be informed (the staff person accused, other staff, parents of other children in the program, the children, the board of directors, provincial/territorial licensing agency), at what point, and by whom.

As with any suspicions of maltreatment, remember that you are legally bound to report, even if another party tries to dissuade you from calling against your better judgment. It is a serious occurrence when the staff, student, or volunteer is suspected of abusing a child when working in the ECLC program. Accusations of abuse that do not involve children in the program (i.e., outside of this role) are handled differently.

Tertiary Prevention

Investigations into child maltreatment may confirm that a child has suffered maltreatment. The alleged offender may be identified and criminal charges may be laid. In **tertiary prevention**, there are a number of objectives. For the child, it means preventing further maltreatment and developing a care plan for the individual child's recovery. For the family, the objective is to work toward short- and long-term change. Beyond any criminal charges for the offenders, treatment must be explored to prevent maltreatment from recurring.

The role of educators in tertiary prevention is threefold:

- They provide a secure and developmentally stimulating environment for the child.

- They support change in parents by providing good role modelling and resources.

- They may maintain ongoing communication with the child protection and other agencies' staff involved with the child and family and be part of a plan for the family. *For example, the child protection agency may request that a parent spend a couple of mornings a week in the program to role model positive discipline strategies.*

Communicating with Child Protection Agencies

High-quality ECLC programs recognize that staff can't be all things to all people. This is why directors establish connections with relevant professionals in their community and collect materials for the program's resource library and for distribution among parents. Depending on the issue, educators are called on to work collaboratively with other professionals—for example, the public health nurse during an outbreak of diarrhea. In the case of child maltreatment, educators may be team members with a child protection worker and possibly other specialists assigned to an individual child.

> The director and educator are requested to participate in the child's recovery process along with the child's play therapist and behavioural therapist. The therapy is conducted and supervised by the trained therapists, but they may have particular recommendations for the educators to incorporate into the child's everyday program. Whether these are specific guidelines for play or for all the educators to manage a child's inappropriate behaviour consistently (i.e., the six-year-old's temper tantrums), the recommendations are an important aspect of the child's ongoing care.

Because children's situations and types of maltreatment vary so greatly, it is impossible to discuss fully the range of professionals and therapies that may be part of an individual child's recovery.

As part of the child's care plan, educators may be asked to observe, document, or complete developmental checklists to aid these professionals in assessing the child's progress. Educators are encouraged to call on the child protection worker when they are uncertain about a particular behaviour (e.g., self-harming) or other community agencies for guidance in supporting children and families who are going through the court process.

There are times when a child who has been maltreated is enrolled in a program for the first time by the child protection agency or another agency as part of the care strategy. Social workers recognize that trained professionals in high-quality ECLC programs enhance the child's well-being. Usually, the goals for enrolling a child who has been maltreated into a program include building positive relationships, overcoming developmental delays, and increasing feelings of self-worth, as well as providing modelling and support for parents. The decision to accept this added responsibility should not be taken lightly. It will not be in anyone's best interest, including the child's, if the educators can't cope with the complexities of the situation. Educators will not yet have an ongoing relationship with the new child and may therefore need increased support.

Making a Difference: The Community Responds to Child Abuse lists the following strategies in working with children identified as victims of maltreatment. Professionals, which includes educators, can help the child to

- develop positive self-esteem,
- trust,
- identify and express emotions,
- learn to communicate,
- identify and solve problem situations,
- continue developmental progress, and
- learn strategies in emergency situations (e.g., include plans such as what to do, where to go, who to contact in a crisis).*

High-quality ECLC programs strive to provide most of these things for all children in their program. You are already participating in the child's recovery regardless of the specific therapies carried out by other professionals. If you refer back to the discussion on the consequences of being maltreated, you will see just how they interconnect with these strategies.

Providing a Secure Environment

Beyond the essentials included in the preceding list, certain aspects of your everyday work come into play when caring for children who have been maltreated:

- Provide predictability and security in the day's routine (e.g., bringing a transition object such as a toy back and forth between home and the program). Routines and rituals are important coping mechanisms for children, especially if their lives have been stressful or disorganized.

- Help children learn appropriate ways to have their needs met, even when that means learning to delay gratification (e.g., an educator explains to the preschooler that he will be able to ride on a tricycle as soon as the next tricycle is free).

- Build a spirit of community in the classroom, with children and adults helping one another, talking through issues, and solving problems together.

- Provide clear and firm, but kind and reasonable, limits as an important part of the ECLC program. Since they suffer from injuries and pain or fear that someone will hurt them again, children who have been maltreated often feel unsafe. As a result, they may take risks even though they may know, or have been told, that an action can result in an injury. Or they may intentionally hurt others because they have learned that others have hurt them.

---

*Source: Adapted with permission from P. Rimer, 2018. *Making a Difference: The Community Responds to Child Abuse*, Eighth Edition (Toronto: Boost Child & Youth Advocacy Centre), pp. 129–131.

- Guide children to help them learn age-appropriate behaviour. Maltreatment may result in children having developmentally inappropriate behaviour.
- Be an active listener. Children can sense when they can trust an educator and express worries, fears, and concerns related to their family. This is not a counselling relationship, but one in which an educator can help the child cope with stress.
- Be aware that a family's situation rarely changes from inadequate to wonderful overnight. The child probably feels frustrated and worried about the family or has fears and concerns about social services or a legal proceeding in which he or she is involved.
- Recognize that children's behaviour can have many different meanings. Consider a child with a short attention span. Although it may be a developmental stage, perhaps it is a learned behaviour that is used as a survival tool (e.g., he or she expects that any activity will be interrupted with yelling or a smack and so is overly attuned to every movement or conversation in the room, always ready to move quickly).

Supporting Change in Parents

Communicate respect for the parent and the parent's own ways of coping and adapting to his or her unique realities. When supported and respected as a person, a parent is more likely to use the ECLC program as a resource to develop the confidence and skills needed to interact successfully with other persons and institutions in his or her life. As was the case for children who are maltreated, educators' communication with the child protection worker is important in providing consistency and support to parents who have been abusive.

All parents bring strengths and weaknesses, past experiences, and expectations to parenting. Most parents who maltreat their children love them and want to stop. Parents and other family members can feel distressed and overwhelmed by the child's maltreatment, whether they were the offenders or believe they failed to protect the child from others. They may experience reactions similar to those of the child: they are preoccupied with the details of what happened, have feelings of helplessness and guilt, and are fearful that it could happen again (Rimer, 2007, p. 84).

The program may play a role in providing respite for parents. Parents may need to work on managing or eliminating stress factors or problems that directly or indirectly relate to their parenting (e.g., counselling or treatment sessions, resolution of marital, housing, education, or employment issues). Programs can provide high-quality care for the child during this time. The child protection worker may request that these parents enroll their children in a program for the first time. This may not only benefit the parents but also encourage the development and recovery of the children. As stated earlier, providing modelling of positive ways to interact with children (e.g., talking, playing) and positively guiding their behaviour may provide parents with ideas and strategies.

Ultimately, the child's rights must be at the forefront of our concerns. In recent years, tragic stories of children who have suffered further or who have been killed while in the care of known offenders have been terrible reminders that not all parents have the support or possibly the will to change their abusive behaviour. Educators who continue to have concerns about the well-being of a child whose report has already been filed must report any new information. In the big picture, re-evaluating existing child protection legislation, policies, and protocols is part of the solution to this important social problem.

REVISITING THE HEALTH PROMOTION ACTION PLAN

Child maltreatment is a major social problem that requires a multidimensional approach by all members and levels of society. With reference to the health promotion action plan introduced in Unit 1, the following examples demonstrate how the plan incorporates child maltreatment prevention.

Individual Problem Solving and Self-Reliance
As individuals, it is important that we

- reflect on our personal and professional values to determine whether we practise respect for children in our everyday lives, built on the UN Convention on the Rights of the Child and our ECE Code of Ethics (provincial/territorial or Canadian Child Care Federation).
- continue to build our knowledge and skills in child development, working with families and policy and legislation to contribute to best practices as professionals. Organize staff training on child maltreatment and invite a child protection worker to speak at a parent meeting.
- follow all legal and ethical responsibilities if you suspect child maltreatment, in order to prevent further maltreatment.
- consider serving on the board at a women's shelter (or family shelter), often affiliated with a range of services. Educators can learn about community needs and contribute valuable knowledge and skills.

Community Action

- After talking with single parents from the program, one educator who is also a single parent organized a support group. The group set up a babysitting exchange that allows a parent to go to the laundromat or grocery store without the children. Besides making these errands less stressful, this arrangement provides the parent with respite time. Parents also exchange clothing and toys. This group provides valuable and enjoyable opportunities for the parents to establish friendships and reduce feelings of isolation.
- From the grassroots, community action can include the establishment of parent resource centres: book, toy, and clothing exchanges and telephone help lines (e.g., Kids Help Phone).

- Interested parents are offered a recognized parenting program with a trained facilitator on a weekly basis at the end of the day, while their children have dinner and are being cared for.

- Internal policies and procedures are regularly evaluated to maintain the focus on supporting children and families and on prevention of child maltreatment and family violence.

- Educators share the information they learn from professional development activities with their colleagues.

- Within some communities, professionals who work in the area or have an interest in child maltreatment form a child protection team (e.g., professionals working in the fields of education, medicine, public health, mental health, social work, law enforcement, law). These teams improve communication among professionals and coordinate more effective prevention programs, training, and child maltreatment response in the community. Educators and parents can be encouraged to become involved as participants.

Societal Change

Here are some examples of advocacy for societal change:

NELSONstudy

To access Resource
Materials, visit NelsonStudy.

- As child advocates, educators can be involved in organizations that work to reduce the acceptance of violence in our society, which is a root cause of maltreatment. Child advocacy associations, for example, are working toward laws against any type of corporal punishment of children (see the Global Initiative to End All Corporal Punishment of Children website in the Resource Materials).

- Social policy can be established that takes measures to reduce poverty and unemployment and subsequently lower ongoing stress for families.

- The Convention on the Rights of the Child can be translated into national laws.

- Federal and provincial policies and practice may be established to provide further high-quality, accessible ECLC programs.

- Police and judicial systems can be strengthened.

- Cultural and social norms that support violence against children and adults can be changed.

- Environmental risk factors can be reduced (e.g., monitoring levels of lead and removing environmental toxins—lead poisoning can go unnoticed while causing permanent damage to children's brains and putting them at higher risk for child maltreatment).

- The availability of alcohol can be reduced (e.g., fetal alcohol syndrome not only affects the child's brain, but also puts the child at risk for maltreatment).

As a society, we must move from focusing on individuals to addressing the root causes of maltreatment, which will take a multifaceted approach. Recognizing the work that needs to be done by all levels of government in addressing the social determinants of health, such as income inequality, housing and food security, and social exclusion (see Social Determinants of Health, page 4), would also have a major impact on preventing child maltreatment in Canada.

CONCLUSION

Whether we are referring to primary, secondary, or tertiary prevention, the prevention of child maltreatment has a lot to do with working collaboratively. This issue, more than any other in the ECLC program, acknowledges that promoting children's health is not done in isolation.

> The problems related to maltreatment of children are complex and they have complex impact on our society. Yet there are solutions to these problems. The choice to find solutions is up to us. If we choose, we have some control of our future. If we, as a society, continue to ignore the laws of biology, and the inevitable neurodevelopmental consequences of our current childrearing practices and policies, our potential as a humane society will remain unrealized. The future will hold sociocultural devolution—the inevitable consequence of the competition for limited resources and the implementation of reactive, one-dimensional and short-term solutions. (Perry & Marcellus, n.d., p. 2)*

ASSESS YOUR LEARNING

Define terms or describe concepts used in this unit.

- abusive head trauma (AHT)
- behavioural and emotional indicators
- child maltreatment
- documentation
- emotional abuse
- family violence
- female genital mutilation/cutting
- neglect
- physical abuse
- primary prevention
- secondary prevention
- sexual abuse
- tertiary prevention

Evaluate your options in each situation.

1. A coworker remarks that there are probably a lot of children in your program who are maltreated because most are part of single-parent families.

2. A month after you reported a case of suspected maltreatment to the child protection agency, there has been no news. The child continues to come to the program each day and is demonstrating the same behaviour that led you to make the report in the first place. You are angry and confused by the lack of response from the agency.

3. A coworker who spanks her children starts a conversation at lunch time about repealing Section 43 of the *Criminal Code*. She suggests that doing so could mean parents would be charged for "a little slap."

---

*Source: Perry & Marcellus, n.d., p. 2, http://teacher.scholastic.com/professional/bruceperry/abuse_neglect.htm

4. Lily, one of the five-year-old children who attends the program in the mornings and school kindergarten in the afternoon, is quiet and listless this morning. When you sit with her for a while, she tells you that she's scared to go home tonight. Lily says that last night her dad was really mad and hit her mom. She comments that she is going to be a good girl tonight so it won't happen again.

5. The director meets with the educators to inform everyone that the child protection agency has requested that a child who has been maltreated be enrolled in your program as part of his treatment. He requires a caring, consistent environment to help reduce developmental delays and build self-confidence. Although you are flattered, and the director obviously wants to say yes, you are concerned because you and the other educators are already feeling stretched meeting the needs of the current children.

APPENDIX 8.1

UN Convention on the Rights of the Child

In Child Friendly Language

"Rights" are things every child should have or be able to do. All children have the same rights. These rights are listed in the UN Convention on the Rights of the Child. Almost every country has agreed to these rights. All the rights are connected to each other, and all are equally important. Sometimes, we have to think about rights in terms of what is the best for children in a situation, and what is critical to life and protection from harm. As you grow, you have more responsibility to make choices and exercise your rights.

Article 1
Everyone under 18 has these rights.

Article 2
All children have these rights, no matter who they are, where they live, what their parents do, what language they speak, what their religion is, whether they are a boy or girl, what their culture is, whether they have a disability, whether they are rich or poor. No child should be treated unfairly on any basis.

Article 3
All adults should do what is best for you. When adults make decisions, they should think about how their decisions will affect children.

Article 4
The government has a responsibility to make sure your rights are protected. They must help your family protect your rights and create an environment where you can grow and reach your potential.

Article 5
Your family has the responsibility to help you learn to exercise your rights, and to ensure that your rights are protected.

Article 6
You have the right to be alive.

Article 7
You have the right to a name, and this should be officially recognized by the government. You have the right to a nationality (to belong to a country).

Article 8
You have the right to an identity—an official record of who you are. No one should take this away from you.

Article 9
You have the right to live with your parent(s), unless it is bad for you. You have the right to live with a family who cares for you.

Article 10
If you live in a different country than your parents do, you have the right to be together in the same place.

Article 11
You have the right to be protected from kidnapping.

Article 12
You have the right to give your opinion, and for adults to listen and take it seriously.

Article 13
You have the right to find out things and share what you think with others, by talking, drawing, writing, or in any other way unless it harms or offends other people.

Article 14
You have the right to choose your own religion and beliefs. Your parents should help you decide what is right and wrong, and what is best for you.

Article 15
You have the right to choose your own friends and join or set up groups, as long as it isn't harmful to others.

Article 16
You have the right to privacy.

Article 17
You have the right to get information that is important to your well-being, from radio, newspaper, books, computers, and other sources. Adults should make sure that the information you are getting is not harmful, and help you find and understand the information you need.

Article 18

You have the right to be raised by your parent(s) if possible.

Article 19

You have the right to be protected from being hurt and mistreated, in body or mind.

Article 20

You have the right to special care and help if you cannot live with your parents.

Article 21

You have the right to care and protection if you are adopted or in foster care.

Article 22

You have the right to special protection and help if you are a refugee (if you have been forced to leave your home and live in another country), as well as all the rights in this Convention.

Article 23

You have the right to special education and care if you have a disability, as well as all the rights in this Convention, so that you can live a full life.

Article 24

You have the right to the best health care possible, safe water to drink, nutritious food, a clean and safe environment, and information to help you stay well.

Article 25

If you live in care or in other situations away from home, you have the right to have these living arrangements looked at regularly to see if they are the most appropriate.

Article 26

You have the right to help from the government if you are poor or in need.

Article 27

You have the right to food, clothing, a safe place to live and to have your basic needs met. You should not be disadvantaged so that you can't do many of the things other kids can do.

Article 28

You have the right to a good quality education. You should be encouraged to go to school to the highest level you can.

Article 29

Your education should help you use and develop your talents and abilities. It should also help you learn to live peacefully, protect the environment, and respect other people.

Article 30

You have the right to practise your own culture, language, and religion or any you choose. Minority and indigenous groups need special protection of this right.

Article 31

You have the right to play and rest.

Article 32

You have the right to protection from work that harms you, and is bad for your health and education. If you work, you have the right to be safe and paid fairly.

Article 33

You have the right to protection from harmful drugs and from the drug trade.

Article 34

You have the right to be free from sexual abuse.

Article 35

No one is allowed to kidnap or sell you.

Article 36

You have the right to protection from any kind of exploitation (being taken advantage of).

Article 37

No one is allowed to punish you in a cruel or harmful way.

Article 38

You have the right to protection and freedom from war. Children under 15 cannot be forced to go into the army or take part in war.

Article 39

You have the right to help if you've been hurt, neglected, or badly treated.

Article 40

You have the right to legal help and fair treatment in a justice system that respects your rights.

Article 41

If the laws of your country provide better protection of your rights than the articles in this Convention, those laws should apply.

Article 42

You have the right to know your rights! Adults should know about these rights and help you learn about them, too.

Articles 43 to 54

These articles explain how governments and international organizations like UNICEF will work to ensure children are protected with their rights.

This text is not an official version of the UN Convention on the Rights of the Child. Access the official text of the Convention at www.unicef.org/crc/crc.htm.

Source: Adapted from the poster entitled *UN Convention on the Rights of the Child in Child Friendly Language.* Reprinted with permission of UNICEF Canada.

Supporting Children's Development

9

CONTENTS

Courtesy of George Brown College/Richmond Adelaide Child Care Centre

High-quality early childhood learning and care (ECLC) programs strive to support children's growth and development in all areas. Educators think about each child holistically to achieve a balance in his or her physical, emotional, and social well-being. This is particularly important as our further understanding of health and illness makes the interconnections between the mind and body obvious, such as the physical wear and tear of stress.

Students and, ultimately, graduates integrate their knowledge of health, safety, and nutrition with what they learn about child development, curriculum, families, diversity, and inclusion to create ECLC programs that meet the needs of both the group and each child. Ongoing research confirms that the brain is the key to our overall health and well-being, including our abilities and coping skills. Prolonged exposure to stress will have a negative effect on a child's brain development. Although many elements influence development, there is general agreement that human development follows predictable sequences in all areas—cognitive, emotional, social, and physical—but that individuals have unique "timing" and a sociocultural context. Children learn through interacting with people, objects, and the environment.

Children's growth and development are primary focus areas in your early childhood education (ECE), and you will be developing your knowledge and skills in observing and facilitating healthy child development before and after you graduate. This textbook examines certain issues relating to children's well-being that readers can integrate with their knowledge of child development, developmental psychology, and sociology. The topics covered here will add to your understanding and ability to support children's well-being. Educators are in an ideal position to support children in their learning of lifelong healthy habits and positive attitudes. The latter portion of this unit is devoted to the health curriculum for children in ECLC programs.

HEALTHY BRAIN DEVELOPMENT

Brain research is continuing to help inform parents and educators about the types of relationships, environments, and experiences that support optimal brain development. According to the Canadian Paediatric Society (CPS) (2013, p. 1),

> The evolving science of brain and early child development (ECD) clearly demonstrates that what happens early lays the foundation for later health and learning. We now know that each child's own world, especially parents and other caregivers, literally sculpts the brain and impacts stress pathways. Early development is, in turn, linked with susceptibility to later disease. Children are launched on trajectories of health and development well before birth. These trajectories are further modified, for better or for worse, by subsequent experiences within their families, care environments and communities. We therefore need a comprehensive system of monitoring early childhood outcomes in Canada.*

The importance of our emotional and social well-being and how these relate to physical well-being cannot be overstated. How you feel about yourself and the effectiveness of your relationships with others profoundly affect your health.

The human brain in early life is far more receptive (commonly termed "plastic") than it is in adulthood. Accordingly, young children's brains are more accessible to learning and enlightening influences. However, if the young child's environment and experiences are impoverished or neglectful, the brain is more susceptible to developmental problems (ZERO to THREE, n.d., p. 1).

Self-Regulation

Self-regulation and our ability to relate to others are two complex and recurring emotional and social tasks that are themes in our lives from birth and essential for positive mental health from infancy. Self-regulation refers to the ability to focus attention, control emotional energy, and initiate and recover from anger, disappointment, joy, or other emotions, as well as manage facial and body movement. How well a child (or adult) can self-regulate has a dramatic effect on that

OBJECTIVE

To outline educators' roles in supporting each child's emotional well-being in terms of the child's

- self-regulation,
- relationship development,
- stress levels, and
- sexuality. (LO 1, 2, 4)

---

*Source: Reprinted with permission from the Canadian Paediatric Society.

individual's quality of daily life. To adapt, the child must be capable of flexible regulation because life requires action and reflection, intensity and calm, and concentration and split attention.

Responsive relationships are the cornerstone of emotional development and self-regulation. This statement is also a foundation of education and training in the early childhood profession, with which you are likely already familiar. A newborn needs the educator to regulate his or her state. As the child grows, regulation becomes dyadic—child and educator work together. During the preschool years, the child begins to self-regulate. The child learns to tolerate strong emotions and recover from arousal in secure, responsive relationships that support regulation. Self-regulation develops when children are exposed to manageable levels of stimulation and are protected from overarousal. Differences exist among children in their ability to regulate emotions and behaviour and to tolerate stress. Children use a variety of sensory and motor skills to self-regulate.

Temperament also accounts for individual differences in a child's emotional arousal and reactivity.

> Temperament is biologically grounded, not chosen by the child. It is part of the individual's distinctive wiring in the nervous system. Temperament affects how we experience the world and relate to people. The many characteristics of temperament create our uniqueness. Temperament includes such aspects as our emotional and sensory intensity, adaptability, and determination. (ZERO to THREE, 2016, p. 1)

But it is through the relationship that the child learns to recover from arousal and stress. When educators remain emotionally available and are sensitive and responsive to individual differences, children learn to regulate. When children anticipate the empathy and understanding of their educator, they are more likely to cope with distress.

Children need to experience a full range of emotions and feel that it is safe to express them. When they do, they learn to regulate emotions and practise the culturally determined display rules for expressing emotions. For example, they learn when to make eye contact and how to show gratitude. They must know how to regulate emotions and behaviour to choose actions that will achieve their goals when exploring and relating to others. A child who wants to play with peers needs to regulate the impulse to take all the toys. Self-regulation is therefore central to the child's social, cognitive, and emotional development. Focusing on self-regulation means understanding individual capacities for stimulation and patterns of recovery from arousal. Educators need to use this information to create a safe environment and relationship for exploration and the development of self-regulation. As the child develops new language and cognitive and social skills, they are tools for regulation. These new skills are practised and sorted out in the context of secure educator–child relationships.

"Relating to others" refers to children's ability to build relationships, which begins at birth with their parents and develops with other significant people. In addition to relationships with adults, peer relationships are very important. Although referenced over 25 years ago, the following statement is true to this day: the three major tasks of early childhood relationships are peer group entry, conflict resolution, and maintaining play (Guralnick, 2010, p. 74). Children need to regulate their emotional energy to accomplish all three tasks. Individual differences exist in the speed, intensity, and duration of emotional responses. Educators must know each child's emotional reactions to promote regulation and recovery before the child can make progress.

Educators support self-regulation when they

- initiate and maintain communication with parents and staff that increases sensitivity to the individual child's security and exploration;
- create an environment that is safe for exploration and the expression of impulses;
- observe and record individual sensory and motor skills that are used to regulate; are responsive to the child's signals and intentions;
- remain emotionally available;
- pair novel stimulation with familiar experience;
- remain sensitive to individual differences in coping and relating;
- avoid the following measures that violate the relationship: emotional withdrawal, punishment, imposition of educator control, and intense expression of the educator's negative emotion;
- create optimal individual stimulation, taking into consideration the type of stimulation, its form, its intensity, and variations in presentation;
- increase stimulation over time in small increments that are responsive to the individual's ability to cope;
- respond to the child's signals and intentions;
- ensure that the child's voice is heard and that the child is able to participate meaningfully in matters that directly affect him or her (as per the UN Convention on the Rights of the Child; see Appendix 8.1, page 529);
- create spaces in the playroom with reduced stimulation;
- create stimulus shelters and comfort zones in the playroom; and
- create spaces for one-to-one interaction in the playroom. (Goulet & Schroeder, 1998, pp. 37–45)*

---

*Source: Adapted from M. Goulet and R. Schroeder, 1998. *How Caring Relationships Support Self-Regulation: Video Guide* (Washington, DC: NAEYC), pp. 37–45. Reprinted with permission from the National Association for the Education of Young Children.

GAABAAGANG GIVES CHILDREN A SPACE OF THEIR OWN

Open the curtain to what looks like a shelf in the Ekwaamjigenang Children's Centre [in Ojibway Ekwaamjigenang means "Our Children, Our Sacred Gifts"] and what one will see instead is a space with toys, pictures, mirrors and enough room for a child to lie down.

This quiet space, also known as a Gaabaagang, is an area where children can choose to go to be alone. Children use the space one at a time and can stay there as long as they need. The curtained-off space is part of every room in the centre, from infant to

(continued)

kindergarten.... "The idea for the Gaabaagang came out of respect for the children...."
The Gaabaagang gives children a private place for downtime or to cry, be angry or upset.... The children are taught to respect the Gaabaagang as an individual space and to give each other their privacy.... "There's a blanket, weighted toys, and different items inside there that really help them calm down. We also put pictures inside on the top so children can focus on something and have that space where they're not bothered."

RECEs [registered early childhood educators] place themselves in view of the Gaabaagang to let the child know they are available for a talk or a hug when the child is ready. The space thus allows for co-regulation between the child and the RECE.

"We feel children are in a moment of vulnerability when they are deeply upset and hurting.... When they're dysregulated they may not understand all those deep feelings they're having. They need the support and help of a caring adult so that the child isn't left to figure out how to regulate themselves. The caregiver helps guide them in co-regulating their emotions, labelling their emotions and talking about their emotions...."

In what it calls a "living document," Ekwaamjigenang says the principles for the Gaabaagang include:

- Encourage and support children's self-control and regulation.
- Foster kindness and respect of children.
- Allow children to take time to calm down until they are ready to act with a clear mind.
- Allow children to be in a better frame of mind which in turn allows them to be open to discuss what happened and what needs to be done.
- Help children form positive beliefs about themselves, their world and their behaviour.
- Support children struggling with emotional regulation and help them identify and validate their feelings

Source: *Gaabaagang Gives Children a Space of Their Own,* College of Early Childhood Educators. n.d., pp. 1–2. Retrieved February 2018 from https://www.ordre-epe.ca/en/Documents/Gaabaagang_EN.pdf. Reprinted by permission of the College of Early Childhood Educators.

Educators must observe the children to determine how each individual regulates emotional energy, preferences for other children, the familiar play situations chosen, the types of toys, and the pretend themes in which the child engages. When these things are known, educators can design environments that maximize the child's interactions with other children.

Making friends during the early years forms the basis for children's future relationships. *Early Learning for Every Child Today* (Best Start Panel on Early Learning, 2007, p. 43) identifies making friends as the dominant skill in the social developmental domain for preschoolers (2½ to 6 years). Indicators of the child's developing skill are

- seeking out others to play with;
- offering play materials and roles to others;
- playing with others cooperatively;
- inviting others to play;

- exchanging ideas, materials, and points of view with others; and

- sustaining play with others.

Educators can enhance children's opportunities to make friends through social play by

- providing equipment and activities that help children learn social rules and roles and practise taking turns and ownership as they are developmentally ready;

- observing children's individual strengths and interests and using these to involve the child with others;

- engaging in play with children, taking turns, exchanging ideas, and modelling how to make friends and sustain play (Best Start Panel on Early Learning, 2007, p. 43);

- actively guiding children to initiate play with one another when an educator observes an opportunity to foster a friendship. Insisting, however, that children play together, or that "we are all friends," is artificial and does not help children make friends. The reality is that although we all need to show respect for one another, children choose friends;

- choosing and arranging furniture to promote social interaction;

- providing equipment that provides the child with the opportunity to release emotional energy; and

- recognizing those school-agers who are having difficulty making friends and using observation to determine how educators can foster these skills. This may also mean making changes in the program.

Robert Nieding/Getty Images

Shankar (2010, p. 2) states that the dynamic nature of self-regulation has five levels operating:

1. Biological (e.g., how well the child regulates her arousal states)

2. Emotional (e.g., how well the child monitors and modifies her emotional responses)

3. Cognitive (e.g., how well the child can sustain and switch her attention; inhibit impulses; deal with frustration, delay, distractions; sequence her thoughts)

4. Social (e.g., the child's mastery of rules of appropriate behaviour; how well the child can co-regulate and thereby develop prosocial attributes)

5. Reflective thinking skills*

Courtesy of George Brown College/Scotia Plaza Child Care Centre

*Source: Shanker, Stuart (2010, July 26). "Self-Regulation: Calm, Alert, and Learning." *Education Canada Magazine*. EdCan Network. Accessible from: www.edcan.ca/articles/self-regulation-calm-alert-and-learning. Reprinted with permission.

Helping Children Cope with Stress

We have heard many times that stress is one of life's realities and that a certain degree of stress is important and positive; it challenges the individual to learn and grow. We also know that the causes of stress are varied. Some stressors are situational and short-lived, such as an upcoming birthday party or a fall that results in scraped knees, and some are chronic and long term, such as living in an abusive home environment or the death of a loved one. In addition, stress factors are unique to individuals: adults should be sensitive to each child's stress factors, realizing that they have meaning for the child. Urging a child to stop worrying, or suggesting that he or she shouldn't be upset, trivializes a child's concerns, causing more stress. Almost anything can cause stress. Regardless of the cause, stress management is crucial for a child. In some ways, many children can be very resilient by developing the ability to

- cope well with challenges and adversity and
- persist and adapt when things don't go well.

NELSONstudy

To access Resource Materials, visit NelsonStudy.

This ability can be supported when primary caregivers practise the strategies to help children develop self-regulation. Additional strategies include guiding children as they try to identify their own and others' feelings, understand cause and effect, and reach out to ask for support from others when they need it (Pearson & Hall, 2006, p. 8) (see the Reaching IN … Reaching OUT website in Resource Materials). However, emotional vulnerability that begins in childhood can affect someone for a lifetime. How?

Stressors arouse pathways in the brain, and very early in life, individuals establish physiological stress responses that either contribute to lifelong health or detract from it. A dramatic example involves cortisol, a chemical produced to respond to stress. Higher cortisol levels are produced in response to stress, and repeated or prolonged elevated cortisol levels can damage organs, including the brain, or body systems. In other words, lifelong health can be affected by the patterns of stress response established early, and this response is highly influenced by early experiences interacting with the brain. The most critical early experiences involve the quality of interactions with primary caregivers.

Although infants, toddlers, and younger preschoolers have personality strengths, they don't yet have the cognitive skills to develop optimal coping on their own. They need adults to create environments that are low in stress and to help them find ways to cope with stress. Young children hear about things that relate to the outside of their bodies (e.g., changing a diaper, putting a coat on because it's cold outside, tying shoes), but beginning in the preschool years, their awareness of how they are affected by stress involves the inside as much as the outside of their body (e.g., their heart beats faster, their mouth becomes dry, and they have butterflies in their tummy). When children become aware of their internal body cues, they can recognize when they are experiencing stress. This leads to adults helping children to learn to regulate their internal responses and acquire coping strategies, such as relaxation techniques (e.g., taking slow, deep breaths) or moving away from the situation that is causing the stress. Coping skills are usually more developed in older children because they have developed the sequential and logical thinking skills to be able to think about their problems and anticipate consequences.

Most children can cope with the usual stress factors arising in everyday living, especially with adult support. Separation protest is a healthy and normal reaction in young children because of the lack of control young children have to affect their environment; in other words, despite the child's protest, the parent can leave anyway. However, as parents and other significant caregivers show consistent and caring responses, the young child begins to integrate feelings of trust and self-control, as was discussed with regard to self-regulation. Confidence in the caregiver leads to confidence in the self with the caregiver and eventually confidence in the self. ECLC program policies and practices on entry into the program should identify ways to reduce stress on infants and young children. An individual's control or perceived control reduces elevations in cortisol. Children who are more certain about their ability to control their distress, and who develop strategies to do so, exhibit less stress and have lower levels of cortisol. Educators must support the development of children's personal control over the environment and over their own internal body state to reduce stress and regulate the production of cortisol.

A study of three- to six-year-olds at a range of child care centres of varying quality in Australia demonstrated that it is possible to identify the immediate impact of the child care environment on children using biomarkers of stress such as cortisol. The cortisol levels were acquired from the children by taking samples of saliva, and the change in cortisol at different times of the child care day was established (Guilfoyle & Sims, 2009–2010, p. 1). Children's lower stress responses (lower cortisol in saliva) were found in high-quality programs where respect for the children was evident, as well as for their social and cultural backgrounds and their individuality. Those programs with lowered cortisol in children also involved parent partnerships and active supervision. These are all important components in developing secure attachments and strong relationships. "The relationship dimension of quality is important, as secure attachments are known to moderate the stress response" (Guilfoyle & Sims, 2009–2010, p. 11). Research on the neuroendocrine system has emerged rapidly due to the use of salivary cortisol measures.

Children's Stress Factors and Responses

It can be difficult to categorize stress factors and responses into those less serious and of short duration and those that are not because a stressor is defined by how the individual perceives it. We can often distinguish among three kinds of responses to stress: positive, tolerable, and toxic. As described below, these three terms refer to the stress response systems' effects on the body, not to the stressful event or experience itself. According to Harvard University, **positive stress** is normal and healthy for children and is characterized by brief increases in hormone production and heart rate. For example, the first day at a new school or a field trip might cause positive stress in a child (Center on the Developing Child, Harvard University, n.d., p. 1).

Generally, the following stress factors are less serious or short term:

- those related to developmental milestones with no other mediating forces (e.g., toilet learning, separation anxiety, new baby in the house, making friends, learning to read, most fears)
- those related to everyday frustrations, such as too many choices, no choices, or no or little control over decisions that affect their life

common but often anxiety-inducing experiences, such as visits to the doctor, the dentist, or a hospital emergency room; short stays in the hospital for minor ailments; short separations from family; moving; transition to an ECLC program; leaving that program to attend school; transitions within a program or school (e.g., from infant to toddler room); rejection from a peer.

Table 9.1 lists some of the common fears of children at different ages (CPS, 2016b).

TABLE 9.1 Common Childhood Fears

Under 2 Years Old	• Loud noises or the dark. If unable to eliminate the noise or the lighting, adults need to be present and reassuring to reduce stress. • Separation anxiety. Dealing with it sensitively and consistently will help the child learn to trust that the parent will return. *For example: Ensuring that parents have a ritual of goodbye when dropping off the child and not "disappearing" without the child's awareness.*
2 to 4 Years Old	• At this age, children have vivid imaginations and have difficulty distinguishing reality from fantasy. • They may also have scary nightmares that wake them up and need reassurance that the things they saw in the dream are not real. When that happens, they may need a trusted adult with them until they fall asleep. • The fears may seem rational (e.g., a fear of dogs) or irrational to adults (e.g., being afraid of what's under the bed). Either way, we must remember that they are real fears to the child. • By age three, most children can separate from their parents with little or no crying.
5 Years Old and Older	• Exposure to visual media from any of the many possible media formats may create fears in young children, including news reports of war or terrorist attacks on television. Some children arriving in Canada, especially refugees from war-torn countries, have firsthand experience. This is also true for younger children if their exposure is not carefully monitored. • Younger school-agers might be afraid of ghosts and other supernatural beings. As they get older, they may have more concrete fears, such as being lost or kidnapped, being disliked, or real-life catastrophes (e.g., floods, fires, armed conflicts). • Their concrete fears, however, are usually out of proportion to their likelihood in the child's life. As they develop cognitive understanding of this fact, these fears generally lessen or cease. • Fear of being humiliated or looking or acting "strange" in front of their peers. • Older children often worry about their parents' relationship or health and may exaggerate mild arguments or complaints that they hear. • Night terrors, not uncommon in 4- to 9-year-olds, are characterized by children not fully arousing from sleep but seeming to wake up, and they are screaming and thrashing. Although they seem awake, they will not respond and will have no recollection of the event.

Source: Reprinted with permission from the Canadian Paediatric Society.

CRITICAL THINKING

Last week, two-year-old Priya, who had just started using the toilet, slipped while seated and almost fell in "bottom first." She now refuses to use the toilet again and cries and points at it whenever she needs to go but insists on wearing diapers. Priya's mom has requested to bring in a potty as Priya feels safe with it and uses one at home. However, the public health department has a policy against potties for hygiene reasons. How can you support Priya in coping with her fear?

There are stress factors that can be more traumatic or long term, but as long as the stressful event is not ongoing, and if the child has support from caring adults to adapt to the event, long-term damage to the child's health is not likely. This response is termed the **tolerable stress response**. Here are some examples of stressors that may be more traumatic:

- parents' separation or divorce; death of a family member
- bias (e.g., racism or a home culture perceived as very different from and not accepted by that of the ECLC program or school)
- bullying (generally in school-age children)
- refugee experiences (e.g., war, the witnessing of torture or death, the separation or loss of family members, different climate or weather, different language)
- witnessing a catastrophe or disaster (e.g., tornado, fire, terrorist attack)

Although this list is incomplete, it conveys the idea that children can have a range of stress factors, some of which they resolve or cope with over time or with experience. Others are overwhelming or begin as something relatively minor and then escalate, resulting in a major negative effect on how the child functions every day.

A **toxic stress response** can result when a child experiences strong, repeated, and/or continuing adversity without adequate adult support. Toxic stress can have cumulative effects on physical and mental health that last throughout a person's life. Developmental delays in childhood and heart disease, depression, and diabetes later in life are some health problems connected to toxic stress in childhood. The likelihood of developing one of these problems increases with the amount of stress experienced. However, studies also show that damage caused by the toxic stress response can be prevented or even reversed by strong and caring relationships with adults that begin early in a child's life.

Identifying Children Who Are Experiencing Stress

Many people assume that signs of stress are easy to pinpoint in children. However, with the exception of some very obvious signs, identification relies on educators' observation skills and sensitivity to individual children. Each child's temperament and personality traits have an effect on how they perceive stress and on their response. Identifying that the child is experiencing stress is only the beginning. Effective communication with parents is critical in determining the stress factors and deciding how you can work together to support the child. Possible signs are endless, but these are some common ones:

- The child seems sad, has a vacant expression, whines a lot, or has frequent temper tantrums.
- The child clings to educators, although he or she has been in the program for an extended period, or hasn't connected with at least one educator.
- The child is constantly worried.
- The child complains about physical symptoms (e.g., headaches or tummyaches, especially for school-agers). Some school-agers do not complain about aches but indicate stress through behaviour such as nail biting, nervous twitches, or sucking their thumb.
- The child seems to be tired and rundown and gets sick a lot (e.g., has frequent colds).
- The child has nightmares or night terrors.
- Bodily functions are not working properly—the child may have trouble with feeding, be constipated, have diarrhea, be unable to sleep or relax, or want to sleep all the time.
- The child self-stimulates constantly (e.g., rocking back and forth, thumb sucking, **self-pleasuring**).
- The child's overall behaviour suddenly changes drastically (e.g., becomes very aggressive or withdrawn).
- The child's development regresses.
- The child is hypervigilant and lives in a state of anxious readiness.

Suggestions for Reducing Children's Stress

Supporting children in their coping with their stress—helping them develop healthy ways to cope with what is usually normal stress—is one of the educators' roles in promoting the child's emotional well-being. Developing coping skills contributes to children's self-control and feelings of self-worth. Educators should also help children become aware of the mind–body–emotion interconnection whenever possible as there are many physiological connections as well.

Help children develop coping skills by responding to needs and cues (e.g., comfort a distressed infant as promptly as possible, respect a toddler's need to try a task independently, offer a preschooler a choice whenever possible, provide a school-ager with opportunities for decision making without adult interference).

Asking a school-ager who has started biting his or her nails lately what the child is thinking and feeling at that moment can help make this connection.

To reduce overall stress for the children in their program, educators can implement a number of strategies to create a **"stress-aware" environment**. Here are some of those strategies:

- Provide a secure, calm environment in which schedules, routines, and transitions contribute to stability, not to heightened stress. Do what you can behind the scenes to reduce stress.
- Maintain an emotional climate of trust. Children will feel that they can express a range of emotions and be supported.
- Be calm and provide security for children.
- Recognize and respond to children's feelings, taking your cues from the child.
- Create a curriculum that supports the development of children's learning about self—feelings, rights, and responsibilities.
- Honour children's right to participate. Ensure that each child's voice is being heard so that children can express their views according to their developing capacities. This supports the UN Convention on the Rights of the Child. Equally important, it helps reduce stress for the child because it contributes to a sense of control.
- Create developmentally appropriate stimulus shelters where a child can choose to be away from the group (e.g., pillows in a cozy corner for infants and toddlers, lofts or tents for preschoolers and school-agers).
- Evaluate the level of stimulation. Remember that some children are very much affected by sensory stimulation. For example,

    - Is the environment too busy and disordered, which can contribute to unfocused play, or uncluttered and organized, to help children feel in control?
    - Is the noise level conducive to focused play? Are there quiet times during the day to encourage calmness?
    - Is music playing, and, when it's playing, does the music fit the mood of the room?
    - Is the lighting natural and adequate or artificial and inadequate?

Courtesy of George Brown College/Richmond Adelaide Child Care Centre

Helping infants and toddlers start to learn they can reduce their own stress levels usually means comforting them, but it also means helping them find ways to comfort themselves, identifying for them what they are experiencing, and guiding them to activities that help them work out some of their anger or frustration (e.g., large motor activities, water and sand play). With preschool and school-age children, educators can help them identify the "inside and outside" body cues for their stressful feelings and suggest ways in which they can alleviate those feelings now and in the future. As children learn about what makes them feel stressed and how they react, they learn a lot about themselves that will be beneficial in the long term.

Some older children may express their fears about terrorist attacks or armed conflicts (i.e., war). The following list of suggestions may help children process these fears. These strategies are similar to those used by parents and educators when helping children deal with other types of fears:

- Reassure children that they are safe, that you will protect them from danger, and that you will continue to help them when they feel afraid, sad, etc. If what is happening is in a far-off location, identify where we are on the globe or map compared with the geographic location of the conflict they fear.
- Know that reactions are usually short term.
- Take the time to listen actively.
- Answer questions as well as you can but don't make promises you can't keep.
- Take their fears seriously; never ridicule or belittle children's fears.
- Be a role model. Share feelings and appropriate ways in which you cope with feelings.

Here are some examples of coping strategies that educators can help children develop:

- deep, slow breathing to help slow down the body.
- stretching exercises (e.g., tensing and relaxing muscles), which can be incorporated into a creative movement activity for preschoolers (e.g., jungle animals), or relaxation exercises, which use imagery (e.g., the children lie down with eyes closed and an educator takes them on an imaginary journey).
- helping individual children identify what is a stress release for them. Some need vigorous physical activity, others prefer time alone looking at books or listening to music, and others may need to pound clay.

Courtesy of Barb Pimento, taken at the Downtown Montessori (Coatsworth) Childcare Centre

- asking children to identify what causes their stress and what they can do to prevent a reaction (e.g., remove themselves from a stressful situation if possible, think about something else).
- resolving conflict—much of school-agers' stress, in particular, is related to interaction with peers. Supporting children in learning to negotiate and ensuring that there are consistent expectations for managing conflict in the program help children build conflict resolution skills.

Helping Specific Children

Educators create a stress-aware environment for all the children, but there are times when an individual child needs extra support because stress is affecting her or him significantly. Educators use their observation skills to identify signs and possible stress factors. The director may also be involved, and certainly parents are fully involved, unless there is a strong suspicion of child maltreatment.

The following example highlights the benefits of program involvement with parents in managing children's stress factors that may be developmentally based and, it is hoped, short term.

A CHILD IS STRESSED, HOW CAN I HELP?

When children's stress reactions are developmentally based, educators and parents are often able to support children through this process in a positive way:

Desmond is four years old. He has always been afraid of the doctor's office, mainly because of the immunization shots. Next month, he is to be hospitalized to have minor surgery. His mother, Lorna, tells you that he is terrified. His stress is evident in the program as well as at home. He is not sleeping well and is having recurring nightmares. At the program, he can't lie still to rest, although he is obviously tired and irritable. Desmond is usually quite involved and able to concentrate for periods of time at play. Lately he flits around aimlessly.

Lorna and Desmond's educators have decided to try to help Desmond in the weeks leading up to the surgery in a number of ways:

Courtesy of George Brown College/Richmond Adelaide Child Care Centre

- Desmond and Lorna will take the guided tour of the hospital, which is designed for children about to have surgery to decrease their anxiety about the unknown.

- Educators will provide Desmond with one-to-one time whenever possible, encouraging him to discuss his feelings when he is comfortable.

- Because Desmond enjoys dramatic play, the educators have set up this area as a hospital. The setting encourages him to act out his feelings and experiences. Since children tend to play about what they already know, the educators realize that his most meaningful play will be after the surgery. However, it is helpful for Desmond to handle the toy medical instruments and for educators to listen to his fears in the context of play with dolls.

Desmond is worried that the doctor will remove a leg or an arm rather than just perform the minor surgery. He's afraid that the doctor is mad at him because he always cries when he gets his shots. He's afraid he is going to be punished. This is helpful information to share with Lorna because until now she thought his only fear was that she was going to leave him in the hospital. During the hospital tour, Lorna focuses her questions on issues that help reduce Desmond's fears.

- She finds out that she can stay in the hospital room with him.

- In the children's playroom, Desmond talks with two children who had minor surgeries and sees that they have both arms and legs.

After the visit, Desmond is more focused at the program. Although he is still stressed, he's playing with other children again and isn't as hesitant to voice his fears. Lorna says that Desmond is sleeping better.

The day of surgery arrives. The doctor assures Desmond that she will only fix what she said she would and that he has done nothing wrong. When Clarissa, an educator, visits with two of Desmond's friends from the program, he is happy to see them and shows them his room and the playroom before checking out of the hospital. Within a week of his return to the program, Desmond seems to be back to his old self. Lorna isn't anticipating that he will love the doctor from now on, but she believes that the preparation and positive hospital experience alleviated Desmond's stress and fear.

When children's stress is due to a very serious or long-term factor such as child abuse, the death of a parent, or an experience as a refugee, educators will likely need to collaborate with others in ensuring that the child receives consistent support. Other agencies may be involved, and educators may be given recommendations from play therapists or other developmental specialists and counselling services.

Some stressors may need additional help for some children but not for others, depending on aspects such as the complexity of the issue and, of course, how it is affecting the child. *For example, divorce may result in minimal or drastic changes to the child's everyday life situation.* Bullying, now recognized as a critical public health issue in many countries, including Canada, can lead to serious and lasting harm. Children as young as early school age can be the victims and/or perpetrators, especially when we consider that bullying has now been defined as encompassing four categories: physical, verbal, relational, and cyberbullying (Canadian Council on Learning, 2008). As with all concerns, educators need to remember the scope and limits of their responsibility in supporting children's development, identifying when children need further help, and working with parents and other professionals in seeking that help.

Sexuality

"Canada is a pluralistic society in which people with differing philosophical, cultural, and religious values live together with a mutual recognition and respect for the basic rights and freedoms that all people are entitled to in a democratic society" (Sex Information and Education Council of Canada, 2015, p. 3). Individual Canadians have diverse values and opinions related to sexuality. The interplay of these two realities requires that democratic values are upheld in policies and practices, while recognizing the rights of individuals in upholding their cultural values as long as these respect human rights and freedoms.

Sexuality is part of all of us, regardless of our age. Yet this topic often makes adults feel uncomfortable because they may be hesitant to acknowledge young children's sexuality. Young children's sexual feelings provide sensory pleasure, but without the erotic overtones that develop during and after puberty. Children's sexuality is an integral part of growth and development.

When children touch or stimulate their genitals in some way, it is often termed "self-pleasuring" or "self-stimulation." Masturbation is an act of stimulating oneself to reach orgasm. Touching oneself for pleasure is a normal and natural behaviour, and in keeping with this positive view, we use the term "self-pleasuring" in this textbook. In fact, self-pleasuring more closely describes the child's intent. The word "masturbation" may evoke negative feelings for some adults due to taboos or messages learned as they were growing up. Self-pleasuring is a healthy behaviour for children unless it becomes the focus and interferes with the child's involvement in activities. When you observe children self-pleasuring, your reaction should be to help children learn social parameters, as with all behaviour. Acknowledge the child's pleasure and help him or her regard it as private, to be performed when alone. If children feel shame or embarrassment for normal, curious, or stimulating behaviour, this negativity about sexual matters may stay with them.

Developing Human Sexuality

With knowledge of child development, educators are able to predict the normal patterns of sexual behaviour and are prepared for and respond calmly to them.

Infants

- Early experiences with sucking and being held, rocked, and cradled provide a foundation that fosters positive feelings toward self and relationships.
- Touching or fondling the genitals when the diaper is off is normal as infants explore all parts of their body.
- Activities such as bouncing, swinging, and jumping may produce sexual pleasure; boys may have an erection, and girls may have vaginal secretions, although they are less noticeable.

Toddlers

In addition to the experiences and activities listed above for infants,

- they learn words for private body parts and toileting, and
- they have increased interest in others' genitals, an interest heightened by learning to use the toilet.

Preschoolers

- They have concerns about their genitals. Boys might worry about their penis falling off, or girls might wonder why they don't have a penis. If they tell an educator of their concern, children must be reassured and not teased. Boys need to know that their penis won't fall off, and girls need to know that they have all their sexual parts, some of which are inside their body and not as obvious as boys' genitals. The following are typical preschooler behaviours:
- They self-pleasure or explore their genitals.
- They observe each other during washroom routines.
- They may sex-play, including "You Show Me and I'll Show You," "Doctor," and so on.
- They question educators about how their body works, where babies come from, why those two dogs in the park are stuck together (i.e., mating), why girls and boys are different, and so on.

School-Agers

- They may sex-play.
- They possibly self-pleasure in public, although most school-agers understand privacy rules.
- They use slang or swearwords for private parts, sexual acts, or sexual orientation.

- They ask educators questions similar to those that preschoolers ask but are somewhat more sophisticated (e.g., "How do babies get into a uterus?" or "What are those animals doing?"). Questions such as "What does homosexual mean?" and "How do people get AIDS?" or those related to puberty (e.g., "When will I get hair down there?") are common. ECE students and educators should also be prepared for personal questions from school-age children, such as "Do you have sex with your boyfriend?" These questions are personal. You should feel confident in responding respectfully by saying that this is a personal question and that you will not answer a question that is private. By asking questions, children learn which questions are private and which we will answer. Here again, educators help children learn social skills. A positive tone is important to ensure that children know they haven't done anything "wrong" by simply asking a question.

Knowledge Promotes Healthy Attitudes

Knowing about sex does not encourage children to become sexually active too early. Of course, this doesn't mean that four- or five-year-olds are interested in sexual intercourse or should be taught about it. A five-year-old may have an idea that a man and a woman rub bodies (and may even play this out with a partner in dramatic play with clothes on). However, the child probably does not understand the specifics of intercourse, and if he or she does, the educators should explore the possibility of sexual maltreatment. Educators should be prepared to discuss anatomical facts related to gender identity and sexual differences. Adults' comfort level concerning sexuality may reduce children's anxiety about this topic. However, developing a common approach to this topic is difficult because of differences in opinion.

Educators should not offer their opinion on sexual intercourse outside of marriage. It is the family's right to convey their moral beliefs. Educators must try not to be judgmental about family beliefs and teachings. However, if there is concern that the child is being physically, emotionally, or sexually abused as a result of the family's sexual values, educators cannot ignore this possibility and must explore it further (see Exploring Your Feelings, page 471).

Around two years of age, children begin to be interested in parts of the body—both theirs and those of another gender. Giving nicknames to genitals rather than the anatomically correct term, or discouraging children from mentioning these body parts, leads to confusion later. When children hear another child or adult call a penis a "wee-wee," they begin to assume that there is something wrong with using the word "penis," although it's acceptable to use the correct names for other body parts. The same confusing message is learned by infants. Adults smile at them when they play with their toes but slap them or say no when they touch their genitals. If these messages are reinforced as children grow, they will view self-pleasuring and their genitals as bad or dirty.

Preschoolers and young school-agers between the ages of three and eight may be eager to explore similarities and differences in their bodies with peers. Sexual games such as "Doctor" or "You Show Me and I'll Show You," often while playing "House," are motivated by natural curiosity, not by erotic drive. Although these games are predictable and part of development, adults often overreact to them.

For preschoolers, one of the important aspects of their emerging sense of self is awareness of their gender. Around age four or five, many focus on gender stereotypes, much to the chagrin of parents and educators who foster less rigid roles for males and females. When children reach the school-age years, many are naturally drawn to stereotypes in clothing, hairstyles, toys, and play behaviour. They also observe and experience gender stereotypes around them. Without devaluing individual children's interests and inclinations, educators must give the same kind of care and attention to girls as to boys and continue to offer them the same range of choices. Ongoing commitment to a nonsexist approach in the program helps counteract the gender stereotypes that children face in society. Adapting to a stereotype is harmful because it replaces behaving in accordance with your own personal identity with behaving in accordance with expectations of how you should behave.

A relatively common stereotype is that boys should not cry. This may result in a boy's reluctance to talk to anyone about what is worrying him for fear that he will cry. This can negatively affect his long-term emotional health.

Gender Identity and Gender Independent Children

In the recent past, the definition of gender identity has undergone, and continues to undergo, various versions with emerging awareness that binary (male and female gender) is not inclusive. The two examples below demonstrate how definitions can have less or more clarity regarding the fluctuating nature of **gender identity**:

- "Gender is used to describe the characteristics of women and men that are socially constructed, while sex refers to those that are biologically determined. People are born female or male, but learn to be girls and boys who grow into women and men. This learned behaviour makes up gender identity and determines gender roles" (World Health Organization, n.d., p. 1).*

- "Gender identity is each person's internal and individual experience of gender. It is their sense of being a woman, a man, both, neither, or anywhere along the gender spectrum. A person's gender identity may be the same as or different from the gender typically associated with their sex assigned at birth" (Government of Canada, 2017, p. 1).**

It is evident from the gender identity definitions above that Canada's federal government has expanded the definition as well as made it clear that discrimination of gender identity is against human rights in Canada.

In addition to diversity in adult gender and sexuality, it is also reality that some children are gender independent: "**Gender independent children** are those

---

*Source: Reprinted with permission from the publisher, from World Health Organization, *Gender: Definitions,* http://www.euro.who.int/en/health-topics/health-determinants/gender/gender-definitions

**Source: *About Gender Identity and Gender Expression.* http://www.justice.gc.ca/eng/csj-sjc/pl/identity-identite/about-apropos.html. Department of Justice Canada, 2017. Reproduced with the permission of the Department of Justice Canada, 2018.

whose gender identity and/or gender expression differs from what others expect of their assigned (natal) sex" (Pyne, 2012, p. 1). The following information offers a beginning understanding of children who may be gender independent. Educators working with a gender independent child or children will require deeper knowledge and appreciation of gender independence.

UNDERSTANDING GENDER INDEPENDENCE IN CHILDREN

- Gender independent children are very diverse. Some may strongly and consistently identify with a gender role that differs from their natal sex. Others may express a gender identity that blends aspects of multiple genders and is fluid or changing. And others may be comfortable in their assigned sex but behave in ways that do not conform to social norms, such as preferring clothing and activities typically associated with the other gender.

- In the majority of situations, gender independent behaviour is simply a natural expression of the diversity of human experience.

- If provided the space to explore a range of activities and gender identities, many will place themselves comfortably on a spectrum between male and female or will grow to feel comfortable in their assigned gender role. For others, however, their cross-gender identification remains certain and consistent, and living in their assigned gender role may be too distressing to be consistent with their healthy growth.

Source: Adapted from *Supporting Gender Independent Children and Their Families: Evidence Brief: Inform Your Practice*, J. Pyne, July 2012, pp. 1 & 6. Retrieved February 2018 from https://www.rainbowhealthontario.ca/wp-content/uploads/woocommerce_uploads/2012/10/RHO_FactSheet_GIC_E1.pdf

---

Parents' Perspectives on Children's Sexuality

We have made some strong comments in this textbook on the advantages of direct communication about children's sexuality. Just as it is important to acknowledge parents' views on issues such as guidance, illness, and safety, the same principle applies to sexuality. Some parents may not agree with this open approach, and educators must respect their position, as parents and guardians are the primary and important source of sexual health education. So how do educators handle situations in which a child's sexual question or behaviour is one that you know the parent discourages or forbids?

First, educators need to come to an agreement among themselves on how they approach sexual questions and behaviour. This type of discussion provides opportunities for staff to talk about differences of opinion. Staff may benefit from additional post-diploma training (in-service) or consultation with a sexual health educator, often affiliated with the local public health agency. Some adults grew up with negative feelings or attitudes about bodies and sexuality. Some have values based on religious or ethnocultural beliefs about sexuality or sex roles. Although you must respect these views, it is inappropriate for a professional working with children to impart them to children.

- John believes that children should not touch or stimulate their genitals under any circumstances. He recognizes that he needs to explore why he feels this way. Meanwhile, he knows that he must avoid reacting negatively to children's self-pleasuring.
- A child asks how babies are born. Amélie is tempted to answer, "A stork drops them from the sky." Amélie must recognize that giving children false information is not helpful. The child will eventually find out that she wasn't telling the truth. Older children already have some idea and may be testing their educator's honesty.

Second, programs' policies on child guidance and curriculum should clarify staff's commitment to answering children's questions, including ones of a sexual nature. Written information that educators develop for parents should mention that children's awareness of self, others, and the world is part of the ongoing curriculum. To avoid misunderstanding, include examples such as "We use anatomically correct names for all parts of the body" and "A preschooler who is exploring his or her genitals is redirected if this occurs in a social situation. The child is reminded that this is a private activity, which is acceptable at nap time."

Third, meeting with the parents at the time of enrollment allows the director to raise this issue and discuss the parents' views and how they wish to handle their child's questions. Differences of opinion may arise, and in those cases, a workable and practical compromise can be reached. In the future, if a sexuality issue arises that is relevant to all parents, it would be beneficial to have a parent meeting facilitated by a sexual health educator (or other expert). The sexual health educator facilitates a discussion to identify concerns and issues that need to be addressed. Changes in a program's policy or practices may be required.

Some children have shown a keen interest in playing "Doctor," and parents have concerns that individual children may be hurt either physically or emotionally. At a parent meeting, a staff person outlines how educators manage these situations in the program:

- The children are clearly told that their individual rights are to be respected and that no one has a right to touch them in a way that makes them feel uncomfortable. They are also not permitted to touch another person against that person's wishes. This rule applies at all times, whether it concerns aggressive behaviour (e.g., hitting, pushing) or sexual behaviour (e.g., kissing, touching private body parts).
- No child is permitted under any circumstances to insert parts of the body (e.g., fingers) or other objects into any part of another child's body.
- If one child is being forced to play "Doctor" against her or his wishes, the children are reminded of individual rights and the importance of respecting those rights. If children are discovered playing "Doctor" (e.g., with clothes off), the educator responds by calmly instructing children to put their clothes on and redirecting their play to another area (i.e., the rule is that children keep their clothes on at the program).

CRITICAL THINKING

A mother asks you to tell her four-year-old son that it is "bad" whenever you see him touch his penis. She tells you that the behaviour is morally wrong. How would your conversation with her proceed?

Role of Educators as Sex Educators

Parents are the primary sexual health educators in children's lives. But educators too have a significant role to play as sex educators, whether they are aware of it or not. How? Children are constantly learning about their sexuality by

- listening to adults and other children,
- observing the way adults interact with each other and react to events and comments,
- absorbing attitudes that are communicated in adult conversation and action, and
- interacting with adults and other children.

In other words, educators are teaching about sexuality simply by the way they act, their body language, what they say, and what they don't say.

A school-age girl is looking at a magazine that has a picture of a girl about the same age posing in a way that looks seductive. The educator who remarks, "Isn't she gorgeous?" is teaching something different from the educator who asks, "What do you think of this advertisement?" The question may initiate a conversation between the girl and the educator about how advertisers use children in inappropriate ways and how they affect the way that girls and boys view females.

Educators contribute to children's sexual learning in a number of ways:

- They contribute to children's positive body image and self-worth by helping them feel proud and in control of their body. *For example, educators need to be aware of the messages they send children as feelings of self will be integrated with feelings of his or her body and body products. "I'm changing your diaper now. When you are a preschooler, you will be using the toilet" is much more affirming than "Oh, what a smelly diaper you have. You need to learn how to use the toilet."*
- They encourage knowledgeable and responsible behaviour by being informed about sexuality, answering questions simply and honestly, and responding gently to normal, curious sexual behaviour—while at the same time setting clear limits that help children learn about boundaries. *For example, a three-year-old girl asks why a boy stands up to use the toilet. The educator responds, "Girls and boys use the toilet differently because boys have a penis and girls have a vagina." If the child wants further explanation, the educator can elaborate with the fact that standing up for boys makes peeing more comfortable, just as sitting down does for girls."* Keep it simple.

- They serve as role models by helping children understand acceptable and unacceptable private and public behaviour. *For example, the child who puts his or her hand on the female educator's breast can be told, "My breast is a private body part, but you can hold my hand."*

Body Image

Think about your **body image**. Is it positive? If not, reflect on your own attitudes about weight and shape and how these can shift to promote your own body image. Granted, many of the obstacles to positive body image are the messages we are inundated with in a society obsessed with a narrow definition of beauty, as well as excessive value placed on attractiveness in this narrow view. In the real world, people come in many shapes, sizes, colours, and abilities. Images in the media are altered in many ways to make the models "appear" perfect. Educators can do their best to counteract this focus on looks by commenting on children's strengths and attempts, not their looks. *For example, say "Alice, you run so fast" instead of "Alice, you look so pretty in that outfit" or "Ramon, your drawing includes such an interesting variety of colours" instead of "Ramon, your hair looks perfect today."* Ensure that children are valued for qualities (having a great imagination, being a good listener to friends, problem-solving abilities, etc.) rather than body size and appearance.

... the mental picture I have of my body + my thoughts and feelings about that picture*

Telnov Oleksii/Shutterstock.com

Children's Questions about Sexuality and Sexual Orientation

Questions about sexuality emerge from children as they become interested. Sexuality, like any other aspect of what is going on inside and around children, is something they naturally want to know about—their body, how it works, and sex. Be sensitive and follow the child's lead. Remember, the story unfolds for children over many years, along with their cognitive development. It is inappropriate to provide a long, detailed explanation that holds more information than the child wants or needs. Even for many older school-agers, the whole idea of sex can sound disgusting. The reality is that many young school-agers are exposed to age-*inappropriate* sexually explicit content on the Internet, movies, television, and music. Their questions may be an attempt to try to make sense of it all. Don't be surprised when at times you feel uncomfortable with a question or panicky at the prospect of answering it. Many educators feel this way. Part of this reaction stems from the fact that you aren't the child's parent and want to avoid saying anything that contradicts what the parents have told, or will tell, their child.

Often a simple answer is all the younger child wants or needs. If he asks, "What are those two dogs doing?" you could answer, "The dogs are making puppies." Remember three key points when answering children's questions at any age:

1. Be sure you understand what it is the child wants to know. For example, when Chantal asks, "Where did I come from?" she might not be interested in the sexual act but rather what city or country she originated from or that she came from her mother's uterus.

---

*Source: Peel Public Health. (2011, June 3). *Fostering Healthy Body Image in Children and Teens.* Retrieved February 2018 from https://www.peelregion.ca/health/commhlth/fostbi/fostint.htm. Reprinted with permission.

Unit 9 **Supporting Children's Development**

2. Find out what the child already knows. For example, ask Chantal, "Where do you think you came from?" This will help you clarify what she is actually asking and what she already knows.
3. If you can't answer immediately, be sure to get back to the child soon.

CRITICAL THINKING

An ECE student who is pregnant is approached by an eight-year-old boy, who asks, "How did you get pregnant? Were you raped?" The student responds angrily, "That's not a very nice question. Do you know you could hurt someone's feelings by asking that?" How would you respond?

Sexual orientation, like race, gender, class, and religion, is part of an individual's identity and must be respected as such. When children ask what the words "lesbian," "gay," "transgender," "bisexual," or "queer" mean, or when they use derogatory names for sexual orientation to name-call, this is a very important learning moment. Some children may be part of an LGBTQ (lesbian, gay, transgender, bisexual, queer) family or be friends with someone who has queer (gay) parents. However, even these children may use negative remarks or stereotypes based on a lack of knowledge or misconceptions due to overwhelming stereotypes and discrimination.

The scenario below occurred between a four-year-old and a five-year-old on a walk in the ECLC program's neighbourhood:

Child 1: *"Why are those two men holding hands?"*

Child 2: *"They're probably gay."*

Child 1: *"What does gay mean?"*

Child 2: *"I don't know how to explain it. Let's ask the teacher."*

Our classroom's book shelf, for instance, was well-stocked with stories about diverse family forms or tales whose primary characters were gay or lesbian themselves. Of these titles, I used a classroom favourite ("Daddy's Roommate") to offer an age-appropriate definition of 'gay.' According to one of the story's main characters, "Gay is another kind of love. And love is the best kind of happiness." To elaborate further on this definition, it was explained to the children that gay is when a man loves a man or a woman loves a woman. Opportunities for further questions were offered but this experience ultimately seemed to resolve the initial curiosity expressed on the neighbourhood walk. (Janmohamed & Campbell, 2009, p. 41)

Source: *Building Bridges: Queer Families in Early Childhood Education* by Zeenat Janmohamed and Ryan Campbell. Atkinson Centre for Society and Child Development, 2009, p. 41. Reprinted with permission.

For most children, it is not the sex act that they generally want to know about but the importance of different kinds of families and relationships. What is important for adults to focus on is the caring part of the relationship in all family structures. *For example, other children may ask a child whose parents are lesbian, "Who is your real mom?" If the child being asked is upset with the question or unsure how to answer, the educator can say that both his moms are real and that both of them are there to love and care for him as he grows up. Similarly, for a child who is adopted, regardless of parents' sexual orientation, we would respond that the "real mom" is the mom who is there for the child growing up, and the "birth mom" is the woman who carried the baby in her uterus and birthed the baby.*

LGBTQ families are much the same as any other family! The legalization of same-sex marriages in Canada (July 2005) supports this fact. In many centres, there are parents or coworkers who are lesbian, gay, bisexual, or transgender. They may have "come out" (self-disclosed their gender identity) or possibly have not. There will also be children whom we are caring for now in programs who will become aware of their non-heterosexual orientation as they get older. Perhaps this reality helps highlight the importance of educators' attitudes in acknowledging LGBTQ families as we do single parents, step-parents, blended families, grandparents bringing up their grandchildren, and so on. This is as integral a part of a child's identity as his or her race, religion, and socioeconomic level:

> Working effectively with LGBTQ people involves having some knowledge and understanding of the social and historical context within which LGBTQ people live and parent. While LGBTQ families in Canada currently enjoy unprecedented social and legal recognition, it is only relatively recently that they have been officially "allowed" to become parents.

> Not only do LGBTQ parents know that their children turn out just fine, but numerous professional associations that work with children have issued official statements in support of LGBTQ parenting.... The Canadian Psychological Association statement (2003) reads, in part: "... there are essentially no differences in the psychosocial development, gender identity or sexual orientation between the children of gay or lesbian parents and the children of heterosexual parents."

> Think about what this means. It means that when someone walks into your program or service, they do not know if you are one of the people who believe this. They do not know how they will be treated. They may be fearful to disclose their sexual orientation, gender identity or family structure, in case they will be met with ignorance, fear or discrimination. (Best Start Resource Centre, 2012, pp. 15, 18)*

Being an LGBTQ-positive educator means being willing to spend some time reflecting on your earliest beliefs about LGBTQ people and, often, a willingness to challenge these beliefs. Our ideas about people who are different from us come from many places, such as family, religion, school, peers, and the media (Best Start Resource Centre, 2012, p. 20).

---

*Source: Best Start Resource Centre. (2012). *Welcoming and Celebrating Sexual Orientation and Gender Diversity in Families: From Preconception to Preschool.* Page 15. Toronto: Author. Retrieved February 2018 from https://www.beststart.org/resources/howto/pdf/LGBTQ_Resource_fnl_online.pdf

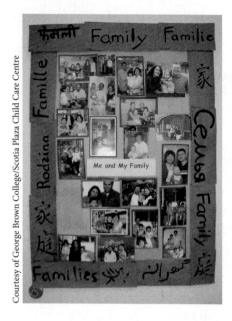

Courtesy of George Brown College/Scotia Plaza Child Care Centre

People who hold negative attitudes about a sexual orientation that is different from their own must recognize that this bias is discriminatory, as is any other form of discrimination (i.e., gender, race, religion, age, and body size). Discrimination perpetuates unjust treatment of individuals based on their identity. Children and families need to be accepted and supported, and if educators are either subtly or overtly disapproving, they are not contributing to the child or family's emotional well-being. Educators can seek out community resources to help build their knowledge and understanding of LGBTQ families and communicate respectfully with all families in their program to best support them. *Welcoming and Celebrating Sexual Orientation and Gender Diversity in Families: From Preconception to Preschool* by the Best Start Resource Centre (2012) is a comprehensive resource that offers many specific strategies for an ECLC environment that is inclusive with language and curriculum, as well as taking advantage of teachable moments for a broader acceptance of sexual orientation and gender expression. (See Resource Materials.)

NELSONstudy

To access Resource Materials, visit NelsonStudy.

OBJECTIVE

To describe essential principles in planning and carrying through with a program that recognizes children's needs for sleep, rest, and physical activity. (LO 2, 4, 6)

RHYTHM OF THE PROGRAM

The **rhythm of a program** refers to the pace of daily routines and activities. Establishing a rhythm that respects and responds to the children is an educator's daily role, beginning with greeting and talking with parents and children at drop-off. The rhythm is influenced by the ages of the children and other factors, such as group size, ratios, interests of the children, time of day, weather, space available, mood of the group, and individual children. Adequate opportunities for physical activity, cognitive stimulation, and nutrition must be balanced with opportunities for rest and relaxation. Children of all ages need opportunities to reduce stimulation and stress. Respect for individual children is paramount in planning and carrying out the day's activities as some children need more opportunity for downtime. This unit includes a discussion of the need for rest and relaxation. The need for physical activity is discussed in Unit 6, and nutritional needs are discussed in Unit 5.

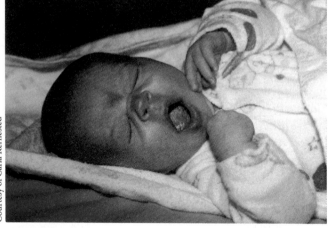

Courtesy of Carla Kernested

The Need for Napping, Rest, and Relaxation

Napping or resting is an issue that arises in every program and with every age group. Educators balance the needs of the group with those of the individual. This requires acknowledging the limitations of group care while recognizing and carrying through with practices and routines that endorse the child's uniqueness. When this is not done, children may be negatively affected. For example,

- they may not get the rest they need, which can have a negative effect on their development;

- they may be forced to comply with rigid rules, such as lying on a cot for over an hour even if they don't need to nap; and

- they may be involved in a lose–lose situation, with the child and the educator developing unhappy relationships around routines such as napping or resting.

Sleep Requirements

Sleep hygiene, as defined by the National Sleep Foundation (n.d.-b, p. 1) is "a variety of different practices and habits that are necessary to have good nighttime sleep quality and full daytime alertness."*

As children grow and develop, the amount of sleep they require changes. This includes how sleep is distributed across day and night. A child's daytime napping steadily decreases. Most children stop napping sometime between three and five years of age. This tends to result in somewhat longer nighttime sleeping (Gruber, n.d., p. 2). Sleep hygiene is now known to have a paramount role in brain and cognitive development of young children, beginning very early in their development.

- Petit and Montplaisir's "Consequences of Short Sleep Duration or Poor Sleep in Young Children" (2012, pp. 3, 4, 5) lists some powerful examples: adequate sleep seems to help structure the foundations of language from six to seven months of age and nurtures its development throughout the early years.

  This implies that a child's very early development of cognitive abilities and language depends on proper development of sleep organization and other physical processes.

  Otherwise, certain unfavourable and irreversible effects on development occur even if the sleep duration later becomes normal. This suggests the existence of a critical maturation period of the nervous system during which sleep plays a key role. It is therefore vital to treat severe dyssomnias as early as possible so as to foster optimal development in children.

- The duration of time that a child sleeps between 12 and 18 months is linked to a child's working memory, impulse control, and mental flexibility.

- Short-term sleep deprivation before a child is three years old can indicate shortfalls in verbal and non-verbal cognitive abilities at five and six years old.

Cristian Zamfir/Shutterstock.com

---

*Source: Republished with permission of National Sleep Foundation, from National Sleep Foundation Online; permission conveyed through Copyright Clearance Center, Inc.

As discussed in Unit 6, additional concerns regarding insufficient sleep for young children include

- possible emotional and behavioural problems later (at five years old) (Sivertsen et al., 2015, p. 574) and
- possible weight gain leading to childhood obesity.

While every child is slightly different in terms of how much sleep he or she needs, most of the children require the following to be fully rested in a 24-hour period (National Sleep Foundation, n.d.-a):

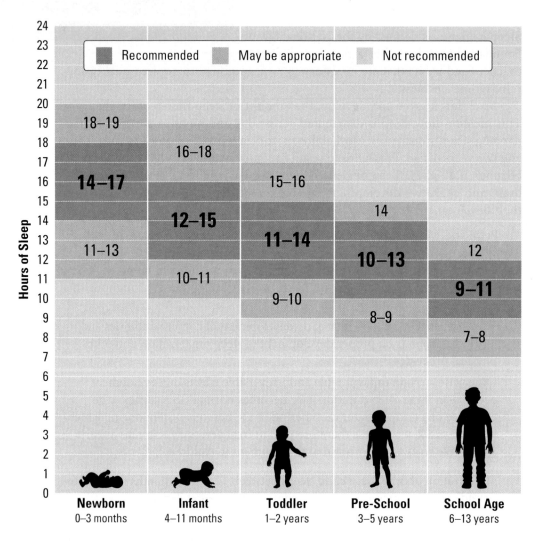

Source: Republished with permission of National Sleep Foundation, from National Sleep Foundation Online; permission conveyed through Copyright Clearance Center, Inc.

HOW THE NEED FOR REST AND RELAXATION ADJUSTS FOR CHILDREN

Opportunities for rest and relaxation take into account the developmental and individual needs of children in the group.

INFANTS:

- Infants follow their own individual nap schedules, which should be somewhat consistent with nap times at home. If the infant goes to nap when tired, rather than falling asleep in an adult's arms, he or she will soon self-soothe and fall asleep, especially if this is the routine at home.

- Infants under one year old are placed on their backs for optimum sleep safety, to prevent the possibility of Sudden Infant Death Syndrome (SIDS). In addition, a loose blanket or other soft bedding, bumper pads, and stuffed toys must be avoided.

TODDLERS AND PRESCHOOLERS:

- For some, their clues that they are overtired can seem atypical. Rather than yawning and looking sleepy, they may be restless, distracted, or fidgety. It is important to set up cots and start the nap routine before children seem overtired, as it is usually easier for a child to settle sooner rather than later.

- If possible, cots should be spaced 90 cm (3 ft.) apart and head to toe to reduce spreading of germs. Children may be allowed to have their own calming object from home (e.g., a small stuffed animal to be brought out at naptime only).

- Read a quiet story, have books that children may look at for a few minutes, or do a guided meditation or breathing exercise to help the transition for some children who need calming.

- Gently remind children of naptime rules (e.g., "speak softly" or "stay on your cot"). When a child awakens, speaking softly is also a rule so as to avoid disturbing others.

- Some preschoolers, especially those close to five years old, don't require a nap any longer but still need to slow down and rest. In many programs, they are only expected to lie on cots for a half hour, and then they can get up and do quiet activities. If another space is unavailable for children who are not asleep, containers with a range of quiet activities let children demonstrate a range of problem solving, sorting and classifying, or fine motor skills (e.g., puzzles, threading activities, small objects to sort and classify).

OLDER PRESCHOOLERS AND SCHOOL-AGERS:

- Some older preschoolers need nap time, and provisions should be made to meet their sleep needs.

- School-agers need comfortable furniture or spaces where they can wind down or do quiet activities, if they would like to, after school. Some prefer personal time, while others like to spend some time with a peer, playing a card game, engaging in another quiet activity, or having a conversation.

The need for rest and relaxation must be balanced with the need for physical activity. The *Canadian Physical Activity Guidelines* call parents, educators, physicians, and community leaders to action to support children's daily active time (see Appendixes 6.1 and 6.2, pages 379, 380). You know the reasons behind this call to action, which are outlined in detail in Unit 6. As a reminder, educators who model a physically active lifestyle contribute to the children's interest in activity. When educators participate with children and observe them in active play, they use their observations to design the environment and to facilitate so that children can challenge themselves and enjoy all the benefits of daily physically active play.

HEALTH CURRICULUM

As with all aspects of early childhood curricula, the **health curriculum** should be designed such that educators identify young children's play and learning interests. Educators rely on information about individual children based on their observation and assessment of children's developmental levels, interests, and cultural context. In other words, children's health education should be integrated into the program in ways that relate to their needs and interests.

Children's Understanding of Health

Children's understanding of health is influenced by the interaction of a number of factors:

- stage of cognitive development and temperament
- family and cultural context (i.e., cultural identity, socioeconomic circumstances, parenting styles)
- peers, their community, and the media

Cognitive Development

Young children's growing cognitive abilities affect what and how they think about health, prevention, and health promotion. Combining Piaget's theory of cognitive development and Natapoff's research on children's understanding of health, Table 9.2 (see page 562) provides examples of how children perceive concepts of health and prevention at each level. The term "prevention," for example, assumes an understanding of future and causality—actions that you take today can affect your health in 20 years. Does a three-, five-, or seven-year-old understand this concept? No. To fully understand and talk about these and other concepts, we have to reach Piaget's formal operational level in our cognitive development (at about age 12). Does that mean that teaching young children about health is pointless? No. It means that the health curriculum, to be relevant, should be based on children's cognitive understanding. Content that fits children's ability to process information is more likely to have a positive effect on long-term health behaviour (Natapoff, 1982).

Appropriate health education focuses on what children want and need now, not on what they'll need in the future. In a study in which four- and five-year-olds were interviewed in a preschool setting, the results revealed that young children's understanding of health was largely related to their ability to participate in healthy activities (e.g., healthy eating, hygiene, physical activity) in a supportive, everyday

OBJECTIVES

To identify and describe four factors that influence children's understanding of health. (LO 4)

To discuss the guidelines in developing an appropriate health curriculum and identifying inappropriate practices. (LO 3, 4)

To identify developmental health needs and interests for each age group. (LO 3, 4)

To offer suggestions for integrating the health curriculum in each age group on topics such as environmental education, oral health education, and hand washing and germs. (LO 3, 4, 6)

To identify the who, what, when, where, and why of cooking with children. (LO 4)

To discuss how educators promote oral health with each age group. (LO 1, 4)

context. This means that children's active involvement should be the emphasis in health promotion (Almqvist et al., 2006).

> Explaining to Jamie, a preschooler, that if he brushes his teeth every day they will be healthy in 20 years is too abstract.

Memorizing rules is fairly easy for children. Yet we *cannot* assume that when Jamie repeats "Brushing my teeth every day will keep them healthy in 20 years," he fully understands what he has said. For him, 20 years from now holds no meaning. It makes more sense to Jamie if we relate health education to his everyday life.

> Brushing your teeth takes all the sticky food off your teeth so you won't get cavities (or a hole in the tooth). Brushing cleans your mouth and makes it smell good too.

Cognitive development is a natural process. We can no more speed up its progress than we can speed up physical development and get a two-month-old to sit up independently. A comparison of several studies that set out to determine whether preschoolers understand a biological germ theory of illness concluded that they do not. Most children in the studies did not link the origin of a symptom (the germ) to transmission. A few children reasoned that certain kinds of symptoms are contagious (e.g., all coughs are contagious). For the most part, the preschool children (four- and five-year-olds) had a physical rather than a biological theory of germs (Siegal & Peterson, 2005). *For example, a cookie dropped on the ground would not have germs because they weren't on the cookie, reinforcing the belief that germs were not present if not visible.*

Learning is an interactive process, and children's exploration and interaction enhance their development. Using the concept of the body as an example, educators can provide experiences, materials, and questions that promote children's learning. Children build on their experiences. During diaper changes, educators can talk to infants about their tummy, knees, and toes and ask them to help lift their bottom to take off the diaper. Toddlers are learning the names and locations of body parts and beginning to identify feelings. Educators help preschoolers progress in their understanding of the body by asking them questions such as "How do you know when you are tired (or hungry, afraid, sick, happy)?" Educators can thus encourage children to become more aware of concrete body cues. School-agers begin to understand how the internal circulatory, digestive, and other systems work.

Temperament

The sequence of development is similar for children, although temperaments are unique (see Temperament, page 534). Temperament is generally considered to refer to characteristic patterns of emotional reactions and emotional self-regulation. Biological characteristics influence behaviour very early in life. Renowned psychologist Jerome Kagan studied shyness in children for many years. He believes that approximately 20% of infants are born with an inhibited temperament. By two

TABLE 9.2 Cognitive Understanding of Health

Concept	Sensorimotor: Birth to 2 Years	Preoperational: 2 to 7 Years	Concrete Operational: 7 to 11 Years
Health	• Concept too abstract for a presymbolic child. Groundwork is laid for later cognitive stages through child's experiences of healthy environments.	• Only the physical dimension of health • Egocentric (e.g., if candy makes me feel good, it must be good for me) • Can't focus on the whole and the part at the same time; for example, child believes that someone with a bandage on the knee is not healthy (the physical signs of injury or illness are less of an abstract concept)	• Beginning awareness of health as more than a physical dimension (e.g., understanding that emotional stress can cause physical symptoms) • Has conservation—believes it's possible to be partly healthy and partly not healthy (e.g., realizes that the child is still healthy even with a sprained ankle)
Causality	• Too abstract—repeated experiences with cause and effect will contribute to development in this realm	• Has "magical thinking" and is intuitive rather than logical—sometimes unrelated practices are thought to affect health or illness (e.g., child believes that getting sick must have been a result of misbehaviour—"Why did Rena give me chickenpox? I wasn't mean to her.")	• Has cause-and-effect reasoning—understands that certain actions or inactions can affect health (e.g., eating breakfast helps you concentrate at school)
Time	• Too abstract—consistent daily routines provide some predictability in their day (e.g., toddlers know that after lunch they will have a nap; they understand sequence)	• Present oriented—here-and-now orientation; does not have an understanding of the future	• Still present oriented • Has reversibility, enabling child to think through a chain of events and back—important in beginning to see more long-term orientation to health
Body	• Beginning awareness of body parts will contribute to later stages	• Has some body awareness but not a holistic view of how systems interrelate • Perceptually bound • Developing an awareness of body cues	• More aware of the body and mind and how they work together • Beginning awareness of body cues (e.g., child with asthma recognizes early symptoms of an episode and by acting on these cues takes medication)

months old, these infants show sensitivity to unfamiliar stimuli, such as strangers and loud noises. They will kick their legs and feet more, display a higher heart rate, and cry longer and louder when exposed to a loud noise, such as a balloon popping, than infants not born with an inhibited temperament (Carducci, 2008). Often such behaviour begins to be labelled as shyness as the child grows older. Shyness doesn't always mean that the child is more anxious than a more outgoing child. However, anxiety in a child is an important consideration because temperament has an effect on the child's understanding and view of health.

Irena's parents let her walk to the corner store by herself. She feels proud, excited, and independent. On the other hand, her older sister, Thea, is relieved now that Irena can go to the store when the family needs milk or bread. She has always felt anxious about going because she worries about all the things that could go wrong (e.g., she could trip and fall, not have enough money, be hit by a car, be approached by a stranger).

Thea has an inhibited temperament compared with her sister. She views many of life's challenges as risky and threatening, whereas Irena sees challenges as positive and exciting. People's temperaments are on a continuum, with those more fearful on one end and those who believe they are invincible on the other. Of course, feeling invincible can also be influenced by development. As we noted in Unit 7, young children may not as yet understand the risks involved in their activity. A preschool child cannot estimate how long it will take a moving vehicle to reach the child's location and therefore may take undue risks, such as running across a street to retrieve a ball. When developing and implementing a health curriculum, educators need to consider the range of temperaments in their group. Remember that increasing children's anxiety or feelings of vulnerability to encourage them to take positive health action has serious ethical questions. We must be careful not to raise anxiety levels in children because increased stress for children does not mean increased health, as discussed earlier.

Educators are planning to teach children to be cautious about crossing streets, ingesting poisons, or approaching animals by focusing on all the dangers. Educators are concerned about some of the children who feel invincible. Although their approach may have a positive effect on the safety behaviour of some children, it may have a negative effect on those who worry. Their fears about crossing streets, exploring new things, or approaching animals are intensified. This negates children's confidence in striving toward self-care.

The Family and Cultural Context

Family is an essential connection to children's identity. The connection between children and their families is a powerful one that has a significant effect on their understanding of health. Members of various ethnocultural groups connect the cause of disease, to varying degrees, to certain theories, such as the imbalance of hot and cold in the body, spiritual or supernatural powers, or magic (e.g., the evil eye causing fever, vomiting, or diarrhea). Illness may be viewed as an invasion of body, mind, soul, and spirit (Waxler-Morrison et al., 2005). A family's health beliefs and practices may be effective in maintaining the health of an individual and his or her family, even if these practices are not based on contemporary medical theories. In fact, traditional remedies may at times help someone feel better when conventional medicine has failed or has no recommendation.

It is essential that the ECLC program respect the significance and dignity of each family's cultural beliefs and practices. Of course, this must be qualified with regard to concerns that children are being mistreated, malnourished, or neglected in any way by a particular family practice. Remember that culture is a broad term and can be defined in many ways. For example, in Bates and Plog's book *Cultural Anthropology*, they have defined culture as "the system of shared beliefs, values, customs, behaviours, and artifacts that the members of society use to cope with their world and with one another, and that are transmitted from generation to generation through learning" (1990, p. 7). Another way of defining culture includes **"inherited" culture** (i.e., race, ethnicity, language, religion) and **"personal" culture** (i.e., acquired, often reflecting values, attitudes, and ideologies). Perhaps gender identity, as defined on page 549, could be considered a combination of both inherited and personal culture. A person's sense of gender identity can come from a combination of genetic and environmental influences.

Influences that may stem from culture are beliefs about health care professionals (e.g., conventional versus complementary practitioners) and types of treatment (e.g., prescription medicine versus herbs). Clearly, a practice that is unfamiliar to an educator is just that—unfamiliar. In their work with families, educators learn about health beliefs and practices other than those learned in their own families or at school and use this knowledge and experience in health curriculum development. The differences in inherited cultural practices can be overshadowed by socioeconomic factors.

As wealth is a better indicator of long-term health outcomes in Canada (Mikkonen & Raphael, 2010), there may be more similarities between the health beliefs or practices of different ethnocultural groups at the same socioeconomic level than there are among the people within the same ethnocultural groups who are from different socioeconomic levels. In other words, if you are wealthy, you probably have more in common with others who are wealthy than you do with people who are poor and from your ethnocultural background. The reverse is true also.

Socioeconomic Factors Affecting Well-Being
The socioeconomic gradient in health status has been a pattern for over a century in all industrialized, wealthy societies. Children who are poor are likely to be living in unhealthy environments that are beyond their ability to change. Poverty usually means food insecurity, substandard housing (e.g., cold, damp, drafty, crowded) in unsafe areas, inadequate clothing, and no access to safe play and recreation opportunities. These living conditions result in a higher incidence of disease, hospitalization, and deaths due to injuries. Families in poverty often deal with insecure employment and rarely see a reason to hope for improvement in their situation.

It is difficult for children to develop a future-oriented attitude toward health when the world they live in is filled with daily crises (e.g., uncertainty over when they will have food). Children who live in families who are comfortable financially have more reason to believe that they have control over and can affect their health and their future.

Peers and the Community

As children grow older, the influence of their peers, community, and the media can have either a positive or a negative effect on their health. Sam was eating a variety of nutritious foods until he was six years old; then he told his mom that he could bring in only those foods that his friends approved. Similarly, Olivia stopped washing her hands because it wasn't "cool" with her friends. On the other hand, if peers are excited about healthy habits or have positive views of health, they tend to influence one another positively. Children's willingness to try new foods that peers, possibly from different ethnocultural backgrounds, bring in fosters an openness that promotes health. Friends who are willing to wait while their peers wash their hands are making a statement about health.

The community—neighbourhood, ECLC program, school, recreation centre, place of worship—in which children live also affects their overall well-being and influences their view of health.

Every morning the program's playground is strewn with broken glass and discarded needles, syringes, and condoms from the night before. To date, nothing proactive has been done to change this, and the children are getting the impression that we have to accept the situation.

Children, educators, parents, and the police work together to develop a plan of action that results in changing the situation. Children see firsthand that it is possible to have an impact on our health.

Developing and Implementing a Health Curriculum

Many of the programs' healthy practices are important for all of us in our everyday lives—hand washing, oral care, healthy eating, physical activity, and stress management. The hygiene practices described in Unit 3 are not of particular educational interest to children, even though they have a direct impact on their health (e.g., food storage, disinfecting mouthing toys). Providing a health curriculum in a program is more than occasionally reading a children's book about a health-related issue. Table 9.3 (see page 567) consists of guidelines for appropriate and inappropriate health curricula for children that educators can refer to in evaluating their ongoing curriculum.

CRITICAL THINKING

Your partner in the preschool room searches the Internet on a regular basis for finding curriculum ideas. She has found a theme-based set of activities on learning about germs, all of it focusing on children learning that germs are not visible to the naked eye, they are everywhere, and we must kill them all. What feedback will you offer, and what would you suggest as an alternative?

Health Needs and Interests of Children

Certain health education topics or behaviours are more appropriate to introduce at particular ages and developmental stages. Beginning to learn about germs, for example, makes much more sense to pre-schoolers and school-agers than it does to infants. The following discussion is by no means exhaustive, but it indicates typical health areas of need or interest for each age group. Of course, each group of young children in ECLC programs is unique, and these general ideas must be responsive to the group's needs and interests.

Infants and Toddlers

The focus in a health curriculum for infants and toddlers is on adults caring for children's health needs and modelling healthy attitudes and behaviour. Environments that support infants' and toddlers' emotional health and development are ones in which children feel safe and secure and trust that adults will meet their physical, emotional, and social needs and respond to their cues. To achieve such environments, ECLC programs need to

- establish effective ongoing communication with parents (e.g., practices around separation for child and parent that promote trust).

- implement good hygiene practice, ensure safety, and actively involve children in routines. This would include as many one-to-one or small-group experiences as possible. The very young child learns about health by experiencing healthy environments and by educators' actions. For example,

  - responding to infants' and toddlers' verbalization and talking about the activity's process, including naming parts of the body while diapering, while toileting, and during other routines;

  - encouraging the child's involvement in undressing (e.g., diapering, getting into a sleeper for a nap after outdoor play) and older toddlers' involvement with dressing; and

  - hand washing with children, who become increasingly involved as time goes on.

- provide opportunities for children's bodies moving in space, minimizing restriction except for safety reasons.

- relate physical activities to growth and development, such as short, flexible tunnels for budding crawlers and large foam blocks for climbers.

- ensure that infants are given a spoon and are encouraged to be as involved as they would like to be in self-feeding. Be patient with toddlers' learning table behaviour and respectful of cultural practices in eating that differ from yours (e.g., using hands to eat or an adult feeding a child). Establish basic limits: food is not to be thrown, for example.

- offer opportunities for various sensory experiences, including foods with interesting natural colours and textures, as appropriate.

- serve nutritious food, encouraging preference for whole foods without a lot of processing and added sugar, salt, and additives.

- monitor and control sudden loud noises in the program because of young children's fears. When adults who are unfamiliar to the children visit the program, or when the children are outside, be sensitive to the children's responses. Support children in daily separation from parents.

TABLE 9.3   Developing a Health Curriculum: Guidelines

APPROPRIATE HEALTH CURRICULUM	
Guidelines	**Examples**
focuses on the children's developmental needs, interests, and level of understanding	Preschoolers' interest and readiness to learn simple safety rules that can be practised, such as "stay away from matches" or "stop, drop, and roll" if clothes catch fire.
is interactive—children learn best when they interact with people and materials in their environment (play based or fit into their daily lives)	Toddlers are encouraged, but not forced, to try new foods (e.g., pineapple). They can see peers and educators eating the food, hear its name, observe it with their other senses, and have opportunities in the home-living centre to play with lifelike fruit and vegetables. They are learning about the food and are therefore more likely to try it.
acknowledges children's rights through participation	The educator supports the children's ideas for incorporating a safety rule for a new activity according to their developing capacities.
has clear and reasonable objectives for children's learning based on developmental areas (cognitive, physical, emotional, social)	The primary objective for the preschool cooking experience is to encourage the child to follow a sequence. Secondary objectives include sensory exploration, cause and effect, promoting turn taking, and small motor skills.
is organized so that much of the health curriculum happens as part of the program's routines—hand washing, rest and relaxation, physical activity, healthy eating, and so on	Infants' hands are washed by the educator after diapering and before eating; school-agers are encouraged to respond to their body cues, such as needing to rest or drink water after vigorous physical activity.
includes practices modelled by educators	Children see educators washing their hands after helping a child in the washroom and before eating with the children.
fits into the natural daily, weekly, monthly, and seasonal rhythm of the program	From the spring to the fall harvest is an ideal time to learn about growing vegetables and flowers from seeds.

(continued)

TABLE 9.3 Developing a Health Curriculum: Guidelines *(continued)*

APPROPRIATE HEALTH CURRICULUM (*continued*)

Guidelines	Examples
is integrated into all curriculum areas—music, movement, science, literature, and so on	Preschooler body awareness: <ul><li>beginning awareness of body cues (e.g., child with asthma recognizes early symptoms of an episode and by acting on these cues takes medication); art—body tracing on paper; children paint in body parts</li><li>music—songs about bodies</li><li>creative movement—body games, challenging children to explore their bodies with questions such as "How tall/small can you be?", "How high can you jump?", and "How angry/happy can you look?"</li><li>science—use a magnifying glass to look at skin</li><li>literature—many children's books (e.g., *The Bare Naked Book*)</li><li>numeracy—graph particular body characteristics (e.g., skin, hair, and eye colour, "inny" or "outy" bellybuttons) by printing names or placing photos of children on paper</li><li>dramatic play—a full-length mirror</li></ul>
is flexible so that educators can take advantage of teachable moments or one-to-one interactions	Answer a preschooler's question during a food experience (e.g., "Why are vegetables good for me?"); show a toddler how to sneeze into the sleeve after the child has sneezed without covering his or her mouth.
builds self-esteem and competence, moving from simple to complex	Use simple three-step recipe cards for "ants on a log" (celery, cream cheese, raisins), allowing children to feel accomplishment in completing a task independently.
is respectful and inclusive of family beliefs, practices, and situations	A parent regularly comes in and teaches tai chi to the school-age children and educators and discusses its advantages to reduce stress in mind and body.
focuses on the concrete rather than the abstract and on present rather than future health	Say "Physical activity helps your body work better" rather than "Physical activity now lowers your risk of heart disease when you are an adult."
emphasizes all aspects of health so that children begin to develop an awareness of holistic health involving physical, emotional, and social well-being	Healthy eating is viewed in terms of its effect not only on growth and physical well-being but also on mental alertness: if you eat well, you learn better and you have opportunities to spend enjoyable, relaxed social time with your friends while eating.
moves toward increased understanding and responsibility for their own health with knowledge about what aspects of their health are in their control	Emphasize to preschoolers that making hand washing a habit before eating and after toileting is something they can take responsibility for, something that helps them take control over how often they get sick; let preschoolers know that they have no control over how safely an adult drives a car, but they do have control over putting on their seat belts to protect themselves.

(continued)

TABLE 9.3 Developing a Health Curriculum: Guidelines *(continued)*

INAPPROPRIATE HEALTH CURRICULUM	
Practices	Examples
a series of lessons are formally taught to children	Talking (or lecturing) to children about the dos and don'ts of hygiene without hands-on practice does not allow interaction with children; reading a book about sexuality in group time is inappropriate.
is based on themes, so a health area is highlighted for a week but is not a priority for the rest of the year	Peacemaking is introduced as a week's theme in the school-agers' room when a conflict is in the news. For the remainder of the year, the principles of peacemaking are ignored by educators, and children are not developing the skills to put peacemaking into practice.
is based on the adults' health interests rather than the children's interests	An educator who does aerobics every day conducts daily instructional exercises and loses patience with the toddlers when they don't seem interested in the activity.
is designed or implemented in a way that instills fear, an inappropriate sense of responsibility, or groundless vulnerability in the child	An educator pressures preschoolers to eat everything on their plate because children elsewhere are starving; an educator cautions children to never talk to strangers because they may hurt them.

Courtesy of Carla Kernested

Toilet learning often begins somewhere between 18 and 36 months. The term "learning" highlights children's active role in this process. As with most aspects of working with children, educators should follow the child's lead. Readiness for using the toilet is demonstrated when all three of the following are observed in a child:

- physical maturity—stays dry for several hours, can get to the toilet, pulls down loose-fitting pants
- awareness—of a full bladder or bowel; the child understands that she or he has wet or soiled diapers
- desire—to use the toilet (or potty) and to have a dry diaper

When all three aspects of readiness are in place, toilet learning is usually a positive process. Educators in toddler (or preschool) rooms often find that children's desire is high when peers are using the toilet. Children's feelings of self-esteem are paramount in the approach to toilet learning. In the best interests of the child, together parents and educators work to provide support through this period. When there is a difference of opinion on the timing or approach to toilet learning, educators and parents work together to reach a compromise.

Preschoolers

This group of children is particularly interested in learning about

- cleanliness, toilet learning and toileting, good grooming, dressing themselves;
- germs and sickness;
- health and safety rules (e.g., cover your mouth with your sleeve when you cough and sneeze, look both ways before crossing the street with an adult);
- safety and injury prevention, at least on an early-awareness level, and especially using simple rules;
- personal safety, again on an early-awareness level, and following child-centred guidelines (see Child Maltreatment Prevention Programs for Children, page 501);
- community helpers (e.g., role of firefighters, police officers, doctors, nurses, dentists) and especially what process takes place in a hospital if the child or a friend has been a patient;
- some common fears: fear of the dark, monsters, loud noises (e.g., thunder, truck backfiring), abandonment (especially if divorce, death, hospitalization, or other trauma has occurred);
- food and good nutrition, how and where foods are grown or are eaten, same and different foods eaten by people and animals;
- the role of sleep and relaxation; and
- the role of physical activity and movement.

The following are usually of more interest and more appropriate developmentally for older preschoolers:

- body awareness, interest in more complex body parts and systems (e.g., internal organs, respiratory system)
- regular brushing, primary teeth coming out, new teeth coming in
- emotions, own feelings, awareness of similarities and differences (e.g., gender, race), manners, own family and others' families, having babies
- beginning awareness of conflict resolution and peacemaking
- basic understanding of importance of caring for the environment

School-Agers

School-agers are interested in more complex issues and want more details, but they still haven't developed abstract reasoning. The following are some examples that particularly interest them:

- illnesses
- loss of primary teeth, emergence of permanent teeth
- body awareness that is more complex than when younger (e.g., interest in body secretions and body noises, changes with puberty)
- consumer health, especially as reflected in advertisements in television commercials, magazines, product labels, prices

- environmental health issues, particularly issues around landfill sites, over-packaging, air quality, climate change, animal extinction, and actions we take, such as observing the three R's (reduce, reuse, recycle), composting, returning bottles and cans, and renewing and refinishing
- personal feelings, making friends, family dynamics, getting along with others (e.g., bullies, peacemaking)
- human rights: racism, sexism, classism, homophobia, and concern for those whose rights have not been respected
- safety and injury prevention (e.g., bicycle, pedestrian, playground, home safety, first-aid treatments)
- awareness of own stressors and positive ways to deal with stress
- how the body works (e.g., how nutrition, rest, and physical activity interrelate)
- physical fitness
- foods friends eat that may be different from theirs and nutrients in foods
- self-care, as in learning to make snacks and meals independently, knowing what to do in an emergency, finding out about personal safety and street proofing
- community awareness and with support from adults work with others to affect health in the community (e.g., neighbourhood, school, ECLC program)

Getting Down to the Health Curriculum

When health is viewed holistically, countless topics and issues can be included in a program's health curriculum. Although this section does not include a multitude of ready-to-use activities for different age groups, it does offer suggestions for implementing health curricula in a selected number of health-related topics. (See Resource Materials.) From here, students will be able to take what they learn from the entire discussion on health curricula and develop a curriculum on topics of their choice. Of course, any specific curriculum must always be based on the needs and interests of the particular group of children as they emerge. The following topics are discussed in more detail in connection with the guidelines for the various age groups:

NELSONstudy

To access Resource Materials, visit NelsonStudy.

- environmental health
- nutrition education
- oral health
- hand washing and germs

Environmental Health Education

For more than two decades, concern about the health of our planet, which ultimately affects all life, has been a major educational focus for everyone. A lot of resources are available that encourage public involvement in environmental health and safety. Of course, increased knowledge about climate change, energy use, land and water use, waste, and other environmental issues is essential for changes in public and personal attitudes and behaviour that will positively affect

the earth. Canadians are slowly becoming environmentally literate and are starting to engage in environmental stewardship to contribute to a healthy future, including advocacy for legislative changes that follow the precautionary principle (see Precautionary Approach, page 402).

> Children are spending more time indoors, in structured learning activities, in front of screens, and away from nature. Without adults to show them the way, our children lack early experiences in nature that are fundamental to nurturing environmental ethics. Without a healthy relationship with nature, our children will lose baseline understanding of what nature should be like and be less concerned with changes.... Once our children become adults, how will the next generation of Canadian children learn to love nature, understand our reliance on it, and actively care for it over time? (Parks Canada, 2014, p. 21)

However, we must never imply or state that children are solely responsible for the future of the planet. Because children have reached only the early stages of cognitive and moral development, they are liable to take this message seriously. Feelings of guilt (e.g., whenever a child uses a paper product), fear or hopelessness for the future, and other feelings will contribute to children's stress levels. They may begin to view the onerous task of saving the planet as theirs alone and become consumed by it.

Environmental health education can be a part of everyday life at home and in programs. Adults who "live gently" or are aware of their "carbon footprint"—both of these terms are used to refer to a way of living that respects life, uses resources without wasting, and causes minimal harm to the planet—are helping children to learn about environmental health. Programs model these practices by

- participating in recycling programs, where available. The most common recycling programs are community-wide and accept glass, plastics, cardboard, and newspapers. Recycling can also include clothing, winter boots and coats, skates, and toy swaps in ECLC programs and between programs.
- composting. Some local waste management programs also accept food waste for composting.
- choosing products that are safer for the environment (e.g., cloth diapers or use of a recycling system for disposable diapers, biodegradable products).
- using energy efficiently.
- repairing, remodelling, and reusing, when possible.
- respecting ecosystems.

Within programs, educators need to be aware of the messages they are sending to children about their role in saving the earth. Our goal is for children to develop a positive attitude and belief that they can make change happen and be part of a community of change by incorporating actions that contribute to that change, but not to be overwhelmed with a sense of personal responsibility. When environmental education is integrated through contact with nature, there is the potential for various benefits for children, as listed in Table 9.4.

TABLE 9.4 Hands-On Contact with Nature and Children's Mental Health and Well-Being

Benefit	Effect
Benefits associated with seeing growth and change, the cycles of life	Builds resilience
Contact with nature is calming	Reduces disruptive behaviour
Gives children a sense of freedom to innovate, to be creative, to discover	Enhances self-esteem
Engages the senses	Creates feelings of wellness
Provides enjoyment	Children enjoy being outside in nature
Gives a sense of achievement, empowerment	Increases self-esteem

Source: Maller, D. (2005). "Hands-on Contact with Nature in Primary Schools as a Catalyst for Developing a Sense of Community and Cultivating Mental Health & Wellbeing." *EINGANA: Journal of the Victorian Association of Environmental Education, 28*(3), 17–22. Retrieved February 2018 from http://www.vaee.vic.edu.au/resources/eingana/einganadec05.pdf#=18. Reprinted with permission.

Outdoor Playscapes: Breaking New Ground by L. Wilson (2014) is a wonderful resource to build your knowledge and curriculum for exploring natural environments with children. (See Resource Materials.) For example, Chapter 6 of *Outdoor Playscapes,* "Greening the Outdoor Environment," discusses the value of greening playgrounds and the impact of nature on children. The author also identifies influences on garden design and offers many ideas and considerations for getting started and involving children.

NELSONstudy

To access Resource Materials, visit NelsonStudy.

Infants and Toddlers

Environmental education for infants and toddlers should focus on role modelling. Children observing educators who respect plants, trees, animals, and insects on walks and children guided by gentle reminders when handling nature inappropriately (e.g., plucking flower petals, stomping on earthworms) are on their way to becoming environmental advocates. Opportunities for walks in the park or other natural environments, each season, provide awareness of nature and may provide a chance for puddle splashing with boots and raincoats on; music recordings of nature sounds such as rain falling, birds singing, insects chirping, or waves lapping may also provide comfort and familiarity when children experience the "real" sounds. Children's natural impulse to jump in puddles is based on their need to learn about and experience the physical world. Using their senses and motor skills to explore natural settings enhances many skills, including cognitive skills such as focus and problem solving. It is important to remember that, developmentally, these very young children are egocentric and that going beyond this level of environmental education would not be good practice.

Preschoolers

As with all learning, preschoolers build on what they have already experienced with the environment. For preschoolers to develop respect for the natural environment, they first need to be part of it and learn about it. However, environmental concepts and issues are complex. Since children learn from the simple to the complex, educators begin with simpler versions of relevant concepts for preschoolers. They learn best when they interact with people and objects.

The environmental concept of life cycles can be introduced at the preschool level in a number of ways. Planting and harvesting, composting, and observing trees change with the seasons are ways that help preschool children begin to understand nature. Ideally, a respect for nature is a part of everyone's value system. Individuals don't necessarily have to love earthworms or spiders to respect the role they play in the environment. Vermicomposting (or red worm composting), for example, is a convenient way for organic waste to decompose. It is a practical, indoor option to help preschoolers see the process of composting "in action." Educators can easily find information on the health and safety considerations for this process.

Educators need to provide experiences through the seasons that serve as springboards for observing, investigating, discovering, and learning about the environment through nature. Adults, including ECE students and educators, sometimes feel that they do not know enough about nature, but they can learn along with children. Adults who demonstrate a quest for learning, rather than pretending to know everything, actually provide very good role modelling.

Children can express their interest in the environment in all areas of the program's curriculum:

- *Art.* Use easels outdoors to inspire children to paint their representation of trees or their feelings about trees; make leaf rubbings; create from recycled materials (e.g., sound-makers, collages).
- *Music.* Sing songs about nature or create chants; identify sounds of nature. Create music with natural materials such as tree stumps and sticks, tap stones together, put sand in funnel and let it pour on different surfaces, and crinkle fall leaves.
- *Creative movement.* Express the rhythms of the earth or move like wind, water, and so on.
- *Science.* Care for a living thing through planting and gardening; adopt a tree in the park and see how it changes with the seasons. Focus on small life forms (e.g., insects, worms); pick them up gently (e.g., large spoon or tweezers); observe them carefully with a magnifying glass, in a bug container, or on a piece of white paper or cardboard. Return them gently to the ground.
- *Literature.* Read and discuss books about nature or about legends that involve nature, possibly stories from the children's backgrounds (e.g., Indigenous legends embody nature).
- *Numeracy.* Compare sizes and shapes of plants, pebbles, or rocks to seriate, classify.

- *Dramatic play.* Add a small recycling box in the home-living centre; play jungle animals; transform the play area into a forest with trees and animals.
- *Field trips.* Walk in your neighbourhood in the different seasons; visit a botanical garden, recycling plant, community playground, garden centre, farm, orchard, bird sanctuary, pond.

Although they are still young, preschoolers could become involved at a simple level with community action, along with their parents or educators.

City developers were planning to cut down trees in the program's neighbourhood to build a parking lot. Educators and concerned parents involved the children in a walk of support for the park, the trees, and the play area. The event got media attention. As well, pictures the children drew of the park and trees were enclosed in a letter to the mayor.

Educators must be careful to ensure that participation of this kind does not instill fear, that children understand the purpose of what they are doing, and that they are not being exploited to gain public support for adults' issues. Many complex environmental issues are beyond a preschooler's cognitive level of understanding (e.g., animal extinction).

Courtesy of George Brown College/Scotia Plaza Child Care Centre

Today's preschoolers will become the adults who make major environmental decisions in the future. The interest in, knowledge of, and concern for the environment that begin in children's preschool years will eventually benefit everyone.

School-Agers

This age group is already targeted more than any other with regard to environmental education resources. School-agers, especially those who have reached a concrete operational level of thinking, can have a fuller understanding of environmental issues, particularly if they have had environmental experiences earlier in life. Children are becoming interested in the democratic process. Those who have been developing decision-making and coping skills may have been involved in some social action. Any number of approaches and activities can be part of school-age ECLC programs. Through a discovery approach supported by educators who believe in the importance of living gently, school-agers can get involved in meaningful and practical experiences. They can also organize and lead regular school yard and neighbourhood litter cleanup campaigns. Through their experiences, school-agers acquire the knowledge and life skills to develop their confidence as change agents. They may also be interested in becoming involved in community action with such activities as writing letters to policymakers about environmental issues that affect them.

> When children put their energy into contributing to change, a health promotion philosophy is put into practice.

By planning and networking with teachers in the children's school, ideally, educators and teachers can coordinate their environmental health policies and practices. As well, they can find out how much time is spent on the environment in the classroom. This policy includes several practices to reduce waste, eliminate toxins (e.g., audit of cleaning products, running water for a few minutes every morning to flush possible lead in the water pipes), and incorporate ways to build child respect for the environment in age-appropriate ways. Your efforts will be in vain if children become turned off when inundated with environmental education rather than motivated and excited by it.

Adults have a major role in protecting children from environmental hazards as there are a number of factors about children that contribute to their greater exposure to substances in the environment (see Environmental Concerns and Children's Well-Being, page 449). Protection must always be a priority, but there are many ways that educators and parents can "gently" integrate environmental health education into children's lives, recognizing their rights to participation in their own health promotion.

CRITICAL THINKING

You have been told at your placement that although the preschoolers are busy exploring fall leaves by jumping in them outdoors and noting their varied colours, public health regulations do not permit you to take any leaves indoors. You believe that the preschoolers would benefit from having the opportunity to explore the leaves indoors, handling them, experiencing their texture and other properties more in-depth, noting the leaf "veins" with a magnifying glass, etc.

What do you think is the rationale behind the public health inspector prohibiting leaves being brought inside? Do you believe that this regulation is warranted? If not, how would you proceed?

Nutrition Education

Nutrition is the easiest health area to integrate throughout the curriculum and from infancy to school age. The possibilities for learning are endless but usually centre on some general concepts. The following nutrition concepts can be appropriately incorporated into children's nutrition experiences:

- Everyone needs food to grow, feel good, and have energy to do things.
- A wide variety of foods are available, and it is best for our body if we have variety every day.
- Foods have unique colours, flavours, textures, smells, sizes, shapes, and sounds.
- Foods that are unfamiliar to you are enjoyed by other people. Trying new foods helps you learn about yourself and the world and gain respect for and insight into other ethnocultural backgrounds.
- Everyone has individual food likes and dislikes.
- Food should be respected for its role in fulfilling needs—and should not be used for art activities.
- Foods have different sources (e.g., some grow on trees or in the ground, some come from animals).
- Foods are made up of nutrients, and the foods that have more nutrients are better for our body.
- The way that food is handled and cooked affects the amount of nutrients in it, its safety, and its taste.
- Food provides the opportunity for social time, and the rights of self and others are considered through the sharing of food.

Nutrition experiences help children develop cognitively, physically, emotionally, and socially. Here are some examples of how food can be incorporated into all areas of the program's curriculum:

- *Art.* Use magazines and grocery store fliers to create collages of various foods; paint food cartons to be recycled after use or use them in box sculpture; draw pictures of how you feel eating different foods (e.g., puckered face after eating a lemon). Using food that will not be eaten in art and craft activities is unacceptable and disrespectful of food and of those who do not have enough to eat.
- *Music.* Sing songs about foods; the words to familiar children's songs can be modified to include nutrition messages.
- *Creative movement.* Pretend to be fruit or vegetables planted, picked, harvested, falling to the ground.
- *Science.* Design activities using one or more senses (e.g., discovery box with foods inside to touch and describe before washing and eating). Grow foods (e.g., gardening in plots or boxes). Compare fruit and vegetables (e.g., fresh, frozen, canned, dried).
- *Literature.* Read books about food, cooking, gardening (include books that portray a diverse array of foods, which expands children's awareness of choices).

- *Numeracy.* Use scales and measures to compare weights of foods. Practise one-to-one correspondence with children for number (e.g., fruit, vegetable, muffins) to ensure that there is enough for each child.
- *Social studies.* Share foods and eating customs with others—activities particularly relevant for older preschool and school-age children. Examples are foods eaten for Diwali, harvest foods, haggis, foods for Kwanza celebrations, the origin or invention of certain foods and eating implements, cooking equipment, utensils.
- *Dramatic play.* Set up a grocery store (e.g., empty cracker and cereal boxes), restaurant, or pizzeria and provide lifelike food. Use cooking and eating utensils that reflect ethnocultural diversity.
- *Field trips.* Visit a grocery store, market, bakery, farm, or local garden, or invite a child's family member to come and cook a traditional dish. Some field trips, such as a sizable grocery store, are most relevant when going for a specific reason (e.g., school-age group and educator have decided on a recipe, visit the grocery store for ingredients, return to the child care setting to prepare the recipe, and share it for snack).

Cooking with Children

Cooking with children is an ideal way to begin their nutrition education. Snacks provide an opportunity each day for children to have food experiences. Food preparation calls on children to use their five senses; to learn about colours, shapes, and textures; and to use simple kitchen utensils. Children can begin to learn the basic principles of hygiene and food safety and, of course, take pride in their accomplishments and eat the "fruit" of their labour. Even older infants love to squeeze bananas or help mash potatoes. When children enjoy cooking and eating nutritious foods and develop food preparation skills, they may be inclined to have a more balanced lifestyle as they get older. Current public health concerns about the mass consumption of unhealthy food, particularly convenience foods with high contents of unhealthy fats, salt, and sugar, require changes in eating habits. Table 9.5 offers suggestions for snacks that children can make.

TABLE 9.5 Some Snacks or Lunches Children Can Make

Age Group	Snack or Lunch Idea
Infants	simple fruit salad, mashed banana, applesauce, blended mango pudding, cottage cheese with a face made with Cheerios, frozen fruit juice on sticks, finger gelatin made with fruit juice and plain gelatin, well-cooked carrot sticks with yogurt dip,* smoothed avocado on crackers, fruit and yogurt blender drinks
Toddlers	devilled eggs using yogurt instead of mayonnaise, cottage cheese salad with crushed pineapple, porridge for a teddy bear picnic, ants on a log (e.g., bread sticks with apple butter and Rice Krispies), fruit or vegetable and cheese kabobs using Popsicle sticks, frozen bananas on sticks served with yogurt or applesauce dips,* banana coins in orange juice, nutritious milk shakes

(continued)

TABLE 9.5   Some Snacks or Lunches Children Can Make (*continued*)

Age Group	Snack or Lunch Idea
Preschoolers	English muffin pizzas, dippidy-doo and vegetables too,* guacamole* and corn tortilla chips, pita sandwiches, unidentified frying objects (i.e., cut a circle out of a slice of bread and fry it with an egg in the hole), home-made butter (shake cream) for sandwiches or crackers, vegetable ("stone") soup, yogurt and fruit sundaes, "people" sandwiches (e.g., hummus on circles of bread with grated carrots, apple smiles, sunflower seeds, banana coins, etc., to make faces), scrambled eggs in an "ice cream" cone
School-Agers	tacos, three-bean salad, muffins, baked apples, rice pudding, Waldorf salad, banana-egg pancakes, chop suey, stir-fried vegetables, bannock, pretzels, fondue,* stuffed pita, hummus with crackers, sticky rice, vegetable sushi, beans and rice, lentil, vegetable, or other soups

* Provide children with individual dishes of dip, guacamole, or fondue. Double dipping in a communal dish spreads germs.

The Five Ws of Cooking with Children
Who?
The ideal educator–child ratios:

- Infants 1:1
- Toddlers 1:2
- Preschoolers 1:3
- School-agers 1:4 maximum

The worst situation:

- A large group of children with one educator

These ratios promote safe cooking practices and allow for individual participation.

What?
Two ways of cooking with children:

- small group with an educator, usually using a recipe that makes enough food for a number of children (e.g., baking)
- individual children following the recipe, often called "production-line cooking," usually using a recipe that makes individual portions

Select nutritious foods that are developmentally appropriate and do not pose a risk for choking. Ensure that allergies and food restrictions (religious, ethnocultural) are considered in planning any food experience.

What children learn from following recipes

1. the names of food and food mixtures
2. sequential learning: recipes that are based on developmental appropriateness, for example,
   - two steps for infants
   - three to four steps for toddlers
   - four to six steps for preschoolers
   - eight steps maximum for school-agers
3. how to measure ingredients

Pictorial and written recipe cards are particularly useful for preschoolers and school-agers. They incorporate sequencing and prereading skills (or reading, for older children) into the experience, and children learn that a lot of food preparation involves recipes. For prereaders, there should be many illustrations with just a few words. It is possible to use one recipe card listing all the steps (e.g., on a piece of construction paper). For individual-portion cooking, a set of recipe cards (one card for each step) makes it easier for children to do one step and then move to the next station.

bulgur

6 Tsp.

mint and parsley, chopped

2 Tsp.

Courtesy of Barb Pimento

Courtesy of Sister Celeste—Fort Norman

Preparing and Baking Bannock Together: Step 1

The following are tips for making recipe cards:

- Cut out pictures or drawings of food, cooking equipment, and utensils used in each step.
- Use a dot system rather than numbers to indicate each step, particularly for preschoolers (e.g., one dot on the first card, two dots on the second).
- Laminate the cards for durability with repeated use.

As children become more familiar with the printed word, you may want to create recipe cards that combine pictures and words (e.g., have a picture of the apple and print the word "apple" or use the dots and symbol for the number two). For readers, the recipe's steps can be presented in a chart format.

When?

The ideal time is during play time, as one choice among several activities. This way, you may be able to work with smaller groups at a time and repeat the recipe until all children

Preparing and Baking Bannock Together: Steps 2 & 3

who want to can do it. With the ideal number of children (or close to it), you are able to focus on each child's questions, reactions, and so on, and each child is truly involved in the process. Your role as facilitator is very important. If children are independently doing a production-line recipe, ensure that other children are not waiting in line. This creates an antisocial climate. Instead, children can sign up and come at their turn.

The worst time is during a circle time or other large group times. It is not realistic to expect a large number of children to work together at something that needs only a few. Passing a bowl around while each child has one stir is not learning—it creates frustration, and your role is focused on crowd control rather than on facilitating.

Where?

The ideal place:

- In a low-traffic area located close to running water and an electrical outlet, if needed

The worst place:

- In a noisy, busy area

Why?

Food experiences (or cooking) with children can be positive in many ways:

- Everyone needs to eat!
- When children are involved in food preparation, they are more likely to try the food.
- Cooking is usually an enjoyable experience for children. They are proud of their accomplishments, which builds self-esteem.

Any well-planned food experience has many advantages for children:

1. Cognitive opportunities are made available and facilitated through foods.
   - Children can see similarities and differences (classification).
   - They can experience temporal relations (sense of time and sequence).
   - They can develop a sense of quantity and measurement.
   - They can problem solve (e.g., What will happen if…?).
   - They can take part in matching (one-to-one correspondence).
   - They can learn about growing plants.
   - They can learn about the origins of foods, such as eggs from chickens, milk from cows and goats.
   - They can see the effect of temperature on substances (e.g., freezing fruit juice, frying potato pancakes, baking muffins).

2. Educators use opportunities to build language skills through food routines and nutritional learning experiences (e.g., by using the correct terms for foods, equipment, cooking processes, and discussions about foods and by following recipe cards).

3. Children regularly have the opportunity to participate in food preparation. This can be integrated into the everyday curriculum. In addition to viewing meal and snack preparation as important aspects of everyday life, children build their cooking skills and have opportunities for cooperation and for appreciating a wider repertoire of foods, enhancing their ethnocultural learning. Most ethnocultural groups have particular breads that are either staples or are familiar to them.

4. Food experiences involve both girls and boys, promoting an atmosphere of equity in both food preparation and cleanup.

To enhance the cooking experience, educators should follow these recommendations:

1. Prepare for the activity:
   - Try out the recipe before using it with the children.
   - Ensure that all ingredients and equipment are available and in working order.
   - Check carefully for any food allergies or restrictions.

2. Promote safety:
   - Have all necessary equipment and ingredients set out in a safe location before beginning the activity (involve school-agers in this aspect).
   - Explain and demonstrate all safety aspects to the children before starting (e.g., using knives) and practise these precautions during the activity.
   - Tips for before the activity:
     - The table is cleaned and disinfected before you begin.
     - Everyone, including you, washes their hands before setting up the ingredients, utensils, and equipment.
     - Food is stored safely, lids are wiped, and fruit and vegetables are washed before use.

- Tips during the activity:
  - Ensure that sharp utensils (e.g., knives) and equipment (e.g., griddle) are out of reach of young children or actively supervised if handled by older preschoolers or school-agers.
  - Children are not left unattended and do not walk or talk with food in their mouth.
- Tips after the activity:
  - Clean and disinfect the utensils, equipment, and table when finished.
  - Include children in the clean-up, if possible.
  - If the snack is not to be eaten immediately, store it safely (e.g., blender drinks in the fridge).
  - Wash hands.

3. Facilitate the activity:
   - Encourage every child to participate.
   - Be receptive to the questions and feelings of each child.
   - Show interest and enjoyment in the activity through facial expression, tone of voice, body language, flexibility, and positive interactions with children.
   - Let the children's comments and questions guide you about what they want to learn.
   - Ask questions that encourage problem solving if children are not initiating questions.
   - Use positive guidance throughout the activity.

4. Evaluate the activity after it is over:
   - Were the expectations appropriate for children's learning?
   - Did each child have opportunities to actively participate?
   - Was the time frame appropriate?
   - What follow-up experiences would be meaningful?

It is important to involve families in your nutritional education curriculum. Some family members may be available to come in and make a favourite recipe with the children; others may send in a recipe or a food that has special meaning in ethnocultural or religious events. Programs may also find ways to share families' favourite recipes through newsletters, bulletin boards, cookbook projects (possible fundraiser), and potluck events throughout the year.

Oral Health Education

"Poor oral health can affect a person's quality of life. Oral pain, missing teeth or oral infections can influence the way a person speaks, eats and socializes. These oral health problems can reduce a person's quality of life by affecting their physical, mental and social well-being" (Canadian Dental Association, 2013, p. 1). Tooth decay or early childhood caries (ECC) is the most common chronic infectious disease in Canadian children. "A 2010 Canadian Health Measures Survey reported that 57% of Canadian children six to 11 years of age have had a cavity, with an average of 2.5 teeth affected by decay. Caries rates are increasing among children two to four years of age" (CPS, 2016a, p. 1).

CPS's position statement on oral health care for children (2016a, p. 1) includes the following points:

- Dental care for both prevention and treatment should be accessible to all children and youth.
- The cost of dental care impacts low-income families more due to their income level and less likelihood that they carry dental insurance.
- Public funding of dental care in Canada is decreasing and varies across the country.
- Research shows that preventive dental care improves our oral health later and in turn reduces treatment costs.
- Fluoridation does decrease the rate of dental carries, especially in higher-risk populations.

Oral health education is a good example of children learning through a daily routine. Oral care is a lifelong health habit. Educators are in an ideal position to take an active role in ensuring that children's teeth are protected while they are in the program and to help children learn good **oral health** practices. Taking good care of teeth and gums is essential, for maintaining both oral health and overall health.

For families who are financially comfortable or who have jobs that include oral benefits, professional oral care is usually not a problem. Families with a low income but not on social assistance are often in a position in which they do not have oral benefits, and the family budget may not be able to include the costs of oral care. However, some communities provide access to free or affordable oral care if they qualify, and it can be very helpful to make that information available to families in the program.

By around age two, children have 20 primary (or baby) teeth. Between ages 6 and 12, primary teeth start to loosen and fall out as the permanent teeth underneath begin pushing through the gums (see Figure 9.1). Most children start by losing the lower two front teeth and then the top two, creating the classic gap-toothed smile.

Everyone gets plaque. This thick, sticky layer, mostly made of bacteria that live in our mouth and "feed" on the sugars and starches we eat, is constantly on our teeth. The bacteria in the plaque mix with food in our mouth in an "acid attack" that lasts up to 20 minutes after we eat. This attack begins eroding the enamel layer of our teeth. Some of us incorrectly assume that the natural sugar in raisins or other dried fruit, or the starch in snacks such as pretzels or crackers, is better for your teeth than less-nutritive snacks such as candy or potato chips. Although saliva helps neutralize the acid and rinse food out of our mouth, especially at mealtime, when more saliva is produced, it can't do it all. Brushing and flossing are needed to remove food and plaque; if the plaque stays there, it hardens and causes tartar, which leads to tooth decay. When young children have the opportunity to learn effective toothbrushing, flossing will be a natural addition to their routine as they reach school age. Brushing our teeth before going to sleep is a good practice. When we are asleep, we don't produce as much saliva, so the bacteria and food left in our mouth produce acid that eats at enamel.

FIGURE 9.1 The Development of the Primary Teeth

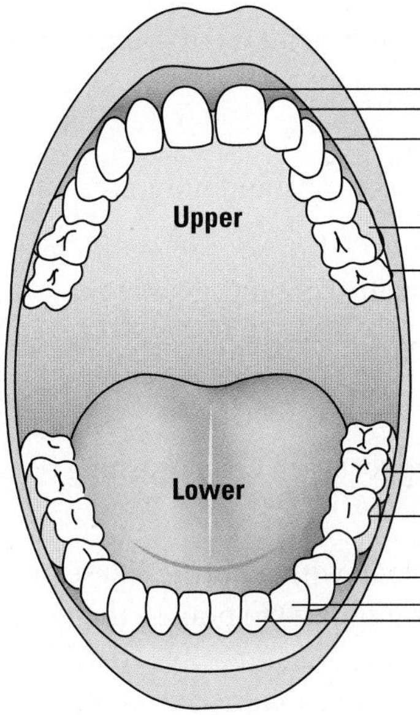

Primary Teeth	When Teeth "come in"	When Teeth "fall out"
Upper		
Central incisors	7–12 mos	6–8 yrs
Lateral incisors	9–13 mos	7–8 yrs
Canines	16–22 mos	10–12 yrs
First molars	13–19 mos	9–11 yrs
Second molars	25–33 mos	10–12 yrs
Lower		
Second molars	20–31 mos	10–12 yrs
First molars	12–18 mos	9–11 yrs
Canines	16–23 mos	9–12 yrs
Lateral incisors	7–16 mos	7–8 yrs
Central incisors	6–10 mos	6–8 yrs

How Do We Promote Oral Health?

Fluoride Fluoride is a mineral that strengthens tooth enamel, which helps prevent cavities, and can even reverse tooth decay that has started. People who live in communities in which the drinking water is supplied through a water treatment plant probably haven't given much thought to fluoride. In many places, fluoride is added to the drinking water before it reaches our homes, which is a decision made by each community's public health agency. Fluoride is also found in various foods, toothpaste, fluoride drops prescribed by physicians, and fluoride treatments by oral professionals.

The controversy, sometimes voiced, about fluoride is usually concern that tap water may contain a higher level than it should. Dental fluorosis occurs when high amounts of fluoride are consumed in early childhood. In its most common form, fluorosis affects how the child's teeth look: small white specks appearing on the teeth. Dental fluorosis is not an issue of concern for the vast majority of children (Canadian Dental Association, 2018a, p. 1). If educators or parents are concerned about fluoride levels, contact your regional public health agency.

Healthy Eating and Drinking Limit or, if possible, avoid offering high-sugar foods, particularly sticky ones (e.g., raisins, pop, candy) and limit foods with cooked starch (e.g., potato chips, pretzels). Serve dentally friendly foods often, especially fresh fruit and vegetables, plain yogurts, cheese, and milk. Frequent snacking (or grazing) is discouraged because food is in our mouth so often that acid production is frequent. Encourage children to drink water between meals and snacks, ensuring that tap water is readily available and easy for preschoolers and school-agers to access independently. Little or no juice for children is good practice, as excessive juice consumption is one of the factors in the development of early childhood tooth decay (CPS, 2016a, p. 2).

"From birth to 12 months" (CPS, 2015, pp. 55–56):

- Wipe a baby's gums with a soft, clean, damp cloth twice a day—only once a day if you know that a parent is doing this too.
- "Never leave a baby in bed with a bottle."
- If a bottle is needed before naptime, offer water or milk and not juice.
- "Never sweeten a soother."
- "Don't give a baby teething biscuits, which usually contain sugar."

For children between 1 and 3 years of age (CPS, 2015, p. 56):

- Use regular cup for all drinks.
- If a routine in your ECLC program, begin to support each child brushing teeth, using water, with educator's support.

Do not prop baby bottles or put children to sleep with a bottle. These practices allow formula or milk (which contains natural sugars) to pool in the mouth for a long period of time. Babies' teeth are soft and very susceptible to acid and decay. *Juice and non-nutritive high-sugar drinks are even more damaging.*

Early childhood tooth decay (ECTD) (formerly called nursing bottle syndrome) can happen very quickly, leading to the painful decay of primary teeth. Dull white spots or lines can appear on newly erupted teeth, seemingly overnight. Parents are encouraged to see a dentist as soon as possible if this happens.

ECTD has a negative impact on children's overall health and can cause pain, making it difficult to sleep, eat, or speak. Pain can also affect a child's ability to concentrate and learn. Children who develop dental decay at an early age are more likely to suffer decay throughout childhood. By making appropriate cleaning practices part of the daily routine and helping families learn about nutrition and oral hygiene, you can play an important role in preventing ECTD. (CPS, 2015, p. 55)*

- Drinking a bottle of water is not a risk for ECTD; putting a child to bed with a bottle increases risk of choking.
- Children's eustachian tubes are shorter and straighter than adults'. When children lie on their back with a bottle in their mouth, the liquid and saliva may run back into the middle ear and cause an ear infection.

It is advisable to switch to a sippy cup for all drinks as soon as possible, preferably by one year of age.

Routine Toothbrushing By the time children are of preschool age, they can learn about "2 for 2": twice daily for two minutes each time. Although this really refers to once in the morning and once before bed, if the ECLC program can support a toothbrushing routine in the day, it reinforces the concept and gives children more practice.

Many centres choose not to brush the children's teeth during the day. There are several reasons for this decision, including

- the public health issue surrounding the logistics of storing the brushes in a manner that keeps them from touching, being able to air-dry, but not open to the air, and the labelling of both the brushes and each child's storage area. Due to the various styles of brushes, finding a hook system that accommodates the brushes is challenging. That being said, some programs have been successful in meeting these issues.
- children dropping the brush into the sink and onto the floor, resulting in the brush needing to be replaced.
- the time that it takes staff to supervise all the children during this routine.

For many programs, this routine follows lunch time as children begin the transition to a nap or quiet activity. On field trips, children can rinse their mouth with water. Flossing is difficult in programs because of the extra time and demands involved. Parents should floss their child's teeth once a day until the child has the skill to floss his or her own teeth as flossing can reduce overall plaque significantly.

Courtesy of Barb Pimento

---

*Source: Reprinted with permission from the Canadian Paediatric Society.

Tips for brushing:

- Use a soft toothbrush.
- Add toothpaste. Use a very small dab for infants and toddlers; preschoolers need an amount only about the size of a pea. Be careful that the tip of the tube doesn't touch the brush. An educator will need to help younger children put on the paste.
- Shop for toothpaste and other oral care products with the CDA seal. "From toothbrushes to mouthwashes, oral care products bearing the Canadian Dental Association (CDA) Seal of Recognition have been reviewed by the CDA and have demonstrated specific oral health benefits" (Canadian Dental Association, 2018b, p. 2).
- Follow the three-step method (see Figure 9.2) and brush or supervise the child's brushing. Start at the far lower back teeth, using a "wiggling," not a scrubbing, motion.
- Move around the mouth, wiggling the brush on all the surfaces. Don't forget to brush the tongue to fight bacteria and freshen the breath.
- Teach children not to swallow the toothpaste but to rinse with water and spit.
- Rinse the brushes well.

FIGURE 9.2 Toothbrushing Pattern

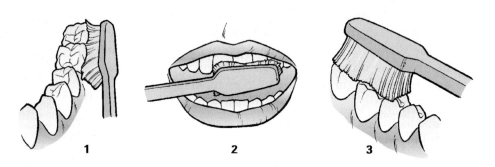

1   2   3

Tips for toothbrushes and for preventing infections:

- Use a baby toothbrush for infants and toddlers and a child-sized one for children up to 12 years old. Ask parents to replace it every three months.
- Each child must have his or her own brush and must never share it.
- Label each child's toothbrush and store it to dry where air will circulate around it and where it doesn't touch other toothbrushes. Educators often have to be very creative in designing a convenient, hygienic storage method.
- Rinse toothbrushes thoroughly after brushing and ensure that each one can dry without touching others.
- Keep brushes out of reach of children to ensure that they are not used by different children and as a safety precaution. Children must learn not to run or walk with a toothbrush in their mouth.

- Ideally, each child should have his or her own travel-sized tube to reduce the likelihood of cross-contamination and promote independence. The tubes must be labelled with the children's names.
- Wash your hands before and after brushing children's teeth.

Infants and toddlers

Educators communicate with parents about wishes for their infant's daily oral care. If the parent agrees, the educator can wipe a young infant's gums with a soft, clean, damp cloth daily. When first teeth appear, CPS (2015) recommends cleaning them with a soft-bristled toothbrush designed for babies while laying the infant on a flat surface or cradling the infant's head in your lap.

When toddlers are able to stand at the sink, they are able to participate more in brushing. Standing behind the toddler and facing the mirror tends to be a convenient position. Educators may either do the brushing for the child or hold the brush with the toddler. For the child between one and three years of age, it's a good idea for the educator to check for ECTD monthly, by gently lifting a child's upper lip to check for signs of tooth decay. Signs are chalky-white or brown spots on the teeth, or near the gum line. If these exist, it is important to inform parents, so that they can soon take their child to a dentist (CPS, 2015, p. 56).

Preschoolers and school-agers

With experience, older preschoolers become more skilled at brushing, and the educator eventually needs only to supervise and possibly offer a little help rather than be actively involved. Being able to print her or his name is usually an indicator that a child has the dexterity to toothbrush. Most school-agers have the dexterity to brush their teeth without supervision and have gained more responsibility and independence in self-care. Although some children simply don't like brushing their teeth or don't like one more routine, most children appreciate the immediate results: brighter teeth and a clean-tasting mouth. Involve children in planning and preparing dentally healthy snacks. Educators can also encourage children to be aware of healthy food choices and explain how some foods promote oral health.

> The muffins offered at lunch time have raisins in them. The educator mentions to the children at her table that having something with dried fruit is best at lunch time because at a meal they have more saliva, which helps take the sticky raisins out of their teeth. Also, their routine is to brush their teeth after lunch.

Learning about oral health can be incorporated into all areas of the program's curriculum:

- *Art.* Paint and draw pictures of food that promote oral health.
- *Creative movement.* Children can wiggle their bodies like they wiggle the toothbrush, an activity more appropriate for younger preschoolers.
- *Music.* Sing songs (e.g., about smiles: Raffi's *You Brush Your Teeth*).
- *Science.* Place a hard-boiled egg in vinegar, which helps illustrate, to preschoolers and school-agers, how enamel dissolves with a lot of acid in time.

- *Literature.* Read books about keeping teeth, losing teeth (e.g., tooth fairy stories), and oral health.
- *Numeracy.* Count teeth (e.g., how many molars); classify pictures of foods that are more and less healthy for your teeth.
- *Lunch time/snacks.* Discuss nutrition and positive roles of good food in our health (e.g., the importance of our strong teeth in crunching carrots and biting into apples).
- *Dramatic play.* Set up a dental office and provide a variety of real props, including a flashlight, a mirror, and a lab coat; avoid needles for safety as well as not to instill fear! If you are involved in the play, offer positive comments about going to the dentist and avoid using negative words such as "drill" or "hurt."
- *Field trips.* Tour a dentist's office; invite a dental hygienist to talk about oral health with children and/or for a parent meeting. Dental professionals often have positive and child-appropriate explanations for their questions.

Contact local resources such as the public health agency or a local college that teaches oral hygiene to inquire about possible resources (such as "big teeth" and toothbrushes, models that children can practise with or observe and talk about).

Hand Washing and Germs

As we discussed in Unit 3, hand washing is the most important routine that we do every day to prevent the spread of infection. It is a health practice that children need to learn for it to become a lifelong health habit. Like oral health, education about hand washing is based on an ongoing routine in the program, and there are many opportunities to reinforce it.

Infants and Toddlers

The hand-washing routine begins in infancy as part of diapering and feeding routines. Educators talk with infants about what they are doing as they are doing it, making comments such as "The water is warm" or "The cloth feels soft and wet." Infants are aware of their hands being washed and feel that it is part of caring.

Once toddlers are physically able to stand at the sink, educators can help them learn to wash their own hands. It is easier for children to learn the proper way and to make it a habit with practice than it is to change poor habits once they are formed. Educators may make the routine enjoyable for children by singing action songs such as *This Is the Way We Wash Our Hands*.

Preschoolers

Preschool children are ready for basic information about germs and what hand washing does to germs. During the preschool years, children become skilled at hand washing when adults provide consistent support built on earlier experience. By the time they are independently washing their hands, with educators now only supervising, they can learn some basic information about germs (e.g., germs are on our hands even when they look clean and they hide between fingers and under nails).

How can preschoolers learn about germs when germs can't be seen on hands? As with all aspects of the curriculum, it is essential to encourage active involvement and introduce concepts in a concrete way. Educators reinforce the fact that we are trying to prevent as many germs as we can from entering our bodies. Because our hands touch many things, there are a lot of germs on them. Most children don't walk around with facial tissue in a pocket; rather than not covering their mouth when they sneeze, and rather than sneezing into their hands, they can put their arm in front of their mouth. This prevents germs from getting on their hands.

Courtesy of George Brown College/Scotia Plaza Child Care Centre

Since we can't see germs, educators can show preschoolers something to compare to germs. Use a spray bottle to spray water into the air; the water droplets seem to disappear in the air and fall onto objects. Germs in the water now float in the air and can land anywhere—including on someone else. When we cough and sneeze, droplets of saliva that carry germs spray out. This helps children understand why covering their mouth before sneezing is a good way to cut down on germs going from one person to another.

Learning about hand washing can be incorporated into different curriculum areas:

- *Art*. Draw what they think germs would look like if they could see them.
- *Music*. Sing songs (e.g., to the tune of *Row, Row, Row Your Boat*, sing "Scrub, scrub, scrub your hands, put the soap between, wash the germs right down the drain, make them nice and clean").
- *Science*. Put a piece of bread in a jar and over the next several days invite the children to watch mould grow. To compare, handle a second piece of bread with dirty hands and put it into the jar. Ask children to predict which piece of bread will grow mould (germs) more quickly and record their predictions and observations over the next week. Educators can explain that for us to actually see germs (like mould), there have to be many, many of them. Do not let the children touch the bread with mould.
- *Literature*. Read books with hygiene topics, or storybooks about a child who had a cold, and so on.
- *Dramatic play*. Use the water table to wash dolls, including the hands.
- *Nutrition*. Show how food can be shared without spreading germs (e.g., serving spoons, cutting a sandwich in half rather than taking turns having a bite, when child touches a cracker or grape that is the one the child eats).

School-Agers

School-age children will be hand washing without supervision, although many need to be reminded. Developmentally, these children are at an age when discussions about germs and the role of hand washing can be more complex.

> Germs are everywhere, and some of them help keep us healthy (e.g., penicillin, yogurt). Skin and nose hairs stop some germs from getting into our bodies. Our body has other ways to defend us: tears, saliva, and stomach juices kill some germs when they get into our body.

Discussion of products such as hand sanitizers and antibacterial soaps can encourage children to think about the pros and cons of killing all germs (see Receiving Mixed Messages, page 159). Are there benefits to killing even the "friendly germs" we have on and in our bodies? How do we find a balance?

Activities such as growing moulds on foods (e.g., apple core in a jar) or growing germs from fingerprints on agar in Petri dishes are appropriate (contact your local hospital or make an agar mixture with the children). Children in the concrete operational stage of development can understand that the mouldy apple is the same apple a week later, and the same with the Petri dish.

REVISITING THE HEALTH PROMOTION ACTION PLAN

Children need to be consulted and participate meaningfully in the decisions and activities that affect them. The skills that children develop in this process include expressing views, decision making, coping, and public participation. These skills don't happen overnight. It takes practice and confidence to develop them. As children get older, they need experiences that encourage them to see themselves as participants, helpers, or agents of change in their communities. Educators and families assist children in finding a balance between having confidence in their own skills and abilities and knowing when to depend on adults, the community, and society.

Health promotion is based on the philosophy that individuals can have both personal and public control over their lives and can improve their own health. Through our awareness, we can make change happen from the individual level to the societal level. Using the three components of the health promotion action plan presented in Unit 1, the following example highlights this philosophy: The *UN Convention on the Rights of the Child in Child Friendly Language* poster has a prominent place in each playroom at the centre for everyone to see. Parents and ECE students often read it over, and several of the four- and five-year-olds and the school-agers have asked a family member or one of the educators to read it to them. Due to the lengthy list of articles in the convention, however, the children lose interest quickly and run off to play.

Recognizing the importance of ensuring that the UN-legislated rights of all children are upheld in our ECLC program and that children become aware of their rights at an age-appropriate level, the director and educators decided to find ways to bring this document to life as their ethical and professional responsibility.

Individual Problem Solving and Self-Reliance

One of the educators designed an arrow with Velcro that points to the current article of interest on the poster. The arrow location is chosen by a child or children who show interest in the poster, and ways to enable discussion of this particular article are explored, ensuring children's input. For the text of all articles, refer to Appendix 8.1: UN Convention on the Rights of the Child (page 529).

The room partners and children identified those articles of most interest to the children. One of the most compelling rights, Article 12, is the one the children and educators agreed would be the best place to start, which states, "You have the right to give your opinion, and for adults to listen and take it seriously" (United Nations, n.d., p. 1). *Every Child's Right to Be Heard: A Resource Guide on the UN Committee on the Rights of the Child General Comment No. 12* (Lansdown, 2011) is a comprehensive resource that has documented many examples worldwide of children's rights to speak and be heard. (See Resource Materials.) In addition to many examples, it begins with the background and context for Article 12. The resource lists why listening to children is important (Lansdown, 2011, cover page, Chapter 1):

NELSONstudy

To access Resource Materials, visit NelsonStudy.

- Participation contributes to personal development
- Participation leads to better decision-making and outcomes
- Participation serves to protect children
- Participation contributes to preparation for civil society development, tolerance, and respect for others
- Participation strengthens accountability

As part of the exploration of Article 12, the educators shared the story examples from the resource, and the children decided if it was of interest to discuss. This simple one caught the preschool children's interest and is as follows (Lansdown, 2011, p. 12):

BUILDING COMPETENCE IN VERY YOUNG CHILDREN IN THE UNITED KINGDOM

In one nursery in the UK, with 20 children up to the age of four years, the staff decided that the children could help themselves to fruit and water when they wanted to. Initially, the children asked for permission, until they understood that they could help themselves. Some spilt the water, but they learned to mop up the spills and to pour the water more carefully, as they acquired experience. In being consulted in this practical way about what they actually preferred, the children were able to practise more independence and respond to their bodily needs for snacks and water.

Source: Save the Children UK and UNICEF (2011). *Every Child's Right to Be Heard*. http://www.unicef.org/adolescence/files/Every_Childs_Right_to_be_Heard.pdf. Reprinted by permission.

The discussion that ensued had children voice their likes and dislikes about snack time in a large group. When one child said, "I don't like it when I'm playing but I have to stop for a snack," several others shouted, "Me too!" The educators asked what would be better, and the children referred back to the story about helping themselves when they were ready. A group discussion led to a compromise to have the snack table ready for three children at a time, available for a 45-minute window of time. Listening to the children's preferences resulted in a sense of pride for the children, who shared the new routine idea with their families at the end of day. The routine was very successful, addressing children's needs, as well as ensuring that an educator was always available as appropriate.

Community Action

Many of the children, particularly the school-agers, were interested in involvement of children's rights. The following example is a story of leadership, which inspired the children to make a difference in their ECLC setting/school community (Lansdown, 2011, p. 6):

CHILDREN AS COMMUNITY LEADERS IN EGYPT

A participatory sanitation and hygiene education program is bringing a transformational change in the socioeconomic conditions of communities living in remote villages of Egypt. The program is involving children in a process of change to improve the habitats in which they reside. It is based on training a group of committed children on various aspects of sanitation and hygiene education, and making them leaders in an initiative designed to have an immediate impact on the living conditions of their respective communities.... The program includes disseminating information about the nutritional value of various kinds of food. Emphasis is placed on the need to have a balanced diet including fruits, milk, and vegetables, rather than just meat. Lessons on environmental protection [[such as keeping the rivers clean]] are also part of the program.... Stress is laid on the civic responsibility not to pollute public spaces.

The impact of the training program is already evident in the daily lives of the villagers. Eleven-year-old Asmaa, who lives with her extended family of 20 people in Zarazra village in Sohag, Upper Egypt, says many of her habits have changed since joining the program. She explains that she has become confident enough to take a lead role in ensuring that other children in the village benefit from her knowledge. "Whenever I see other children throwing rubbish on the street or in the river, I tell them not to and I explain why. They do listen to me, and are willing to learn just like I was. I also tell them never to swim in the river or the canal, because they might get sick, which is what we have learned at school." Her mother, Labiba, is proud of her daughter: "The conditions in our village are poor. But it is the children's progress that gives otherwise impoverished families hope."

Source: Save the Children UK and UNICEF (2011). *Every Child's Right to Be Heard.* http://www.unicef.org/adolescence/files/Every_Childs_Right_to_be_Heard.pdf. Reprinted by permission.

A few days after talking about the children community leaders in Egypt, several of the school-agers talked about their interest in being leaders to help make the school and community playgrounds more friendly to the environment. Some talked about all the plastic bottles that kids are using and throwing away and how bad and unnecessary they are. Others brought up the safety concern of unnecessary garbage strewn in the school playground during recesses, at lunch time, and after school. The garbage caused some minor but unnecessary injuries, such as sprained ankles caused by tripping over plastic bottles, and a broken glass bottle resulting in a child's cut hand. This led to interest in working with staff and parents to help the children learn about and follow through with environment-positive practices, which also made the playground safer.

Throughout the year, the group of children, with support from resource persons and parents, brought the whole school community on board with a school waste audit, a school policy on waste reduction and recycling, and an action plan that started with a waste-free lunch program launched during waste reduction week in October. (See Resource Materials.) The committee meets monthly with children, teachers, and early childhood educators, and all voices are heard and considered. A number of parents and relatives of the children and educators are also becoming involved, and this community action is contributing to a cohesive vision for change. Article 29 of the UN Convention on the Rights of the Child states, "Your education should help you use and develop your talents and abilities. It should also help you learn to live peacefully, protect the environment, and respect other people" (United Nations, n.d., p. 1).

NELSONstudy

To access Resource Materials, visit NelsonStudy.

Societal Change

Due to their further knowledge of the UN Convention on the Rights of the Child, and their involvement at the community level, children, their families, and educators have the impetus to become engaged in advocacy for broader societal change.

Canada has some dynamic role models who became advocates as children and are making remarkable headway with regard to human rights. Two renowned examples are as follows:

- Hannah Taylor, who started the Ladybug Foundation in 2001, which addresses the homelessness issue in Canada, when she was five years old. Hannah is the youngest member of the jury panel of children from around the world that selects the annual recipient of the World's Children's Prize for the Rights of the Child in Stockholm and is the recipient of the 2007 Future Leader Award (Canada's Most Powerful Women: Top 100). In 2016, she was presented with the Meritorious Service Cross by Canada's governor general. In 2017, she was one of six Muhammad Ali Humanitarian Award winners from around the world. (See Resource Materials.)

NELSONstudy

To access Resource Materials, visit NelsonStudy.

- Craig Kielburger, at 12 years old, along with his brother, Marc, co-founded Free the Children and later the WE movement. The WE movement believes that when we come together we can create a better world. People are empowered to transform their local and the global communities by shifting their thinking from "me" to "we." Every year WE Days are held in various Canadian cities. Free the Children received the World's Children's Prize for the Rights of the Child (also known as the Children's Nobel Prize). (See Resource Materials.)

NELSONstudy

To access Resource Materials, visit NelsonStudy.

With such inspiring young advocates, the school-agers, often with family involvement, have started on their long-term commitment to societal change that will one day benefit all children. Early childhood educators also recognize the importance of advocating for well-funded, integrated ECLC programs in Canada as one of the essential ways to address the desired outcomes of the UN Convention on the Rights of the Child. The educators are child advocates who are members of a professional organization with this goal.

CONCLUSION

A holistic view of children's health is based on the premise that the whole child must always be considered. This view is particularly important when discussing issues that at first glance seem to relate to only one dimension of well-being, such as stress (emotional) or rest (physical). We quickly realize that there are physical, emotional, and social considerations for all health issues. Health policies and procedures based on the program's philosophy are written and reviewed regularly to ensure that this holistic view of health is put into practice on an ongoing basis.

A health curriculum is determined by the developmental needs and interests of the children and their sociocultural context. It is integrated into the everyday life at the program. The relevance of the health curriculum to the children's lives and viewing children as partners are paramount in planning, implementing, and evaluating a health curriculum.

ASSESS YOUR LEARNING

Define terms or describe concepts used in this unit.

- body image
- children's understanding of health
- early childhood tooth decay (ECTD)
- five Ws of cooking with children
- gender identity
- gender independent children
- health curriculum
- inherited culture
- oral health
- personal culture

- positive stress
- rhythm of the program
- self-pleasuring
- self-regulation
- sexuality
- sleep hygiene
- stress-aware environment
- temperament
- tolerable stress response
- toxic stress response

Evaluate your options in each situation.

1. You overhear an ECE student say to a three-year-old, "You have to play with Daniel. We are all friends at day care."

2. A parent approaches you and asks that you do not allow his son to play with his friend Brent, because Brent likes to play with dolls and dress in girls' clothes.

3. An eight-year-old in your program is being teased by her peers for being so tall. Katie has been growing quickly lately and is much taller than the rest of the children. She storms off crying, and when you go to comfort her, she asks you, "Will I always be different from everyone else? I hate being tall."

4. You and a classmate have been asked to plan a curriculum to help preschoolers learn about poison prevention. You agree that it would be a good idea to bring

in real objects. Next day, your colleague arrives with a bag of potentially hazardous products, including oven, window, and toilet cleaners used at home.

5. The program where you are doing a placement does not promote good nutrition. You are responsible for the weekly after-school cooking club and have submitted your plan to the educator. You would like to begin with simple recipes such as "dippidy-doo and vegetables too" and move to more complex recipes, such as soups and breads. The educator discourages you with the comment, "This will never work. The children only want to make cookies and cakes."

Bibliography

UNIT 1

Acupuncture Canada. (n.d.). *Regulation and education.* Retrieved April 2018 from https://www.acupuncturecanada.org/acupuncture-101/regulation-and-education/

Block, S. (2013, April). *Brief to the Standing Committee on Finance regarding study of income inequality in Canada.* Toronto: Wellesley Institute.

Butler, M., & Pang, M. (2014). *Current issues in mental health in Canada: Child and youth mental health (in brief)* (Publication No. 2014-13-E). Ottawa: Library of Parliament.

Campaign 2000. (2017). *A poverty-free Canada requires federal leadership: 2017 Report Card on Child and Family Poverty in Canada.* Retrieved April 2018 from https://campaign2000.ca/wp-content/uploads/2017/11/EnglishNationalC2000ReportNov212017.pdf

Campaign 2000. (2016). *A road map to eradicate child and family poverty: 2016 Report Card on Child and Family Poverty in Canada.* Retrieved April 2018 from http://campaign2000.ca/wp-content/uploads/2016/11/Campaign2000NationalReportCard2016Eng.pdf

Campaign 2000. (2012). *Needed: A federal action plan to eradicate child and family poverty in Canada. 2012 Report Card on Child and Family Poverty.* Toronto: Family Service Association of Canada. Retrieved July 2013 from http://www.campaign2000.ca/reportCards/national/C2000reportCardNov2012.pdf

Canadian Council on Learning. (2006, May 31). *Why is high-quality child care essential? The link between quality child care and early learning.* Retrieved April 2018 from http://www.child-encyclopedia.com/sites/default/files/docs/suggestions/high-quality-child-care.pdf

Canadian Institute for Health Information. (2016, July). *Trends in income-related health inequalities in Canada: Technical report.* Retrieved April 2018 from https://secure.cihi.ca/free_products/trends_in_income_related_inequalities_in_canada_2015_en.pdf

Canadian Medical Association. (2013, July). *Health care in Canada: What makes us sick? Canadian Medical Association town hall report.* Retrieved April 2018 from http://nccdh.ca/resources/entry/health-care-in-canada

Canadian Paediatric Society. (2018, February 28). *A harmonized immunization schedule for Canada: A call to action.* Position statement. Retrieved April 2018 from https://www.cps.ca/en/documents/position/harmonized-immunization-schedule-Canada

Canadian Paediatric Society. (2015, October). *Housing need in Canada: Healthy lives start at home.* Position statement. Retrieved April 2018 from https://www.cps.ca/en/documents/position/housing-need

CBC News. (2008, June 11). *Prime Minister Stephen Harper's statement of apology.* Retrieved April 2018 from http://www.cbc.ca/news/canada/prime-minister-stephen-harper-s-statement-of-apology-1.734250

Conference Board of Canada. (2012). *Adults with inadequate literacy skills.* Retrieved April 2018 from http://www.conferenceboard.ca/hcp/provincial/education/adlt-lowlit.aspx

Early Childhood Development Intercultural Partnerships. (n.d.). *Cultural safety in practice with children, families and communities.* Retrieved April 2018 from http://www.ecdip.org/docs/pdf/Cultural%20Safety%20Poster.pdf

Epp, J. (1986). *Achieving health for all: A framework for health promotion.* Ottawa: Health and Welfare Canada.

Gestwicki, C., & Bertrand, J. (2012). *Essentials of early education* (4th Canadian ed.). Toronto: ITP Nelson.

Gonzalez-Mena, J. (2014). *Foundations in early childhood education: Teaching children in a diverse society* (6th ed.). New York: McGraw-Hill.

Government of Canada. (2018a, February 26). *Canada's health care system.* Retrieved April 2018 from https://www.canada.ca/en/health-canada/services/health-care-system/reports-publications/health-care-system/canada.html#a4

Government of Canada. (2018b, January 30). *Health literacy: About health literacy.* Retrieved April 2018 from https://www.canada.ca/en/public-health/services/chronic-diseases/health-literacy.html

Government of Canada. (2016a). *Towards a poverty reduction strategy: Discussion paper.* Retrieved April 2018 from https://www.canada.ca/en/employment-social-development/programs/poverty-reduction/discussion-paper.html

Government of Canada. (2016b). *What we heard: Shaping Canada's National Housing Strategy.* Retrieved April 2018 from http://publications.gc.ca/collections/collection_2017/edsc-esdc/Em12-30-2016-eng.pdf

Government of Canada. (2015a, May 4). *Licensed natural health products database (LNHPD).* Retrieved April 2018 from https://www.canada.ca/en/health-canada/services/drugs-health-products/natural-non-prescription/applications-submissions/product-licensing/licensed-natural-health-products-database.html

Government of Canada. (2015b, July 31). *World conference on social determinants of health.* Retrieved April 2018 from https://www.canada.ca/en/public-health/services/health-promotion/population-health/what-determines-health/world-conference-on-social-determinants-health.html

Government of Canada. (2014, May 6). *Mental health promotion.* Retrieved April 2018 from https://www.canada.ca/en/public-health/services/health-promotion/mental-health/mental-health-promotion.html

Government of Canada. (2013, January 15). *What is the population health approach?* Retrieved April 2018 from https://www.canada.ca/en/public-health/services/health-promotion/population-health/population-health-approach/what-population-health-approach.html#health

Government of Canada. (2011, October 21). *Determinants of health: What makes Canadians healthy or unhealthy?* Retrieved April 2018 from https://www.canada.ca/en/public-health/services/health-promotion/population-health/what-determines-health.html # determinants

Government of Canada. (2010, May 12). *Healthy workplaces*. Retrieved April 2018 from https://www.canada.ca/en/health-canada/services/health-care-system/health-human-resources/strategy/healthy-workplaces.html

Health Council of Canada. (2013, September). *Better health, better care, better value for all: Refocusing health care reform in Canada*. Retrieved April 2018 from https://healthcouncilcanada.ca/files/HCC_Summative_Report_Accessible_FA.pdf

Hertzman, C. (2010, November). Framework for the social determinants of early child development. In *Encyclopedia on early childhood development*. Retrieved April 2018 from http://www.child-encyclopedia.com/sites/default/files/textes-experts/en/669/framework-for-the-social-determinants-of-early-child-development.pdf

Hertzman, C. (1998). The case for child development as a determinant of health. *Canadian Journal of Public Health, 89*(Suppl. 1), S14–S19.

Hertzman, C., & Power, C. (2004). Child development as a determinant of health across the life course. *Current Paediatrics, 14*, 438–443.

Indigenous Corporate Training Inc. (n.d.). *Indigenous peoples: A guide to terminology*. Retrieved April 2018 from https://cdn2.hubspot.net/hubfs/374848/docs/Indigenous_Peoples_Guide_to_Terminology_v2.pdf?t=1523023710106

Ipsos Reid Public Affairs. (2011, January 13). *Natural health product tracking survey, 2010: Final report*. Ottawa: Health Canada. Retrieved September 2013 from http://epe.lac-bac.gc.ca/100/200/301/pwgsc-tpsgc/por-ef/health/2011/135-09/ report.pdf

Justin Trudeau, for the record: "We beat fear with hope." (2015, October 20). *Maclean's*. Retrieved April 2018 from http://www.macleans.ca/politics/ottawa/justin-trudeau-for-the-record-we-beat-fear-with-hope/

Lum, Z.-A. (2014, October 3). Canada is the only UN member to reject landmark Indigenous rights document. *Huffington Post*. Retrieved April 2018 from https://www.huffingtonpost.ca/2014/10/02/canada-un-indigenous-rights_n_5918868.html

Macdonald, D., & Wilson, D. (2016, May 17). *Shameful neglect: Indigenous child poverty in Canada*. Canadian Centre for Policy Alternatives. Retrieved April 2018 from https://www.policyalternatives.ca/publications/reports/shameful-neglect

McCain, M. N., et al. (2007). *Early Years Study 2: Putting science into action*. Toronto: Council for Early Child Development. Retrieved April 2018 from http://earlylearning.ubc.ca/media/publications/early_years_study_2.pdf

Mikkonen, J., & Raphael, D. (2010). *Social determinants of health: The Canadian facts*. Toronto: York University School of Health Policy and Management. Retrieved April 2018 from http://thecanadianfacts.org/The_Canadian_Facts.pdf

Mustard, J. F. (2010, February). Early brain development and human development. In *Encyclopedia on early childhood development*. Retrieved April 2018 from http://www.child-encyclopedia.com/sites/default/files/textes-experts/en/669/early-brain-development-and-human-development.pdf

Ng, E. O., & Omariba, D. W. R. (2010, March). *Health literacy and immigrants in Canada: Determinants and effects on health outcomes*. Canada Council of Learning. Retrieved April 2018 from https://pdfs.semanticscholar.org/7f7d/78e6f2f0e183a02adee41ce1989a3fc2c714.pdf

O'Campo, P. (2013, September 9). Social policy is strong health policy. *Winnipeg Free Press*. Retrieved April 2018 from https://www.winnipegfreepress.com/opinion/analysis/social-policy-is-strong-health-policy-222921361.html

Organisation for Economic Co-operation and Development. (n.d.). *What we do and how*. Retrieved April 2018 from http://www.oecd.org/about/whatwedoandhow/

Raphael, D., et al. (1999). The community quality of life project: A health promotion approach to understanding communities. *Health Promotion International, 14*(3), 197–210. Retrieved April 2018 from https://academic.oup.com/heapro/article/14/3/197/615047

Savigny, M. (2017, August). *Increasing access to early childhood education and care in Canada: The case for a more equitable system for Canadians under 5*. Retrieved April 2018 from http://openresearch.ocadu.ca/id/eprint/1978/1/Savigny_Meghan_2017_MDES_SFI_MRP.pdf

Shonkoff, J., & Phillips, D. (2001). *From neurons to neighbourhoods: The science of early childhood development*. Ottawa: National Academy of Sciences.

Shonkoff, J. P. (2010, January/February). Building a new biodevelopmental framework to guide the future of early childhood policy. *Child Development, 81*(1), P357–367.

Shulte, B. (2015). *Overwhelmed: Work, love and play when no one has the time*. London, UK: Picador Pan Macmillan.

Timmons, B. W., et al. (2007). Physical activity for preschool children—how much and how? *Applied Physiology, Nutrition, and Metabolism, 32*, S122–S134.

Truth and Reconciliation Commission of Canada. (2015). *Truth and Reconciliation Commission of Canada: Calls to action*. Retrieved April 2018 from http://www.trc.ca/websites/trcinstitution/File/2015/Findings/Calls_to_Action_English2.pdf

Turcotte, M. (2015, May 20). *Spotlight on Canadians: Results from the General Social Survey. Trends in social capital in Canada*. Ottawa: Minister of Industry. Retrieved April 2018 from http://www.statcan.gc.ca/pub/89-652-x/89-652-x2015002-eng.pdf

UNICEF Office of Research. (2016, April). Fairness for children: A league table of inequality in child well-being in rich countries. *Innocenti Report Card 13*. Innocenti, Florence: Author. Retrieved April 2018 from https://www.unicef-irc.org/publications/pdf/RC13_eng.pdf

Wilkinson, R., & Marmot, M. (Eds.). (2003). *Social determinants of health: The solid facts* (2nd ed.). Copenhagen, Denmark: WHO Regional Office for Europe. Retrieved April 2018 from http://www.euro.who.int/__data/assets/pdf_file/0005/98438/e81384.pdf

World Health Organization. (2013a). *The Ottawa Charter for Health Promotion*. Retrieved April 2018 from http://www.who.int/healthpromotion/conferences/previous/ottawa/en/index4.html

World Health Organization. (2013b). *What is the WHO definition of health?* Retrieved April 2018 from http://www.who.int/suggestions/faq/en/

World Health Organization. (2005). *Health impact assessment toolkit for cities: Document 1*. Retrieved April 2018 from http://www.euro.who.int/__data/assets/pdf_file/0007/101500/HIA_Toolkit_1.pdf

World Health Organization. (1997). *The Jakarta Declaration on Leading Health Promotion into the 21st Century*. Retrieved April 2018 from http://apps.who.int/iris/bitstream/handle/10665/63698/WHO_HPR_HEP_4ICHP_BR_97.4_eng.pdf;jsessionid=12DE0F18945DBDD338ACBE851B2BF12E?sequence=1

World Health Organization & Commission on the Social Determinants of Health. (2008). *Closing the gap in a generation: Health equity through action on the social determinants of health*. Geneva, Switzerland: Author. Retrieved April 2018 from http://apps.who.int/iris/bitstream/handle/10665/43943/9789241563703_eng.pdf?sequence=1

Alberta Centre for Active Living. (n.d.-a). *Physical Activity @ Work: Community level: Tapping into community physical activity resources.* Retrieved April 2018 from https://sites.ualberta.ca/~active/workplace/ideas/community.html

Alberta Centre for Active Living. (n.d.-b). *Physical Activity @ Work: Individual level: Helping your employees be more active.* Retrieved April 2018 from https://sites.ualberta.ca/~active/workplace/ideas/individual.html

Alberta Centre for Active Living. (n.d.-c). *Physical Activity @ Work: Social level: Being active with your co-workers.* Retrieved April 2018 from https://sites.ualberta.ca/~active/workplace/ideas/social.html

Beach, J., & Flanagan, K. (n.d.). *People, programs and practices: A training strategy for the early childhood education and care sector in Canada.* Toronto: Child Care Human Resources Sector Council.

Best Start: Ontario's Maternal, Newborn and Early Child Development Resource Centre & Health Nexus. (2011). *Health before pregnancy workbook.* Retrieved November 2017 from http://www.beststart.org/resources/rep_health/Health_Before _pregnancy_2011_FULL.pdf

Best Start Resource Centre. (2012). *When compassion hurts: Burnout, vicarious trauma and secondary trauma in prenatal and early childhood service providers.* Toronto: Author. Retrieved November 2017 from https://www.beststart.org/resources/howto/pdf/Compassion_14MY01_Final.pdf

Burczycka, M. (2016). Trends in self-reported spousal violence in Canada, 2014. In M. Burczycka & S. Conroy, *Family violence in Canada: A statistical profile, 2014* (Statistics Canada Catalogue No. 85-002-X). Retrieved April 2018 from https://www.statcan.gc.ca/pub/85-002-x/2016001/article/14303/01-eng.htm

Burczycka, M., & Conroy, S. (2017, February 16). *Family violence in Canada: A statistical profile, 2017* (Statistics Canada Catalogue No. 85-002-X). Retrieved November 2017 from http://www.statcan.gc.ca/pub/85-002-x/2017001/article/14698-eng.pdf

Canadian Centre for Occupational Health and Safety. (2016a, February 2). *Joint health and safety committee: What is a joint health and safety committee?* Retrieved June 2018 from https://www.ccohs.ca/oshanswers/hsprograms/hscommittees/whatisa.html

Canadian Centre for Occupational Health and Safety. (2016b, July 13). *OH&S legislation in Canada: Basic responsibilities.* Retrieved November 2017 from http://www.ccohs.ca/oshanswers/legisl/responsi.html

Canadian Centre for Occupational Health and Safety. (2015, May 22). *Foot comfort and safety at work.* Retrieved November 2017 from http://www.ccohs.ca/oshanswers/prevention/ppe/foot_com.html#_1_14

Canadian Centre for Occupational Health and Safety. (2014, April 3). *Stretching—at the workstation.* Retrieved November 2017 from http://www.ccohs.ca/oshanswers/ergonomics/office/stretching.html

Canadian Centre for Occupational Health and Safety. (2013). *Musculoskeletal disorders (MSD) awareness* [E-course]. Retrieved April 2018 from http://www.ccohs.ca/products/courses/msd_awareness/

Canadian Centre for Occupational Health and Safety. (2012, June 7). *Workplace stress: General.* Retrieved April 2018 from http://www.ccohs.ca/oshanswers/psychosocial/stress.html

Canadian Child Care Federation. (1992). *Safety in the arts.* Retrieved November 2017 from http://www.cccf-fcsge.ca/wp-content/uploads/RS_21-e.pdf

Canadian Paediatric Society. (2015). *Well beings: A guide to health in child care* (3rd rev. ed.). Ottawa: Author.

Canadian Standards Association Group & Bureau de normalisation du Québec. (2013). *Psychological health and safety in the workplace—prevention, promotion, and guidance to staged implementation* (CAN/CSA-Z1003-13/BNQ 9700-803/2013). Retrieved November 2017 from http://www.csagroup.org/documents/codes-and-standards/publications/CAN_CSA-Z1003-13_BNQ_9700-803_2013_EN.pdf

Centre for Applied Research in Mental Health and Addiction. (2012). *What is psychological health and safety?* Retrieved November 2017 from https://www.guardingmindsatwork.ca/info/safety_what

Child Care Human Resources Sector Council. (2013a). *Occupational standards for child care administrators.* Ottawa: Author. Retrieved April 2018 from http://www.ccsc-cssge.ca/sites/default/files/uploads/Projects-Pubs-Docs/EN%20Pub%20Chart/OS_Admin_Web(final).pdf

Child Care Human Resources Sector Council. (2013b). *You bet we still care! A survey of centre-based early childhood education and care in Canada: Highlights report.* Ottawa: Author. Retrieved April 2018 from http://www.ccsc-cssge.ca/sites/default/files/uploads/Projects-Pubs-Docs/EN%20Pub%20Chart/YouBetSurveyReport_Final.pdf

Dietitians of Canada. (2016, October 28). *Fat.* Retrieved April 2018 from https://www.dietitians.ca/Your-Health/Nutrition-A-Z/Fat.aspx

Edwards, S., et al. (2008). *A research paper to inform the development of an early years learning framework for Australia.* Melbourne, Australia: Office for Children and Early Childhood Development, Department of Education and Early Childhood Development.

Environmental Health Association of Nova Scotia. (2004). Household cleaners. In *Guide to less toxic products.* Retrieved November 2017 from http://www.lesstoxicguide.ca/index.asp?fetch=household#carp

Government of Canada. (2017, February 16). *Psychological health in the workplace.* Retrieved November 2017 from https://www.canada.ca/en/employment-social-development/services/health-safety/reports/psychological-health.html#h2.3

Government of Canada. (2016, July 27). *Boric acid.* Retrieved November 2017 from https://www.canada.ca/en/health-canada/services/chemicals-product-safety/boric-acid.html

Government of Canada. (2015, June 18). *Reduce humidity, moisture and mould.* Retrieved April 2018 from https://www.canada.ca/en/health-canada/services/air-quality/indoor-air-contaminants/reduce-humidity-moisture-mould.html

Government of Ontario. (2017, September 3). *Calories on menus.* Retrieved November 2017 from https://www.ontario.ca/page/calories-menus#section-4t

Guarding Minds @ Work. (2012). *The 13 psychological factors in GM@W.* Retrieved November 2017 from https://www.guardingmindsatwork.ca/info/risk_factors

Hales, D., & Lauzon, L. (2018). *An invitation to health* (5th Canadian ed.). Toronto: Nelson.

Health Canada. (2018, March). *Canada's food guide consultation: Phase 2* (Health Canada Catalogue No. H164-207/1-2017E-PDF). Retrieved April 2018 from https://www.canada.ca/content/dam/hc-sc/documents/services/health/publications/food-nutrition/canada-food-guide-phase2-what-we-heard.pdf

Health Canada. (2016, October). *Healthy eating strategy* (Health Canada Catalogue No. H164-196/2016E-PDF). Ottawa: Minister of Health. Retrieved November 2017 from http://publications.gc.ca/collections/collection_2016/sc-hc/H164-196-2016-eng.pdf

Health Canada. (2011a). *Eating well with Canada's Food Guide.* Retrieved June 2013 from http://www.hc-sc.gc.ca/fn-an/alt_formats/hpfb-dgpsa/pdf/food-guide-aliment/view_eatwell_vue_bienmang-eng.pdf

Health Canada. (2011b). *Eating well with Canada's Food Guide: A resource for educators and communicators.* Retrieved June 2013 from http://www.hc-sc.gc.ca/fn-an/alt_formats/hpfb-dgpsa/pdf/pubs/res-educat-eng.pdf

Health Canada. (2008). *Best advice on stress risk management in the workplace: Part 1 of 2* (Health Canada Catalogue No. H39-546/2000E). Ottawa: Minister of Public Works and Government Services Canada. Retrieved April 2018 from http://mentalhealthworks.cmhaontario.ca/sites/default/files/stress-part-1_e.pdf (Part 1) and http://www.mentalhealthpromotion.net/resources/best-advice-on-stress-risk-management-in-the-workplace---part-2.pdf (Part 2)

Hoeger, W. K., et al. (2009). *Principles and labs for fitness and wellness* (1st Canadian ed.). Toronto: Nelson Education.

Ioannone, P., & Pimento, B. (2017). *Workplace predictors of health among registered early childhood educators in Ontario.* Toronto: George Brown College Office of Research and Innovation.

King, P. M., et al. (2006). Ergonomic recommendations and their impact on child care workers' health. *Work: A Journal of Prevention, Assessment and Rehabilitation, 26,* 13–17. Retrieved April 2018 from https://www.ncbi.nlm.nih.gov/pubmed/16373975

Kuk, J. L., et al. (2011). Edmonton Obesity Staging System: Association with weight history and mortality risk. *Applied Physiology, Nutrition, and Metabolism, 36,* 570–576. Retrieved April 2018 from http://www.nrcresearchpress.com/doi/10.1139/h11-058?url_ver=Z39.88-2003&rfr_id=ori:rid:crossref.org&rfr_dat=cr_pub%3dwww.ncbi.nlm.nih.gov#.Ws_01i7wYuU

Lepp, A., et al. (2013). The relationship between cell phone use, physical and sedentary activity, and cardiorespiratory fitness in a sample of U.S. college students. *International Journal of Behavioral Nutrition and Physical Activity, 10,* 79. doi:10.1186/1479-5868-10-79. Retrieved April 2018 from https://ijbnpa.biomedcentral.com/articles/10.1186/1479-5868-10-79

Ortega, F. B., et al. (2013). The intriguing metabolically healthy but obese phenotype: Cardiovascular prognosis and role of fitness. *European Heart Journal, 34,* 389–397. doi:10.1093/eurheartj/ehs174. Retrieved April 2018 from https://www.ncbi.nlm.nih.gov/pmc/articles/PMC3561613/

Ratey, J. J. (2008). *SPARK: The revolutionary new science of exercise and the brain.* New York: Little, Brown & Company.

Statistics Canada. (2012, November 29). *Body composition of Canadian adults, 2009 to 2011.* Retrieved April 2018 from http://www.statcan.gc.ca/pub/82-625-x/2012001/article/11708-eng.htm

Winsa, P. (2013, June 17). National survey of post-secondary students in Canada shows stress and anxiety are major factors in mental health. *Toronto Star.* Retrieved April 2018 from https://www.thestar.com/news/gta/2013/06/17/national_survey_of_postsecondary_students_in_canada_shows_stress_and_anxiety_are_major_factors_in_mental_health.html

World Health Organization. (n.d.). *BMI classification.* Retrieved April 2018 from http://apps.who.int/bmi/index.jsp?introPage=intro_3.html

UNIT 3

American Academy of Pediatrics. (2015). *Red book 2015: Report of the Committee on Infectious Diseases.* Elk Grove Village, IL: Author.

Canadian Centre for Occupational Health and Safety. (2014, September 25). *Hand washing: Reducing the risk of common infections.* Retrieved December 2017 from http://www.ccohs.ca/oshanswers/diseases/washing_hands.html

Canadian Paediatric Society. (2018, February 38). *A bite in the playroom: Managing human bites in child care settings.* Position statement. Retrieved May 2018 from https://www.cps.ca/en/documents/position/human-bites-in-child-care-settings

Canadian Paediatric Society. (2016a, February 1). *Antimicrobial products in the home: The evolving problem of antibiotic resistance.* Position statement. Retrieved December 2017 from https://www.cps.ca/en/documents/position/antimicrobial-products-in-the-home#Reallife

Canadian Paediatric Society. (2016b, February 1). *Autistic spectrum disorder: No causal relationship with vaccines.* Position statement. Retrieved December 2017 from https://www.cps.ca/en/documents/position/autistic-spectrum-disorder-no-causal-relationship-with-vaccines

Canadian Paediatric Society. (2016c, February 1). *A harmonized immunization schedule for Canada: A call to action.* Position statement. Retrieved December 2017 from https://www.cps.ca/en/documents/position/harmonized-immunization-schedule-Canada

Canadian Paediatric Society. (2015). *Well beings: A guide to health in child care* (3rd rev. ed.). Ottawa: Author.

Ecojustice. (2017, January 31). *Canada still won't ban unsafe triclosan from your family products.* Retrieved January 2018 from http://www.huffingtonpost.ca/ecojustice/triclosan-ban_b_14437592.html

Government of Canada. (2016, November 25). *Triclosan.* Retrieved January 2018 from https://www.canada.ca/en/health-canada/services/chemicals-product-safety/triclosan.html

Kramer, A., et al. (2006). How long do nosocomial pathogens persist on inanimate surfaces? A systematic review. *BMC Infectious Diseases, 6,* 130. doi:10.1186/1471-2334-6-130. Retrieved December 2017 from https://bmcinfectdis.biomedcentral.com/articles/10.1186/1471-2334-6-130

Ottawa Public Health. (2017). *Environmental cleaning and disinfection in child care centres and schools.* Retrieved December 2017 from http://www.ottawapublichealth.ca/en/professionals-and-partners/environmental-cleaning-and-disinfection-in-child-care-centres-and-schools.aspx

Public Health Agency of Canada. (2017a). *Canadian immunization guide chapter on influenza and statement on seasonal influenza vaccine for 2017–2018.* Retrieved December 2017 from https://www.canada.ca/content/dam/phac-aspc/documents/services/publications/healthy-living/canadian-immunization-guide-statement-seasonal-influenza-vaccine/naci-stmt-2017-2018-eng.pdf

Public Health Agency of Canada. (2017b, March 3). *Canadian immunization guide: Introduction.* Retrieved December 2017 from https://www.canada.ca/en/public-health/services/canadian-immunization-guide/introduction.html

Public Health Agency of Canada. (2017c, August 29). *Canadian immunization guide: Part 5—passive immunization.* Retrieved December 2017 from https://www.canada.ca/en/public-health/services/publications/healthy-living/canadian-immunization-guide-part-5-passive-immunization.html

Public Health Agency of Canada. (2017d, November 16). *Page 13: Canadian immunization guide: Part 1—key immunization information.* Retrieved December 2017 from https://www.canada.ca/en/public-health/services/publications/healthy-living/canadian-immunization-guide-part-1-key-immunization-information/page-13-recommended-immunization-schedules.html

Public Health Agency of Canada. (2016, September 1). *Page 2: Canadian immunization guide: Part 1—key immunization information.* Retrieved December 2017 from https://www.canada.ca/en/public-health/services/publications/healthy-living/canadian-immunization-guide-part-1-key-immunization-information/page-2-immunization-in-canada.html

ScienceDaily. (2008, April 28). *Daycare attendance early in life cuts childhood leukemia risk by 30 percent, analysis finds.* Retrieved December 2017 from http://www.sciencedaily.com/releases/2008/04/080428084232.htm

Statistics Canada. (2017, June 28). *Childhood national immunization coverage survey, 2015.* Retrieved December 2017 from https://www.statcan.gc.ca/daily-quotidien/170628/dq170628a-eng.htm

UNIT 4

Allergy/Asthma Information Association. (n.d.). *Dust, pet and mold: Allergies.* Retrieved December 2017 from http://www.aaia.ca/en/dust_brochure_en.pdf

Allergy/Asthma Information Association. (2006). *Drug allergy: How you can help your allergist make the diagnosis.* Retrieved December 2017 from http://www.aaia.ca/en/drug_allergy.htm

Allergy/Asthma Information Association. (2004). *Scents in the workplace.* Retrieved December 2017 from http://aaia.ca/en/scents_in_the_workplace.htm

Asthma Canada. (n.d.-a). *Medicines and treatment.* Retrieved December 2017 from https://www.asthma.ca/get-help/asthma-3/treatment/

Asthma Canada. (n.d.-b). *Who gets asthma?* Retrieved December 2017 from https://www.asthma.ca/get-help/asthma-3/diagnosis-3/who-gets-asthma/

Asthma Canada. (2017, June). *Asthma facts and statistics FAQs.* Retrieved December 2017 from https://www.asthma.ca/wp-content/uploads/2017/06/Asthma-Facts-and-Stats.pdf

Canadian Allergy, Asthma and Immunology Foundation. (n.d.). *Natural rubber latex allergy: A guideline for allergic patients.* Retrieved December 2017 from http://www.allergyfoundation.ca/index.php?page=64

Canadian Paediatric Society. (2016a, September). *Head lice.* Retrieved December 2017 from https://www.caringforkids.cps.ca/handouts/head_lice

Canadian Paediatric Society. (2016b, September 22). *Head lice infestations: A clinical update.* Practice point. Retrieved December 2017 from https://www.cps.ca/en/documents/position/head-lice

Canadian Paediatric Society. (2016c, February 1). *Health implications of children in child care centres Part B: Injuries and infections.* Position statement. Retrieved December 2017 from https://www.cps.ca/en/documents/position/child-care-centres-injuries-infections

Canadian Paediatric Society. (2016d, February 1). *Preventing varicella: Recommendations for routine two-dose varicella immunization in children.* Position statement. Retrieved December 2017 from http://www.cps.ca/en/documents/position/preventing-varicella

Canadian Paediatric Society. (2016e, February 1). *School and daycare exclusion policies for chickenpox: A rational approach.* Position statement. Retrieved December 2017 from https://www.cps.ca/en/documents/position/exclusion-policies-for-chickenpox

Canadian Paediatric Society. (2016f, February 1). *Treating cough and cold: Guidance for caregivers of children and youth.* Position statement. Retrieved December 2017 from https://www.cps.ca/en/documents/position/treating-cough-cold

Canadian Paediatric Society. (2015). *Well beings: A guide to health in child care* (3rd rev. ed.). Ottawa: Author.

CBC News. (2007, January 12). *Cough syrup dangerous for babies, U.S. officials warn.* Retrieved December 2017 from http://www.cbc.ca/news/cough-syrup-dangerous-for-babies-u-s-officials-warn-1.632413

Comack, E., & Lyons, J. (2010, September 9). *Fast facts: Winnipeg needs a bed bug plan.* Canadian Centre for Policy Alternatives. Retrieved December 2017 from http://www.policyalternatives.ca/publications/commentary/fast-facts-winnipeg-needs-bed-bug-plan

Government of Alberta & Alberta Health Services. (2011, September). *Healthy hands at work: Being sick at work is everyone's business.* Retrieved January 2018 from https://www.hwmh.ca/workfiles/staff/worker-handbook.pdf

Government of Canada. (2017, September 15). *Common food allergens.* Retrieved December 2017 from https://www.canada.ca/en/health-canada/services/food-nutrition/food-safety/food-allergies-intolerances/food-allergies.html

Government of Canada. (2015, February 27). *Bedbugs: What are they?* Retrieved December 2017 from https://www.canada.ca/en/health-canada/services/pest-control-tips/bedbugs-what-are-they.html

Health Canada. (2012, March). Antibiotic resistance. *It's Your Health.* Retrieved December 2017 from http://www.hc-sc.gc.ca/hl-vs/alt_formats/pacrb-dgapcr/pdf/iyh-vsv/med/antibiotic-eng.pdf

The Lung Association. (2015, October 2). *Asthma: Asthma medications.* Retrieved December 2017 from https://www.lung.ca/lung-health/lung-disease/asthma/medications

Manitoba Early Learning and Child Care. (n.d.). *Bed bug guide for licensed child care facilities.* Winnipeg: Author. Retrieved December 2017 from https://www.gov.mb.ca/fs/childcare/resources/pubs/bed_bug_guide.pdf

Province of Manitoba. (2018, January 8). *The Community Child Care Standards Act (C.C.S.M. c. C158) Child Care Regulation.* Retrieved January 2017 from https://web2.gov.mb.ca/laws/regs/current/_pdf-regs.php?reg=62/86

Shum, M., et al. (2012). Bed bugs and public health: New approaches for an old scourge. *Canadian Journal of Public Health, 103,* e399–403. Retrieved December 2017 from http://journal.cpha.ca/index.php/cjph/article/view/3426

UNIT 5

Baby Food Safety. (2009, April 13). *Baby first foods.* Retrieved February 2018 from https://babyfirstfoods.wordpress.com/category/baby-food-safety/

Best Start Resource Centre & Nutrition Resource Centre. (2012). *Feeding your baby from six months to one year.* Toronto: Author. Retrieved February 2018 from https://www.beststart.org/resources/nutrition/pdf/feeding_baby_rev2012_LR.pdf

Canadian Paediatric Society. (2017, January). *Vegetarian diets for children and teens.* Retrieved February 2018 from https://www.caringforkids.cps.ca/handouts/vegetarian_diets_for_children_and_teens

Canadian Paediatric Society. (2016a, February 1). *Concerns for the use of soy-based formulas in infant nutrition.* Position statement. Retrieved February 2018 from https://www.cps.ca/en/documents/position/use-soy-based-formulas

Canadian Paediatric Society. (2016b, February 1). *Dietary exposures and allergy prevention in high-risk infants.* Position statement. Retrieved February 2018 from https://www.cps.ca/en/documents/position/dietary-exposures-and-allergy-prevention-in-high-risk-infants

Canadian Paediatric Society. (2015). *Well beings: A guide to health in child care* (3rd rev. ed.). Ottawa: Author.

Carruth, B. R., et al. (2004). Prevalence of picky eaters among infants and toddlers and their caregivers' decisions about offering a new food. *Journal of the American Dietetic Association, 104*(1 Suppl.), S57–S64.

CBC News. (2017, September 15). *Health Canada trans fat ban takes effect next year: Artificial trans fat will be off Canadians' dining plates as of 1 year from today.* Retrieved March 2018 from http://www.cbc.ca/news/health/trans-fats-1.4292241

Darmon, N., & Drewnowski, A. (2015, October 1). Contribution of food prices and diet cost to socioeconomic disparities in diet quality and health: A systematic review and analysis. *Nutrition Reviews, 73*(10), 643–660. https://doi.org/10.1093/nutrit/nuv027. Retrieved March 2018 from https://academic.oup.com/nutritionreviews/article/73/10/643/1848128

Dietitians of Canada. (2014). *Are organic foods better for my health?* Retrieved February 2018 from https://www.dietitians.ca/Downloads/Factsheets/Organic-foods-are-they-better.aspx

Draxten, M., et al. (2014, July). *Parental role modeling of fruits and vegetables at meals and snacks is associated with children's adequate consumption.* Retrieved March 2018 from https://www.ncbi.nlm.nih.gov/pmc/articles/PMC4034448/pdf/nihms581041.pdf

Dunedin, A. (2014, March 19). *Food additives banned by one or more countries.* Ragged University. Retrieved March 2018 from https://www.raggeduniversity.co.uk/2014/03/19/food-additives-banned-countries-alex-dunedin/

Eat Right Ontario. (2017a, October 18). *I have recently heard about stevia. Is it safe to use?* Retrieved March 2018 from http://www.eatrightontario.ca/en/Articles/Food-technology/I-have-recently-heard-about-stevia-Is-it-safe-to.aspx

Eat Right Ontario. (2017b, October 18). *Understanding genetically modified foods.* Retrieved March 2018 from https://www.eatrightontario.ca/en/ViewPDF.aspx

European Environment Agency. (2013). *Late lessons from early warnings: Science, precaution, innovation—summary.* Retrieved February 2018 from http://www.agripressworld.com/_STUDIOEMMA_UPLOADS/downloads/Late.pdf

Fisher, J. O., et al. (2007). Effects of portion size and energy density on young children's intake at a meal. *American Journal of Clinical Nutrition, 86,* 174–179. Retrieved February 2018 from https://www.ncbi.nlm.nih.gov/pmc/articles/PMC2531150/

Gilbert, J. A., et al. (2012). After-school snack intake among Canadian children and adolescents. *Canadian Journal of Public Health, 103,* e448–e452. Retrieved February 2018 from https://www.ncbi.nlm.nih.gov/pubmed/23618026

Gillis, D. (1989). *Promoting nutritional health during the preschool years: Canadian guidelines.* Ottawa: Network of the Federal/Provincial/Territorial Group on Nutrition and National Institute of Nutrition.

Government of Canada. (2017, July 24). *Food labelling changes.* Retrieved February 2018 from https://www.canada.ca/en/health-canada/services/food-labelling-changes.html?_ga=2.241694978.1256372131.1519498383-1678291144.1512943202

Government of Canada. (2016a, November 16). *Fats.* Retrieved February 2018 from http://healthycanadians.gc.ca/eating-nutrition/healthy-eating-saine-alimentation/nutrients-nutriments/fats-lipides-eng.php#a2

Government of Canada. (2016b, December 14). *Food additives.* Retrieved February 2018 from https://www.canada.ca/en/health-canada/services/food-nutrition/food-safety/food-additives.html

Government of Canada. (2016c, October 31). *Food irradiation.* Retrieved March 2018 from http://www.inspection.gc.ca/food/information-for-consumers/fact-sheets-and-infographics/irradiation/eng/1332358607968/1332358680017

Government of Canada. (2016d, December 22). *Genetically modified (GM) foods and other novel foods.* Retrieved February 2018 from https://www.canada.ca/en/health-canada/services/food-nutrition/genetically-modified-foods-other-novel-foods.html

Government of Canada. (2016e, May 16). *Health claims.* Retrieved February 2018 from https://www.canada.ca/en/health-canada/services/food-nutrition/food-labelling/health-claims.html

Government of Canada. (2015, August 18). *Nutrition for healthy term infants: Recommendations from birth to six months.* Retrieved February 2018 from https://www.canada.ca/en/health-canada/services/food-nutrition/healthy-eating/infant-feeding/nutrition-healthy-term-infants-recommendations-birth-six-months.html#a6

Government of Canada. (2013, January 9). *Food safety tips for microwaves.* Retrieved February 2018 from https://www.canada.ca/en/health-canada/services/general-food-safety-tips/microwaves.html

Government of Canada. (2012, July 25). *Household food insecurity in Canada: Overview.* Retrieved February 2018 from https://www.canada.ca/en/health-canada/services/food-nutrition/food-nutrition-surveillance/health-nutrition-surveys/canadian-community-health-survey-cchs/household-food-insecurity-canada-overview.html#fnb2

Government of Canada. (2011, April 12). *Food safety tips for leftovers.* Retrieved February 2018 from https://www.canada.ca/en/health-canada/services/general-food-safety-tips/food-safety-tips-leftovers.html

Government of Canada. (2007, February 5). *Make wise choices.* Retrieved February 2018 from https://www.canada.ca/en/health-canada/services/food-nutrition/canada-food-guide/food-guide-basics/make-wise-choices.html

Health Canada. (2018, March 21). *Canada food guide: Revision process.* Retrieved June 2018 from https://www.canada.ca/en/health-canada/services/canada-food-guides/revision-process.html#a2

Health Canada. (2017a, April 5). *Food front-of-package nutrition symbol consumer consultation.* Retrieved March 2018 from https://www.healthyeatingconsultations.ca/front-of-package

Health Canada. (2017b). *Let's eat healthy Canada!* Retrieved March 2018 from https://www.canada.ca/content/dam/hc-sc/documents/services/publications/food-nutrition/infographic-lets-eat-healthy-canada/infographic-lets-eat-healthy-canada.pdf

Health Canada. (2015, March). *Safe food handling for children ages five and under.* Retrieved March 2018 from https://www.canada.ca/content/dam/canada/health-canada/migration/healthy-canadians/alt/pdf/eating-nutrition/healthy-eating-saine-alimentation/safety-salubrite/vulnerable-populations/children-under-5-moins-enfant-eng.pdf

Health Canada. (2011a). *Eating well with Canada's Food Guide.* Retrieved June 2013 from http://www.hc-sc.gc.ca/fn-an/alt_formats/hpfb-dgpsa/pdf/food-guide -aliment/view_eatwell_vue_bienmang -eng.pdf

Health Canada. (2011b). *Eating well with Canada's Food Guide: A resource for educators and communicators.* Retrieved June 2013 from http://www.hc-sc.gc.ca/fn-an/alt_formats/hpfb-dgpsa/pdf/pubs/res-educat-eng.pdf

Health Canada. (2011c, August). Risks associated with sprouts. *It's Your Health.* Retrieved February 2018 from http://www.hc-sc.gc.ca/hl-vs/alt_formats/pdf/iyh-vsv/food-aliment/sprouts-germes-eng.pdf

Health Canada. (2009a, March). *Mercury and human health.* Retrieved February 2018 from http://www.hc-sc.gc.ca/hl-vs/alt_formats/pacrb-dgapcr/pdf/iyh-vsv/environ/merc2008-eng.pdf

Health Canada. (2009b, June 23). *Monograph: Calcium.* Retrieved February 2018 from http://webprod.hc-sc.gc.ca/nhpid-bdipsn/monoReq.do?id=57&lang=eng

Health Canada. (2007, December 14). *Mercury: Your health and the environment: A resource tool.* Retrieved February 2018 from https://www.canada.ca/en/health-canada/services/environmental-workplace-health/reports-publications/environmental-contaminants/mercury-your-health-environment-resource-tool.html

Heart and Stroke Foundation of Canada. (2017). *Trans fatty acids ("trans fat") and heart disease and stroke.* Position statement. Retrieved February 2018 from http://www.heartandstroke.ca/-/media/pdf-files/canada/2017-position-statements/transfatty-acids-ps-eng.ashx?la=en&hash=1462D8CF328665A124340833F1362C3AE633B7D4

Heart and Stroke Foundation of Canada. (2014, August). *Dietary sodium, heart disease and stroke.* Position statement. Retrieved February 2018 from http://www.heartandstroke.ca/-/media/pdf-files/canada/2017-position-statements/dietary-sodium-ps-eng.ashx?la=en&hash=E7A61CBBB69B9DC33366E4198862017424EDC1E4

Infant and Toddler Forum. (2010, September). *Nutrients: Functions, sources and requirements. Toddler factsheet 1.1i.* Retrieved February 2018 from https://www.infantandtoddlerforum.org/media/upload/pdf-downloads/1.1i_-_Nutrients_Functions_Sources_and_Requirements.pdf

Islamic Food and Nutrition Council of America. (n.d.). *What is in our food? Is it permissible?* Retrieved February 2018 from http://www.ifanca.org/Pages/staticwebpages.aspx?page=Whatisinourfood

Kirkey, S. (2007, October 26). Salt has invaded Canada's food supply. *The Gazette* (Montreal). Retrieved February 2018 from https://www.pressreader.com/canada/montreal-gazette/20071026/281578056302368

Kramer, M., et al. (2008). Breastfeeding and child cognitive development: New evidence from a large randomized trial. *Archives of General Psychiatry, 65,* 578–584. Retrieved February 2018 from https://www.researchgate.net/publication/5395191_Breastfeeding_and_Child_Cognitive_Development_New_Evidence_From_a_Large_Randomized_Trial

Lambert-Lagacé, L. (2003). *Feeding your baby the healthiest foods: From breast milk to table foods.* Toronto: Fitzhenry & Whiteside.

Latner, J. D., et al. (2007). Childhood obesity stigma: Association with television, videogame, and magazine exposure. *Body Image, 4,* 147–155. Retrieved February 2018 from http://www2.hawaii.edu/~jlatner/downloads/pubs/Body-image-media2007.pdf

Latner, J. D., & Stunkard, A. J. (2003). Getting worse: The stigmatization of obese children. *Obesity Research, 11,* 452–456. Retrieved February 2018 from http://onlinelibrary.wiley.com/doi/10.1038/oby.2003.61/full

Li, R., et al. (2010). Do infants fed from bottles lack self-regulation of milk intake compared with directly breastfed infants? *Pediatrics, 125,* e1386–e1395. Retrieved February 2018 from https://fhop.ucsf.edu/sites/fhop.ucsf.edu/files/wysiwyg/peds%202009-2549v1.pdf

McCann, D., et al. (2007). Food additives and hyperactive behaviour in 3-year-old and 8/9-year-old children in the community: A randomised, double-blinded, placebo-controlled trial. *The Lancet, 370,* 1560–1567. Retrieved February 2018 from http://www.thelancet.com/journals/lancet/article/PIIS0140-6736(07)61306-3/abstract

McIntyre, L., et al. (2012). Coping with child hunger in Canada: Have household strategies changed over a decade? *Canadian Journal of Public Health, 103,* 428–432. Retrieved February 2018 from http://journal.cpha.ca/index.php/cjph/article/view/3296/2716

Mennella, J. A., et al. (2005). Infant feeding practices and early flavor experiences in Mexican infants: An intra-cultural study. *Journal of the American Dietetic Association, 105*(6), 908–915. doi:10.1016/j.jada.2005.03.008

National Eating Disorder Information Centre. (2014). *Prevention and health promotion.* Retrieved February 2018 from http://nedic.ca/give-get-help/prevention-health-promotion

National Initiative for Eating Disorders. (2017). *Canadian research on eating disorders.* Retrieved February 2018 from http://nied.ca/wp-content/uploads/2017/11/Canadian-Research-on-Eating-Disorders-Formatted.pdf

National Institutes of Health. (2015, June). *Osteoporosis: Peak bone mass in women.* Retrieved February 2018 from https://www.bones.nih.gov/health-info/bone/osteoporosis/bone-mass

Oddy, W. H., et al. (2012). The long-term effects of breastfeeding on development. *Contemporary Pediatrics.* Retrieved February 2018 from http://cdn.intechopen.com/pdfs/31651/InTechThe_long_term_effects_of_breastfeeding_on_development.pdf

Ratey, J. J. (2013). *SPARK: The revolutionary new science of exercise and the brain* (repr. ed.). New York: Little, Brown & Company.

Rich, T. R. (n.d.). Kashrut: Jewish dietary laws. *Judaism 101.* Retrieved February 2018 from http://www.jewfaq.org/kashrut.htm#Rules

Satter, E. (n.d.). *Child of mine: Feeding with love and good sense.* Palo Alto, CA: Bull Publishing. Retrieved February 2018 from http://www.EllynSatter.com

Satter, E. (2006). *Helping children be good eaters: Provider guidelines.* Retrieved February 2018 from https://www.ellynsatterinstitute.org/wp-content/uploads/2016/11/Handout-HelpingChildrenBeGoodEaters-Child-Care-2013.pdf

Satter, E. (1990). *How to get your kid to eat … but not too much.* Palo Alto, CA: Bull Publishing.

Shields, M. (2006, August). Overweight and obesity among children and youth. *Health Reports, 17*(3) (Catalogue No. 82-003). Ottawa: Statistics Canada. Retrieved February 2018 from http://ibis.geog.ubc.ca/courses/geob370/students/class10/ddchan/www/images/docs/Shields.pdf

Simpson, J. A. R., et al. (2007). Nutrition Screening Tool for Every Preschooler (NutriSTEP™): Validation and test-retest reliability of a parent-administered questionnaire assessing nutrition risk of preschoolers. *European Journal of Clinical Nutrition, 62,* 770–780.

Sizer, F., & Whitney, E. (2012). *Nutrition concepts and controversies* (13th ed.). Toronto: Wadsworth Thomson Learning.

World Health Organization. (2017, October 11). *Tenfold increase in childhood and adolescent obesity in four decades: New study by Imperial College London and WHO.* Retrieved June 2018 from http://www.who.int/en/news-room/detail/11-10-2017-tenfold-increase-in-childhood-and-adolescent-obesity-in-four-decades-new-study-by-imperial-college-london-and-who

Zhang, Y.-J., et al. (2015). Antioxidant phytochemicals for the prevention and treatment of chronic diseases. *Molecules, 20,* 21138–21156. doi:10.3390. Retrieved March 2018 from https://www.researchgate.net/publication/284903544_Antioxidant_Phytochemicals_for_the_Prevention_and_Treatment_of_Chronic_Diseases

UNIT 6

Active Healthy Kids Canada. (2013a). *Are we driving our kids to unhealthy habits? (Short Form). 2013 Active Healthy Kids Canada: Report card on physical activity for children and youth.* Retrieved February 2018 from http://dvqdas9jty7g6.cloudfront.net/reportcard2013/AHKC-Summary-2013.pdf

Active Healthy Kids Canada. (2013b). *Highlights from the 2013 Active Healthy Kids Canada report card on physical activity for children and youth.* Retrieved February 2018 from http://dvqdas9jty7g6.cloudfront.net/reportcard2013/AHKC-2013-Fact-Sheet-FINAL.pdf

Active Healthy Kids Canada. (2008). *It's time to unplug our kids: Canada's Report Card on Physical Activity for Children & Youth—2008.* Toronto: Author. Retrieved February 2018 from http://dvqdas9jty7g6.cloudfront .net/reportcard2008/AHKCLongFormEN.pdf

Alberta Health Services. (2010, March). *Childhood overweight and obesity: Summary of evidence from the* Cost of Obesity in Alberta *report.* Retrieved March 2018 from https://www.albertahealthservices.ca/ poph/hi-poph-surv-phids-childhood-overweight-obesity-2010.pdf

Arenz, S., et al. (2004). Breast-feeding and childhood obesity—a systematic review. *International Journal of Obesity, 28,* 1247–1256. Retrieved February 2018 from https://www.nature.com/ articles/0802758.pdf

Barnes, S. (2012, October). *Reducing childhood obesity in Ontario through a health equity lens.* Toronto: Wellesley Institute. Retrieved February 2018 from http://www.wellesleyinstitute.com/wp-content/ uploads/2012/10/Reducing-Childhood-Obesity-in-Ontario.pdf

Barr, R., & Linebarger, D. N. (2017). *Media exposure during infancy and early childhood: The effect of content and context on learning and development.* Switzerland: Springer International Publishing. Retrieved March 2018 from https://reader.paperc.com/books/ media-exposure-during-infancy-and-early-childhood/638763/ ACoverHTML

Bell, A. C. (2007, October 3). *The contribution of green school ground design to moderate activity levels.* Toronto: Evergreen. Retrieved February 2018 from http://www.cuhi.utoronto.ca/seminars/ supportingdocs/Oct0307_ABell.pdf

Bell, A. C., & Dyment, D. E. (n.d.). *Grounds for action: Promoting physical activity through school ground greening in Canada.* Toronto: Evergreen. Retrieved February 2018 from https://www.evergreen.ca/ downloads/pdfs/Grounds-For-Action.pdf

Boldemann, C., et al. (2006). Impact of preschool environment upon children's physical activity and sun exposure. *Preventive Medicine, 42,* 301–308.

Brussoni, M., et al. (2012). Risky play and children's safety: Balancing priorities for optimal child development. *Inernational Journal of Environmental Research and Public Health, , 9*(9), 3134–3148. Retrieved March 2018 from https://www.ncbi.nlm.nih.gov/pmc/articles/ PMC3499858/

Butler, D. (2008, February 8). Area parents turn blind eye to obesity. *The Ottawa Citizen.* Retrieved March 2018 from http://www.canada .com/ottawacitizen/news/story.html?k=17974&id=fcf3724a-9dbb- 45f7-93fa-f2544edef301

Canada WALKS. (n.d.). *What makes communities great places to walk?* Retrieved March 2018 from http://canadawalks.ca/about/walkability/

Canadian Paediatric Society. (2017, November 27). *Screen time and young children: Promoting health and development in a digital world.* Position statement. Retrieved February 2018 from https://www.cps .ca/en/documents/position/screen-time-and-young-children

Canadian Paediatric Society. (2015). *Well beings: A guide to health in child care* (3rd rev. ed.). Ottawa: Author.

Canadian Paediatric Society. (2012, April 1). *Healthy active living: Physical activity guidelines for children and adolescents.* Position statement. Retrieved February 2018 from https://www.cps.ca/en/documents/ position/physical-activity-guidelines

Canadian Society for Exercise Physiology. (n.d.-a). *Canadian physical activity guidelines: For the early years—0–4 years.* Retrieved February 2018 from http://csep.ca/CMFiles/Guidelines/ CSEP_PAGuidelines_0-65plus_en.pdf

Canadian Society for Exercise Physiology. (n.d.-b). *Canadian sedentary behaviour guidelines: For the early years—0–4 years.* Retrieved February 2018 from http://www.csep.ca/CMFiles/Guidelines/bcfiles/ BC_CSEP_SBGuidelines_early-years_en.pdf

Childhood Obesity Foundation. (2015, April). *What is childhood obesity?* Retrieved March 2018 from http://childhoodobesityfoundation.ca/ what-is-childhood-obesity/

Children's Hospital of Eastern Ontario (CHEO). (n.d.). *Unplug and connect: Keeping families strong in a wired world.* Retrieved March 2018 from http://www.cheo.on.ca/uploads/Mental%20Health/ Technology%20info%20for%20parents.pdf

City of Vancouver. (2009). *EcoDensity: How density, design, and land use will contribute to environmental sustainability, affordability, and livability.* Retrieved February 2018 from https://www. civicinfo.bc.ca/practices_innovations/eco_density_initiative-- vancouver--2009.pdf

Dennisson, B. A., et al. (2002). Television viewing and television in bedroom associated with overweight risk among low-income preschool children. *Pediatrics, 109,* 1028–1035. Retrieved February 2018 from http://pediatrics.aappublications.org/content/109/6/1028.long? sso=1&sso_redirect_count=1&nfstatus=401&nftoken=00000000 -0000-0000-0000-000000000000&nfstatusdescription=ERROR%3a +No+local+token

Dietitians of Canada & Canadian Paediatric Society. (2010). *Promoting optimal monitoring of child growth in Canada using the new WHO growth charts.* Retrieved February 2018 from https://www.dietitians .ca/Downloads/Public/tcg-position-paper.aspx

Dreamfilm Productions. (2017, July 15). *Programmed to be fat?* [CBC documentary]. Retrieved February 2018 from http://www.cbc.ca/ natureofthings/m/episodes/programmed-to-be-fat

Epigenome NoE. (2013). *What is epigenetics?* Retrieved February 2018 from http://www.epigenome-noe.net/aboutus/epigenetics. php. html

Evergreen. (2004). *Small wonders: Designing vibrant natural landscapes for early childhood.* Retrieved June 2018 from https://www.evergreen .ca/downloads/pdfs/Small-Wonders.pdf

Gallahue, D. L., & Donnelly, F. C. (2007). *Developmental physical education for all children* (4th ed.). Champaign, IL: Human Kinetics.

Garriguet, D., et al. (2016, September 26). *Physical activity and sedentary behaviour of Canadian children aged 3 to 5.* Retrieved April 2017 from https://www.participaction.com/en-ca/thought-leadership/ research/are-young-children-inactive-and-sedentary

Government of Canada. (2017, December 14). *What is active transportation?* Retrieved March 2018 from https://www.canada.ca/ en/public-health/services/health-promotion/healthy-living/ physical-activity/what-active-transportation.html

Government of Canada. (2016, January 22). *Children and physical activity.* Retrieved March 2018 from https://www.canada.ca/en/ public-health/services/being-active/children-physical-activity.html

Government of Canada. (2010, May 3). *Section 2: Integrated Pan-Canadian Healthy Living Strategy 2005—The integrated Pan-Canadian Healthy Living Strategy.* Retrieved February 2018 from https://www.canada.ca/en/public-health/services/health-promotion/ healthy-living/2005-integrated-canadian-healthy-living-strategy/ key-elements.html#strat_d

Government of Manitoba. (2014, October). *Moving forward with school nutrition guidelines.* Retrieved June 2018 from http://www.gov.mb.ca/ healthyschools/foodinschools/documents/mfsng/mfsng.pdf

Health Canada. (2011). *Eating well with Canada's Food Guide.* Retrieved June 2013 from http://www.hc-sc.gc.ca/fn-an/alt_formats/hpfb-dgpsa/pdf/food-guide -aliment/view_eatwell_vue_bienmang-eng.pdf

Jacobson, M. F. (2005, June 1). *Liquid candy: How soft drinks are harming America's health.* Washington, DC: Center for Science in the Public Interest. Retrieved February 2018 from https://cspinet.org/sites/default/files/attachment/liquid_candy_final_w_new _supplement.pdf

Kneas, K., & Perry, B. (n.d.). *Using technology in the early childhood classroom.* Retrieved February 2018 from http://teacher.scholastic .com/professional/bruceperry/using_technology.htm

Lippmann, W. (1914). *Drift and mastery.* Madison: The University of Wisconsin Press.

MacDonald, M. (2017, June 25). *Ban on junk food sales in Canadian schools having positive effect: Study.* CTV News. Retrieved March 2018 from https://www.ctvnews.ca/health/ban-on-junk-food-sales -in-canadian-schools-having-positive-effect-study-1.3475201

MediaSmarts. (n.d.). *Marketing and consumerism—special issues for young children.* Retrieved March 2018 from http://mediasmarts .ca/marketing-consumerism/marketing-consumerism-special -issues-young-children

Miller, A. L., et al. (2017). *Early life stress and childhood obesity risk.* Durham, NC: Healthy Eating Research. Retrieved March 2018 from http://healthyeatingresearch.org/wp-content/uploads/2017/06/ her_stress_obesity_5-30.pdf

National Sleep Foundation. (n.d.). *Sleep hygiene: What is sleep hygiene?* Retrieved February 2018 from https://sleepfoundation.org/sleep-topics/sleep-hygiene

Ontario Ministry of Education. (2004, October 20). *Making Ontario schools healthier places to learn.* Toronto: Government of Ontario. Retrieved February 2018 from http://www.edu.gov.on.ca/eng/document/reports/healthyschools/report.pdf

Pardee, M., et al. (2005, June). *Community Investment Collaborative for Kids, resource guide 4: Creating playgrounds for early childhood facilities.* Retrieved February 2018 from http://www.lisc.org/media/filer_public/c6/c8/c6c8b045-d3c9-46ad-ab6d-65d6b807a666/2005 _cick_guide_vol4_playgrounds.pdf

ParticipACTION. (n.d.-a). *Canadian 24-hour movement guidelines for children and youth: An integration of physical activity, sedentary behaviour, and sleep.* Retrieved March 2018 from https://www .participaction.com/sites/default/files/downloads/participaction -24hguidelines-05-17en.pdf

ParticipACTION. (n.d.-b). *Canadian 24-hour movement guidelines for the early years (0-4 years): An integration of physical activity, sedentary behaviour, and sleep.* Retrieved March 2018 from https://www.participaction.com/sites/default/files/downloads/PAR7972_24Hour_Guidelines_EY_En.pdf

ParticipACTION. (2016a). *Are Canadian kids too tired to move? 2016 ParticipACTION Report Card on Physical Activity for Children and Youth.* Retrieved March 2018 from https://www.participaction.com/sites/default/files/downloads/2016%20ParticipACTION%20Report%20Card%20-%20Full%20Report.pdf

ParticipACTION. (2016b). *The Report Card on Physical Activity for Children and Youth: Are Canadian kids too tired to move?* Retrieved March 2018 from https://www.participaction.com/sites/default/files/downloads/2016%20ParticipACTION%20Report%20Card%20-%20 Presentation.pdf

ParticipACTION. (2015). *The biggest risk is keeping kids indoors: The 2015 ParticipACTION Report Card on Physical Activity for Children and Youth.* Retrieved April 2018 from https://www.participaction.com/sites/default/files/downloads/Participaction-2015ReportCard -FullReport_4.pdf

PHE Canada. (2018a). *Physical literacy: What is physical literacy?* Retrieved March 2018 from http://www.phecanada.ca/programs/physical-literacy/what-physical-literacy

PHE Canada. (2018b). *Physical literacy: Why is it important?* Retrieved March 2018 from http://www.phecanada.ca/programs/physical-literacy/what-physical-literacy/why-it-important

Plourde, G. (2006, March). Preventing and managing pediatric obesity: Recommendations for family physicians. *Canadian Family Physician, 52,* 322–328. Retrieved February 2018 from https://www.ncbi.nlm .nih.gov/pmc/articles/PMC1479709/

Public Health Agency of Canada. (2016, December). *Health status of Canadians 2016: A report of the Chief Public Health Officer.* Retrieved March 2018 from http://healthycanadians.gc.ca/publications/department-ministere/state-public-health-status-2016-etat-sante -publique-statut/alt/pdf-eng.pdf

Public Health Agency of Canada. (2005). *The Integrated Pan-Canadian Healthy Living Strategy.* Retrieved February 2018 from http://www .phac-aspc.gc.ca/hp-ps/hl-mvs/ipchls-spimmvs/pdf/ipchls-spimmvs -eng.pdf

Raine, K., et al. (2012). Coming to consensus on policy to create supportive built environments and community design. *Canadian Journal of Public Health, 103*(Suppl. 3), eS5–eS8. Retrieved February 2018 from http://journal.cpha.ca/index.php/cjph/article/view/3446/2674

Ratey, J. J. (2008). *SPARK: The revolutionary new science of exercise and the brain.* New York: Little, Brown & Company.

Roberts, K. C., et al. (2012, August). Overweight and obesity in children and adolescents: Results from the 2009 to 2011 Canadian Health Measures Survey. *Component of Statistics Canada Health Reports, 23*(3) (Catalogue No. 82-003-XPE). Ottawa: Statistics Canada. Retrieved March 2018 from http://www.statcan.gc.ca/pub/82-003-x/2012003/article/11706-eng.pdf

Scaglioni, S., et al. (2011, November 16). Determinants of children's eating behavior. *The American Journal of Clinical Nutrition, 94* (Suppl. 6), 2006S–2011S. https://doi.org/10.3945/ajcn.110.001685. Retrieved March 2018 from https://academic.oup.com/ajcn/article/94/suppl_6/2006S/4598037

Shields, M. (2006, August). Overweight and obesity among children and youth. *Health Reports, 17*(3) (Catalogue No. 82-003). Ottawa: Statistics Canada. Retrieved February 2018 from http://ibis.geog.ubc .ca/courses/geob370/students/class10/ddchan/www/images/docs/Shields.pdf

Simpson, J. A. R., et al. (2007). Nutrition Screening Tool for Every Preschooler (NutriSTEP™): Validation and test-retest reliability of a parent-administered questionnaire assessing nutrition risk of preschoolers. *European Journal of Clinical Nutrition, 62,* 770–780.

Statistics Canada. (2015, November 27). *Health at a glance: Select health indicators of First Nations people living off reserve, Métis and Inuit.* Retrieved March 2018 from http://www.statcan.gc.ca/pub/82-624-x/2013001/article/11763-eng.htm

Timmons, B., et al. (2012). Systematic review of physical activity and health in the early years (aged 0–4 years). *Applied Physiology, Nutrition, and Metabolism, 37*(4), 773–792. Retrieved March 2018 from http://www.nrcresearchpress.com/doi/10.1139/h2012-070#.WqQYt4PwYuU

Timmons, B. W., et al. (2008, March 7). Physical activity of preschool children—sum and method? *Applied Physiology, Nutrition, and Metabolism, 32*(Suppl. 2F), s136–s149. Retrieved March 2018 from http://www.nrcresearchpress.com/doi/10.1139/H07-166#.WqRL74PwYuV

Toronto Parks and Recreation Department. (2004, May). *Toward a healthy, active future: Toronto Parks and Recreation strategic plan. A draft for review and comment.* Toronto: City of Toronto. Retrieved February 2018 from http://www.dufferinpark.ca/research/pdf/strategicdraftplanspring04.pdf

Tremblay, M., et al. (2015). Position statement on active outdoor play. *International Journal of Environmental Research and Public Health, 12*(6), 6475–6505. doi:10.3390/ijerph120606475. Retrieved March 2018 from http://www.mdpi.com/1660-4601/12/6/6475

Tucker, P., et al. (2006, August). Preventing paediatric obesity: Recommendations from a community-based qualitative investigation. *Obesity Reviews, 7,* 251–260. Retrieved February 2018 from https://www.ncbi.nlm.nih.gov/pmc/articles/PMC5017874/

Veugelers, P. J., & Fitzgerald, A. L. (2005). Prevalence of and risk factors for childhood overweight and obesity. *Canadian Medical Association Journal, 173,* 607–613. Retrieved February 2018 from https://www.ncbi.nlm.nih.gov/pmc/articles/PMC1197160/

Weber, B. (2018, March 7). Canada to push "plastics charter" at G7: McKenna at Mexico Oceans Summit. *CityNews.* Retrieved March 2018 from http://toronto.citynews.ca/2018/03/07/environment-minister-catherine-mckenna-to-push-plastics-charter-at-g7/

Whiting, S., et al. (2004). Factors that affect bone mineral accrual in the adolescent growth spurt. *The American Society for Nutritional Sciences Journal of Nutrition, 134,* 696S–700S.

Williams, L. M. (2013, May). *Between health and place: Understanding the built environment.* Toronto: Wellesley Institute. Retrieved February 2018 from http://www.wellesleyinstitute.com/wp-content/uploads/2013/05/Between-Health-and-Place.pdf

Williamson, P., & Roberts, J. (2004). *First Nations peoples* (2nd ed.). Toronto: Emond Montgomery Publications Limited.

Wilson, L. (2014). *Outdoor playscapes: Breaking new ground.* Toronto: Nelson.

World Health Organization. (2018, February). *Obesity and overweight: Fact sheet.* Retrieved February 2018 from http://www.who.int/mediacentre/factsheets/fs311/en/

World Health Organization. (2017a, November). *Diabetes: Fact sheet.* Retrieved February 2018 from http://www.who.int/mediacentre/factsheets/fs312/en/

World Health Organization. (2017b). *Report of the Commission on Ending Childhood Obesity: Executive summary.* Retrieved March 2018 from http://apps.who.int/iris/bitstream/10665/259349/1/WHO-NMH-PND-ECHO-17.1-eng.pdf

UNIT 7

Canadian Cancer Society. (2018). *Melanoma skin cancer statistics.* Retrieved January 2018 from http://www.cancer.ca/en/cancer-information/cancer-type/skin-melanoma/statistics/?region=qc

Canadian Medical Association. (n.d.). *Environment and health.* Retrieved January 2018 from https://www.cma.ca/En/Pages/environment-health.aspx

Canadian Paediatric Society. (2016, April 4). *Preventing choking and suffocation in children.* Position statement. Retrieved January 2018 from http://www.cps.ca/en/documents/position/preventing-choking-suffocation-children

Canadian Paediatric Society. (2015). *Well beings: A guide to health in child care* (3rd rev. ed.). Ottawa: Author.

Canadian Paediatric Society. (2014, November 7). *Preventing playground injuries.* Position statement. Retrieved January 2018 from http://www.cps.ca/documents/position/playground-injuries

Canadian Partnership for Children's Health and Environment. (n.d.). *Lung cancer: Reduce the risk. Test for radon.* Retrieved January 2018 from http://www.healthyenvironmentforkids.ca/content/reduce-radon

Canadian Partnership for Children's Health and Environment. (2010a, October). *Focus on bisphenol A: Statement of health and environmental organizations on endocrine disrupting chemicals.* Retrieved January 2018 from http://www.healthyenvironmentforkids.ca/sites/healthyenvironmentforkids.ca/files/BPA-Eng-Oct-2010.pdf

Canadian Partnership for Children's Health and Environment. (2010b, March). *Your child's skin may act more like a sponge than a shield.* Retrieved January 2018 from http://www.healthyenvironmentforkids.ca/sites/healthyenvironmentforkids.ca/files/Skin-Eng-Fr.pdf

Canadian Partnership for Children's Health and Environment. (2005). *Child health and the environment—a primer.* Retrieved January 2018 from http://www.healthyenvironmentforkids.ca/sites/healthyenvironmentforkids.ca/files/cpche-resources/Primer.pdf

Canadian Partnership for Children's Health and Environment & Canadian Child Care Federation. (2017, March). *Radon: What you can do. Reduce the risk of the #1 cause of lung cancer in non-smokers.* Retrieved January 2018 from http://www.cela.ca/sites/cela.ca/files/RadonChildCareProfessionalsEN.pdf

Canadian Red Cross. (2013, June 6). *Canadians underestimate measures needed to prevent child drowning, Red Cross research suggests.* Retrieved January 2018 from http://www.redcross.ca/who-we-are/newsroom/news-releases/latest-news/canadians-underestimate-measures-needed-to-prevent

Canadian Standards Association. (2016, September). *Children's playspaces and equipment* (CAN/CSA-Z614-14). Mississauga, ON: Author.

CAREX Canada. (2017, November 27). *Radon in schools: A summary of radon testing across Canada.* Retrieved January 2018 from https://www.carexcanada.ca/en/announcements/radon_in_schools/

Cribb, R. (2017, October 14). In Sarnia's chemical valley, is "toxic soup" making people sick? *Toronto Star.* Retrieved March 2018 from https://www.thestar.com/news/world/2017/10/14/in-sarnias-chemical-valley-is-toxic-soup-making-people-sick.html

CTV News. (2016, March 29). *Alarming number of canned foods still contain BPA, new report warns.* Retrieved January 2018 from https://www.ctvnews.ca/health/health-headlines/alarming-number-of-canned-foods-still-contain-bpa-new-report-warns-1.2837540

Dennis, J., et al. (2013). Helmet legislation and admissions to hospital for cycling related head injuries in Canadian provinces and territories: Interrupted time series analysis. *BMJ, 346,* f2674. Retrieved January 2018 from http://www.bmj.com/content/346/bmj.f2674

Environmental Defence. (2008, February). *Toxic baby bottles in Canada.* Retrieved January 2018 from https://environmentaldefence.ca/reports-guides/report-toxic-baby-bottles-in-canada/

Government of Canada. (2017a, November 8). *Battery safety.* Retrieved January 2018 from https://www.canada.ca/en/health-canada/services/toy-safety/battery-safety.html

Government of Canada. (2017b, March 3). *How to use the UV index.* Retrieved January 2018 from https://www.canada.ca/en/environment

-climate-change/services/weather-health/uv-index-sun-safety/how
-to-use.html

Government of Canada. (2017c, December 22). *Safe drinking water for First Nation communities*. Retrieved January 2018 from http://www
.aadnc-aandc.gc.ca/eng/1506514143353/1506514230742

Government of Canada. (2017d, November 7). *Sunscreens*. Retrieved January 2018 from https://www.canada.ca/en/health-canada/services/
sun-safety/sunscreens.html

Government of Canada. (2017e, June 14). *Toxic substances list*. Retrieved January 2018 from https://www.canada.ca/en/environment-climate
-change/services/canadian-environmental-protection-act-registry/
substances-list/toxic.html

Government of Canada. (2017f, June 2). *Wind chill index*. Retrieved January 2018 from https://www.canada.ca/en/environment-climate
-change/services/weather-health/wind-chill-cold-weather/wind-chill
-index.html#X-201501151120261

Government of Canada. (2016a, July 21). *Insect repellents*. Retrieved January 2018 from https://www.canada.ca/en/health-canada/
services/about-pesticides/insect-repellents.html

Government of Canada. (2016b, August 15). *OSH answers fact sheets: Humidex rating and work*. Retrieved January 2018 from https://www
.ccohs.ca/oshanswers/phys_agents/humidex.html?=undefined&
wbdisable=true

Government of Canada. (2016c, February 10). *West Nile virus*. Retrieved January 2018 from https://www.canada.ca/en/public-health/services/
diseases/west-nile-virus.html

Government of Canada. (2015a, May 22). *Lead and cadmium in children's jewellery*. Retrieved January 2018 from https://www.canada.ca/en/health
-canada/services/injury-prevention/lead-cadmium-children-jewellery.html

Government of Canada. (2015b, April 14). *Magnet safety*. Retrieved January 2018 from https://www.canada.ca/en/health-canada/
services/toy-safety/magnets.html

Government of Canada. (2015c, June 26). *Risks of West Nile virus*. Retrieved January 2018 from https://www.canada.ca/en/public
-health/services/diseases/west-nile-virus/risks-west-nile-virus.html

Government of Canada. (2014a). *Radon: Is it in your home?* Retrieved January 2018 from https://www.canada.ca/en/health-canada/services/
environmental-workplace-health/radiation/radon.html

Government of Canada. (2014b, December 1). *Small parts in toys*. Retrieved January 2018 from https://www.canada.ca/en/health
-canada/services/toy-safety/small-parts-toys.html

Government of Canada. (2012, January 12). *Stroller and carriage safety*. Retrieved January 2018 from https://www.canada.ca/en/health
-canada/services/infant-care/strollers-carriages.html

Government of Canada. (2001, September). *A Canadian perspective on the precautionary approach/principle*. Retrieved June 2018 from http://www.ibrarian.net/navon/paper/A_Canadian_Perspective_on
_the_Precautionary_Appro.pdf?paperid=990195

Health Canada. (2018, May 2). *New Government of Canada regulations protect children from exposure to lead and cadmium* [Media release]. Retrieved June 2018 from https://www.newswire.ca/news-releases/
new-government-of-canada-regulations-protect-children-from-
exposure-to-lead-and-cadmium-681501991.html

Health Canada. (2014, April). Canada Consumer Product Safety Act: *Quick reference guide*. Retrieved January 2018 from https://www
.canada.ca/content/dam/hc-sc/migration/hc-sc/cps-spc/alt-for-
mats/hecs-sesc/pdf/pubs/indust/ccpsa_ref-lcspc/ccpsa_ref-lc-
spc-eng.pdf

Health Canada. (2013, February). *Lead and human health*. Retrieved January 2018 from http://publications.gc.ca/collections/collection
_2013/sc-hc/H13-7-101-2013-eng.pdf

Helmets.org. (2018, June 2). *Statistics: Statistics from the children's safety network*. Retrieved January 2018 from https://helmets.org/stats.htm#child

Institute for Agriculture and Trade Policy. (2008). *Smart plastics guide: Healthier food uses of plastics*. Retrieved July 2013 from https://
foodsecurecanada.org/sites/foodsecurecanada.org/files/smart
_plastics_guide.pdf

Klasing, A. (2016, June 7). *Make it safe: Canada's obligation to end the First Nations water crisis*. Retrieved January 2018 from https://www
.hrw.org/report/2016/06/07/make-it-safe/canadas-obligation-end
-first-nations-water-crisis

Leitch, K. (2007). *Reaching for the top: A report by the advisor on healthy children and youth* (Catalogue No. H21-296/2007E). Ottawa: Health Canada. Retrieved January 2018 from https://www.canada.ca/content/
dam/hc-sc/migration/hc-sc/hl-vs/alt_formats/hpb-dgps/pdf/child
-enfant/2007-advisor-conseillere/advisor-conseillere-eng.pdf

Mackenzie, C. A., et al. (2005). Declining sex ratio in a First Nation community. *Environmental Health Perspectives, 113*(10). Retrieved January 2018 from https://www.ncbi.nlm.nih.gov/pmc/articles/
PMC1281269/

Marsit, C. J. (2015). Epigenetics of nutrition and environmental effects: Influence of environmental exposure on human epigenetic regulation. *Journal of Experimental Biology, 218*(1), 71–79. Retrieved January 2018 from http://jeb.biologists.org/content/jexbio/218/1/71.full.pdf

National Geographic Society. (2017, April). *Seven things to know about climate change*. Retrieved January 2018 from https://www
.nationalgeographic.com/magazine/2017/04/seven-things-to
-know-about-climate-change/

Parachute. (2015, June). *The cost of injury in Canada: The clock is ticking …* Retrieved January 2018 from http://www.parachutecanada
.org/downloads/research/Cost_of_Injury-2015.pdf

Parachute. (2014). *Annual Report—2014*. Retrieved November 2017 from http://www.parachutecanada.org/downloads/corporate/
Annual_Report_2014.pdf

Phipps, E., et al. (2017, September. 25). Call for action on radon in child care settings. *Environmental Health Review, 60*(3), 77–81. Retrieved January 2018 from http://pubs.ciphi.ca/doi/pdf/10.5864/d2017-020

Public Health Agency of Canada. (2013). *Leading causes of injury hospitalizations, Canada, 2009/10* (Pub.: 120177; Catalogue No. HP32-6/2010E-PDF). Ottawa: Her Majesty the Queen in Right of Canada.

Public Health Agency of Canada. (2012). *Injury in review: 2012 edition—spotlight on road and transport safety* (Catalogue No. HP15-14/2012C-PDF). Ottawa: Author. Retrieved January 2018 from http://publications.gc.ca/collections/collection_2013/aspc-phac/
HP15-14-2012-eng.pdf

Saunders, N. R., et al. (2017). *Unintentional injuries in children and youth from immigrant families in Ontario, Canada: A population-based cross-sectional study*. Retrieved January 2018 from http://cmajopen.ca/
content/5/1/E90.full.pdf

Scott, D. N. (2012, January 4). Beyond BPA: We need to get tough on toxics. *The Globe and Mail*. Retrieved January 2018 from https://
www.theglobeandmail.com/opinion/beyond-bpa-we-need-to-get
-tough-on-toxics/article4085163/

Weir E., et al. (2010). A Canadian framework for applying the precautionary principle to public health issues. *Canadian Journal of Public*

Health, 101(5), 396–398. Retrieved January 2018 from http://journal. cpha.ca/index.php/cjph/article/view/2635

World Health Organization. (n.d.). *Ultraviolet radiation and health.* Retrieved January 2018 from http://www.who.int/uv/uv_and_health/en/

World Health Organization. (2010). *Exposure to benzene.* Retrieved March 2018 from http://www.who.int/ipcs/features/benzene.pdf

UNIT 8

Afifi, T. O., et al. (2017, May 23). The relationships between harsh physical punishment and child maltreatment in childhood and intimate partner violence in adulthood. *BMC Public Health, 17*, 493. doi:10.1186/s12889-017-4359-8. Retrieved February 2018 from https://www.ncbi.nlm.nih.gov/pmc/articles/PMC5442668/

Barr, R. G. (2012, October 16). Preventing abusive head trauma resulting from a failure of normal interaction between infants and their caregivers. *Proceedings of the National Academy of Sciences, 109* (Suppl. 2), 17294–17301. Retrieved February 2018 from http://www .pnas.org/content/pnas/109/Supplement_2/17294.full.pdf

Barr, R. G. (2006, April). Crying behaviour and its importance for psychosocial development in children. *Encyclopedia on early childhood development* (pp. 1–10). Retrieved February 2018 from http:// www.child-encyclopedia.com/sites/default/files/textes-experts/ en/799/crying-behaviour-and-its-importance-for-psychosocial -development-in-children.pdf

Bennett, S. (2010). Female genital mutilation/cutting. In C. Jenny (Ed.), *Child abuse and neglect: Diagnosis, treatment, and evidence.* St. Louis, MO: Saunders Elsevier.

California Childcare Health Program. (2010, February). *Coining: What you need to know.* Fact sheets for families. Retrieved February 2018 from https://cchp.ucsf.edu/sites/cchp.ucsf.edu/files/Coining _En0210.pdf

Canadian Child Welfare Research Portal. (n.d.). *Frequently asked questions (FAQs).* Retrieved February 2018 from http://cwrp.ca/faqs#Q2

Canadian Paediatric Society. (2015). *Well beings: A guide to health in child care* (3rd rev. ed.). Ottawa: Author.

Canadian Paediatric Society. (2005, September 1). *Joint statement on shaken baby syndrome.* Position statement. Retrieved February 2018 from https://www.cps.ca/en/documents/position/ shaken-baby-syndrome

Canadian Women's Foundation. (2014, April). *Fact sheet: Moving women out of violence.* Retrieved February 2018 from https://www .canadianwomen.org/wp-content/uploads/2017/09/Facts-About -Violence.pdf

Department of Justice Canada. (2013, February 4). *Sexual offending against children and youth.* Retrieved February 2018 from https:// www.canada.ca/en/news/archive/2013/02/sexual-offending-against -children-youth.html

Department of Justice Canada. (2002, April 23). *Child abuse: A fact sheet from the Department of Justice Canada.* Retrieved February 2018 from http://publications.gc.ca/collections/Collection/J2-295 -2002E.pdf

Global Initiative to End All Corporal Punishment of Children. (2016, June). Corporal punishment of children: Review of research on its impact and associations. Retrieved February 2018 from http://www .kodomosukoyaka.net/pdf/2016-GI-review.pdf

Gonzalez, M., et al. (2008, August). What predicts injury from physical punishment? A test of the typologies of violence hypothesis. *Child Abuse & Neglect, 31*, 752–765. Retrieved February 2018 from https:// www.sciencedirect.com/science/article/pii/S0145213408001191

Government of Canada. (2017, February 27). *Family violence: How big is the problem in Canada?* Retrieved February 2018 from https://www .canada.ca/en/public-health/services/health-promotion/stop-family -violence/problem-canada.html

Government of Canada. (2014, August 4). *What is family violence?* Retrieved February 2018 from https://www.canada.ca/en/public -health/services/health-promotion/stop-family-violence/family -violence.html

Hall, D. K., & Pearson, J. (2004). *Reaching in … Reaching out. Resilience training: Introducing thinking skills that help children bounce back.* Toronto: The Child Development Institute.

Jordan, B., & Sketchley, R. (2009, September). A stitch in time saves nine: Preventing and responding to the abuse and neglect of infants. *Child Abuse Prevention Issues, 30.* National Child Protection Clearinghouse. Published by the Australian Institute of Family Studies. Retrieved February 2018 from https://aifs.gov.au/cfca/ publications/stitch-time-saves-nine-preventing-and-responding-th

Jud, A., & Trocmé, N. (2013). *Information sheets: Physical abuse and physical punishment in Canada.* Canadian Child Welfare Research Portal. Retrieved February 2018 from http://cwrp.ca/infosheets/ physical-abuse-and-physical-punishment-canada

Lamont, A. (2010a, April). *Effects of child abuse and neglect for adult survivors.* NCPC Resource Sheet. National Child Protection Clearinghouse. Published by the Australian Institute of Family Studies. Retrieved February 2018 from https://www.theactgroup.com .au/documents/EffectsofChildAbuseandNeglectforAdultSurvivors.pdf

Lamont, A. (2010b, April). *Effects of child abuse and neglect for children and adolescents.* NCPC Resource Sheet. National Child Protection Clearinghouse. Published by the Australian Institute of Family Studies. Retrieved February 2018 from https://www.theactgroup .com.au/documents/EffectsofChildAbuseandNeglectfor ChildrenandAdolescents.pdf

Macdonald, D., & Wilson, D. (2013, June). *Poverty or prosperity: Indigenous children in Canada.* Ottawa: Canadian Centre for Policy Alternatives. Retrieved February 2018 from http://www .policyalternatives.ca/sites/default/files/uploads/publications/ National%20Office/2013/06/Poverty_or_Prosperity_Indigenous _Children.pdf

Odhayani, A., et al. (2013, August). Behavioural consequences of child abuse. *Canadian Family Physician, 59*, 831–836. Retrieved June 2018 from http://www.cfp.ca/content/59/8/831

Office of the Federal Ombudsman for Victims of Crime. (n.d.). *Every image, every child backgrounder: Recommendations to the Government of Canada.* Retrieved February 2018 from http://www .victimsfirst.gc.ca/media/news-nouv/bg-di/20090507a.html

Packer, C., et al. (2015, April 7). Canada's response to female genital mutilation: Are we failing our girls? *CMAJ-JAMC, 187*(6), E188–E189. Retrieved February 2018 from https://www.ncbi.nlm.nih.gov/pmc/ articles/PMC4387059/

Payne, E. (2015, July 20). Shaken baby syndrome: A medical term of the past. *Ottawa Citizen.* Retrieved February 2018 from http://ottawacitizen.com/news/local-news/shaken-baby-syndrome -a-medical-term-of-the-past

Perry, B. D. (2004). *Maltreatment and the developing child: How early childhood experience shapes child and culture*. Inaugural lecture. London, ON: The Margaret McCain Lecture Series, Centre for Children and Families in the Justice System. Retrieved February 2018 from http://www.lfcc.on.ca/mccain/perry.pdf

Perry, B. D., & Marcellus, J. (n.d.). *The impact of abuse and neglect on the developing brain*. Retrieved February 2018 from http://teacher.scholastic.com/professional/bruceperry/abuse_neglect.htm

Public Health Agency of Canada. (2016, October). *A focus on family violence in Canada*. Retrieved February 2018 from http://www.healthycanadians.gc.ca/publications/department-ministere/state-public-health-family-violence-2016-etat-sante-publique-violence-familiale/alt/pdf-eng.pdf

Public Health Agency of Canada. (2010). *Canadian Incidence Study of Reported Child Abuse and Neglect—2008*. Ottawa: Her Majesty the Queen in Right of Canada. Catalogue No. HP5-1/2008E-PDF. Retrieved February 2018 from http://cwrp.ca/sites/default/files/publications/en/CIS-2008-rprt-eng.pdf

Public Safety Canada. (2015, May 27). *2013–2014 evaluation of the National Strategy for the Protection of Children from Sexual Exploitation on the Internet: Final report*. Retrieved June 2018 from https://www.publicsafety.gc.ca/cnt/rsrcs/pblctns/vltn-prtctn-chldrn-2013-14/vltn-prtctn-chldrn-2013-14-eng.pdf

Rimer, J. (2007). *Literature review: Responding to child and youth victims of sexual exploitation on the Internet*. Toronto: Boost Child & Youth Advocacy Centre.

Rimer, P. (2018). *Making a difference: The community responds to child abuse* (8th ed.). Toronto: Boost Child & Youth Advocacy Centre.

Rimer, P., & Prager, B. (2016). *Reaching out: Working together to identify and respond to child victims of abuse* (2nd ed.). Toronto: Nelson Canada.

Schwartz, D. (2015, June 2). Truth and Reconciliation Commission: By the numbers. Summary report is only one step in reconciliation. *CBC News: Indigenous*. Retrieved February 2018 from http://www.cbc.ca/news/indigenous/truth-and-reconciliation-commission-by-the-numbers-1.3096185

Shonkoff, J. P., et al. (2009). Neuroscience, molecular biology, and the childhood roots of health disparities: Building a new framework for health promotion and disease prevention. *JAMA, 301*, 2252–2259. Retrieved February 2018 from https://jamanetwork.com/journals/jama/article-abstract/184019?redirect=true

Statistics Canada. (2011). *Aboriginal peoples in Canada: First Nations people, Métis and Inuit: National Household Survey, 2011* (Catalogue No. 99-011-X2011001). Ottawa: Minister of Industry. Retrieved February 2018 from http://www12.statcan.gc.ca/nhs-enm/2011/as-sa/99-011-x/99-011-x2011001-eng.pdf

Trocmé, N. (2012, February). Child maltreatment and its impact on psychosocial child development epidemiology. In *Encyclopedia on early childhood development*. Retrieved February 2018 from http://www.child-encyclopedia.com/sites/default/files/textes-experts/en/779/child-maltreatment-and-its-impact-on-psychosocial-child-development-epidemiology-.pdf

UNFPA & UNICEF. (2014). *UNFPA-UNICEF joint programme on female genital mutilation/cutting: Accelerating change. Summary report of phase 1 2008–2013*. Retrieved February 2018 from https://www.unicef.org/protection/files/Joint_Programme_on_FGMC_Summary_Report.pdf

UNICEF. (2013, July). *Female genital mutilation/cutting: A statistical overview and exploration of the dynamics of change*. Retrieved February 2018 from http://data.unicef.org/wp-content/uploads/2015/12/FGMC_Lo_res_Final_26.pdf

World Health Organization. (2008). *Eliminating female genital mutilation: An interagency statement*. Geneva: Author. Retrieved February 2018 from http://apps.who.int/iris/bitstream/10665/43839/1/9789241596442_eng.pdf

UNIT 9

Almqvist, L., et al. (2006). I can play—young children's perceptions of health. *Pediatric Rehabilitation, 9(3)*, 275–284.

Bates, D. G., & Plog, F. (1990). *Cultural anthropology*. New York: McGraw-Hill.

Best Start Panel on Early Learning. (2007). Early learning for every child today: A framework for Ontario early childhood settings. Toronto: Ontario Ministry of Children and Youth Services. Retrieved February 2018 from http://www.edu.gov.on.ca/childcare/oelf/continuum/continuum.pdf

Best Start Resource Centre. (2012). *Welcoming and celebrating sexual orientation and gender diversity in families: From preconception to preschool*. Toronto: Author. Retrieved February 2018 from https://www.beststart.org/resources/howto/pdf/LGBTQ_Resource_fnl_online.pdf

Canadian Council on Learning. (2008, March 20). *Bullying in Canada—how intimidation affects learning*. Retrieved February 2018 from http://en.copian.ca/library/research/ccl/bullying_in_canada/bullying_in_canada.pdf

Canadian Dental Association. (2018a). *Fluoride and your child*. Retrieved February 2018 from https://www.cda-adc.ca/en/oral_health/cfyt/dental_care_children/fluoride.asp

Canadian Dental Association. (2018b). *Oral health articles*. Retrieved February 2018 from http://www.cda-adc.ca/en/about/media_room/health_month/publicity/oral_health_articles.asp

Canadian Dental Association. (2013). *Oral health: Good for life™*. Retrieved February 2018 from http://www.cda-adc.ca/en/oral_health/cfyt/good_for_life/default.asp

Canadian Paediatric Society. (2016a, February 1). *Oral health care for children—a call for action*. Position statement. Retrieved February 2018 from https://www.cps.ca/en/documents/position/oral-health-care-for-children

Canadian Paediatric Society. (2016b, November). *Taming the monsters: Helping children deal with their fears*. Retrieved February 2018 from https://www.caringforkids.cps.ca/handouts/taming_the_monsters

Canadian Paediatric Society. (2015). *Well beings: A guide to health in child care* (3rd rev. ed.). Ottawa: Author.

Canadian Paediatric Society. (2013, March 14). *Measuring in support of early childhood development*. Position statement. Retrieved February 2018 from http://www.cps.ca/documents/position/early-childhood-development

Carducci, B. (2008, June 16). Are we born shy? Genetics, environment, and bashfulness. *Psychology Today*. Retrieved February 2018 from https://www.psychologytoday.com/blog/breaking-the-ice/200806/are-we-born-shy

Center on the Developing Child, Harvard University. (n.d.). *Toxic stress: The facts.* Retrieved February 2018 from https://developingchild .harvard.edu/science/key-concepts/toxic-stress/

College of Early Childhood Educators. (n.d.). *Gaabaagang gives children a space of their own.* Retrieved February 2018 from https:// www.ordre-epe.ca/en/Documents/Gaabaagang_EN.pdf

Goulet, M., & Schroeder, R. (1998). *How caring relationships support self-regulation: Video guide.* Toronto: National Association for the Education of Young Children.

Government of Canada. (2017, September 18). *About gender identity and gender expression.* Retrieved February 2018 from http://www .justice.gc.ca/eng/csj-sjc/pl/identity-identite/about-apropos.html

Gruber, R., for the Canadian Sleep Society. (n.d.). *Children: Patient information brochure.* Retrieved February 2018 from https://css-scs .ca/resources/brochures/children

Guilfoyle, A., & Sims, M. (2009–2010). Cortisol changes and the quality of child care in Australian preschool and kindergarten children. *Illinois Child Welfare, 5*(1). Retrieved February 2018 from http:// www.illinoischildwelfare.org/archives/volume5/icw5-guilfoyle.pdf

Guralnick, M. (2010). Early intervention approaches to enhance the peer-related social competence of young children with developmental delays: A historical perspective. *Infants & Young Children, 23*(2), 73–83. Retrieved February 2018 from https://depts.washington.edu/isei/ iyc/23.2_gural.pdf

Janmohamed, Z., & Campbell, R. (2009). *Building bridges: Queer families in early childhood education.* Retrieved February 2018 from https://www.oise.utoronto.ca/atkinson/UserFiles/File/Resources _Topics/Resources_Topics_Diversity/BuildingBridges.pdf

Lansdown, G. (2011). *Every child's right to be heard: A resource guide on the UN Committee on the Rights of the Child General Comment No. 12.* London: Save the Children UK. Retrieved February 2018 from https:// www.unicef.org/adolescence/files/Every_Childs_Right_to_be_Heard.pdf

Maller, C. (2005). *Hands-on contact with nature in primary schools as a catalyst for developing a sense of community and cultivating mental health and wellbeing. EINGANA: A Journal of Environmental Education, 28*(3), 17–22.

Mikkonen, J., & Raphael, D. (2010). *Social determinants of health: The Canadian facts.* Toronto: York University School of Health Policy and Management. Retrieved April 2018 from http://thecanadianfacts.org/ The_Canadian_Facts.pdf

Natapoff, J. N. (1982). A developmental analysis of children's ideas of health. *Health Education Quarterly, 9,* 130–141.

National Sleep Foundation. (n.d.-a). *How much sleep do we really need?* Retrieved February 2018 from https://sleepfoundation.org/how-sleep -works/how-much-sleep-do-we-really-need

National Sleep Foundation. (n.d.-b). *Sleep hygiene: What is sleep hygiene?* Retrieved February 2018 from https://sleepfoundation.org/ sleep-topics/sleep-hygiene

Parks Canada. (2014). *Connecting Canadians with nature—an investment in the well-being of our citizens.* Ottawa: Parks Canada. Retrieved February 2018 from http://www.parks-parcs.ca/english/ ConnectingCanadians-English_web.pdf

Pearson, J., & Hall, D. K. (2006, April). *Reaching IN … Reaching OUT resiliency guidebook.* Retrieved February 2018 from http://www .reachinginreachingout.com/documents/Guidebook-06.pdf

Peel Public Health. (2011, June 3). *Fostering healthy body image in children and teens.* Retrieved February 2018 from https://www. peelregion.ca/health/commhlth/fostbi/fostint.htm

Petit, D., & Montplaisir, J. (2012, December). Consequences of short sleep duration or poor sleep in young children. In R. E. Tremblay et al. (Eds.), *Encyclopedia on early childhood development.* Retrieved February 2018 from http://www.child-encyclopedia.com/sleeping -behaviour/according-experts/consequences-short-sleep-duration -or-poor-sleep-young-children

Pyne, J., for Rainbow Health Ontario. (2012, July). *Supporting gender independent children and their families.* Evidence brief: Inform your practice. Retrieved February 2018 from https://www.rainbowhealthontario.ca/wp-content/uploads/ woocommerce_uploads/2012/10/RHO_FactSheet_GIC_E1.pdf

Save the Children UK & UNICEF (2011). *Every child's right to be heard.* Retrieved February 2018 from http://www.unicef.org/adolescence/ files/Every_Childs_Right_to_be_Heard.pdf

Sex Information and Education Council of Canada. (2015). *Sexual health education in the schools: Questions and answers.* Retrieved February 2018 from http://sieccan.org/wp/wp-content/uploads/ 2015/08/SIECCAN-QA-Sexual-health-education-in-the-schools -2015-Ontario.pdf

Shankar, S. (2010, July 26). *Self-regulation: Calm, alert, and learning.* EdCan Network. Retrieved February 2018 from https://www.edcan .ca/articles/self-regulation-calm-alert-and-learning/

Siegal, M., & Peterson, C. C. (Eds.). (2005). *Children's understanding of biology and health.* Cambridge, UK: Cambridge University Press. Retrieved February 2018 from https://books.google.ca/books?hl =en&lr=&id=52Nm_WEuw-UC&oi=fnd&pg=PP1&dq=Children%E2 %80%99s+understanding+of+biology+and+health&ots=CqxGJZR3H 4&sig=ZWchOeuOg3SPv-NR6l57KFKLm50#v=onepage&q =Children%E2%80%99s%20understanding%20of%20biology%20 and%20health&f=false

Sivertsen, B., et al. (2015, June). Later emotional and behavioral problems associated with sleep problems in toddlers: A longitudinal study. *JAMA Pediatrics, 169*(6), 575–582. Retrieved February 2018 from https://jamanetwork.com/journals/jamapediatrics/ fullarticle/2214166

United Nations. (n.d.). *UN Convention on the Rights of the Child in child friendly language.* Retrieved February 2018 from https://www.unicef .org/rightsite/files/uncrcchilldfriendlylanguage.pdf

Waxler-Morrison, N., et al. (Eds.). (2005). *Cross-cultural caring: A handbook for health professionals* (2nd ed.). Vancouver: UBC Press. Retrieved February 2018 from https://www.ubcpress.ca/asset/ 12508/1/9780774810258.pdf

World Health Organization. (n.d.). *Gender: Definitions.* Retrieved February 2018 from http://www.euro.who.int/en/health-topics/ health-determinants/gender/gender-definitions

ZERO to THREE. (n.d.). *Frequently asked questions about brain development.* Retrieved February 2018 from https://www.zerotothree .org/resources/series/frequently-asked-questions-about-brain- development

ZERO to THREE. (2016, February 16). *Temperament: What makes your child tick.* Retrieved February 2018 from https://www.zerotothree .org/resources/159-temperament-what-makes-your-child-tick

Index

Natural health products, 20–21
Natural Health Products Regulations, 20
Neglect, 476–477. *See also* Child maltreatment
Networking, 53–56, 503
Neuroscience, 28
New foods, 275–276, 289
New host, 137
Noise level, 95
Noncustodial parents, and pickup times, 463
Nonlocomotor skills, 338
Nutrients
    food sources, 315–318
    functions of, 239–240, 315–318
    key nutrients, 251, 253
    role of, 239–240
    table of, 315–318
NutriSTEP, 356
Nutrition, 231
    body image and, 235–237
    child nutrition programs, 296–297
    developmental characteristics related to eating, 273–274
    digestion, 247–250
    eating habits, factors shaping, 232–239
    economics and, 237–239
    educators and, 65–70
    emotional component, 233
    food insecurity, 238–239
    healthy eating habits (*see* Healthy eating habits)
    infant nutrition (*see* Infant nutrition)
    menu planning, 297–300
    nutrients, 239–240, 251, 253, 315–318
    nutrition education, 577–583
    nutrition labels, 262–264, 270–271
    physical component, 232–233
    positive eating environment, 275–277
    preschool nutrition, 289–290
    school-age nutrition, 290–292
    social and cultural components, 233–235
    toddler nutrition, 287–289
    vegetables and fruit, consumption of, 242–244
    vegetarianism, 258–261
    See also Food
Nutrition education, 577–583
Nutrition Facts table, 263
Nutrition labels, 262–264, 270–271

Obesity
    biology and, 327–330
    body mass index (BMI), 67, 324
    carbonated drinks, contribution of, 361–363
    childhood obesity, concerns about, 322–330
    childhood obesity, factors affecting, 324–325
    epigenetics, 328
    overweight, 324
Observation
    of child development and interests, 566–571
    children's safety and, 400
    health observations (*see* Health observations)
    safety checks, 415–416
Occupational health
    checklists, 122–126
    physical well-being (*see* Physical well-being of educators)
    psychological well-being (*see* Psychological well-being of educators)
Omega-3 fatty acids, 245–246
Oral health, 584
    early childhood tooth decay (ECTD), 586–587
    fluoride, 585–586
    healthy eating and drinking, 586–587
    infants and toddlers, 589
    plaque, 584–585
    preschoolers, 589
    promotion of oral health, 585–590
    school-aged children, 589
    toothbrushing, 587–589
Organic foods, 264
OTC medication, 195–197
Otitis media (ear infection), 225
Outdoor air quality, 95
Outdoor play. *See* Play (outdoor)
Outdoor play equipment. *See* Play equipment
Over-the-counter (OTC) medication, 195–197
Overeating, 358–361
Overweight, 324

Pandemic, 162–163
Parents
    children's sexuality, perspectives on, 550–551
    communication, where suspected child maltreatment, 515
    effective parenting skills, 485
    intoxicated parents, 463–464
    noncustodial parents, 463
    parenting style, 28–29
    supporting change in, 524–525
ParticipACTION, 354
Partner abuse. *See* Family violence
Peers, influence of, 565
Personal culture, 564
Personal Health Information Act, 179
Personal stress factors, 102
Personal wellness, 63
Pesticides, 264, 455–456